THE EVOLVING HOUSE

The Economics of Shelter

The Evolving House

VOLUME II

THE ECONOMICS OF SHELTER

BY

ALBERT FARWELL BEMIS

THE TECHNOLOGY PRESS

MASSACHUSETTS INSTITUTE OF TECHNOLOGY

CAMBRIDGE · MASSACHUSETTS

DEDICATED
TO THE
BETTERMENT OF THE HOME
THE CRADLE OF
THE BODY
THE MIND
THE SPIRIT

Abbreviations Used in References

GPO	United States Government Printing Office
ILO	International Labour Office
NBER	National Bureau of Economic Research
NICB	National Industrial Conference Board
USBLS	United States Bureau of Labor Statistics
USC	United States Census
USDC	United States Department of Commerce
USDL	United States Department of Labor

Foreword To All Volumes

THE general purpose of this three-part work is to deal with one of the fundamental features of human existence, housing or shelter. The subject offers a rich field for investigation, and the economic and social questions involved press urgently, in one form or another, upon society and upon the individual.

For more years than I like to contemplate it has seemed to me that the means of providing homes in modern America and elsewhere have been strangely out of date. The provision of food and clothing has been organized, increased, and facilitated to an extraordinary degree, and the same is true of the more complex needs of heat, light, transportation, luxuries, recreation, information. Why is the house which one builds for his family to live in for a generation, why is the house almost outside the influence of modern mass production methods? Should it be brought within their scope? If so, how? Such questions have been surging within me now for at least eight or ten years and these volumes contain my effort to answer them.

The method of attack necessitates first, in Volume I, a review of the evolution of the home and the social and economic forces which have influenced its development; then in Volume II an analysis of current housing conditions and trends and comparisons with the methods of other industries. Thus we should be able to find out what is the matter with housing and wherein it lags behind in the march of civilization. Finally, a solution of such problems will be offered in the third volume in the form of a rationalization of the housing industry, thus harmonizing the means by which our homes are provided with those mostly used in supplying the other major needs.

This rather large task, I am frank to say, I have approached with the distinct preconceived idea that the chief factor of the modern housing problem is physical structure. A new conception of the structure of our modern houses is needed, better adapted not only to the social conditions of our day but also to modern means of production: factories, machinery, technology, and research. Other industries have made use of such forces to a far greater extent than the building industry has done. The peculiar and complex nature of the building industry has thus far thwarted basic improvement in methods of house construction; but rationalization of it with respect to the other industries is imminent in all countries where, in varying degrees, mass production prevails.

Mass productive methods have come to stay, because they are simply the further development of the division of labor. It seems to be a law of life that function or labor is divided and subdivided, specialized and further specialized, infinitely and forever. Further extensions of mass production into both old and new fields may be confidently predicted. A study of housing as one of the chief factors in the " cost of living " in comparison with all other factors quite clearly indicates its backwardness compared with those other things which our present-day life demands. To bring it into harmony with the others is primarily an engineering problem which has gradually developed in character and importance during the last century and particularly in the last decade. It has not been adequately dealt with, probably because of its very complex and diverse character; it is easily seen in its generalities but hard to grasp in its details.

The solution is obviously through rationalization because the present methods of house production are old and out of harmony with methods used in other industries. The factors involved are by no means wholly structural or industrial; but social custom, living standards, public welfare, property, finance, esthetics, and still other factors must be balanced.

But balance among these factors can not be established until the housing structure, which is the basis of the whole problem, has been rationalized. The existing house structure was mostly developed before the industrial age, and grew out of the materials and methods and social standards of earlier centuries. The structure is physically sound but not well adapted to recent technical advances in materials and applied mechanics. Its elements are not well suited to manufacture by mass production or to ready field erection. It is not adapted to large-scale credit financing at low cost. Furthermore, it is very ill-fitted to include the accessories which, in these days, make the home. We are clearly putting new wine into old bottles when we implant modern heating, lighting, and plumbing into the house structure and architecture of two centuries ago. Finally, from the esthetic viewpoint it does not adequately express the spirit of the present era or utilize the wealth of adornment available through new materials, colors, and textures.

The whole world today is experiencing an evolutionary maladjustment far more significant than any unbalance between industries. Productive means have far outstripped control means and distributive means. Potential production, including transport, is sufficient to supply the necessaries of life in abundant quantity to every man, woman, and child throughout the world. But our economic and political control methods are out of date and full of flaws. Millions are pinched and even starving in the midst of plenty. But the time is nearly here, and the forces are working toward it, when improved technology of control and distribution will tend to harmonize and balance with our technology of production. The great communistic experiment of the Soviets, the autocracy of Mussolini, the spiritual democracy of Gandhi, the flounderings of all entrenched political and economic forces, including those of the United States, the philosophy and suggestions of the scientists, including " Technocracy," are all valuable contributions to this end. Rationalization between world production and distribution through which we shall make better use of our recent great

advances in productive technique for the general public good
is clearly on the horizon. The present depression is drawing it
towards us. But its approach will not stop the continued play
of evolutionary forces in the field of production in general and
housing in particular. In fact, improved technique of control
between methods of production and distribution can hardly
occur until the existing maladjustment between the building
industry and our other great industries has been annulled.

It is a very far cry from the time when primitive man first
used the protecting shelter of a tree or a cave down to present-
day complex life and the home which it demands. Yet during
this period of a half million or million years man and his home
have been evolving under exactly the same natural forces as
exist today, and we can draw a picture of the evolution of his
home and some of the influences which have brought it to the
present point. We can note the interplay through the ages of
man's physical, mental, and spiritual urges. The interplay of
these forces has tended always, though in waves, toward further
and further specialization in supplying man's wants and crav-
ings. Increasing technique has meant increased knowledge, more
knowledge has furthered man's higher aims, and so in continuous subdivision of man's work the human race has progressed.
The home, one of man's primary needs, has helped to conserve
and pass down to subsequent generations and ages his mental
accomplishments; and within the home man's vague super-
human sense, the spirit, has evolved, ever urging onward and
upward. No inquiry could be more interesting, more illuminating, more profound or more far reaching, more significant or
more pertinent to present needs, than a study of the houses of
mankind.

ALBERT FARWELL BEMIS

Preface to Volume II

VOLUME I dealt extensively with the development of man's abode and the interrelations between it and his social and spiritual life. That review was intended to form the background for the serious study of the economic and physical actualities of the American home of today. This volume brings us face to face with these actualities. It makes no attempt to evaluate purely social factors, but this must not be construed to mean that it fails to recognize their importance.

In the Foreword to All Volumes, the statement is made that the chief factor of the modern housing problem is physical structure. This has been criticized as failing to recognize the importance of social aspects, as failing to take any account of group housing — in fact, as indicating a bias which vitiated the conclusions of the work. This second volume, however, should go far to make clear what was meant. Whatever may be its social values, housing requires work, it costs money; the economic element is vital to its character, and social achievements in housing cannot be made without cost, whether the housing be individual or communal in type. At the present time housing costs too much, compared with other things. Its economic aspect is therefore dominant.

Definitions are often troublesome in a work of this sort. The words " house " and " housing " are used indiscriminately by many writers. In this book " house " is used to mean any building sheltering one or more families in permanent residence, be it a cottage, a two-family structure, or a multi-

family apartment; " housing " is used in its collective sense
synonymously with " shelter " to define the conglomerate house
of the group or nation. Other words, too, are perplexing, on
account of the changes that occur in their meanings. " Capi-
talism " necessarily exists in some degree in every social order,
and the basic meaning of the word does not justify its increasingly popular use to define an individualistic economy. I have
used this and other words in their perverted sense with the
greatest reluctance. Here and there, to make my meaning clear,
I have essayed by other words to fortify and clarify the basic
meaning; but always to do so would encumber the flow of
thought, and I have usually deferred to common parlance.

By studying housing conditions in all their economic phases,
we may see what aspects of the home-providing process are out
of balance and need bringing up to date. We commence with a
section setting forth the importance of housing relative to other
economic factors; the product of the industry, chiefly in the
United States, is then defined; and finally we show that the cost
of that product is entirely too high.

The second and longest section of the book examines the
reasons for this high cost. It rehearses the often-told story of
the disabilities in the building industry, describes its organization, and compares its efficiency with that of others. It then
examines in greater detail the four cost factors which seem
most to need detailed analysis.

The final section gives attention to some of the governmental
efforts which have been made to improve minimum housing in
quality and cost. It concludes with a suggested solution by
other means. In view of the intense demand for government
participation in the expense of housing, we present a careful
study of the results of this participation in nations where it
has been carried out on a large scale. From this study he who
runs may read that it is not a fitting solution of the problem
of cost, however desirable, indeed essential, governmental control of city planning and building regulations may be. The
soundest way out is clearly through reduction of the cost of

the product by normal means. The last chapter, on rationalization, points the way, a way which will be enlarged upon in the final volume of this series.

The importance of the home as an economic factor has received relatively slight attention. In making an economic study like this, one constantly encounters a blank wall of inadequate statistics — at once scanty, inaccurate, and poorly suited for comparison. Numerous things of far less value than housing have been made the subject of endless analysis, study, discussion, statistical review, and research. Effort and expense galore have been devoted to the investigation of manufactures, machinery, railways, bridges, canals, mines, churches, motor-cars, sheep, yes, and even radishes and popcorn. But on the subject of housing, as will be apparent to the reader, information is equally scarce and sporadic whether in government or private files. At almost every point independent investigation has been required. And obviously the present disturbed economic condition throughout the world adds greatly to the difficulty of analyzing data and drawing conclusions therefrom. Where comparisons have been made between different periods and different countries, allowance has been attempted for abnormal differences of currency values.

At my request and under my direction, Luther Conant has for five years worked at the collection of data on nearly every aspect of present-day housing. His findings in the form of text, tables, charts, and footnotes are here combined with my conclusions from and views of those findings. The reader who is interested to pursue such economic data will find additional material in the appendices and the bibliography. A few of the charts, though based on all available data, are somewhat conjectural and marked accordingly. By this use of conjecture certain trends and relationships are made more clear.

The excellent charts and graphs are by John W. Germond. Numerous government and private research bureaus, trade associations, and journals, as well as private individuals, have been most generous in responding to requests for information.

A list of these will be found at the end of the volume, and to each I tender my sincere appreciation of their aid. I am much indebted to Marjorie True Gregg for her aid in editing the manuscript, and to John Burchard, 2nd, for assistance in its preparation for publication.

ALBERT FARWELL BEMIS

BOSTON, MASS.
MAY, 1934.

Contents

List of Charts

List of Illustrations

List of Tables

APPENDIX

THE EVOLVING HOUSE

The Economics of Shelter

CHAPTER I

The Economic Importance of Housing

EFORE embarking on an analysis of housing as a factor in the economic life of the family and the nation, it is desirable to restate several definitions and concepts fundamental to economics. The word " economics " itself, with happy appropriateness, comes from the Greek *ôikonomikós*, a composite of two words, the original meaning of which was " home management." From such a simple beginning, economics has grown to its present great and complex significance. It can with difficulty be briefly defined, but may be said to be the science of wealth; agriculture, commerce, industry, finance, building, mining, fisheries, transport, the trades, even the means of living, are all included in its scope.

The word " wealth " derives from the Anglo-Saxon *weola*, meaning " weal, prosperity, well-being, happiness, joy." From such a delightful origin, wealth has come to include the objects which are the *cause* of happiness, and hence material things — the ownership and distribution of which only too often create the converse of happiness.

In its modern, technical meaning, wealth is chiefly the result or product of work, and may be classified as permanent or capital goods and temporary or consumable goods. Of the former, some are the direct gift of nature, requiring the labor of man; such as crude natural resources. The chief capital assets of all primitive countries and of most of the more advanced ones lie in this group: forest, pasture, tillable lands, mines, fisheries, and waterways. Permanent wealth also includes durable things derived from these resources; such as buildings, tools, machinery, roads, canals, and railways, which result from work not needed for providing the necessaries of life. Temporary or quickly consumable wealth develops from the synchronized use of permanent wealth.

The efficiency of a nation as a producer and accumulator of wealth varies inversely with the percentage of its people employed in the production of sustenance commodities. Obviously if all the man-power be required for such sustenance, as was the case in primitive times, there is none left for producing permanent wealth. But as knowledge and technique develop, the ability and desire to provide more durable types of wealth increase. From the viewpoint of present-day economics, the countries of relatively small wealth are those in which the bulk of the people is engaged in providing the basic necessities. The wealthiest countries are those the wants and industries of which are the most extensive and diverse, and in which daily sustenance is provided by relatively few workers. India and Brazil, for instance, rank low in per-capita wealth, despite their enormous territories, while Great Britain and the United States rank high. Chart 1 (conjectural) shows the tendency of types of wealth to increase or decrease with advancing civilization. Chart 2 gives the per-capita wealth and income for various nations, showing how the wealthiest countries are precisely those which by Western standards are the most civilized. In daily life the less wealthy countries lie nearer to starvation than do the wealthier ones, but it by no means follows that in a crisis the complicated economic structure of the latter may not produce a condition of starvation much more severe than ever occurs in a poorer or more backward land. The complexities of transport and communication in economically advanced countries are such that their breakdown would be a catastrophe; the people in primitive countries have a direct contact with the production of necessities.

Consumable wealth concerns the individual more directly than permanent wealth; all effort in primitive times was de-

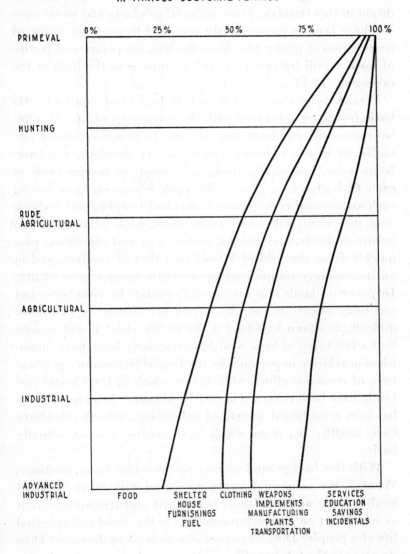

— CHART I —

PERCENTAGE OF SOCIAL EFFORT EXPENDED ON VARIOUS ACTIVITIES
IN VARIOUS CULTURAL PERIODS

	0%	25%	50%	75%	100%
PRIMEVAL					
HUNTING					
RUDE AGRICULTURAL					
AGRICULTURAL					
INDUSTRIAL					
ADVANCED INDUSTRIAL	FOOD	SHELTER HOUSE FURNISHINGS FUEL	CLOTHING IMPLEMENTS MANUFACTURING PLANTS TRANSPORTATION	WEAPONS	SERVICES EDUCATION SAVINGS INCIDENTALS

voted to its production, and that impulse continues. It is indeed a far cry from the condition under which each individual or family was a separate economic entity, directly supplying and consuming all material requirements, to the present condition in this country, where material products and social services have been so tremendously amplified through the enforced cooperation of group life. None the less, the primary objective of work is still temporary wealth or income in the form of the necessaries of life.

Wealth may also be classified as basic and non-basic. Its basic forms are concerned with the necessaries of life; its non-basic ones with comforts and luxuries. In primitive society virtually all wealth is basic, but, as society develops, non-basic forms arise, continually tending, however, to become basic as each finds its place as a social want. Some non-basic forms, such as personal embellishments incident to ephemeral fashion, soon die, along with their progenitors, while others, such as improved foods, waterworks, motor-cars, and airplanes, pass quickly from the field of luxury into that of comfort, and in an increasingly complex social structure become basic wealth. In primitive lands it is easy to differentiate between basic and non-basic effort; in complex urban life it may be extremely difficult, as shown by Chart 3. From this chart it will be seen that a few types of basic wealth, particularly land, have diminished in relative importance in the United States during a century of economic effort, while others which in 1805 would certainly have been regarded as non-basic cannot be so now. There has been a continual growth of subsidiary and sub-subsidiary basic wealth; i.e., items which in themselves are not actually basic.

With this background we may now consider these questions: What is the value of housing compared with other forms of wealth, basic and non-basic, permanent and temporary? Is it as important an item in economics as in the social and spiritual life of a people? Does its importance increase or decrease? Does its place in the total wealth and the annual income grow less or

— CHART 2 —

PER-CAPITA WEALTH AND PER-CAPITA INCOME IN VARIOUS COUNTRIES
IN VARIOUS YEARS: 1925-1928

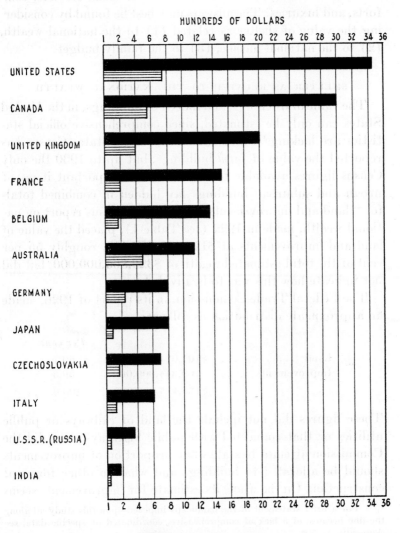

HUNDREDS OF DOLLARS

PER CAPITA WEALTH
PER CAPITA INCOME

more as countries become more mature or more industrialized, richer or poorer? What does it contribute to the annual income? What is its annual cost per capita and per family? What is its relation to other requirements and to the social services, comforts, and luxuries? The answers may best be found by considering the value of shelter as related (1) to the national wealth, (2) to the national income, (3) to the family budget.

SHELTER AS RELATED TO THE NATIONAL WEALTH

The value of dwellings, and indeed of buildings, in the United States can only be estimated, since comprehensive official statistics are lacking.[1] Since 1900 the United States Census has reported the value of *farm* buildings, but up to 1930 the only Census figures available for the far more important items of urban and suburban buildings lay hidden in combined totals for " land and improvements." The latest Census report on national wealth, made in 1922 (see Table 1), placed the value of land and improvements at $176,415,000,000, roughly 55 per cent of the total estimated wealth of $320,800,000,000, but did not indicate how this was to be divided.

The Federal Trade Commission, in its report of 1926,[2] made an approximate distribution as follows:

		Per cent
Land	$107,071,000,000	60.7
Improvements	69,344,000,000	39.3
	$176,415,000,000	100.0

These figures did not include the land of railways or public utilities or that connected with public highways. Nor did the Commission attempt to state what proportion of improvements should be allocated to buildings and what to other forms of construction. On the whole its estimate for improvements seems

[1] For a brief statement of the handicaps imposed upon this study all along the line because of a lack of comprehensive, coordinated or specific data, see Appendix, p. 509.

[2] Federal Trade Commission, " National Wealth and Income " (Government Printing Office, Washington, 1926), p. 34.

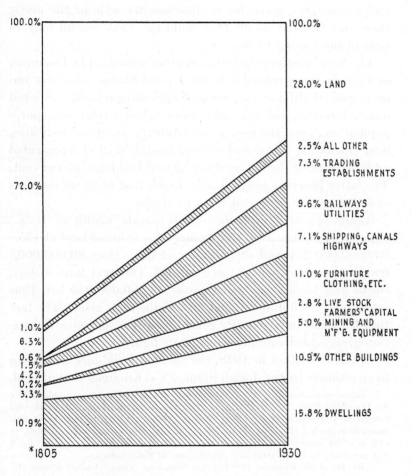

— CHART 3 —

PERCENTAGE DISTRIBUTION OF WEALTH IN THE UNITED STATES
BY PRINCIPAL ITEMS (APPROXIMATE): 1805 AND 1930

100.0%   100.0%

                                                28.0% LAND

                                                2.5% ALL OTHER
                                                7.3% TRADING
                                                      ESTABLISHMENTS
72.0%
                                                9.6% RAILWAYS
                                                      UTILITIES

                                                7.1% SHIPPING, CANALS
                                                      HIGHWAYS

                                                11.0% FURNITURE
                                                       CLOTHING, ETC.

                                                2.8% LIVE STOCK
                                                      FARMERS' CAPITAL
1.0%   5.0% MINING AND
6.3%   M'F'G. EQUIPMENT

0.6%   10.9% OTHER BUILDINGS
1.5%
4.2%
0.2%
3.3%
                                                15.8% DWELLINGS
10.9%

*1805   1930

* EXCLUSIVE OF SLAVES
  DOES NOT INCLUDE LOUISIANA PURCHASE TERRITORY

conservative. A total of $75,000,000,000 for buildings, with
a correspondingly lower figure for land, is perhaps nearer
the truth. This distribution of improvements and land, together with the major items in the Census estimate of 1922, may
be drawn from Table 1. Parallel with the 1922 values, the
table presents original estimates for 1930. Even if the 1930
valuations there given for comparison are wide of the mark,
there can be little doubt that buildings rank second only to
land in the United States.

The same relationship is true of other nations. The Dominion
of Canada is, compared with the United States, relatively undeveloped; it still has vast areas of agricultural land, unworked
mines, forests, great mineral resources, and a relatively sparse
population; none the less, as an arbitrary analysis [3] indicates,
land (including forest and mineral lands) in 1930 represented
42.5 per cent of the national wealth and buildings 17 per cent.
The latter percentage was nearly double that of steam railways
and that of livestock and farm products.

Again, a recent estimate of the private wealth of Italy,[4]
apparently for the year 1929, placed the value of land at 155,-
000,000,000 lire and of buildings at more than 80,000,000,-
000 lire,[5] or 16.5 per cent of the total. The next largest item,
stocks and bonds, was a little over 52,000,000,000 lire, thus
easily giving buildings second rank in the total assets. The fact
that Italy has only recently come forward as an industrial nation gives added significance to these figures.

In Great Britain in 1928, the value of buildings, according
to an estimate by Sir Josiah Stamp,[6] was five times that of land,

[3] Based on estimates of the total national wealth of Canada as published by
the Dominion Bureau of Statistics of the Canadian Department of Trade and
Commerce ("Canada, 1932" [F. A. Acland, Ottawa, 1932], p. 41). These estimates disregarded the value of undeveloped agricultural and mineral land, as
well as other undeveloped natural resources, so that to arrive at our ratios, it
was necessary to make arbitrary calculations of these values.

[4] By Dr. degli Epinosa, in "Foreign Financial News," United States Department of Commerce, Bulletin No. 103.

[5] One lira = 5.2 cents in United States currency at par.

[6] "The National Wealth" (The Economist [London, November 22, 1930],
p. 946). The value of farm buildings was included under farm values instead of
under buildings.

being placed at £4,500,000,000, or was 25 per cent of the net wealth; i.e., gross wealth less £6,400,000,000, representing the national debt,[7] and taking first place among the national as-

TABLE 1

APPROXIMATE DISTRIBUTION OF WEALTH OF THE UNITED STATES IN 1922 AND 1930

	1922 [a]	Per cent [d]	1930 [b]	Per cent [d]
Land	$101,400,000,000	29.6	$125,000,000,000 [c]	29.4
Buildings				
Dwellings	48,000,000,000	14.0	70,000,000,000	16.5
All other	27,000,000,000	7.9	45,000,000,000	10.6
Manufactured products	28,400,000,000	8.3	30,000,000,000	7.1
Furniture, clothing, etc.				
House furnishings	21,000,000,000	6.1	27,000,000,000	6.3
Clothing, jewelry, etc.	18,800,000,000	5.5	20,000,000,000	4.7
Streets, public roads, etc.	22,000,000,000	6.4	27,000,000,000	6.3
Railways	20,000,000,000	5.8	22,000,000,000	5.2
Manufacturing machinery, tools, etc.	15,800,000,000	4.6	20,000,000,000	4.7
Livestock	5,800,000,000	1.7	4,500,000,000	1.1
Farm products	5,500,000,000	1.6	4,500,000,000	1.1
Street railways	4,900,000,000	1.4	3,500,000,000	0.8
Motor vehicles	4,600,000,000	1.3	6,000,000,000	1.4
Electric light and power stations	4,200,000,000	1.2	6,000,000,000	1.4
Miscellaneous utilities	3,400,000,000	1.0	3,500,000,000	0.8
Shipping and canals	2,900,000,000	0.9	2,000,000,000	0.5
Farm implements and machinery	2,600,000,000	0.8	2,000,000,000	0.5
All other	6,500,000,000	1.9	7,000,000,000	1.6
Totals	$342,800,000,000	100.0	$425,000,000,000	100.0

(a) Census data (in round numbers), except for the item of $22,000,000,000 for streets, public roads, etc., which was not included by the Census in its total of $320,800,000,000. The Census did not show values for land and buildings separately, but merely gave a grand total of $176,415,000,000 for land and improvements.

(b) Estimated. These do not allow for the unusual depreciation of values resulting from the general change in economic conditions which began in 1929. With this allowance made, it is almost certain that 1933 values would be less than for 1922.

(c) Takes account of the shrinkage of $20,000,000,000 in the value of farm land between 1920 and 1930, as reported by the Census.

(d) Although distributions in this and many other tables are carried out to decimal places, this does not imply a corresponding precision for the data. Even the round percentages are subject to a margin of error.

[7] The question whether government bonds (which represent a large part of the national debt) should be included in the aggregate wealth of a nation has been widely debated.

In most estimates of the wealth of Great Britain the value of certain imsets. Yet a century ago the value of land in the United Kingdom was placed by Colquhoun [8] at three and one-half times the value of buildings.

This striking development represents the culmination of a trend to be observed in other countries. In the early development of a nation, the value of buildings is small as compared with that of land; but as civilization progresses, the former comes to exceed it. This tendency is made clear by Chart 4, which gives percentages for the approximate distribution of the wealth of Great Britain in 1812 and in 1930.

That the relative value of buildings is increasing in the United States is indicated by local statistics, as well as in Chart 3 (*q.v.*). In 1890 the total value of real estate in Massachusetts was about equally divided between land and buildings; in 1931 buildings represented 65 per cent of the combined total. A similar movement is seen in the few other states which keep records of building valuations, and doubtless would be shown for many others if statistics were available. There can be little doubt that in time, and perhaps in the near future, the value of buildings in the United States will exceed the value of the land.

DWELLING-HOUSES

It is, then, a fair conclusion that in economically advanced nations buildings occupy second and sometimes first place in the national assets, and constantly tend to overtake land. Dwelling-houses, furthermore, form a large proportion of the value of buildings; but to determine their exact position, it is necessary to analyze the figures for buildings more closely.

In 1896 Mulhall,[9] who devoted a large amount of study to

---

portant items is arrived at by capitalizing profits rather than by inventorying the tangible assets connected therewith.

[8] Colquhoun, Patrick, "Treatise on the Population, Wealth, Power and Resources of the British Empire" (Joseph Mawman, London, 1815), p. 55.

[9] Mulhall, Michael George, "Industries and Wealth of Nations" (Longmans, Green and Co., London, 1896), Table No. XXXIV, p. 392. A summary of Mulhall's data is given in the Appendix (p. 513).

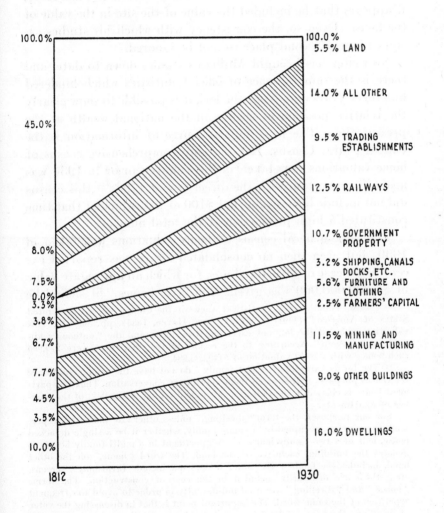

— CHART 4 —

PERCENTAGE DISTRIBUTION OF WEALTH OF GREAT BRITAIN
BY PRINCIPAL ITEMS (APPROXIMATE): 1812 AND 1930

100.0%   100.0%
                                          5.5% LAND

                                          14.0% ALL OTHER

45.0%
                                          9.5% TRADING
                                               ESTABLISHMENTS

                                          12.5% RAILWAYS

                                          10.7% GOVERNMENT
                                                PROPERTY
8.0%
                                          3.2% SHIPPING, CANALS
                                               DOCKS, ETC.
7.5%   5.6% FURNITURE AND
0.0%   CLOTHING
3.3%   2.5% FARMERS' CAPITAL
3.8%
6.7%   11.5% MINING AND
                                                 MANUFACTURING
7.7%   9.0% OTHER BUILDINGS
4.5%
3.5%
                                          16.0% DWELLINGS
10.0%

1812   1930

national wealth and national income, published figures covering the previous year in a number of countries. For every leading country he assigned second place in the national wealth to houses, except in the United Kingdom, where he placed them first. His figures were largely estimated, often from insufficient or even doubtful data, and contain many variations; moreover, it appears that he included the value of the site in the value of the house. Even so, the consistency with which his studies assigned houses second place cannot be ignored.

No writer has brought Mulhall's studies down to date, and there is the same absence of official statistics which hindered him forty years ago. None the less, it is possible to show clearly the relative position of shelter in the national wealth at the present time. The most logical source of information is the United States Census. But the only comprehensive census of home valuations ever taken in this country prior to 1930 was made in connection with the direct tax of 1798;[10] this census did not include homes valued at $100 or less, which at that time constituted a high proportion of the total number.

The next general census of home valuations was taken in 1930; but even then no consolidated figure was reported except in the case of farm dwellings, for which an aggregate value of $7,000,000,000 was given. Non-farm homes,[11] it should be

[10] Pitkin, Timothy, "A Statistical View of the Commerce of the United States of America" (Durrie & Peck, New Haven, 1835), pp. 309–310. This valuation included the lot, not exceeding two acres, and the "outhouses appurtenant thereto." According to the results of this tax, there were 276,695 such homes with a total valuation of $140,683,984.

[11] The terms "dwelling" and "family" do not have the same significance for census purposes that is given them in ordinary conversation. Thus an apartment-house is classed in the Census as a single dwelling, regardless of the number of apartments.

For our purposes, the term "dwelling," unless otherwise indicated, represents the quarters occupied by a single family, whether it be a single detached house, half of a two-family house, or an apartment in a multi-family house; it denotes the building, exclusive of the land. The word "home," on the other hand, includes the land or its value; it does not include furnishings, screens, etc., which are ordinarily included in the cost of construction. The terms "house" and "dwelling" are used indifferently in order to avoid too frequent repetition of the same word. The important point is that in discussing the value of dwellings the value of land is excluded, whereas in discussing the value of homes it is included.

realized, represent over 75 per cent of the total number of homes in the United States, and a much higher percentage of their total value; yet for this major group the Census gave neither

—— CHART 5 ——

MEDIAN VALUES OF OWNED NON-FARM HOMES
IN THE UNITED STATES BY STATES: 1930

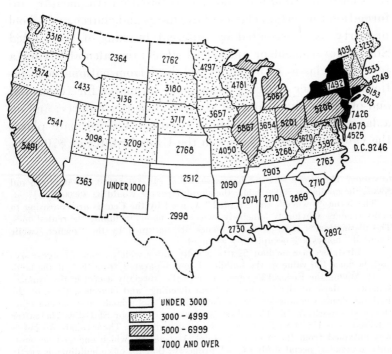

□	UNDER 3000
▒	3000 - 4999
▨	5000 - 6999
■	7000 AND OVER

totals nor averages, confining itself to *median values* by states for owned homes and to *median rentals* for rented homes, with classifications by value or rental groups, respectively.[12]

12 The median values of non-farm homes for urban and rural communities separately and the average values of farm dwellings in 1930 as reported by the Census are given in the Appendix, p. 514.

The Census defines the median value as "the value of that home which would stand in the middle of the series if all the homes were arranged according

These Census medians for "owned" non-farm homes by states are shown in Chart 5; it is impossible to construct from them a satisfactory valuation of the country's dwelling-houses.[13] The records of individual states are equally insufficient. So far as we can ascertain, only Connecticut compiles a record of dwelling valuations separately from those of land. It was, therefore, necessary to construct an original estimate for dwelling-house valuations in the United States in 1930.

This estimate (see Chart 6) was nearly completed before the Census of 1930 was taken. It is based on fragmentary information for certain classes of dwellings and church and school property as represented by different bureaus of the United States Government or of various states; on calculations for a few other classes of buildings obtained from national associations and other sources; on original estimates for residential and other buildings arrived at from state tax reports; and on a large amount of miscellaneous data.[14] The estimate places the value of dwelling-houses in the United States at $70,000,-

---

to value." Thus for a series of homes valued at $10,000, $8000, $5000, $4000, and $3000, the median is $5000, while the simple average would be $6000.

The terms "owned" and "rented" as used by the Census are confusing to many readers. Obviously somebody owns every home, including the rented ones. The distinction is that "owned" homes are occupied by the "owner," while "rented" homes are occupied by a tenant.

[13] First, because median figures usually differ widely from averages; second, because the value of the building is not separated from that of the land.

[14] Among the Federal Government reports especially useful in this connection were those of the Census for farm dwellings and churches, those of the Federal Trade Commission for public buildings and schools, and the construction cost reports of the United States Bureau of Labor Statistics (hereafter referred to as USBLS) for various classes of buildings. The estimate for hotels was obtained from the American Hotel Association, which engaged accountants to make a special study of such property; that for office buildings is partly based on data furnished by the National Association of Building Owners and Managers.

The valuation here used is in dollars current at the time of the census. As compared with values prior to the World War, part of the increase merely reflects the change in the value of the dollar and not a change in the volume of building. The total here given, however, cannot be divided by an index number of construction costs in order to make comparisons with pre-War figures, since in arriving at this estimate the value of pre-War structures was not increased in accordance with the rise in the building cost index.

—— CHART 6 ——

APPROXIMATE VALUATIONS OF BUILDINGS
IN THE UNITED STATES BY MAJOR CLASSES: 1930

Estimated Total Value	$ 115 000 000 000
Dwellings	$ 70 000 000 000
Hotels	$ 4 000 000 000
Non-Residential	$41 000 000 000

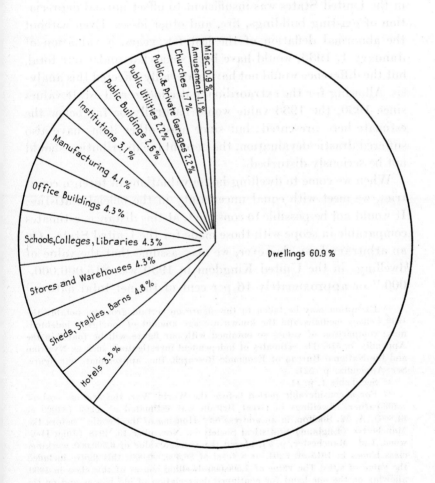

000,000.[15] This total exceeds that for any other class of buildings, and indeed is more than 60 per cent of the total for all classes combined. It easily places dwelling-houses in the second position among the nation's tangible assets; [16] it is more than the entire wealth of France, more than twice that of Canada, and more than four times that of the Argentine Republic.

The years of depression have, it is true, reduced this figure. Between 1930 and 1933 the value of new building construction in the United States was insufficient to offset normal depreciation of existing buildings, fire, and other losses. Even without the abnormal deflation of the last few years, a valuation of January 1, 1933, would have been somewhat under our total, but the difference would not have materially affected this analysis. Allowing for the extraordinary decline in real estate values since 1930, the 1933 value would naturally be far below the estimate here presented; but since most other items have also suffered drastic devaluation, the percentage distribution should not be seriously disturbed.

When we come to dwelling-house valuations in foreign countries, we meet with equal uncertainty in the official statistics. It would not be possible to construct, at this distance, estimates comparable in scope with those made for the United States. On an arbitrary basis, however, we may assume that the value of dwellings in the United Kingdom in 1930 was $15,000,000,-000,[17] or approximately 16 per cent of the net total national

[15] Exception may be taken to this figure on certain grounds, notably the 1930 Census medians and the known average amount of mortgage indebtedness; comparison of values so obtained with our figure will be found in the Appendix, p. 516. The estimates of independent investigators, such as Nystrom and the National Bureau of Economic Research, Inc., approximate our figure. See Appendix, p. 521.

[16] See Table 1, p. 11.

[17] For a considerable period before the World War, the average cost of wage-earners' dwellings in Great Britain was estimated at £200 ($1000 at $4.866). A. W. Shelton, in an address on " Housing of the People " before the Manchester (England) Statistical Society on November 13, 1918 (John Heywood, Ltd., Manchester, p. 3), placed the average value of 6,500,000 working-class homes in 1915 at £204, or a total of $6,500,000,000; this figure included the value of sites. The value of 7,500,000 dwelling-houses of this class in 1930, allowing on the one hand for continued depreciation of old houses and on the

wealth; and that the indicated total value of dwellings in Germany in the same year was $19,500,000,000,[18] or 22.5 per cent of the national wealth.[19] An arbitrary estimate of the aggregate value of all dwellings in France exclusive of site values is $10,-000,000,000, or 16.5 per cent of the national wealth.[20]

The dwellings of India offer striking contrast to those of highly industrialized countries. Nearly nine-tenths of the population is in agricultural communities, and the typical dwelling is a small one-story structure, built of mud with a wooden roof-frame and grass thatch. Where the owner is fortunate enough to have access to a bamboo grove, he is not compelled to purchase any materials whatsoever, and even where these are purchased, the cost is by Occidental standards trifling — only a

---

other for market appreciation, and also for the large number of new dwellings erected in the interval at relatively high costs, may be placed at $10,000,000,000, exclusive of sites. (The Inter-Departmental Committee on the Rent Restrictions Acts estimated that of 7,500,000 houses [not dwellings] in England and Wales in 1914, between 5,000,000 and 6,000,000 were " working-class " houses; in 1930 the total number of houses was about 9,000,000; the number of dwellings was somewhat greater. " Ministry of Health Report " [His Majesty's Stationery Office, London, 1931], pp. 18, 19). Including dwellings of higher-income groups at a much higher average valuation and dwellings in Northern Ireland, we arrive at the figure quoted in the text.

18 The average pre-War cost of wage-earners' dwellings in Germany is placed by one authority at about 6000 marks or $1400 (" Housing Policy in Europe " [Geneva, 1930, published in the United Kingdom for International Labour Office (hereafter ILO) by P. S. King and Son, Ltd., London], p. 345). Including dwellings of the higher-income groups, the average value would be greater, and the average cost of dwellings erected in recent years was considerably higher than that prevailing before the War. The average *value* of all such dwellings in existence in 1930, however, would be less than $1400. A general average of $1200 has led to the total we give.

19 See Table 2, note (b), p. 20.

20 An estimate of dwelling-house values in France in 1910, ostensibly official, placed the total at 59,600,000,000 francs, or a little less than $12,000,000,-000, but the site was probably included. It is known that many small dwellings erected in France before the War cost only a few hundred dollars each. On the other hand, as will be noted in Chapter XI, p. 431, under a five-year program of state-aided housing, inaugurated in 1928, it was proposed to erect 200,000 " cheap " dwellings at an average cost of 35,000 francs, and 60,000 moderate-rent dwellings at an average cost of 70,000 francs. (In 1910 the par value of the franc expressed in United States currency was 19.3 cents; in 1933 it was 3.92 cents.) These figures serve as the basis for the estimate here presented.

few dollars per dwelling. These dwellings are usually erected by the owner with family and communal assistance, but even allowing for such labor the average value of rural dwellings in India can hardly equal $20. Including dwellings of all types, from the hovels of the poorest to the palaces of the native princes,[21] the average value per dwelling may be placed at $50

TABLE 2

COMPARISON OF ESTIMATED VALUE OF DWELLING-HOUSES WITH TOTAL
NATIONAL WEALTH OF SELECTED COUNTRIES IN 1930

(Exclusive of site value)

Country	Number of dwellings	Estimated total value[a]	Per cent of total national wealth	Value per dwelling
United States ..	29,900,000	70,000	16.5	$2,340
Canada	2,000,000	3,000	8.5	1,500
United Kingdom.	10,500,000	15,000	16.5	1,430
France	11,500,000	10,000	16.5	870
Germany	16,200,000	19,000	22.5[b]	1,170
Netherlands ...	1,500,000	1,750	21.0	1,160
India	55,000,000	3,300	7.0	60

NOTE: The term " dwelling " here signifies the abode of a family, not, as by the Census definition, an entire apartment-house or a single house indiscriminately.

(a) In millions of dollars. These estimates are necessarily arbitrary.

(b) The indicated percentage is 34, but this is based on post-War estimates of a total national wealth of $55,000,000,000, which is much below the pre-War total; a ratio of 22.5 per cent would be a more representative figure under normal conditions.

to $70. With $60 as the mean, we may estimate the value of all dwellings at $3,300,000,000, or 7 per cent of the total wealth.

The estimates of total dwelling-house values for several leading countries, together with their relative importance in the total national wealth and the average value per dwelling, are shown in Table 2. The relative position of land, dwellings, and other buildings in the total wealth of certain of these countries

[21] Because of their comparatively small number, these have less effect on the average value than might be supposed.

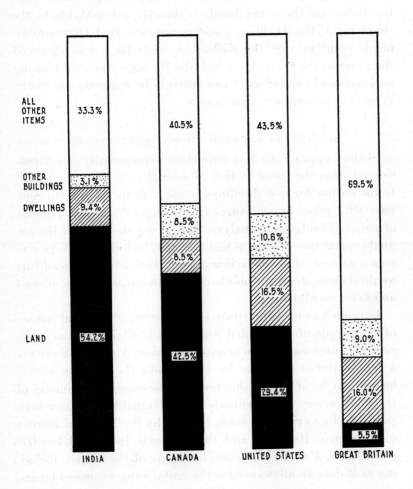

—— CHART 7 ——

RELATIVE POSITION OF LAND, DWELLINGS, AND ALL OTHER BUILDINGS
IN THE TOTAL WEALTH OF SELECTED COUNTRIES: 1930

ALL OTHER ITEMS

INDIA 33.3%
CANADA 40.5%
UNITED STATES 43.5%
GREAT BRITAIN 69.5%

OTHER BUILDINGS

INDIA 3.1%

DWELLINGS

INDIA 9.4%
CANADA 8.5%
UNITED STATES 10.6%
GREAT BRITAIN 9.0%

CANADA 8.5%
UNITED STATES 16.5%
GREAT BRITAIN 16.0%

LAND

INDIA 54.2%
CANADA 42.5%
UNITED STATES 29.4%
GREAT BRITAIN 5.5%

INDIA CANADA UNITED STATES GREAT BRITAIN

appears in Chart 7; the table and chart indicate that as a rule dwelling-houses constitute from one-sixth to one-fifth or more of the wealth of these countries. A distinctly lower ratio in the case of Canada is chiefly due to the relatively sparse population and the high value of other items, and does not necessarily indicate a low standard of housing. The low percentage for India, on the other hand, is directly attributable to the character of the dwelling, and demonstrates that from an economic point of view the civilization of India is less advanced than that of the West. Even in India the importance of housing as a national capital asset can scarcely be ignored, and in the West it is of primary significance.

SHELTER AS RELATED TO NATIONAL INCOME

Shelter appears no less important economically when considered from the point of view of annual cost. The yearly cost to the nation for new dwellings is not a proper figure to compare with other expenditures from income [22] for the purpose of national budgetary analysis. Rather we should take the annual expenditures for home maintenance, including average economic interest on the home investment. Such a total expenditure would include items for obsolescence, upkeep, economic interest and taxes on all homes.

Inasmuch as no authoritative *application* of the total income of the people of the United States was available, it was again necessary to construct an original estimate. Although there are a few scattered estimates by individuals, they are on such a basis as to be of little value for this discussion.[23] Estimates of the total *income* of individuals in the United States have been prepared by various agencies, notably by the National Bureau of Economic Research and the National Industrial Conference Board. For our purposes, the figure of the former, including as it does an allowance for the rental value of owned homes,

[22] This expenditure is discussed in Chapter V, p. 210.

[23] For an estimated distribution of total expenditures, including purchases made with borrowed funds, see p. 30.

—— CHART 8 ——

DISTRIBUTION FOR EXPENDITURE OF THE INCOME OF THE PEOPLE
OF THE UNITED STATES BY MAJOR ITEMS (APPROXIMATE): 1928

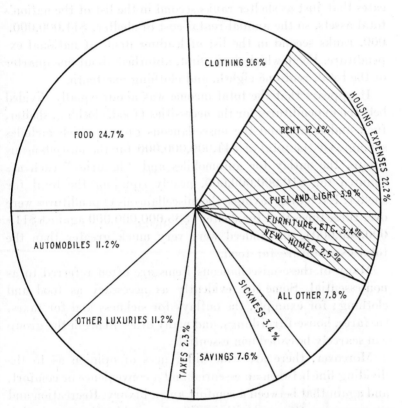

CLOTHING 9.6%

FOOD 24.7%

RENT 12.4%

HOUSING EXPENSES 22.2%

FUEL AND LIGHT 3.9%

FURNITURE, ETC. 3.4%

NEW HOMES 2.5%

AUTOMOBILES 11.2%

ALL OTHER 7.8%

OTHER LUXURIES 11.2%

SICKNESS 3.4%

TAXES 2.3%

SAVINGS 7.6%

is the more satisfactory. It shows a total " realized income " [24]
of individuals in the United States in 1928, the latest reported
year, of $89,400,000,000, exclusive of additions to plant or
other capital account by corporations or other establishments.[25]

[24] This consists in the main of the amounts received by individuals in the
form of wages, salaries, pensions, compensation for injuries, interest, dividends, rents, royalties, services of durable consumers' goods, and profits withdrawn from business.

[25] This includes an item of " imputed " income (amounting since 1922 to

In Table 3, an original estimate of the application of this total is given; percentage comparisons appear in Chart 8.

Table 3 covers the entire population and not merely wage-earners. Moreover, it includes savings and is therefore not simply a statement of actual expenditures. This compilation indicates that just as shelter ranks second in the list of the nation's total assets, so the annual rental cost of shelter, $11,000,000,-000, ranks second in the list of leading items of national expenditure. Food, which ranks first, absorbed about one-quarter of the total, rent one-eighth, and clothing one-tenth.

It appears that the total income was about equally divided between expenditures for the necessities (food, clothing, shelter, fuel, and light) and the miscellaneous group, which includes savings. Of the total of $44,000,000,000 for the miscellaneous group, the outlay for automobiles and " luxuries " each accounted for $10,000,000,000, nearly equaling the total for shelter. Excluding savings, the miscellaneous expenditures were over three times that for shelter ($35,000,000,000 against $11,-000,000,000), and indeed were very much greater than the total expenditure for food.

Many of these miscellaneous items are often referred to as non-essential. Some are evidently as necessary as food and clothing; for example, the outlays for sickness and for taxes, carfares, house-furnishings, and many other items in the group can scarcely be called non-essential.

Moreover, there are wide differences of opinion as to the dividing line between an essential and a convenience or comfort, and again that between a comfort and a luxury. Recreation and pleasure are often and with justification held to be as essential,

---

about $5,250,000,000 annually) covering "the estimated value of the services rendered to their owners by durable direct or consumers' goods," as for instance the rental value of a house occupied by the owner. It does not include such items as "the income which might be imputed to housewives and house-holders for services rendered to their own families" or "income arising from changes in the value of property" (King, W. I., "The National Income and Its Purchasing Power" [National Bureau of Economic Research, Inc., 1930], pp. 42, 73–74).

TABLE 3

 APPROXIMATE DISPOSITION FOR EXPENDITURE OF THE INCOME OF THE
PEOPLE OF THE UNITED STATES IN 1928[a]

(Estimated)

		Per cent
Food	$22,000,000,000	24.7
Clothing	8,500,000,000	9.6
Shelter	11,000,000,000	12.4[b]
Fuel and light	3,500,000,000	3.9
Miscellaneous:		
Automobiles	10,000,000,000	11.2
" Luxuries "	10,000,000,000	11.2
Sickness[c]	3,000,000,000	3.4
Furniture and house furnishings ..	3,000,000,000	3.4
Individual taxes[d]	2,000,000,000	2.3
Savings[e]	9,000,000,000	10.1
Education	2,500,000,000	2.8
Religion	1,000,000,000	1.1
Sundries	3,500,000,000	3.9
	$89,000,000,000[f]	100.0

(*a*) The totals for food, clothing, rent, and fuel and light were estimated in part from average per-family expenditures for these items as reported in various cost-of-living studies by the USBLS and other agencies. The results thus obtained were checked from other data. (See p. 104.) The sources of the estimates for most of the miscellaneous items are indicated in the notes to Table 19.

(*b*) In many cost-of-living studies, which exclude savings and some other items included here, this percentage runs substantially higher (see pp. 104–111).

(*c*) Including incidental costs. Based upon United States Department of Commerce data.

(*d*) Chiefly income taxes; exclusive of taxes on dwellings (included in rent), taxes of corporations, etc., which are deducted before estimating the total income, and excise and other taxes, which are included in the cost of goods consumed.

(*e*) This item does not include the savings of business enterprises in the form of additions to plant, new equipment, etc., since our distribution deals with the expenditures of individuals. It does, however, attempt to include investment in new dwelling-houses (about $2,000,000,000).

(*f*) The total is the National Bureau of Economic Research's estimate of the realized income of the people of the United States in 1928. (See p. 23.) All items in the table are derived by taking percentages, arrived at by the authors, of this NBER total.

if not to man's existence, at least to his efficiency and well-being, as suitable shelter and proper clothing. For example, when in 1931 it was proposed to place a tax on cosmetics, objection was promptly made that they should not be classed as luxuries.[26] The radio, because of its educational and recreational value, to say nothing of its political significance, cannot be strictly classed as a luxury, although it is certainly a newcomer in the field of useful accessories. Likewise a minor and undefinable portion of the outlay for passenger automobiles is for business purposes.[27]

An original estimate [28] of the total expenditures of United States families for so-called luxury items appears in Table 4. For purposes of comparison, this table also includes the estimated expenditures for new dwelling-houses and for housing maintenance. Chart 9 offers a comparison of the expenditures for " luxuries " with those for major necessities — food, clothing, fuel and light, and certain others.

The largest single outlay in the " luxury " group is for passenger automobiles. An allowance of $10,000,000,000 may seem excessive; as a matter of fact, for 1928 it is conservative, and some estimates run much higher. As already stated, the annual national expenditure for shelter, $11,000,000,000, was almost equaled in 1928 by that for passenger automobiles, and by

[26] *Boston Post,* November 30, 1931.

[27] Various estimates of the amount of so-called luxury expenditures have been prepared in recent years. The National Education Association has on several occasions prepared incomplete compilations for a comparison with expenditures for education; one such estimate, issued in 1929, is given in the Appendix, p. 520. It placed the total for certain major luxury or non-essential expenditures in 1926 at $18,200,000,000, of which nearly $12,000,000,000 was charged against passenger automobiles.

Stuart Chase ("Play," in "Whither Mankind," edited by Charles A. Beard [Longmans, Green & Co., New York, 1930], pp. 336–337; see the Appendix, p. 521), places the total outlay coming under the general head of luxury expenditures in 1928 at $21,000,000,000. This author estimated the cost of passenger automobiles at only $5,000,000,000, which is certainly too low. On the other hand, some of his other items — as for instance an allowance of $3,000,-000,000 for entertaining, visiting, night clubs, and road houses — seem excessive.

[28] Based on studies by college and other research staffs, and on data secured from government bureaus, national associations of manufacturers, circulars and prospectuses of banking and brokerage houses, and other sources.

— CHART 9 —

EXPENDITURES BY PEOPLE OF THE UNITED STATES
BY MAJOR ITEMS (ESTIMATED): 1928

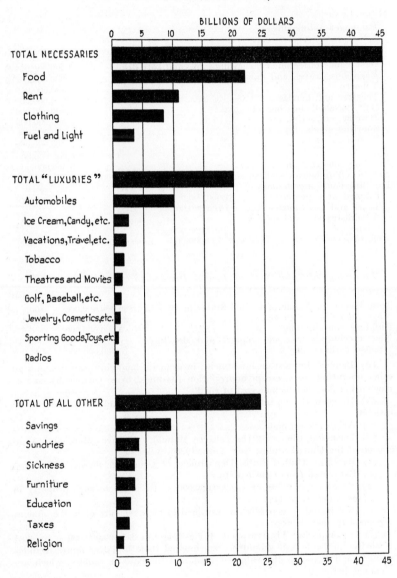

TABLE 4

ESTIMATED TOTAL EXPENDITURES IN THE UNITED STATES FOR CERTAIN MAJOR LUXURIES AND FOR CONSTRUCTION AND MAINTENANCE OF DWELLING-HOUSES IN 1928

Major Luxuries
Passenger automobiles

New cars	$3,300,000,000	
Operating costs a	6,700,000,000	$10,000,000,000

Ice-cream, confectionery, chewing-gum, and soft drinks ..	2,500,000,000 b
Vacations, travel, and day-trips	2,000,000,000 c
Tobacco	1,500,000,000 d
Theatres and movies	1,200,000,000 b
Golf, baseball, boating, etc.	1,000,000,000 c
Jewelry, cosmetics, etc.	800,000,000
Sporting goods, toys, etc.	500,000,000
Radios	500,000,000 e
	$20,000,000,000

Building construction		5,000,000,000 f
New dwelling-houses and repairs	$3,000,000,000	

Dwelling-house maintenance

Interest at 6 per cent	$4,000,000,000 g		
Taxes and assessments	1,700,000,000		
Administration and miscellaneous	600,000,000		
Obsolescence h	700,000,000	7,000,000,000 i	10,000,000,000

Percentage of Total National Income Devoted to Certain Expenditures

		Per cent
Total income of people of United States in 1928 ..	$89,000,000,000	100.0
Major luxuries (as above)	20,000,000,000	22.4
Building construction	5,000,000,000	5.6
New dwelling-houses and repairs and dwelling-house maintenance	10,000,000,000	11.2

(a) Includes interest on investment, insurance, chauffeurs' salaries, and all other operating costs, except depreciation (assumed to be covered by cost of new cars); does not include cost of roads.

(b) Based partly on information secured by correspondence and partly on estimates.

(c) Arbitrary estimate.

(d) Dushkind, Charles, "The Tobacco Manual" (Tobacco Merchants Association of the United States, New York, 1926), p. 26.

(e) Based on United States Department of Commerce data.

(f) Estimated from Census data.

(g) Based on estimate of $70,000,000,000 as the value of such property in 1930 (see Table 1, p. 11).

(h) Not including depreciation, assumed to be taken care of in the amount expended for new houses.

(i) In comparing this figure with the estimate of $11,000,000,000 as the cost of shelter in Table 3, it should be remembered that the latter figure includes interest and taxes on the value of land and the cost of repairs, which are excluded here.

that for " luxuries." It is often asserted that large portions of
our people cannot afford adequate housing. This statement
will be further discussed in other sections of the book, but at
this point a question with important social implications may
be raised. The usual solution proffered for the *impasse* is the
use of public funds for furnishing housing to these people. But
is the proposal really to buy houses or to buy automobiles?

Another approach to the question of annual expenditures in
the United States is the distribution of the total expenditures
of the people of the United States in selected recent years. Such
a distribution, compiled by The Business Week, is presented in
Table 5. It deals with total expenditures rather than with the
total national income, so that the ratio of housing to total naturally differs from that already given in Table 4. Moreover, the
cost of housing as here reported included the cost of house furnishings, fuel, electricity, servants' wages, and various other
items, and not merely economic rent. Nevertheless, Table 5
also indicates the importance of the cost of shelter in the national economy, placing it second only to that of food.

Table 5 suggests another thought. For several years prior
to 1930 the total expenditures of the people of the United
States considerably exceeded the total national income; this is
largely explained by heavy purchases on the instalment plan
and by other forms of borrowing to finance purchases. Such a
condition cannot of course continue for any length of time. In
our complex economic organism, each worker performs only a
minute part in the work of production and distribution. In a
primitive country, or, less apparently, the developed nation,
consumption cannot long exceed production. If it does, the
primitive family hungers and dies; the modern economic structure disintegrates, collapses perhaps, along with the social and
physical well-being of its people. The difference between the two
is that the cooperative labor of the modern state serves as a
leveler. It spreads among its people the group benefits from
time averages, production averages, and place averages — an
economic process in which improvement is sorely needed. If in

TABLE 5

DISTRIBUTION OF TOTAL VALUE OF GOODS AND SERVICES BOUGHT, DI-
RECT TAXES PAID, AND SAVINGS BY INDIVIDUALS IN THE
UNITED STATES IN SELECTED YEARS[a]

(Millions of dollars)

	1919	1921	1927	1929	1930
Food	21,495	18,036	23,194	24,392	21,712
Housing[b]	12,757	12,948	17,229	18,337	16,178
Wearing-apparel	9,577	7,923	9,277	9,313	8,044
Transportation	6,998	7,110	12,281	13,815	12,360
Personal	6,933	6,610	9,390	10,497	8,903
Savings	6,042	5,371	10,054	12,543	7,892
Recreation	1,754	1,750	4,151	5,250	4,171
Health	1,896	2,104	3,286	3,776	3,330
Direct taxes[c]	2,364	2,033	2,448	2,685	2,457
Education	1,352	1,251	2,051	2,308	1,994
Social activities	1,140	1,224	1,735	2,030	1,874
Civil	594	640	972	1,155	1,203
	72,902	67,000	96,068	106,101	90,118

Percentages

	1919	1921	1927	1929	1930
Food	29.5	26.9	24.2	22.9	24.1
Housing	17.5	19.3	17.9	17.2	18.0
Wearing-apparel	13.1	11.9	9.7	8.8	8.9
Transportation	9.6	10.6	12.8	13.0	13.7
Personal	9.5	9.9	9.8	9.9	9.9
Savings	8.3	8.0	10.5	11.9	8.8
Recreation	2.4	2.6	4.3	5.0	4.6
Health	2.6	3.1	3.4	3.6	3.7
Direct taxes[c]	3.2	3.0	2.5	2.5	2.7
Education	1.9	1.9	2.1	2.2	2.2
Social activities	1.6	1.8	1.8	1.9	2.1
Civil	0.8	1.0	1.0	1.1	1.3
	100.0	100.0	100.0	100.0	100.0

(a) From The Business Week, " The American Consumer Market " (Mc-
Graw-Hill Publishing Co., Inc., New York, 1932), Table 1. This is not a distribution of the *income* of individuals but of their expenditures (approximate) and
savings. These exceed the income partly because purchases on instalment plans
or other forms of credit are included and partly for other reasons.

(b) Includes the cost of fuel and electricity, furnishings, servants' wages,
and other items, not merely the cost of shelter (economic rent) as given in
Table 3, p. 25.

(c) Not paid in connection with any other expenditure.

time of prosperity modern society could store up its needs for those of adversity, much waste and many economic ills would be avoided. The tendency of post-War Europe and America seems rather to have been to drink too fully from the springs of plenty with no thought for the morrow. In the life of the individual, excess of expenditure over income quickly destroys solvency. In the life of a nation, great complexities of social and political structure and policy becloud the results of its annual economy, the trends of which are difficult to see clearly. But a nation is not exempt from a day of reckoning; the same factors of income and outgo that affect the economic position of the individual also affect that of the nation.

Search in economic publications has failed to reveal distributions for other countries similar to that just given. One such distribution [29] of income of the people of Great Britain in 1881 placed the percentage outlay for house rent at 8.8, but a considerable part of the item of taxes, which was credited with 5.4 per cent, should, it seems, have been added to it. Another estimate, by Sir Robert Giffen in 1903,[30] placed house rent expenditure at 10.5 per cent of the total national per-capita expenditure. These calculations imply that the national per-capita expenditure for this purpose in Great Britain was relatively less than that in the United States as stated above.

The proportion of the national income devoted to shelter naturally varies in different lands, and is more or less directly dependent on the general economic status of the people concerned. In countries like India and China, the proportion of national income expended for food is very much higher than in countries like the United States, Canada, Great Britain, and Germany. An increased ratio devoted to food is ordinarily accompanied by a lower one for shelter, although it is in many cases compensated by decreased expenditures for miscellaneous items.

Contemporary European statistics are beclouded by the

[29] Levi, Leoni, quoted in Mulhall, Michael G., "Dictionary of Statistics" (George Routledge and Sons, Ltd., London, 1899), p. 359.

[30] "The Wealth of the Empire, and How It Should Be Used" (Journal of the Royal Statistical Society, September, 1903, pp. 594–595).

greater or less degree of government participation in housing.[31] It is commonly said that taxes in Europe are far in excess of those in the United States. A considerable but not readily ascertainable proportion of these taxes in recent years has been directed to government participation in the provision of shelter. If this allotment could be added to the direct expenditures for housing, it is likely that the national annual expenditure for housing in economically advanced European countries would be a large item, second only to that for food, although perhaps not equaling that in the United States. No country is yet so civilized that food does not dominate the annual expenditure; but the chief nations of Europe have progressed far beyond the primitive condition where starvation is just over the horizon, so that their expenditure for shelter comes to occupy a strong second position. It is conceivable that future economic development may render relatively unimportant the pursuit of food, shelter and clothing. But that time seems remote, and it suffices for our purpose to be able to affirm that in nations of advanced economic status shelter is definitely the second item of expenditure in the national budget, as its value is in capital assets.

SHELTER AS RELATED TO THE FAMILY BUDGET

In concluding the discussion of the economic importance of shelter, we must anticipate that of family budgets, reserved for Chapter III. While the percentages previously given for the annual cost of shelter compared with the national income closely reflect the relation of that cost to family income, the connection in the latter case is somewhat different. Family expenditures take no account of national savings in the form of additions to plant and to working capital by business organizations. Moreover, most discussions of family budgets deal with annual expenditures and disregard the item of individual savings. The cost of shelter thus represents a considerably higher proportion of family than of national expenditure. In countries like the United States, Great Britain, and Germany, shelter,

[31] Government aid is further discussed in Chapter XI.

about one-eighth of the national annual expenditure, ordinarily represents from one-sixth to one-fifth of the annual family budget. In newly or partially developed countries like Canada and Australia, it tends to run somewhat higher until a condition of economic maturity is attained. In countries such as those of the Orient, where a large part of the family income is of necessity devoted to providing food, and where shelter is of a primitive character, the housing cost ordinarily represents a much smaller proportion of the family outlay — sometimes less than 10 per cent.[32]

According to the International Labour Office, the proportions of family expenditure devoted to rent in several European countries just before the War were as follows: [33]

Per cent		Per cent	
Poland	18.1	Norway	15.7
Germany	18.0	Denmark	14.2
Hungary	18.0	Sweden	11.9
Great Britain ..	16.0	Finland	11.8
Austria	14.6	Italy	11.4
France	12.0	Switzerland	10.4

Owing to the fact that in many European countries the family outlay for rent has been reduced because of government subventions to housing in one form or another, these percentages have in some instances been sharply reduced, but if to the actual outlay made by the family there be added the cost of such governmental aid, the relative cost of shelter in the family budget will be fully as large as in the pre-War period, and in some cases even larger.

It appears, then, that the cost of shelter represents 10 per cent or even less of the family budget in countries of a comparatively primitive status and ranges from that up to 15 per cent or 20 per cent in the case of developed industrial countries,

[32] In Japan, which is sharply distinguished from most Oriental countries, the relative importance of shelter in family economics is only slightly less than that in the industrialized countries of the Occident.

[33] ILO, "European Housing Problems since the War" (Geneva, 1924), p. 30.

with a somewhat higher percentage in the case of a few countries which, though modern in their civilization, have not yet reached their full development.

From the facts here presented certain broad generalizations for economically advanced countries may be drawn: shelter is the second item in the national wealth, and its importance tends to increase; it ranks second only to food cost in the national annual expenditure, and it forms an important element in the family budget.

May we not expect that the provision of housing in the modern state shall be comparable in efficiency to that of other important requirements? Regarding the housing industry as vital to the national welfare, may we not demand that it be well organized and its strength preserved? As the following chapters will show, the answer to these questions is " yes," but our demands have not been met.

That this industry is out of joint is evident from the many politico-economic experiments that have been made with it, and that are so familiar to all of us today. Shelter is obviously a form of basic wealth for any social group, whatever its size or location, and whether it be conducted under the principle of individual or of common ownership. The sum total of a nation's housing is an essential part of its total wealth, whether viewed as a capital asset or as a consumable item (" rent ") in the nation's budget. A people without land to use or live upon is an impossibility, and one without shelter is unknown to economics. A people can live without the radio, the telephone, motor-cars, diamonds, and railways, but clearly not without land and food and shelter. Such elements form the very foundation of any economic structure; this being so, they should fit completely into the social and politico-economic policies of a people regardless of what those policies may be. Otherwise the economic structure will be undermined and threatened with destruction; for that structure is based on principles similar to those controlling other material forms: the machine, the plant, the industry, the state.

It is by no means improbable that eventually the basic necessaries of life, including housing, will become available to everyone through the better functioning of community life. But means to this end have still to be evolved; they are not available today even in communistic Russia, where economic equality amounts to a religious principle.

Integrity and harmony are just as vital in the economic structure as in the physical or social one — just as vital as in the working of a crew or the framework of a legal code. The provision of housing is one of the chief activities of human society. Its position in the group economy should be consistent and harmonious with other similar activities. Everyone, regardless of the amount of his personal property and income, has a vital and personal interest in the methods by which the housing industry is conducted, and in the place of shelter in the group economy.

CHAPTER II

The Present-Day House

BEFORE setting out on our study of the economic questions confronting the house of today, it will be desirable to see what it is like. To develop a composite picture for the whole world or even for the United States, with the dwelling-house's bewildering multiplicity and variety, is manifestly impossible. The best that may be done is to present a descriptive statement of the extent to which the typical dwelling in representative nations has become modified by the inclusion of new equipment and facilities.

There is no necessity to recapitulate in this place the story of evolution told in Volume I, " The History of the Home." There we found that the house, originally merely a shelter of one room, has through subdivision and inclusion of accessories and the growth of social customs become a complex mechanism in which the original function of shelter has been overshadowed by the conveniences and luxuries that have come to be regarded as essential. Its development is like a rapidly moving motion-picture film daily recording new problems and new solutions in housing; but we may profitably concentrate on a " still " photograph.

The complex factors which in all places condition the homes of today may be recalled. The house best suited to the semitropical climate of Florida, Spain, or Southern California will hardly suit the dweller in Minnesota or Norway. The building structure indigenous to the wooded regions of our own northeastern and northwestern coasts and southern conifered lands does not rise naturally on the brick-clay soils of the deforested regions or the adobe deserts of the Southwest. The customs of life in Europe and the United States are different; even more do both differ from those of India and Japan. Within a single country geography and materials may cause wide variation in the *natural* development of the plan, structure, and finish of a house; these are even more influenced, if not controlled, by the conditions of urban, suburban, or rural, of industrial or agricultural life. The city or suburban home commands useful public services, but is subject to concomitant restrictions; community life is continually changing physical requirements and demanding additional labor-saving and socially valued accessories, as well as features of pure comfort. The life of the farm and of distant regions, on the other hand, perpetuates housing of a more primitive character. That of the cotton-growing millions of the South, of the Spanish-Americans and Indians of the Southwest, and of the rock-soil farmers of the Northeast has come down through three generations. But even these homes are being transformed and freed from isolation by the motor-car and the telephone, the radio and the newspaper.

One specific social factor which is modifying the home of the Western world is reduction of the size of the family — a tendency that has been manifest in advanced nations during the past fifty or one hundred years. The decrease in the average size of families for certain countries over several decades is indicated in Chart 10, which also shows the number of persons per dwelling.[1] A similar reduction is to be found in other nations. The result inevitably affects at least the size of the home.

A related factor, and one of greater significance, is that of urbanization. This has appeared again and again in history at definite points in the development of civilizations. It has been marked in America since the beginning of the nineteenth century; abroad, the Industrial Revolution enormously accelerated the massing of European populations and stimulated the growth of cities. Urbanization involves public services and welfare and health regulations; it modifies the character of the ru-

[1] For the significance of the Census terms " family " and " dwelling " see p. 14, reference 11.

ral home, while specially developing the large apartment build-ing. This tendency toward multi-family dwellings is typical of all urbanization in the past as well as the present. The rise of urban land values primarily demands economy in the use of living space, and modern machinery makes practicable the de-velopment of ten- to twenty-storied apartments on a scale im-practicable in ancient Rome. Though group life inevitably results in social abuses, it accelerates evolution through in-creased opportunity for cooperation and the need of functional subdivision of labor.

The rapid rise of Babylon to political preeminence and fabu-lous wealth exemplifies this truth, as do the commanding impor-tance of the Greek city-states, with their swiftly flowering civilization, and the imperial power of Rome. For hundreds of years the Teutons and the Goths moved westward through the forests of Europe, changing their abodes but not their man-ners, yet when settled in the half-ruined but compact Roman cities they began to develop a genuine culture. Again, the Han-seatic cities contributed immensely to the trade and culture of Northern Europe, and the Italian cities contained and ex-pressed the glorious values of the Renaissance. Bearing these instances in mind, we may associate with the word " urbaniza-tion " not merely congestion, slums, traffic problems, and dis-ease, but cultural advance, organized living, and enhanced social values.

Cities are but a congeries of homes, buildings for housing the people, in both their private and group life: the factory, the home of industry; the office building, that of commerce. In the church, the school, the library, the theater, the assembly hall the city-dweller develops his social contacts and his intel-lectual and spiritual powers. The economic strength of this con-geries lies in its houses, factories, and office buildings, and the supplementary forms of capital wealth which these represent. Community government must control and foster these basic ele-ments for community good; thus will it best provide for the daily sustenance of its people and for sound growth. Public services include not only water supplies, sewage disposal, and

—— CHART 10 ——

NUMBER OF PERSONS PER FAMILY AND PER DWELLING IN THE UNITED
STATES, CANADA, AND ENGLAND AND WALES IN VARIOUS YEARS

Charted from Census data

PERSONS PER FAMILY

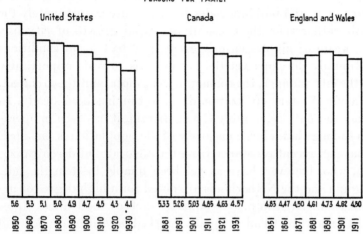

PERSONS PER DWELLING

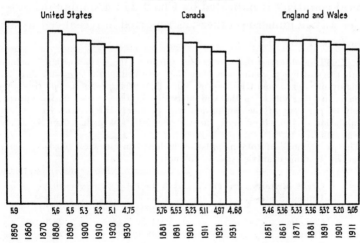

sanitary and building regulations, but also libraries and schools for intellectual advancement, and parks and playgrounds for recreation.

As a direct result of urbanization and its acceleration of evolution, appurtenances and comforts of the urban home continually increase. The public services and the laws regulating their use — and building codes as well — are unfortunately the result rather than the cause of the rapid growth of city life. The waste of obsolescence is great, and bad social conditions continually develop; yet these very evils provide opportunity for the city planner, the community engineer, and the architect.

In our Western civilization urbanization has been steady. In some older nations, notably Great Britain, it has been in operation so long that a large majority of the population is included. It has met recent resistance from the advocates of decentralization, who, however, have as yet been unable to stem the tide. Belgium and the Netherlands are noted for a high degree of urbanization. Even in newer countries such as the United States and Canada the trend is equally marked, and if continued will in the not distant future result in as high a degree of urbanization as has been reached in some older nations. The trend for several countries is indicated by Chart 11; a similar process is under way in numerous others, as reported in recent census surveys (see Table 6).[2]

[2] It will be observed that for census purposes the term "urban" includes communities of much smaller size than the word ordinarily suggests; in nearly all highly urbanized countries, however, a substantial proportion of the population is in large cities. In the United States in 1930, for example, approximately 30 per cent of the population was in ninety-three cities each having a population of 100,000 or more; nearly one-sixth was included in the twelve largest cities.

The proportions of total population included in cities of 100,000 or more in several leading countries are as follows:

	Year	Per cent (approximate)
Great Britain	1931	60.0
United States	1930	29.5
Germany	1925	26.7
Canada	1930	23.3
France	1930	20.1
Japan	1930	16.9
Italy	1930	17.5
India	1931	3.2

—— CHART II ——

PERCENTAGES OF URBAN POPULATION
IN VARIOUS COUNTRIES IN VARIOUS YEARS

Note:-The term "Urban" does not have the same significance in all countries; therefore, the percentages for different countries are not comparable.

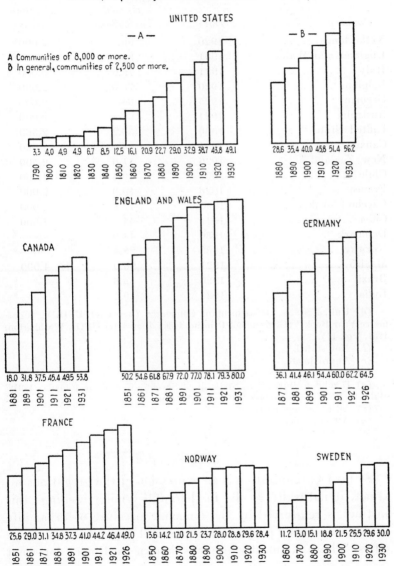

UNITED STATES

— A —

— B —

A Communities of 8,000 or more.
B In general, communities of 2,500 or more.

3.3 4.0 4.9 4.9 6.7 8.5 12.5 16.1 20.9 22.7 29.0 32.9 38.7 43.8 49.1

1790 1800 1810 1820 1830 1840 1850 1860 1870 1880 1890 1900 1910 1920 1930

28.6 35.4 40.0 45.8 51.4 56.2

1880 1890 1900 1910 1920 1930

ENGLAND AND WALES

GERMANY

CANADA

18.0 31.8 37.5 45.4 49.5 53.8

1881 1891 1901 1911 1921 1931

50.2 54.6 61.8 67.9 72.0 77.0 78.1 79.3 80.0

1851 1861 1871 1881 1891 1901 1911 1921 1931

36.1 41.4 46.1 54.4 60.0 62.2 64.5

1871 1881 1891 1901 1911 1921 1926

FRANCE

NORWAY

SWEDEN

25.6 29.0 31.1 34.8 37.3 41.0 44.2 46.4 49.0

1851 1861 1871 1881 1891 1901 1911 1921 1926

13.6 14.2 17.0 21.5 23.7 28.0 28.8 29.6 28.4

1850 1860 1870 1880 1890 1900 1910 1920 1930

11.2 13.0 15.1 18.8 21.5 25.5 29.6 30.0

1860 1870 1880 1890 1900 1910 1920 1930

TABLE 6

URBAN POPULATION OF SELECTED COUNTRIES IN RECENT YEARS [a]

Country	Date	Percentage of population classed as urban	Minimum population of urban areas
Netherlands	1920	96.0	2,000
England and Wales	1931	80.0	—— [b]
Italy	1921	79.0 [c]	3,000
Belgium	1920	78.0	2,000
Germany	1925	64.4	2,000
Australia	1921	62.1	3,000
United States [d]	1930	56.2	2,500
Canada [e]	1931	53.7	1,000
New Zealand	1926	51.6	2,500
Chile	1930	49.4	1,000
France	1926	49.0	2,000
Czecho-Slovakia	1930	47.8	2,000
Cuba	1919	44.7	1,000
Denmark	1930	44.0	—— [f]
Norway	1930	28.4	—— [g]
Mexico	1921	25.0	4,000
Brazil	1920	15.6	—— [b]
India	1921	10.2	—— [b]

(a) United States Department of Commerce (hereafter USDC), "Commerce Year Book" (Government Printing Office [hereafter GPO], Washington, 1931, Vol. II).

(b) Not stated.

(c) Approximate.

(d) Statistical Abstract, 1932, p. 46.

(e) Dominion Bureau of Statistics, "Seventh Census of Canada, 1931," Bulletin XX (F. W. Acland, Ottawa, 1932), p. 6.

(f) All towns and cities.

(g) All incorporated cities.

TYPE OF DWELLING

So far as urbanization is an expression of the gregarious instinct, it naturally results in the multi-family dwelling; this instinct is reinforced by the economic pressure of urban life when a substantial proportion of the total population is in large cities. The apartment-house was known in Rome; tenement structures of Europe date back at least to the Middle Ages; many European countries today favor them over the single-family house.

—— CHART 12 ——

PERCENTAGES OF FAMILIES, BY TYPES OF DWELLING, PROVIDED FOR BY NEW CONSTRUCTION IN 257 CITIES OF THE UNITED STATES IN 1921 AND 1932

Charted from United States Bureau of Labor Statistics data

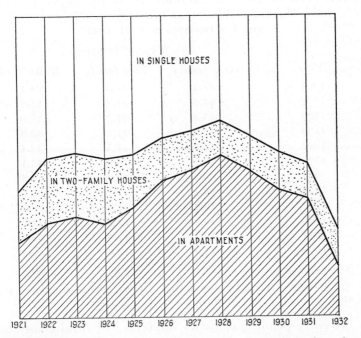

All this is likely to be overlooked by the American, for whom the single-family dwelling has long been the social ideal. It has been and still is the predominating type in this country, and houses fully three-quarters of the population. In the past thirty years, however, and especially since the World War, there has been a marked trend in urban and suburban communities to-

ward the multi-family dwelling; in many cities a majority of
families provided with new housing has been sheltered in such
dwellings. This is clearly brought out by Table 7, compiled by
the United States Bureau of Labor Statistics and based upon
building-permit data for 257 American cities; the data are
shown graphically in Chart 12. The figures, as stated, are for
cities, and do not represent conditions for the country as a
whole; they are for new construction only, undertaken or
projected.

TABLE 7

PERCENTAGE OF FAMILIES PROVIDED FOR IN DIFFERENT TYPES OF
NEW DWELLINGS PROJECTED IN THE SAME 257 CITIES OF
THE UNITED STATES, 1921–1932 [a]

	Type of Dwelling		
Year	*One-family*	*Two-family*	*Multi-family*
1921	58.3	17.3	24.4
1922	47.5	21.3	31.2
1923	45.8	21.2	33.0
1924	47.6	21.5	30.9
1925	46.0	17.5	36.4
1926	40.7	13.9	45.4
1927	38.3	13.4	48.3
1928	35.2	11.1	53.7
1929	40.2	11.4	48.5
1930	45.7	12.1	42.2
1931	49.2	11.5	39.3
1932	71.3	12.4	16.3
True averages	44.3	16.5	39.2

(a) USBLS, "Monthly Labor Review" (GPO, Washington, April, 1933),
p. 846.

No corresponding statistics for farm and rural houses have
been collected by the Government. For these, embracing approximately 44 per cent of the total population in 1930, the
single-family dwelling is the predominant type. More than
80 per cent of our two-family dwellings are found in urban communities; for farm and rural sections multi-family dwellings
may be left out of consideration.

In 1930, for the first time, the Census classified families in the United States by the type of dwelling occupied, i.e., single-family, two-family, and multi-family. The percentage distribution is as follows:

In single-family dwellings 76.3
In two-family dwellings 11.6
In multi-family dwellings 12.1
                                        ──────
                                         100.0

Table 8 gives the number of families and the number of dwellings, thus classified, for urban and for rural sections.[3] A percentage distribution of families by type of dwelling occupied and by type of community is shown in Chart 13.

The proportion of the population living in single-family dwellings is doubtless somewhat higher than the proportion of families, the average number of persons per single-family dwelling being larger than the average number per apartment; in any case, less than one-eighth of the total population in 1930 was housed in multi-family structures. However, the data presented show a decided trend toward that type of dwelling in urban communities, which today include well over one-half of the country's population. During very recent years, it is true, there has been a marked increase in the proportion of single-family dwellings in new construction. While this may mark the beginning of a permanent change, the decrease in apartment-house construction is probably due to the economic depression, which has made the financing of such structures almost impossible.

The United States Bureau of Labor Statistics has noted that if the apartment-house movement continues a majority of the population of many cities will soon be housed in multi-family structures.[4] This development has many important social con-

[3] The total number of occupied dwellings, by principal type, for each state will be found in the Appendix, p. 523.

[4] While multi-family dwellings are found in nearly all large cities, certain communities are noted for exceptionally high percentages of such structures. The outstanding example in the United States is, of course, New York City, especially the Borough of Manhattan, where in several recent years 99.9 per

TABLE 8

NUMBER OF OCCUPIED DWELLINGS AND OF FAMILIES, BY TYPE OF
DWELLING, IN THE UNITED STATES IN 1930 [a]

Area and class of dwelling	Dwellings Number	Per cent	Families Number	Per cent
Total	25,204,976	100.0	29,904,663	100.0
1-family	22,833,110	90.6	22,833,110	76.4
2-family	1,728,087	6.9	3,456,174	11.6
3-or-more-family	643,779	2.6	3,615,379	12.1
Urban	13,046,699	100.0	17,372,524	100.0
1-family	11,001,861	84.3	11,001,861	63.3
2-family	1,430,570	11.0	2,861,140	16.5
3-or-more-family	614,268	4.7	3,509,523	20.2
Rural	12,158,277	100.0	12,532,139	100.0
1-family	11,831,249	97.3	11,831,249	94.4
2-family	297,517	2.4	595,034	4.7
3-or-more-family	29,511	0.2	105,856	0.8

(a) United States Census (hereafter USC), " Population Bulletin, Families, 1930 " (GPO, Washington, 1933), Table 13. The percentages here given have been computed on the basis of the number of private families (29,904,-663), thus excluding approximately 75,000 institutional and other quasi-family groups.

Census Note. It has been found difficult in some cases, particularly in cities where the houses are built in solid blocks, to make this classification. The enumerators were instructed to return as one dwelling a two-family house with one apartment above the other, even though there was a separate front door for each apartment. On the other hand, where two families occupied parts of a building separated by a solid wall running up through the building, each part was counted as a dwelling, and likewise each "house" in a section of "row" houses.

---

cent of *new* dwelling-house construction has been of the multi-family type. Other cities noted for a large number of such dwellings are Boston, Cleveland, Detroit, Chicago, and St. Louis; more than one-third of all multi-family dwellings in the United States are in these six cities. In Philadelphia the apartment has thus far been relatively unpopular.

Two-family dwellings constitute a substantial proportion of the housing of Greater New York, Chicago, Cleveland, Detroit, Milwaukee, and St. Louis. In Greater New York in 1930 there were 136,568 dwellings of this type as against 294,037 one-family dwellings. In Chicago in the same year there were 116,340 two-family as against 209,685 single-family houses. In Los Angeles, on the other hand, there were only about 11,305 two-family as compared with 282,382 single-family dwellings. In Philadelphia, of nearly 400,000 dwellings only 24,400 were of the two-family type. This low figure is partly explained by the large number of " row " houses in Philadelphia, which have some characteristics of the two-family dwelling.

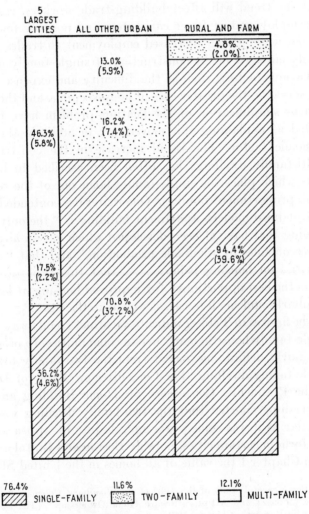

—— CHART 13 ——

PERCENTAGE DISTRIBUTION OF FAMILIES IN THE UNITED STATES
BY TYPE OF DWELLING OCCUPIED AND BY TYPE OF COMMUNITY: 1930

5
LARGEST
CITIES   ALL OTHER URBAN   RURAL AND FARM

4.8%
(2.0%)

13.0%
(5.9%)

16.2%
(7.4%)

46.3%
(5.8%)

94.4%
(39.6%)

17.5%
(2.2%)

70.8%
(32.2%)

36.2%
(4.6%)

76.4%
⧹⧹⧹ SINGLE-FAMILY

11.6%
▒ TWO-FAMILY

12.1%
☐ MULTI-FAMILY

KEY TO PERCENTAGES
Upper Figure is Percentage of Population Group
Lower Figure is Percentage of Total Population

sequences, the Bureau has contended, particularly a smaller proportion of home owners, "which means less settled communities, for people who own their homes move less frequently than people who live in rented dwellings." It further prophesies that the trend will affect building-trade workers, resulting in the employment of fewer carpenters and possibly fewer bricklayers, while giving increased employment to trades not ordinarily engaged in the construction of single-family dwellings.

Various factors, such as the difficulty and expense of securing servants, the greater ease of housekeeping, and the elimination or simplification of the heating problem have been presented as explaining this movement; in addition there is the economic factor. The rapid increase in the construction of multi-family dwellings has often been ascribed to high land costs which place the single-family home out of the reach of a large proportion of families.[5] One writer has contended that the well-planned modern apartment building is " the only form of housing that has yet been developed which effects any reasonable economies by wholesale production," and that " some authorities on housing believe . . . that this type of building offers the best opportunity for improved housing at lower cost, in suburbs and small towns, as well as in the cities." [6]

The figures in Table 7 indicate a distinct trend away from the single-family house in many urban communities. In others there is a fairly definite movement from the two-family toward the single-family dwelling. The Committee on Types of Dwellings of the President's Conference on Home Building and Home Ownership reported that the two-family dwelling was not so popular as it was some years ago, despite its appearance in a new form in certain cities, notably Boston and Buffalo.

In Chapter I the value of all homes in the United States was

[5] For a careful study of this subject see Woodbury, Coleman, " Apartment House Increases and Attitudes toward Home Ownership" (The Institute for Economic Research, Chicago, 1931).

[6] Holden, Thomas S., Vice-President of the F. W. Dodge Corporation, " Building and Loan Annals " (United States Building and Loan League, Chicago, 1930), p. 36.

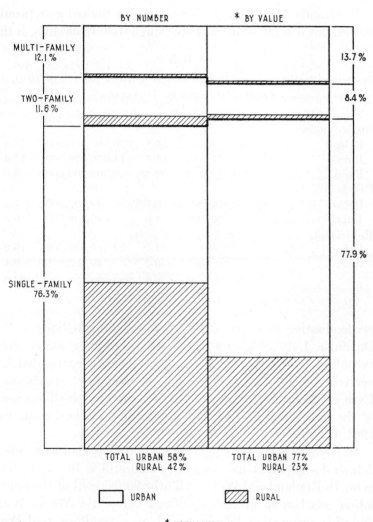

— CHART 14 —

DISTRIBUTION OF HOMES IN THE UNITED STATES BY TYPE
OF DWELLING AND BY TYPE OF COMMUNITY : 1930

BY NUMBER   * BY VALUE

MULTI-FAMILY
12.1 %

13.7 %

TWO-FAMILY
11.6 %

8.4 %

SINGLE - FAMILY
76.3 %

77.9 %

TOTAL URBAN 58%   TOTAL URBAN 77%
RURAL 42%   RURAL 23%

☐ URBAN   ▨ RURAL

* ESTIMATED

estimated at $70,000,000,000; including land, that value is about $90,000,000,000. In Table 9 an attempt is made to distribute this total by principal types of home; its distribution by type of dwelling and by type of community is the aim of Chart 14.

In Canada there is a similar movement toward apartment-houses, but it is not so defined; the single-family dwelling is the

TABLE 9

ESTIMATED VALUE OF THE HOMES OF THE UNITED STATES IN 1930, BY PRINCIPAL TYPES OF DWELLING [a]

Type of Home	Number	Per cent	Estimated value	Per cent
Single-family				
Urban	11,000,000	36.8	$50,800,000,000	56.4
Rural	5,100,000	17.1	11,350,000,000	12.6
Farm	6,700,000	22.4	8,000,000,000	8.9
Two-family				
Urban	2,900,000	9.7	6,700,000,000	7.5
Rural	600,000	2.0	820,000,000	0.9
Multi-family				
Urban	3,500,000	11.7	12,250,000,000	13.6
Rural	100,000	0.3	80,000,000	0.1
	29,900,000	100.0	$90,000,000,000	100.0

(a) For a more detailed estimate see Appendix, p. 526.

predominating type. In 1921, of 1,764,129 dwellings in the Dominion 1,497,305, or 85 per cent, were single houses, even excluding 76,471 row or terrace houses which represented 4.3 per cent of the total; less than 2 per cent were apartments. Even in cities, less than 4 per cent of residential dwellings were of the multi-family type; it is expected that the Census for 1931 will show an increase in this type of housing.

In Great Britain the single-family dwelling (not as a rule a detached structure) has long been and still is the prevailing type. In England and Wales well over 90 per cent of the population was housed in such dwellings before the World War, and this proportion has increased as a result of post-War construction. The apartment-house has until recently been distinctly unpopular in England and Wales; according to one authority,[7] it housed less than 3 per cent of the population in 1921. In the last few years such construction has shown an increase, but not enough materially to affect average conditions. In Scotland a considerable proportion of the urban population is housed in tenements and apartments.

Most of the countries on the western fringe of continental Europe favor the single-family or two-family dwelling. The former prevails in France, Belgium, and the Netherlands, and is common in Denmark. But in all these countries the multi-family dwelling is commonly found in cities, and in none does the single-family dwelling predominate as it does in England and Wales. A good many low-income Belgian families have for many years been housed in apartments, but a pre-War trend toward single-family dwellings has strengthened since the Armistice. A feature of Danish post-War construction is an increase in the number of two-family houses, one dwelling being occupied by the owner.

In Central Europe, on the other hand, the apartment is the characteristic type of dwelling in Germany, Austria, Hungary, Czechoslovakia, Poland, and Italy, and in urban communities of Sweden and Norway. In Germany the multi-family dwelling prevails in the cities, but after the War there was a decided drift toward the single house [8] in rural communities. Nevertheless, a large percentage of the total population is housed in multi-family dwellings.

The trend in Germany is directed toward large blocks of apartment-houses of comparatively few stories, either with large interior courts or so arranged as to have an open rectangle providing good light and space for lawns and gardens. In a number of instances apartment-houses have been arranged in parallel rows so as to give the desired exposure to all apartments. The general effect is unsatisfactory, and it is more usual to

[7] Carr-Saunders, A. M., and Jones, D. C., "The Social Structure of England and Wales" (Oxford University Press, London, 1927), p. 16.
[8] This does not necessarily mean a detached house.

arrange the apartments in blocks with large central courts, or in U-shaped blocks with one end open. In some cases the houses in such blocks have been placed in a zigzag or saw-tooth design to secure more sunlight.

Along with this development has come that of the construction of single-family dwellings. A large number of *Siedlungen,* or settlements providing for both single-family dwellings and apartments in the proportions suggested by the needs of the particular area, have been developed in German cities in recent years. Nearly 10 per cent of the population of the city of Frankfurt was rehoused in them between 1925 and 1930.[9]

In Austria the apartment is distinctly characteristic of urban housing. Some of the post-War structures are very large, including more than 1000 dwellings as well as shops, drug-stores, doctors' offices, a kindergarten, and playrooms, while in the basement are steam laundries and communal baths.[10]

In India, the single-family dwelling, consisting of a single room, is to be found throughout the rural population, which comprises over 85 per cent of the total population; the single-family dwelling is also common in cities.

NUMBER OF ROOMS

With the increase in multi-family housing, and partly because of it, has come in recent years a tendency, especially in the United States, toward a smaller number of rooms per family. One reason for this is the steady reduction in the average number of persons per family; another is the increase in the number of individuals, especially self-supporting women, who desire a separate home, often only a single room or one room and kitchenette. After the War this tendency was enhanced by the decided rise in building costs, which compelled many families to accept narrower quarters.

Statistical evidence for the country at large is conflicting.

---

[9] This is discussed in greater detail under "Living Conditions" (p. 78).
[10] Chaddock, Robert E., "Housing in Vienna: A Socialistic Experiment" (The American Journal of Sociology, January, 1932, pp. 560–568).

A movement toward a smaller number of rooms is suggested by the cost-of-living studies of the United States Bureau of Labor Statistics for 1901 and 1918. The 1901 study, covering wage-earning groups, showed an average of 5.92 rooms per family owning its home and 4.73 rooms per family renting.[11] The 1918 investigation did not discriminate between owned and rented homes, but showed an average of 5 rooms per family in houses and 4.5 rooms per family in apartments.[12] On the other hand, a government authority [13] states that with respect to small houses there has been little tendency since the War to reduce the number of rooms, and that fewer three- and four-room houses of this class have been erected than before the War.

In the case of apartments alone, there is definite evidence of a trend toward fewer rooms. In New York City, for example, the average number of rooms per *new* apartment fell from 4.69 in 1902 to 3.01 in 1932. By boroughs these averages in selected years were as follows: [14]

	Manhattan	Bronx	Brooklyn	Queens	Richmond	New York City
1902	4.71	4.63	4.66	3.33	5.33	4.69
1915	4.42	3.91	3.96	4.48	4.31[a]	4.09
1930	3.79	3.27	3.20	3.08	3.03	3.39
1931	2.90	3.23	3.14	2.86	3.06	3.05
1932	2.54	3.33	3.08	2.83	2.71	3.01

(*a*) In 1910.

This tendency is shown still more clearly by comparing the numbers of one-room, two-room, and three-room apartments in new construction. The proportion of one-room apartments in New York City increased from less than 0.5 per cent in 1912—

[11] United States Department of Labor, " 18th Annual Report of the Commissioner of Labor " (GPO, Washington, 1904), p. 370.

[12] USBLS, " Cost of Living in the United States " (GPO, Washington, 1924), p. 333.

[13] Taylor, James S., Chief, Division of Building and Housing, United States Department of Commerce. Address before the Homebuilders' and Subdividers' Division, National Association of Real Estate Boards, Boston, Massachusetts, June 26, 1929.

[14] Data furnished by Tenement House Department, Borough of Manhattan, New York City.

18 to 9.3 per cent in 1931; that for two-room apartments rose from less than 2 per cent in 1912–16 to 17 per cent in 1932; at the same time the proportion of apartments with more than three rooms fell from nearly 80 to about 25 per cent.[15] For the borough of Manhattan alone the increase in one-room and two-room apartments was even more striking. But these percentages, as stated, relate to new construction, and the average number of rooms in *all* apartments is a good deal higher.

The number of persons per suite in New York City has also fallen, as shown by the following comparison, which covers all types of dwellings: [16]

Year	Suites per 1000 population	Persons per suite
1913	239	4.18
1915	241	4.14
1920	235	4.25
1925	274	3.65
1929	321	3.12

Not only has there been a trend toward fewer rooms, but the average size of rooms likewise seems to have lessened.

Canada, on the other hand, is noted for its large houses. In 1921, excluding the Yukon and the Northwest Territories, pioneering regions, 52 per cent of the dwellings had six rooms or more, and nearly 6 per cent had ten or more. Houses of four and five rooms comprised 25.5 per cent of the total; those of three rooms, two rooms, and one room, 7.88, 6.22, and 2.86 per cent respectively. The one-room houses, which in general are the dwellings of agricultural homesteaders, fell from 73,621 in 1911 to 50,459 in 1921. The large number of rooms per house is the more surprising in view of the fact that the average number of persons per household fell from 5.33 in 1881 to 4.63 in 1921.

Tendencies in post-War building in Europe have been dis-

[15] Furnished by Tenement House Department, City of New York; see the Appendix, p. 525. In 1918 not a single one-room apartment was erected in the entire city.

[16] State Board of Housing, New York, Legislative Document (1930) No. 84, p. 56.

tinctly toward smaller dwellings. This may be explained by the factors previously mentioned, and perhaps even more directly by the relatively high cost of construction and the difficulty of raising capital on advantageous terms. There has, however, been an increase in the number of rooms. Five- or six-room cottages have been featured in most post-War British construction, where four or five rooms were general before the War.

In Germany before the War 53 per cent of the dwellings in large towns and 48 per cent of those in towns of medium size had from one to three rooms. From 1924 to 1927 there was a marked increase in larger dwellings, which in the principal towns represented nearly two-thirds of the total number of new houses. But since 1927 this trend has been reversed, the proportion of small dwellings rising from 34.2 per cent of new construction in that year to 57 per cent in 1931; medium dwellings — those with four to six rooms — dropped from 62.6 to 41.1 per cent; while the dwellings of more than six rooms fell from 3.2 to 1.9 per cent. These and intervening annual figures for a group of 96 cities are given in the following table: [17]

	1927	1928	1929	1930	1931
Small (1–3 rooms)	34.2	35.6	43.0	49.4	57.0
Medium (4–6 rooms)	62.6	60.4	53.8	48.2	41.1
Large (over 6 rooms)	3.2	4.0	3.2	2.4	1.9

In Holland the proportion of all dwellings of three rooms or more, both new and old, has shown a marked increase, rising from 41 per cent in 1899 to 67 per cent in 1927.[18] In Switzerland the small dwelling predominates, with the three-room type featuring the recent construction in cities. Figures for the entire country are not available. Of 3242 dwellings erected in the Canton of Zurich in 1929 one-half contained three rooms, 991 had four, 219 had five, and 121 had six. There were 11 one-room and 283 two-room dwellings.[19]

The prevailing number of rooms per dwelling in several other

[17] ILO, " Industrial and Labour Information," March 21, 1932, p. 312.
[18] USDC, " Housing in Holland under the Housing Act " (Special Report).
[19] See pp. 80–82.

European countries is shown in Table 17, p. 80. It will be seen there that dwellings of only two rooms and even of one room are common in Austria, Poland, Sweden, and Finland. In Sweden in 1926, according to a survey by the Royal Social Board, slightly over one-half the dwellings in 53 towns and communes, including Stockholm and Gothenburg, consisted of two rooms or less, counting the kitchen as a room. In few of these countries have there been more rooms in the dwellings erected since the War.

CONSTRUCTION MATERIALS

While the number of rooms and the additions to accessory equipment keep pace with changing customs and environment, the choice of building materials is more or less governed by tradition. In the United States wooden frame is easily the predominating type of construction. A survey by the United States Department of Commerce [20] in 1923–25 indicated that about 80 per cent of dwellings in communities of over 2500 population, and fully 90 per cent of those in smaller communities, were constructed of wood. In the state of Washington the proportion of wooden dwellings was 98 per cent, in Oregon 97 per cent, in Idaho and New Hampshire 95 per cent, and in seven other states 90 per cent or more. In a large number of states the proportion ranged from 80 to 90 per cent, and in only three cases did it fall below 55 per cent.[21]

Statistics for individual cities show considerable differences. In Los Angeles virtually all the single and two-family houses are of frame construction. In Detroit, according to an estimate by the Department of Buildings and Safety Engineering, from 65 to 75 per cent of the dwellings are of frame. In Philadelphia in 1928, on the other hand, of 415,045 dwellings only 9248, or less than 2.3 per cent, were wooden.[22] " Frame construction is

[20] "Domestic Market Possibilities for Sales of Paints and Varnishes" (GPO, Washington, 1925), pp. 18, 20.

[21] *Viz.*, District of Columbia 20 per cent, Utah 15 per cent, and Arizona 10 per cent. Percentages by states are given in the Appendix, p. 527.

[22] Newman, Bernard J., "What the Rest of the Country Can Learn from

gradually disappearing in Philadelphia." [23] The same tendency is indicated in Washington, D. C.

A survey by the Fidelity-Phenix Fire Insurance Company in 1932 covering 40 cities in the United States showed that 68 per cent of all buildings were of frame construction.[24] The percentage for dwelling-houses alone would undoubtedly be higher, since many other types of building must be of fireproof construction.

The number of frame buildings in 20 cities increased 26.5 per cent during the decade 1920–30, according to a survey by the Continental Mortgage Guarantee Company of New York; non-frame structures in the same period increased 73.4 per cent. While these percentages covered all classes of buildings, the survey revealed a more extensive use of fire-resisting materials for dwellings. This is partly accounted for by the increase in apartment-house construction, since in many of the selected cities the use of wood for such structures is illegal. Up to the present a negligible number of single-family dwellings have been erected by new methods involving the use of steel and other materials in place of wood,[25] though such schemes have had considerable publicity.

While there have been few major changes in basic materials for dwelling-houses in this country, there has been considerable alteration in the kinds of lumber and other materials employed. In particular the use of gypsum products has shown a marked increase. Some of these changes are indicated by Table 10, consisting of index numbers compiled by the National Lumber Manufacturers Association. The figures relate to the production of these various materials and not to the quantities used in dwelling-house construction.

Philadelphia," in "Housing Problems in America" (National Housing Association, New York, 1929), Vol. X, p. 40.

[23] Newman, Bernard J., "Housing in Philadelphia" (Annual Report, Philadelphia Housing Association, 1929), p. 15.

[24] New York Times, Oct. 9, 1932.

[25] This matter will be referred to at more length in the third volume of this series.

One of the chief reasons for the use of wood is its relative cheapness; it is unreasonable to expect marked lessening in its employment for our dwellings until fireproof and other new materials approximate it in cost and efficiency.

TABLE 10

INDEX NUMBERS OF PRODUCTION OF VARIOUS BUILDING MATERIALS IN THE UNITED STATES FROM 1923 TO 1929 [a]

(1919 = 100, unless otherwise indicated)

	1919	1923	1925	1926	1927	1928	1929
Softwood lumber	100	113	116	111	104	103	— [b]
Hardwood lumber	100	88	93	91	85	81	— [b]
Oak flooring	100	298	453	475	434	438	330
Maple flooring	100	117	88	96	95	78	65
Wood shingles	100	82	80	65	70	61	—
Roofing tile [c]	100	246	318	434	391	373	393
Prepared roofing	100	122	131	128	136	146	150
Building stone [c]	100	207	240	262	249	246	265
Common brick	100	153	159	158	149	135	119
Face brick	100	244	313	308	305	305	268
Sand-lime brick	100	145	215	225	218	213	—
Hollow building tile	100	162	181	176	177	171	178
Architectural terra cotta	100	215	267	254	233	236	187
Floor and wall tile	100 [d]	184	176	212	205	228	217
Portland cement [c]	100	170	200	204	214	218	211
Wood lath	100	193	183	179	138	110	—
Metal lath [e]	100	270	422	450	—	—	—
Wall-plaster, wall-board, and floor compositions [f]	100	275	338	—	312	—	259
Gypsum [c]	100	196	235	233	221	211	207
Gypsum plaster-board [c]	100 [d]	219	354	403	796	807	756
Gypsum wall-board [c]	100 [d]	266	570	653	559	619	706
Gypsum partition tile [c]	100 [d]	206	377	355	354	335	340
Fibre-board (Celotex) [e]	100 [g]	281	1,125	1,833	2,917	—	—

(a) Compiled by the National Lumber Manufacturers Association from USC data and other sources.

(b) The index for softwood lumber for 1929 was 107 and for hardwood lumber 98, but the Association states that the 1929 figures for lumber are not comparable with the other lumber percentages for 1926, 1927, and 1928, owing to the fact that the 1929 data are much more comprehensive.

(c) From United States Bureau of Mines.

(d) 1921 = 100.

(e) These percentages are based on estimates by the Celotex and metal lath interests; they cannot be confirmed.

(f) Value of products was reported every two years.

(g) 1922 = 100.

In Canada also frame construction predominates; but the proportion of houses so built declined from 80 per cent in 1891 to 73 per cent in 1921, a lower ratio than that estimated for the United States. Nearly all construction other than wood was of brick, and the majority of the brick houses were situated in Ontario and Quebec.

In the southern portion of Europe and in Great Britain the higher cost of lumber due to the depletion of the forests in many countries led centuries ago to a lessened use of wood, and other types of construction have largely replaced it. In Great Britain the frame dwelling, originally common, is now distinctly the exception, and brick has for several centuries been the predominating material. Since the War only 10 or 12 per cent of the construction there has been of concrete. There has, however, been extensive experimentation with so-called " alternate " (other than brick) construction; " steel houses," houses of cinder and concrete slabs, and even of timber have been erected, but with the exception of concrete most of the departures have failed to contribute substantially to the housing of the nation. In some cases the use of such new materials was attempted largely to resist the exactions of building-trade labor. In general the British people preferred to retain the traditional brick construction.

The Scandinavian countries, Finland, and Northern Russia use wood extensively in minor building construction, but it is rare in Germany; it is even rarer in Holland and France, brick in the former and stone or stucco in the latter being the prevailing materials. Satisfactory statistics are not available.

In Asia Minor stone masonry is the most popular, while in Persia brick or dried clay is still used as it was in the days of Cyrus and Darius.

In India the typical rural dwelling consists in a single room, constructed of bamboo and mud with a thatched roof of grass. There are no windows or doors to fit apertures, and no hardware — not even nails, the bamboo poles being held together with flexible fibers or roots. Such dwellings shelter nearly 300,000,-

000 of India's 350,000,000 population. In cities a crude brick prevails.

In China the use of light bamboo continues to be common among the native population; in Japan frame dwellings are still the rule, although some of the larger cities have adopted more permanent types of construction.[26]

In Australia and New Zealand wood predominates, but stone and concrete are extensively employed. In the former country dwellings of such materials in 1901 comprised 265,000 out of a total of 760,000 against 452,000 of wood,[27] while in the latter frame construction is more popular, 80 per cent of all new private dwellings being of wood in the fiscal years 1924–26.

INCREASE IN ACCESSORY EQUIPMENT

By far the most sweeping changes in homes in the past century have occurred in connection with accessory equipment. The principal items for which approximate data are obtainable are:

(1) Plumbing and sanitary facilities.

(2) Heating services.

(3) Lighting equipment.

(4) Electrical appliances.

(5) Motor transport, involving the garage as a part of, or an adjunct to, the house.

(6) Communication facilities, principally the telephone and the radio.

The recent development of air conditioning promises to add another item to the list, with some significant change in structure.

(1) Plumbing and Sanitary Facilities

Prior to 1830 [28] the bathroom was practically unknown in America, and its appearance was the signal for much criticism

26 For a fuller discussion of contemporary house construction throughout the world, see Volume I, Part III.

27 Webb, A. D., "The New Dictionary of Statistics" (George Routledge and Sons, Ltd., London, 1911), p. 303.

28 See Volume I, pp. 277–8, 306–308.

and even denunciation; in some states heavy taxes were imposed on the innovation, primarily, it seems, in order to discourage its use. During the last half of the nineteenth century there was a gradual increase in plumbing facilities, and since 1900 the increase has been rapid, until today a bathroom is generally regarded as an essential in the urban and suburban dwelling, many houses having several, with supplementary lavatories. In rural sections, however, the bathroom is not so common, and this is true also of the poorer sections of cities. Of 6,288,648 farms covered by the 1930 Census only 994,202, or 16 per cent, reported water piped into the house; in about 531,248, or 8.4 per cent, water was piped into a bathroom. Some housing authorities [29] hold that the bathroom is not strictly essential for very low income families, and this has been recognized in the planning of a number of European developments.

In July, 1930, there were in the United States 21,000,000 bathrooms in 24,000,000 non-farm homes; [30] but many homes had more than one tub. There were 23,100,000 water-closets in these homes, and 300,000 more lavatories than closet combinations. A survey of urban homes made for the General Federation of Women's Clubs in 1925–26 indicated that 68 per cent were equipped with stationary bathtubs, 82 per cent with flush toilets, 71 per cent with stationary wash-basins, 84 per cent with kitchen sinks, and 28 per cent with stationary laundry tubs.

An official survey in 1918,[31] covering 92 industrial cities, showed that 52 per cent of the wage-earning families living in houses and 60 per cent of such families living in apartments had bathrooms. The percentages doubtless are much higher today, because bathrooms have generally been included in new houses erected since 1918. A conservative estimate for the entire country in 1933 would be that upwards of 70 per cent of all non-

29 Among them the Chicago Homes Economic Council.
30 Data furnished by the Plumbing and Heating Industries Bureau.
31 USBLS, "Cost of Living in the United States" (GPO, Washington, 1924), Bulletin 357, p. 333.

farm homes were equipped with at least one bathroom, while a materially higher percentage had inside toilets.

For Canada statistics are not available, but there is little doubt that in urban housing the introduction of plumbing facilities has made substantial progress, although the proportion of homes so equipped is much lower than it is in the United States; in farming regions such conveniences are still the exception. The 1931 Census shows that only one Canadian farmhouse in nine had water piped into the kitchen; in only one in twenty was it piped into a bathroom.

Until after the War bathrooms and other plumbing accessories were found in only a small proportion of European dwellings, even in the most advanced countries; indeed the proportion of all dwellings having such equipment is still small. In the case of dwellings erected since the War, however, there has been a marked advance.

In Great Britain the bathroom was gradually being introduced before the War. Since then it has been required by law in most government-aided construction and has been generally included in other post-War houses; so that nearly 2,000,000 bathrooms have been added in new construction alone since 1918. In Germany plumbing equipment is a general feature of post-War housing. In Austria the private bathroom is the exception, but most new apartment-houses have communal ones, frequently located in the basement. The same is true of Italy. In France the number of new houses erected since the War outside the devastated areas has not been great enough appreciably to change average conditions, and only a small proportion of French houses have bathrooms. The post-War housing of Belgium, while representing a high standard of construction, has as a rule not been provided with bathrooms. In Denmark likewise the bathroom is the exception but most new dwellings have a separate water-closet.

According to a report of the Royal Social Board of Sweden,[32]

[32] "Social Work and Legislation in Sweden" — Survey Published by Order of the Swedish Government (P. A. Norstedt and Söner, Stockholm, 1928), p. 230.

published in 1928, only about 5 per cent of town dwellings in that country had bathrooms. Even in Stockholm the proportion in 1920 was only about 10 per cent. In new construction in that city, however, a bathroom or a shower-bath had been very frequently included, nearly 50 per cent of dwellings erected in 1927 having one of these conveniences. It may be assumed that the bathroom is infrequent in farm and other rural dwellings.

(2) *Heating Services*

Central heating is taken more or less for granted in the northern and central portions of the United States. Stoves are still extensively used by the lower-income classes, but there has been a decided increase in the number of hot-air furnaces and other central installations. It has been calculated [33] that there were in 1930 about 17,000,000 heating systems in residences in the United States. Allowing for homes in various sections of the country where such systems were not needed, this would indicate that about 75 per cent of dwellings had some heating system other than stoves.

European countries are on the whole far behind the United States with respect to heating standards. Central heating is the exception in Great Britain, the coal stove and the fireplace being the usual sources of heat. In many post-War houses one or more bedrooms are provided with a gas stove. Electric heaters for individual rooms are coming into use, but this method is doubtless confined in the main to the higher-income groups.[34]

On the Continent central heating is distinctly uncommon, albeit some progress with it has been made in Germany and Denmark. In Sweden, according to the report already quoted,[35] central heating systems in 1928 were to be found in barely one-twentieth of the dwellings, even in the towns.

In 1931, according to the American Gas Association, there

[33] By the Plumbing and Heating Industries Bureau.

[34] "Panel heating" by radiation has also received considerable recent attention in England.

[35] Royal Social Board, "Social Work and Legislation in Sweden" — Survey Published by Order of the Swedish Government (P. A. Norstedt and Söner, Stockholm, 1928), p. 230.

were nearly 15,000,000 domestic gas consumers in the United States, of whom 9,848,000 used manufactured gas and 5,090,-000 natural gas.[36] In the great majority of homes having gas service this fuel is used for cooking. The methods of cooking in the United States as of January 1, 1929, have been estimated as follows:

	Families	Per cent
Gas, manufactured	9,500,000	33.9
Gas, natural	3,470,000	12.4
Coal and wood	8,290,000	29.6
Oil	6,000,000	21.5
Electricity	725,000	2.6
	27,985,000	100.0

Cooking is evidently still done to a considerable extent on the coal or wood range, although gas is more generally adopted in urban communities. The use of electricity is gradually increasing in this country.[37] While gas is utilized to some extent in Great Britain and continental Europe, wood or coal stoves, fireplaces, and brick ovens continue to be largely employed. Electricity is seldom used for cooking in European homes.

(3) Lighting Equipment

In July, 1932, according to the National Electric Light Association, approximately 20,440,000 homes in the United States were receiving electric service; 700,000 of them were farm homes.[38] On the basis of 7,000,000 [39] farm homes and 30,-500,000 homes of all classes, these figures indicate that about 10 per cent of farm homes, 67 per cent of all homes, and 85 per cent of non-farm homes were receiving electric service; virtually all of these had electric lighting. Presumably the oil lamp

[36] Apparently there was a small number of consumers using gas obtained from various distillates.

[37] In July, 1932, more than 1,000,000 homes were equipped with electric ranges.

[38] As the Census reports that 841,000 farm dwellings were lighted by electricity in 1930, it would appear that about 140,000 farms had private electric plants.

[39] Estimated figure, taking account of the drift from cities to farms as a result of the depression.

was the principal source of lighting in the other **10,000,000** homes. In Canada the electric lighting of urban homes is becoming general, and its extent is approaching that in the United States.

European housing compares better with this country in electric lighting than in some of the other accessories mentioned. As far back as 1924 over 60 per cent of the population of France were living in electrically lighted homes; in Switzerland the proportion was over 90 per cent, and in Czechoslovakia a majority of homes were thus lighted.[40] The rapid growth of hydro-electric properties in Sweden has led to considerable progress in this direction; in 1928, 80 per cent of the town dwellings had electric lighting.

Great Britain in 1928 lagged behind some continental European countries in this respect, with only about 25 per cent of the dwellings wired for electricity. However, facilities for extending this service are rapidly being installed, and present plans contemplate that by 1940 electric service will be available to approximately all the homes of Great Britain and Northern Ireland.

Central European countries apparently as yet have made only a modest advance in this respect, although the extensive water-power developments of recent years presumably will result in a radical change. In some countries of Eastern Europe electric lighting is the rare exception. In 1924 only 2 per cent of the population in Turkey and a negligible percentage in Roumania were living in electrically lighted dwellings.[40]

Electric lighting has made rapid progress in Japan. According to the Japan Year Book for 1931, in 1928 there were 33,-909,000 electric lamps in Japan proper, equaling 54.5 lamps per 100 persons, or 310 lamps per 100 households. The extent to which electric lighting prevails in various countries is shown in Table 11.

[40] With the exception of Great Britain, Sweden and Japan, most of these data are from the Electric World of January 9, 1926. The reliability of some of the figures is doubtful.

(4) Electrical Appliances

Perhaps the most phenomenal change in the American home is the increased use of electric appliances, from the flatiron to the refrigerator and range. In nearly all homes wired for elec-

TABLE 11

NUMBER OF DOMESTIC CONSUMERS OF ELECTRIC CURRENT IN VARIOUS COUNTRIES IN SPECIFIED YEARS

Year	Country	Number of consumers [a]	Number per 1000 population [b]
1932	United States	20,440,000	166
1930	Canada	1,207,457	122
	South America		
1926	Venezuela	500,000	153
1930	Argentina	993,318	86
1928	Chile	135,501	31
1930	Costa Rica	15,183	29
1931	Colombia	21,738	3
	Europe		
1929	Switzerland	842,530	207
1928	Denmark	718,000	202
1928	France	6,339,266	153
1929	Germany	9,744,164	152
1929	Sweden	840,000	137
1928	Czechoslovakia	1,607,240	109
1930	Italy	4,000,000	97
1931	United Kingdom	3,472,043	75
1929	Hungary	198,077	22
1929	Poland and Danzig	552,702	17
1930	Irish Free State	37,700	13
	Other		
1930	New Zealand	266,000	177
1928	Australia	876,200	136
1929	Japan (proper)	10,847,000	168
1929	Union of South Africa	156,057	20
1932	India	187,507	0.5

(a) Computed by the Electrical Equipment Division of the USDC, Bureau of Foreign and Domestic Commerce.

(b) Computed by the authors. In some cases the population was estimated from the returns of the most recent census.

tricity there is an electric flatiron, and in nearly one-half a vacuum cleaner. The numbers of homes having certain electrical appliances on January 1, 1932, are shown in Table 12.

TABLE 12

NUMBER OF HOMES IN THE UNITED STATES HAVING CERTAIN ELEC-
TRICAL APPLIANCES ON JANUARY 1, 1932 [a]

(Total number of wired homes 20,441,000)

Appliance	Number of homes	Per cent of wired homes	Per cent of all homes [b]
Irons	19,772,325	96.7	64.8
Vacuum cleaners	9,281,750	45.4	30.4
Washing machines	8,356,250	40.8	27.4
Toasters	8,245,950	40.3	27.0
Percolators	5,894,000	28.8	19.3
Refrigerators	3,498,750	17.1	11.5
Sewing machines	3,350,000	16.4	11.0
Clocks	3,350,000	16.4	11.0
Heaters	3,339,080	16.3	11.0
Waffle irons	2,735,000	13.4	9.0
Hot plates	2,238,863	10.9	7.3
Heating pads	2,236,800	10.9	7.3
Cookers	1,242,000	6.1	4.1
Ranges	1,095,000	5.3	3.6
Ironers	735,990	3.5	2.4
Floor machines	306,400	1.5	1.0
Egg cookers	293,000	1.4	0.9
Dishwashers	114,000	0.6	0.4

(a) Electrical Merchandising, January, 1932, p. 29.
(b) Computed by the authors on an estimated basis of 30,500,000 homes.

The expenditure for such accessories is high, and has in recent years run well over three-quarters of a billion dollars annually, as follows: [41]

1928	....	$832,000,000
1929	....	863,000,000
1930	....	790,000,000

[41] Electrical Merchandising, January, 1931, p. 22.

The annual operating expense likewise mounts to impressive totals, as shown in Table 13, which gives total expenditure for electric current for various appliances in 1930.

TABLE 13

Total Expenditure for Electric Current by Domestic Consumers in the United States in 1930 for Certain Appliances[a]

Appliance	Expenditure
Refrigerators	$48,600,000
Ranges	42,750,000
Flatirons	41,175,000
Radio sets	30,744,000
Vacuum cleaners	13,945,000
Toasters	9,455,000
Water heaters	9,300,000
Percolators	7,320,000
Washing machines	6,735,000
Fans	5,740,000
Oil burners	5,562,000
Ironing machines	3,752,000
Space heaters	3,233,000
Total	$228,311,000

(a) Compiled by the National Electric Light Association.

Little information is available as to the use of electrical appliances in other countries. Canada doubtless ranks fairly high, and the introduction of such appliances in British homes appears to be making rapid progress; indeed, some of the dwellings erected in recent years by the London County Council for moderate-income groups are termed " all-electric homes." Most other European countries, however, are far behind the United States.

(5) Motor Transport

The growth of cities has produced profound changes in housing owing to the problems of transportation. Only twenty-five years ago it was unusual for a workman of Paris, living in one section, to go to another to work. The increase in rapid and cheap transportation has altered this condition until now people travel long distances between home and employment. The garden-city movement [42] has as one of its aims to counteract this tendency and to restore the old relation of living place and work place.

So far as the individual housing unit is concerned, the only agency which intimately affects its design is the automobile. The garage, often incorporated into the shell of the house, has become an essential feature in the United States in suburban and rural communities. In large cities, notably in the case of apartment-house dwellers, it is often necessary to rely on public garages, while in farm and some other rural sections a shed, barn, or stable serves the purpose.

Building-permit data [43] for leading cities from 1921 to 1929 show that over 40 per cent of the families provided with new dwellings had private garages. Since many of these families were housed in apartments without garages, it follows that a large proportion of single-family and two-family houses had their own garages.

The total number of passenger automobiles in use in the United States on January 1, 1932, has been estimated at 20,-327,000, as compared with 30,500,000 families.[44] The number of registrations is considerably greater, but since large numbers of cars are replaced each year their number exceeds that of cars actually in use. Owing to the fact that many families have several cars, the number of families without one is substantially larger than the difference between total cars and total families. Since many owners put their cars up during the winter months, those in use on January 1 may be less than those owned. Nevertheless, it seems likely that at the beginning of 1932 there were more than 10,000,000 families in the United States without automobiles.

This country, as is well known, leads all others in the ratio of passenger automobiles to population, with an average on Janu-

---

[42] See p. 86.

[43] As collected by the USBLS.

[44] Scoville, John W., "The Automobile Industry — Review of 1931 and Outlook for 1932" (Chrysler Corporation), p. 3.

ary 1, 1932, of one car for every 4.8 persons. Canada and New Zealand each came second, with one car for every 8 persons. Comparisons for selected countries are given in Table 14 and are shown graphically in Chart 15. It is apparent from the table that with the exception of the United States, Canada, and New Zealand the motor-car presents no pressing problem in connec-

TABLE 14

Average Number of Persons per Automobile in Selected Countries, January 1, 1932 [a]

United States	4.8
Canada	8
New Zealand	8
Australia	12
France	24
England	28
Denmark	29
Argentina	35
Sweden	41
Norway	56
Iceland	59
Netherlands	63
Germany	95
Cuba	97
Chile	105
Spain	129
Italy	141
Czechoslovakia	161
Mexico	245
Brazil	250
Egypt	508
Peru	575
Guatemala	593
Japan	643
Poland	1,063
India	1,872
Soviet Russia	2,405
China	11,376
Ethiopia	30,769

(a) USDC, "Motor Vehicle World Census," January 1, 1932 (issued by the Bureau of Foreign and Domestic Commerce), p. 4, 5.

— CHART 15 —

AVERAGE NUMBER OF PERSONS PER AUTOMOBILE
IN VARIOUS COUNTRIES: JANUARY 1, 1932
Charted from U.S. Department of Commerce: Vehicle Census

COUNTRY	NUMBER
United States	4.8
Canada	8
New Zealand	8
Australia	12
France	24
England	28
Denmark	29
Argentina	35
Sweden	41
Norway	56
Iceland	59
Netherlands	63
Germany	95
Cuba	97
Chile	105
Spain	129
Italy	141
Czechoslovakia	161
Mexico	245
Brazil	250
Egypt	508
Peru	575
Guatemala	593
Japan	643

tion with housing. It may be noted that motorcycles are common in England, while in many European nations, particularly England, Holland, Belgium, and France, bicycles are extensively used.[45] The development of the airplane may be carried to a point where private hangars will be regarded as an essential feature of the dwelling, but this appears to be well in the future.

(6) Communication Facilities

With respect to telephone equipment the United States and Canada are far in advance of other countries. The American Telephone and Telegraph Company estimates that there were over 13,000,000 telephones in residences in the United States on January 1, 1930, and that in April, 1931, 42 per cent of the homes of the country had them. The proportion in 1933 was appreciably less, through relinquishment of service due to economic conditions. The United States leads the world in the number of telephones per capita, with an average on January 1, 1931, of 16.4 instruments per 100 population. Chart 16 gives a comparison of the number of telephones per 100 population in various countries.

Another increasingly important accessory is the radio. In 1930, according to the Census, over 12,000,000 families in the United States, or 40.3 per cent of the total number, had radio sets.[46] The ratios by principal geographic sections follow:

	Per cent
Middle Atlantic	55.3
New England	53.8
East North-central	50.2
Pacific	49.2
West North-central	43.1
Mountain	30.9
South Atlantic	19.0
West South-central	16.5
East South-central	12.3

[45] It is stated that in 1933 there were more than 40,000,000 bicycles in Europe. In Holland 35 per cent of the entire population own them. Robbins, L. H., " The Bicycle Comes Around the Corner " (New York Times, January 15, 1933, and New York Times Magazine, March 5, 1933).

[46] This total includes sets operated by battery as well as those operated by supplied electricity.

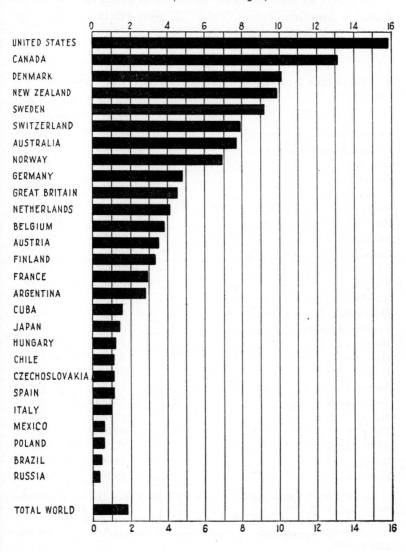

— CHART 16 —

NUMBER OF TELEPHONES PER 100 POPULATION
IN VARIOUS COUNTRIES : JANUARY 1, 1932

From Telephone and Telegraph Statistics of the World
American Telephone and Telegraph Co.

UNITED STATES
CANADA
DENMARK
NEW ZEALAND
SWEDEN
SWITZERLAND
AUSTRALIA
NORWAY
GERMANY
GREAT BRITAIN
NETHERLANDS
BELGIUM
AUSTRIA
FINLAND
FRANCE
ARGENTINA
CUBA
JAPAN
HUNGARY
CHILE
CZECHOSLOVAKIA
SPAIN
ITALY
MEXICO
POLAND
BRAZIL
RUSSIA

TOTAL WORLD

As shown in Table 15, more than two-thirds of the total number of sets were in three countries: the United States, the United Kingdom, and Germany. The number per 1000 population was almost as high in the United Kingdom as in the United States.

As a further indication of the extent to which accessories are found in American homes, Table 16, giving data for two wage-

TABLE 15

ESTIMATED NUMBER OF RADIO SETS ABOUT THE YEAR 1930 [a]

	No. of sets	No. per 1000 population [c]
United States	10,500,000 [b]	85.5
United Kingdom	3,093,000	67.1
Germany	3,066,682	47.8
France	1,500,000	36.2
Japan	641,774	10.0
Spain	500,000	22.1
Russia	500,000	3.1
Sweden	450,000	73.3
Canada	423,557	42.7
Argentina	400,000	34.9
Austria	371,011	55.3
Australia	311,322	48.5
Denmark	343,000	96.8
Czecho-Slovakia	300,000	20.4
Italy	250,000	6.1
Hungary	240,000	27.7
Poland	202,586	6.5
Brazil	175,000	4.4
Netherlands	152,000	19.2
Mexico	100,000	6.1
Finland	90,232	24.8
Switzerland	77,959	19.2
Norway	75,000	26.7
Peru	70,000	11.2

(a) USDC, "Radio Markets of the World, 1930," (GPO, Washington, 1930), pp. 11–13.

(b) As stated in the text, the Census reported over 12,000,000.

(c) Ratios approximate as census figures for population are from years 1928 to 1931.

TABLE 15 (*continued*)

	No. of sets	No. per 1000 population
Belgium	63,125	7.8
New Zealand	52,124	35.7
Chile	35,000	8.2
Cuba	28,875	7.8
Irish Free State	26,000	8.8
Union of South Africa	20,000	2.5
Uruguay	17,150	9.0
China	10,000	0.02
World Total [d]	24,297,561 [e]	

(d) Including countries not enumerated above.

(e) The total on January 1, 1932, was estimated by the Department at 30,000,000 (United States Daily, March 19, 1931).

TABLE 16

HOME EQUIPMENT OF TWO GROUPS OF WAGE-EARNERS' FAMILIES IN THE UNITED STATES

Equipment of homes	100 Ford Company families, 1930 [a]	467 families of unskilled wage-earners in Chicago, 1924 [b]
Number of rooms	Per cent	Per cent
Four	34	44.7
Five	42	20.4
More than five	16	17.2
Bath	72	42.5
Inside toilets	86	77.8 [c]
Electric light	100	70.7
Stoves	56	87.0
Telephone	5 [d]	19.7
Radio	36	7.1
Piano	13	20.2

(a) Monthly Labor Review, June, 1930, pp. 11–54.

(b) Houghteling, Leila, "The Income and Standard of Living of Unskilled Laborers in Chicago" (The University of Chicago Press, Chicago, 1927), pp. 106, 110, 111, 116, 119, 120.

(c) For one family.

(d) Number having telephone in home; 43 per cent of families reported expenditure for telephone.

TABLE 16 (*continued*)

Equipment of homes	100 Ford Company families, 1930	467 families of unskilled wage-earners in Chicago, 1924
	Per cent	Per cent
Victrola	45	40.3
Automobile	47	3.0
Washing-machines		
Electric	49	
Hand	2	
Vacuum cleaners		
Electric	19	
Hand	2	not given
Electric appliances		
Iron	98	
Toaster	6	
Fan	4	
Families reporting savings	37	31.1

earning groups, one of Ford Company employees earning approximately $7 a day in 1930 and the other for unskilled workers in Chicago earning approximately $1500 per family per year in 1924, is suggestive. The first of these groups enjoyed a relatively high income; the second was below the average of wage-earning groups in that year. In the case of families of distinctly low incomes these accessories would, of course, be much less frequent, while some of them would be absent. The proportion of homes in the United States having certain accessories, by type of community, is shown in Chart 17. The frequency of various accessories in various countries is shown in Chart 18.

OTHER CHANGES

It has been shown that the character of the present-day dwelling has been affected by the inclusion of an ever-increasing number of accessories. Another influence is that of public welfare legislation, notably the building and health codes so general in all advanced countries, and, closely related to them, zon-

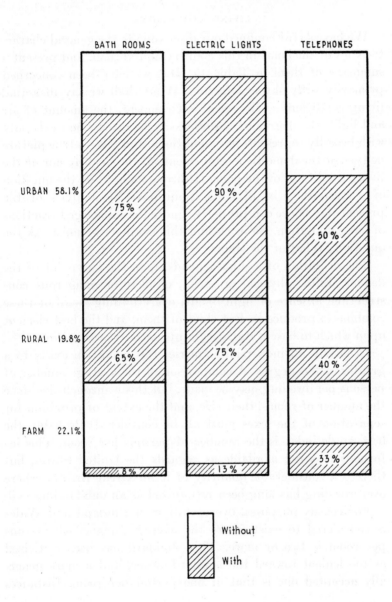

— CHART 17 —

PROPORTIONS OF HOMES IN THE UNITED STATES HAVING
CERTAIN ACCESSORIES, BY TYPE OF COMMUNITY: 1930

BATH ROOMS   ELECTRIC LIGHTS   TELEPHONES

URBAN 58.1%   75%   90%   50%

RURAL 19.8%   65%   75%   40%

FARM 22.1%   8%   13%   33%

Without

With

ing and city-planning regulations. These are discussed more fully in Chapter VIII.

LIVING CONDITIONS

We have so far confined our discussion to the general characteristics of the home in this country and abroad, and present a summary of them in Table 17. But we have been concerned primarily with physical factors. What shall we say of actual living conditions — the social environment, the amount of air and light, the degree of cleanliness? Our discussion deals only with broadly representative conditions, and gives a true picture neither of the domestic arrangements of the wealthy nor of the living conditions of the poor. It throws no light on the question of overcrowding or of slum conditions. No analysis of the present-day house can properly ignore the submerged fractions of our population. So in closing this chapter, we must ask the question: What of the slum?

The definition of a slum depends upon the viewpoint of the definer. Filth, physical or social, obsolete or dangerous construction, absence of light or air, overcrowding — all of these combine to produce it. But chief of them, and the best element upon which to base a statistical approach, is overcrowding.

In nearly all industrial countries this condition exists to a greater or less degree. A comparison of the average number of persons per dwelling may be made, but this is inconclusive since the number of rooms, their size, and the extent of provision for separation of the sexes must all be considered. Probably the best single index is the number of persons per room. This information is not available as regards the United States, but there is a considerable quantity of it for Great Britain, where overcrowding has long been recognized as an outstanding evil.

For census purposes, overcrowding in England and Wales is considered to exist where the average number of persons per room is two or more. This standard has been criticized as too lenient toward the landlord-owner, and a more generally accepted one is that of one person per room. Instances

—— CHART 18 ——

APPROXIMATE PROPORTIONS OF HOMES HAVING CERTAIN ACCESSORY EQUIPMENT IN VARIOUS COUNTRIES: 1930

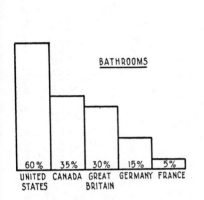

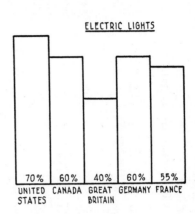

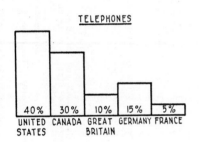

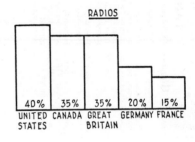

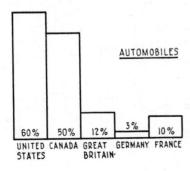

TABLE 17

Representative Housing Conditions in Various Countries in 1931

	United States	Canada	England and Wales	Scotland	France	Germany
Predominant type	Single houses, but two-family houses and tenements fairly common. Marked increase in apartment-houses since the War	Single houses. Recent increase in apartments	Pre-War: row houses; many tenements in London Post-War: single (not detached) cottages	Tenements in cities; more single cottages since the War	Tenements in cities	Tenements; more single houses since the War in smaller communities
Number of rooms	4 to 6; average about 5	6 or more most common	Pre-War: 4 and 5 Post-War: 4, 5 and 6	2 and 3	3 and 4	3 and 4
Bathrooms	In 1918 about 50 per cent of wage-earners' homes had them; found in most post-War houses	Not common before the War. General in post-War urban houses	Bathroom a standard feature of most post-War houses; required by law in state-aided housing	Common in post-War housing	Infrequent	Private bathroom not common, but water-closet and running water for each apartment the rule
Heating	Stoves pre-War; furnace heat or steam fairly common at present	Stoves	Stoves; also fire-places in many post-War houses	Stoves and fire-places	Stoves and fire-places	Stoves; central heating increasing
Miscellaneous equipment	About 80 per cent of all non-farm houses and 10 per cent of farm homes have electric light; electric irons in 65 per cent of all homes	Electrical conveniences fairly common	Electrical conveniences common in post-War houses, but relatively infrequent in others	Electrical conveniences infrequent	Electric lighting common	Electric lighting fairly general
Telephone	In 42 per cent of all homes	Second to United States in number of telephones per capita	Not common	Not common		
Number telephones per 100 population, Jan. 1, 1931 [a]	16.4	14.0	4.3 [b]		2.8	5.0
General	"Except for poorer sections of cities people have been well housed"	Many small and poor houses in rural provinces	Much pre-War housing unsatisfactory — many slum areas; new houses high-grade	Slum conditions exceptionally bad	Sanitary conditions in rural districts often poor	Few slum areas in cities

(a) American Telephone and Telegraph Company, "Telephone and Telegraph Statistics of the World," January 1, 1931 (Comptrollers Department, March 1, 1932), p. 4.   (b) Great Britain and North Ireland.

TABLE 17 (*continued*)

REPRESENTATIVE HOUSING CONDITIONS IN VARIOUS COUNTRIES IN 1931

	Italy	Austria	Switzerland	Russia	Belgium	Finland
Predominant type	Tenements and apartments	Apartments; single-family dwellings	Single-family dwellings fairly common; many apartments	Apartments in cities	Apartments; some increase in single-family dwellings in recent years	Apartments
Number of rooms	1 and 2 rooms frequent	1, 2 and 3	3 and 4	1 and 2 rooms frequent	4 and 5	1 and 2 rooms
Bathrooms	Few private bathrooms; each apartment-house supplied with baths and shower-baths	Infrequent in old buildings; communal baths in many apartment-houses	Fairly general in new dwellings	Very rare	Not general	Infrequent
Heating				Stoves		Stoves
Miscellaneous equipment	Many conveniences: hot water, gas stoves, communal laundries		Electric lighting general	Scanty	Electric lighting general	Electrical equipment infrequent
Telephone		Not general	Fairly common	Very infrequent except in a few cities	Not general	Not general
Number telephones per 100 population, Jan. 1, 1931 [a]	0.9 [b]	3.4	7.3	0.2 [c]	3.6	3.5

General

(a) American Telephone and Telegraph Company, "Telephone and Telegraph Statistics of the World," p. 4.
(b) June 30, 1930.
(c) October 1, 1930 (including Siberia and Associated Republics).

TABLE 17 (*Concluded*)

REPRESENTATIVE HOUSING CONDITIONS IN VARIOUS COUNTRIES IN 1931

	Netherlands	*Denmark*	*Sweden*	*Norway*	*New Zealand*	*Japan*	*India* (rural)
Predominant type	One- and two-family houses almost universal except in Amsterdam and Rotterdam	Single-family and two-family dwellings fairly general; apartments in cities	Apartments in cities; single- and two-family houses more common since the War	Apartments in cities	Single-family houses; few apartments		Single-family dwellings
Number of rooms	4 and 5		2 and 3	2 and 3	4 to 6	2 and 3	1
Bathrooms	Not general	Infrequent: separate water-closets the rule in apartment-houses	Infrequent. In only about 5 per cent of town dwellings in 1928	Infrequent			None
Heating		Some increase in central heating in recent years	Stoves; central heating in only 5 per cent of town dwellings in 1928	Stoves			
Miscellaneous equipment	Electric light general	Electric lighting fairly general	Electric light in over 80 per cent of town dwellings	Electric light fairly common		Electric lighting general	None
Telephone	Not general	Fairly common	Fairly common	Fairly common	General	Very infrequent except in a few cities	None
Number telephones per 100 population, Jan. 1, 1931 [a]	3.9	9.9 [c]	8.7	6.7 [d]	10.2 [c]	1.4 [c]	.02 [b]

General

(a) American Telephone and Telegraph Company, "Telephone and Telegraph Statistics of the World," p. 4.
(b) For British India. Partly estimated. (c) March 31, 1931. (d) June 30, 1930.

of families of from eight to sixteen persons with only two bedrooms per dwelling have been reported by British health officers.

In 1921, according to one analysis, approximately 3,500,000 persons in England and Wales had less than one room to two persons, and nearly 17,500,000, or about 50 per cent of the total population, had less than one room per person. Of 8,750,-000 private families there were nearly 1,750,000, or 20 per cent, sharing their dwelling with one or more other families. "This crowding of two or more families into a dwelling may or may not imply overcrowding in the medical sense," it is stated. "It certainly does imply conditions under which family privacy is impossible." [47]

In Scotland in 1921 conditions were still less satisfactory: 11.8 per cent of the dwellings contained only one room and over 40 per cent more had only two; the one-room houses contained 8 per cent of the total population of 4,700,000 (excluding persons on ships and in large houses and households) and the two-room houses 39.3 per cent. If certain large houses, large households, and persons living on board ship be excluded, 9 per cent of the remaining population were living more than four to a room, 21 per cent more than three to a room, and 43 per cent more than two to a room. The average for all of Scotland was 1.42 persons per room.[47]

Owing to differences in the size of rooms, comparisons are not wholly satisfactory, but these figures leave no doubt that there was excessive overcrowding in Great Britain in 1921. In view of the extensive building operations since the War, we may expect that the returns of the 1931 Census will show some improvement, although it is generally agreed that the extensive housing program of Great Britain since the War has not made an important change in slum conditions. This matter is discussed further in Chapter XI.

Doubtless similar conditions could be shown for many other

[47] Carr-Saunders, A. M., and Jones, D. C., "A Survey of the Social Structure of England and Wales," pp. 14-24.

countries. For instance, in Sweden [48] in 1926 the census returns indicated for small dwellings an average of 1.49 persons per room in Stockholm, 1.69 in Gothenburg, and 1.51 for fifty-three communes including these two cities. If the general formula of one room per person be accepted, these figures indicate extensive overcrowding. For large dwellings, on the other hand, the average was approximately 0.84 persons per room. It may be noted that the number of persons per room was decidedly less in the case of owned homes than in that of rented dwellings or of dwellings where rent was provided free as part compensation.

It is impracticable to present a survey for all countries on these points. It is generally agreed that in Germany there are no such extensive slum areas as exist in the United States and Great Britain, but in all European countries there are considerable sections of the population for which housing conditions are distinctly low. One writer [49] estimates that there are in France 500,000 dwellings, or nearly 5 per cent of the total number standing, which need reconditioning and replacing; in Germany, he asserts, there are 300,000 dwellings which should have been demolished during the past twenty years, and another 200,000 should be scrapped during the next decade — 500,000 in all, or more than 3 per cent of the total number of dwellings. He states that in Belgium there are more than 100,-000 unsanitary or otherwise unsatisfactory dwellings, approximately 6 per cent of the dwellings in that country. In the whole of Europe, he estimates, there are 2,000,000 to 3,000,000 dwellings which should be replaced, but not all these are necessarily slum dwellings.

As a result of such statements, which are frequently made, together with the lack of information in the United States,[50]

[48] Royal Social Board, "Social Work and Legislation in Sweden," p. 230.

[49] Méquet, G., "Housing Problems and the Depression" (International Labour Review, February, 1933, pp. 175–178). Méquet quotes another writer (M. Augustin Rey in the Journal de la Société de Statistique de Paris, October, 1932) as stating that 3,000,000 houses in France need reconstruction, complete renovation, or replacement).

[50] Other factors are the "100 per cent Americanism" attitude and the

there is a tendency to regard European slum conditions as worse than our own. A small group of social workers, on the other hand, moved by the extensive slum clearance in a number of districts of Europe, take the opposite extreme and affirm that we have worse and more slums than Europe. It is impossible to settle this argument; a narrow nationalism or a narrow internationalism is equally prejudicial to good judgment. A development in Vienna often looks more important than one occurring under our own eyes. The garden-cities, the employers' villages, the apartment groupings of the Old World have their counterparts, even though on a smaller scale, in Sunnyside, Radburn, Mariemont, Shawsheen, and the Negro quarters of Chicago; on the other hand, the European post-War effort has unquestionably been more far-reaching and fruitful than our own.

The European slums even more than the American have resulted from decay of once-important residential sections. At their worst, on account of ingrained habits, they are doubtless inferior to anything to be found in this country except in extreme cases of overcrowding among the foreign-born. But in England with its garden-cities and Local Authorities, in Holland with its socially controlled apartments, in Germany and Austria with their extensive *Siedlungen,* the American may find food for thought. Each of these developments merits longer attention than it can be given here, but even brief consideration will serve to point a moral.

After the World War practically every European country was confronted with a housing shortage. Involved political and economic motives, together with the oft-repeated sentiment " homes fit for heroes to live in," found their expression in extensive government participation in housing. This took many different forms; its economic consequences are discussed at length in Chapter XI. Here we are concerned, not with how the buildings were financed nor with the cost of tenancy, but merely

---

observations that the American tourist makes in Paris, London, or Amsterdam where historical spots have degenerated. He does not often visit the same sort of places in his own land.

with the type of home provided. Even before the War the socialistic tendency was more advanced in Europe than in this
country, and many of these magnificent housing developments
were really but a flowering of ideas that had been current for
some time prior to the War.

Most definitely developed in England is the garden-city
movement. This was not primarily an attempt to provide housing, but a scheme for regional planning and decentralization of
industry, an effort to bring the abode of the worker near to his
place of work. A recent English definition is this: " A garden-
city is a town planned for industry and healthy living; of a size
that makes possible a full measure of social life, but not larger;
surrounded by a permanent belt of rural land; the whole of the
land being in public ownership or held in trust for the community." [51] Garden-cities do not build houses and sell no land
except for schools, municipal buildings, churches, and institutions which are required to have title. The leases of the land on
which the houses are built do, however, run for long periods,
from 99 to 999 years.

Although Bournville Village was the first garden-city, and
even as early as 1914 had established a very low death rate as
compared with that of Birmingham, or England and Wales as
a whole,[52] the most striking of the garden-cities are Letchworth
and Welwyn. These two cities in Hertfordshire are demonstra-
tions of the ideas of Ebenezer Howard. They look much like
other English towns, but their planning by Sir Raymond
Unwin has preserved charm and peace during growth so that
they do not sprawl as do some ordinary towns.

The garden-city does not, it is clear, strike directly at the
heart of the slum problem. To be sure, if all industry were de-
centralized, if all workers were housed in garden-cities, the slum

[51] Wood, Edith Elmer, " Housing Progress in Western Europe " (E. P.
Dutton and Company, New York, 1923), p. 24.

[52] 4.9 per thousand for Bournville in the five years ending in 1914, 14.4 for
Birmingham, and 13.8 for England and Wales. Vital statistics are often
deceptive. See p. 442. (Wood, E. E., " Housing Progress in Western Europe,"
p. 17).

might largely disappear. But the garden-city, in order to be a complete unit, must house fully as many people who would not otherwise live in slums as workers who would. It is significant also that after twenty-five years some of the promoters of the garden-city movement are beginning to have doubts as to its ultimate success — not as to its value, but as to the possibility of extending it far enough to remedy the slum problem. The rate of development has been very slow, and many of the garden-city's most ardent proponents are dismayed. In many respects the garden-city is a *tour de force*. It has been copied in some other nations,[53] though not on the same scale as in England.

A more direct approach to the slum situation in England has been made by the various Local Authorities, and particularly by the London County Council. This body, which has been working on the problem since 1889, and up to the outbreak of the War had built dwellings for 59,000 people, has since the Armistice acquired large estates on the fringes of London, equipped them with services and even rapid transit, and then covered the countryside with planned towns of suburban laborers. The original London County Council houses were two- and three-room apartments, with toilets in the basement, oil lighting, and running water in the hall. Today the standard is a five-room cottage with bathroom, wood floors, electric lights, and a garden. Becontree is the largest of the really impressive developments; it was planned to house about 130,000 persons. The buildings are of red or yellow brick, or of brick covered with stucco. A few are cottage flats of three or four rooms and bath, but the majority consist of single cottages of four to seven rooms and bath.[54] The standard of Becontree is the row house; the main plan is to have the living-room on the garden side and to have the houses not more than two rooms deep. There is no

[53] Notably in France, at Le Trait near Caudebec. This shipbuilding community has sixteen different types of houses with dormitories for bachelor workers, lodgers thus being eliminated. There is an allowance of rent for householders who play in the band or the orchestra. The infant death rate is 20 per cent less than that of the department in which it is located.

[54] It should be emphasized that in speaking of single dwellings in Europe detached dwellings are seldom meant.

such effort to obtain sun exposure as has been made in Germany, the English apparently preferring a really charming and haphazard-appearing community to the orderly and scientifically healthy one of Germany. There can be no question that the London County Council effort has effected a considerable social improvement in the lives of the people it houses; but in view of the total slum population it is evident that a great deal of work must still be done.

The development in Holland, as manifested most strikingly in Amsterdam, although reflected in The Hague, Rotterdam, and Hilversum, is quite different; the slums of Amsterdam are still among the worst in the world. The shortage of housing there was acute until the community built tremendous blocks and rows of apartments and single houses, mostly the former. The Dutch prefer the single house, but economy has dictated the development of large colonies of apartments. In the building of this really great mass of housing, spread on the outskirts of the four quarters of Amsterdam, the services of the best Dutch architects have been enlisted, and side by side the work of Wijdeveld, de Klerk, Kramer, and others may be seen. These architects have remained steadfast to beautiful Dutch brick, but have had a distinct inclination toward an extreme international style. Gardens and orientation seem to play a smaller part than they do in Central Europe, and planting is much less carefully attended to. On the other hand, social control is strongly exercised; the municipality recognizes that people make the slums quite as much as the dwellings do, and watch the inhabitants of the buildings carefully. In fact, communities have been developed for the reclamation of "undesirable" families whose unsocial behavior makes them a menace to a peaceful and orderly life. These people are taken from the good buildings and housed in observation stations or dwellings for the "economically weak." Here an effort is made to train them in clean living and in the principles of social give-and-take. The observation stations when empty are quite attractive; when occupied by an undesirable family they are likely to be most unpleasant. People who cannot be reclaimed after a proper probation period are released from state care and left to shift for themselves, or in extreme cases are placed in institutions.

There is much argument as to the efficacy of these measures. The experiment is significant as indicating outright recognition of a very important fact, one altogether too often overlooked by social workers, that some portions of the population fail to live decently fully as much because of lack of will as for lack of economic opportunity. The extent of government or community control is also significant, and permits the pertinent question: assuming the desirability of this method, to what extent would it conflict with the American philosophy of individualism? The effect of the whole Amsterdam experiment has, of course, been good, and has eliminated a considerable slum area.

But by far the greatest efforts in group housing and community building during the past decade have been made in Central Europe, particularly Germany and Austria. Here there has been an extensive and valuable " demonstration of the civic and social values arising from orderly communities." [55] The *Siedlungen* of Berlin, Stuttgart, Frankfurt, and Vienna may here be considered for what they reveal. No one *Siedlung* will show all of the achievements, but by mentioning individual ones the various facets of the movement may be displayed. By far the most extensive development has taken place in the city of Vienna.

Fundamentally the *Siedlung* represents an attempt to provide for the lower classes a community in which every dwelling shall have an equal access to light, air, sun, and garden; the architecture of the group as a whole is carefully considered. An individual *Siedlung* may or may not be a town, with the usual services of the town; sometimes an extremely large building contains many services usually associated with a community, or several building groups designed by several architects are com-

[55] Wright, Henry, " Are We Ready for an American Housing Advance? " (Architecture, June, 1933, p. 310).

bined into a community under the directorship of one. The architects are much attracted by the esthetic possibilities in such buildings, and have chosen varying modes of expression. If these may be criticized, it is because they tend to produce a mass effect which impresses the passerby but fails to provide the homelier domestic effect so desirable for the individual dweller. The tendency, particularly in Germany, is toward monotony; it expresses the great organizing power of the German nation, but charm such as the English village possesses is entirely lacking.

Throughout the *Siedlungen* there is a grouping of row houses and apartments in proper relation, the former being normally two and one-half stories and the latter, which formerly had four stories, now commonly having three. The apartments do not usually have gardens except for a central court, but a notable exception is in Siedlung Britz, in Berlin, where the gardens for each apartment are arranged in terraces. It cannot be said that within the *Siedlung* there is sufficient attention to the diverse needs of separate families, but perhaps this is too much to expect. Special care is directed to orientation and the two-room-deep structure is always the aim. It is intended not to have any dark rooms.

Individual *Siedlungen* reveal the various features desired, but not all are achieved in any one. Thus Siedlung Britz, in Berlin, builds its apartments in a horseshoe with terraced gardens, and around the periphery of the horseshoe the row houses are grouped. Weissenhofsiedlung, in Stuttgart, surveyed from the northeast displays impressive horizontal lines, broken at the top by the grouping of the taller apartments behind the two-story buildings, while the plan is interrupted by curved elements. But the whole has a decidedly institutional effect.

In Vienna there is decided variety. Fountains are common in the courtyards, which are seldom closed on all sides. The Reumannhof has a high arched arcade, pool, pergolas, and bow windows, and suggests an expensive Park Avenue apartment building. It raises the question whether esthetic value has not been

gained at the cost of something more important, or whether the
total cost has not been too high. The Schlingerhof has markets
in the square, and focuses attention on the common use of vista
and light, the value of which has always been recognized on the
Continent in connection with public buildings. Here is an extension from the planned city to planned public living. Garden-
cities of two and one-half stories of row houses are found in the
Weissenböckstrasse. Gable-end architecture is revealed in the
Hoffingergasse. Flat-roofed modern architecture appears in
Wien-West, and the English cottage style in the Flötzersteig.
In many buildings there are common laundries with modern
conveniences. The Fuchsenfeldhof, among others, has a swim-
ming pool. Sand-boxes for the children are provided in the
Sandleitengasse. The tree planting and the quiet to be found in
the row houses of Hermesweise exemplify the attention paid to
such planting throughout the Central European developments.
The kindergarten building in the Lindenhof is better than
many provided in American nursery-schools for the wealthy,
particularly as regards beauty and light and air, and the same
may be said for the Pastaozzihof. Other buildings have libraries, barber-shops, and clinics, dental and medical.

It is small wonder that the splendid achievements of Central
European housing have lured many American social workers
into the conviction that we have erred in this country in stress-
ing the single-family house; they are awaiting the day when we
shall copy the German and Austrian efforts. Unquestionably
these efforts have achieved remarkable social results. The economic solution is another matter which is deferred for later
discussion.[56]

In considering the social application of this development to
America, certain factors must be remembered. There is nothing
in the buildings themselves, other than their original environment, which would prevent their degenerating rapidly into
slums; this rests with the occupants. The Volkswohnhaus in
Felix-Mottl-Strasse, in Vienna, for instance, has a high central

[56] See Chapter XI.

building in a court surrounded by lower buildings with straight rectangular windows. The building provides light and air, but removal of the curtains at the windows and the accumulation of junk in the courtyard might easily transform this section into a slum. Again, Dr. Josef Frank [57] has designed a remarkable group of buildings in Wien XVII. These buildings have uncovered balconies with iron rails. The Italian population of the lower East Side of New York, with their custom of hanging laundry and blankets from railings and the like, could easily give a group like this at least the appearance of a slum. Such conversion is prevented in Europe by planning which takes care of the disposal of junk and the airing of washing and bedding, but far more by the bureaucratic regulation natural in Central Europe. We need not attempt to decide whether some such supervision in America would be desirable; the fact is that from birth or entry to this country every person is taught that he has a right to do as he pleases, and this attitude stands in the way of effective social control. Acute resentment would undoubtedly be engendered by any marked effort in that direction.

Finally, with respect to the question of our overemphasis of the single unit, the words of Dr. Frank are significant: " The Werkbund takes the point of view that different types of people need different types of houses. Later on one may determine which model has been the most popular. Of course one will probably never be able to come to a general conclusion as to whether the one-story house or the apartment-house better answers our needs. But this is not only impossible, it is also unnecessary. Since earliest times all kinds of houses have existed one beside the other, and all kinds of houses will probably go on existing one beside the other for a long time to come." [58]

None the less, there is no doubt that city growth has been best fostered abroad. One of the most hopeful signs of the pres-

[57] One of the foremost Viennese architects, very interested in the *Siedlung* development.

[58] Frank, Josef, "International Housing Exposition, Vienna, Austria " (Architectural Forum, October, 1932, p. 328).

ent time is increasing reliance upon intelligent, trained planning of the city. Both in the percentage and the character of slum areas, several nations of Europe are much in advance of us. Of all nations, none seems to have been more foresighted and progressive in this regard than Germany. Instead of the city being left to grow into an incoherent mass with much waste space, foresight, direction of consistent growth, and expert technical counsel control construction. We may have to admit that the capitalistic-individualistic state is unable to achieve what has been done in this direction by states which during their city development have been largely socialistic.

With this background of present European conditions and with our previous picture of the present-day house, we may now fairly ask the question: " Are the American people well housed? "

The distribution of income, according to Mrs. Edith Elmer Wood, author of several books on housing, " is such that a substantial portion of the population cannot pay a commercial rent, much less a commercial purchase price, for a home fulfilling the minimum health and decency requirements." [59] Again, in " Housing Progress in Western Europe," published in 1923, she stated that the widespread opinion in the United States that European housing conditions are worse than our own is fallacious, and that public opinion in that field in Europe is at least a generation ahead of that in our country. Referring to a survey of various French, English, Dutch, and Belgian cities in 1923, she states:

" I have nowhere seen houses even remotely comparable to the ten thousand old-law tenements of lower Manhattan, built before 1879, with their hundreds of thousands of inhabited rooms devoid of any opening to the outer air.[60] Nor have I seen any surviving

[59] " Recent Trends in American Housing " (The Macmillan Company, New York, 1931), p. 1.
[60] There were 34,453 old-law tenement houses in the Borough of Manhattan in 1920; by 1930 the number had been reduced to 29,509.

layout as bad as that of the North End of Boston, with its four- to seven-foot streets between five-story buildings and labyrinths of rear tenements filling the interior of its blocks." [61]

There can be no doubt that the housing conditions in certain sections of the United States are distinctly bad. In some of the larger cities the housing for about one-eighth of the population is considered by expert observers to approximate slum conditions. In 1930 the Housing Association of the City of New York reported that 2,000,000 persons were still living in " old-law tenements," of a type that it had been unlawful to build since 1901, and many of which had been erected long before.[62]

A number of these tenement-houses are of the " dumb-bell " type, wherein the tenement occupies nearly all the land space, leaving only a narrow margin in the rear for light and air; a so-called air-shaft from 50 to 60 feet long but only 28 inches wide is the only means of supplying light and air for the five rooms on each side of the house. Only four out of fourteen rooms on each floor receive direct light and air from the street or yard; the rooms are very small, and the bedrooms are wholly dependent upon the air-shaft. In the hallway on each floor are two water-closets, lighted and ventilated by the air-shaft, each of which is used by two families. While many such apartments may not fairly be termed slums, they are admittedly far below a satisfactory standard. It is of interest that this type of apartment when first produced, in 1879, received a prize award.[63]

Again, a survey covering 5,242 dwellings in minor streets and alleys in Philadelphia in 1929 showed that 96 per cent of the houses were without furnaces, and nearly 93 per cent without bathrooms; in 30 per cent of this group lamps were used for artificial lighting.[64] It was estimated in 1932 that about 250,000 persons, or approximately 12.8 per cent of the population, in Philadelphia were living in slums or in areas coming

[61] " Housing Progress in Western Europe," p. 3.
[62] " Recent Trends in American Housing," p. 281.
[63] State Board of Housing, New York, " Annual Report," 1932. Legislative Document, 1932, No. 84, pp. 11–12.
[64] Newman, Bernard J., " Housing in Philadelphia, 1929," p. 11.

under the influence of slums.[65] Again, it has been estimated that nearly one-third of the population of Cleveland is included in the so-called " blighted areas "; the proportion living in slums would be much smaller.[66]

The reports of local agencies which have investigated housing in American cities give the impression that the state of things in America is intolerable, so numerous are the instances of overcrowding, of rooms without access to the open air, and of the lack of essential sanitary facilities. Although conditions in slums are extremely bad, they are not representative of the country at large. In 1901, for instance, the following general conditions for wage-earners' homes were reported: [67]

	Sanitation	Furniture	Cleanliness
Good	64%	64%	81%
Fair	29	26	13
Bad	7	10	6

There can be little doubt that conditions today are even better.

Lawrence Veiller, a recognized authority on American housing, and an earnest advocate of high standards, has said:

" The great mass of the people throughout the country live in small one-family dwellings. Some of these are not very attractive architecturally, some of them lack many of the facilities of living that people in America have come to think are essential to a modern home, many of them are built much too close to each other to provide adequate light and ventilation, but the great majority of them are very satisfactory homes. It may be fairly said that the great mass of the people in the United States is, on the whole, well housed — if one always excepts the great centres of population." [68]

[65] Newman, Bernard J.
[66] Millar's Housing Letter, April 3, 1933.
[67] USDL, " 18th Annual Report of the Commissioner of Labor," p. 21.
[68] " The Housing Problem in the United States " (National Housing Association Publications, New York, March, 1930), p. 6. Mr. Veiller is Secretary of the National Housing Association and formerly was Secretary of the New York State Tenement Commission.

It is high time that critical scrutiny be turned upon the accessories which the machine age provides for our comfort, but which so largely control us instead. While the structure of our dwellings has remained much the same for generations, accessory features have developed to a marked degree, and now constitute a large and increasing proportion of the cost of the home. This is especially true of the United States, but since the World War the European nations have exhibited the same tendency. Bathrooms, central heating, electric lighting, and labor-saving appliances are not basic needs except to the minimum extent to which urbanization may require them.[69] And since many of these are not essential even to the urban home, they are surely not necessary in the country. Minimum standards for decent living and a normal social life may, from an economic viewpoint at least, fall far below those pronounced essential by overzealous reformers.[70] Much of the finish and accessories of the present-day American home, while gratifying to the social pride of the owners, may clearly be classed as unnecessary. Even if one admits as essential to comfort many of these non-basic features, the number of pure luxury features in the average American home looms large. Sound planning of the city and of the homes of which it is composed should fully recognize the social and economic values of all the physical features involved; the community will thereby acquire a sense of social and spiritual values, and the ability to strike the right balance between essentials on the one hand and comforts and luxuries on the other.

Of distinct interest in this connection is a study made of the relative importance attached to various accessories by teachers and home-makers, shown in Table 18. It was too limited in scope to be conclusive, but it demonstrates that essential facilities and equipment such as running water and screens are likely to be overlooked in the mad rush for mechanical gadgets.

[69] Fisher, Ernest M., "The Minimum House" (Architecture, January, 1933, p. 45).

[70] As our hard-headed European friends often recognize. See the discussion of state housing under "Living Conditions," p. 89 f.

TABLE 18

RELATIVE IMPORTANCE OF CERTAIN ACCESSORIES AND UTILITIES IN THE HOME [a]

Average Preference as Reported by

	Teachers	Home-makers
Running water	15.01	15.80
Sewage disposal	13.61	12.43
Screens	13.08	10.77
Modern bathroom	10.43	9.83
Power for housework	9.65	7.83
Sufficient house room	8.43	6.43
Electric lighting	8.00	9.25
Telephone	7.90	8.30
Central heating	7.75	10.47
Refrigerator	6.14	8.87
	100.00	99.98

(a) Research study by Department of Sociology of Connecticut Agricultural College. Clark, Carroll D., "Evaluating Certain Equipment of the Modern Rural Home" (Journal of Home Economics, December, 1930, p. 1011).

To sum up, the varied character of the composite American home may be broadly visualized. Its outstanding feature is the separate house for single-family occupancy, comprising three-quarters of all homes and a still higher percentage in value; half of these are found in urban sections. Regardless of the increasing number of city apartment-houses, the country home in the United States has already been submerged through the growth of community life. The city home outnumbers the country home by nearly six to four; if value be taken as the unit of measure, urban homes dominate by more than three to one. The urban single-family home, housing over one-third of all families and representing well over one-half of the entire $90,000,000,000 [71] of total home wealth of this country, is clearly the most important social and economic factor of the problem to which this study is directed.

The norm of this type of dwelling may be seen in great numbers upon entering any of our cities by train or motor. It is

[71] Dwellings $70,000,000,000. See p. 50. Land $20,000,000,000.

usually of two stories, though the one-and-a-half-story cottage and single-story bungalow are common. Its architecture is undistinguished, and both the color and atmosphere might well be called drab. A small grass plot lies in front, and perhaps a small garden and a garage behind. In northern sections the house has a cellar; in southern sections it is frequently without one; in either case the first floor is far enough above the ground to provide for cellar windows and to avoid dampness. A small porch shelters the entrance door, and large double-hung windows are a noticeable and none-too-pleasing feature of the exterior. The upper half of a window is all too often nailed to the casing and covered inside by the conventional dark roller-shade, so that it seldom serves for either light or ventilation. Brickwork, shingles, or wooden siding cover the wooden frame of the walls, and on the conventional pitched roof are wooden or composition asphalt or asbestos shingles.

Inside are a small living-room, a dining-room, a kitchen, two to four bedrooms, and a bathroom. The floors are mostly of low-grade hard wood, and in the kitchen are usually covered with thin linoleum. The type of wooden trim varies with the section of the country; hard pine, perhaps, in the South, and fir in the Northwest. The lath-and-plaster walls are mostly papered or calcimined. The kitchen is generally supplied with a gas stove, one or two built-in cabinets, and a laundry tub, and the bathroom with a tub, toilet, and lavatory, all of simple design in white enameled finish. A one-pipe steam system supplies the heating, the pleasant open fireplace of former days being absent. Half these homes have a telephone, and perhaps more a radio; all are wired for electricity, and all have running water.

This norm is typical of half our homes. But the other half is split into widely differing kinds; one-eighth includes the city apartment, both for rich and poor, taking in most of our slum dwellers. Another eighth comprises the semi-city two-family type — the ugly double-decker; these homes skirt our urban centers in painful prominence, and though they mostly lack the rudiments of esthetic value, they are not without their practical worth and have in plan the elements of attractiveness. The third eighth is well above the norm — the larger house in city, suburb, and country, the newer home, the leader in accessory and plan, the reconditioned ancient house, or the one the architect designs. And last of all, an eighth is scattered over farm, orchard, and ranch, industrial village, hill and dale, desert and shore; these are the simple, more primitive homes built close to the soil and close to basic living needs, but for the most part with the elements essential to a healthy life.

It is asserted by many that the city slums house at most one-eighth of all our city people. The higher and somewhat popular estimate of a third is evidently extreme, and is based on questionable analysis or unusual definition. The extent of slums in any community is doubly a matter of opinion.

If by slums minimum housing is meant, then indeed a third of our people live therein; for that classification includes many a farm and ranchhouse and simple country home, the city-encircling shack and double-decker, and the industrial worker's home, as well as the city slum itself. But the minimum home may possess as much decency and charm as the maximum one — perhaps much more.

Most slums occur in sections with multi-family housing; but the nation's entire equipment of such dwellings holds less than an eighth of our families. The double-decker sections (housing a tenth) and single-family shacks encircling the cities (the number of whose occupants is undeterminable) may indeed have bad slum spots. They have open spaces, however, and figure little in slum reports. So our congested slum areas can hardly comprise a sixteenth of our homes.

For at least three-quarters of our homes, however, the foregoing analysis calls for marked improvement and lower cost. Structure and finish should be more nearly integrated. More homogeneous materials and the resulting simpler treatment of structure and design would mean lower cost. Furthermore, a new type of structure would better accommodate the increasing number and variety of accessories. Though such a new structure should be specially fitted to city life, it should not ignore the other needs of our widely varied national life. The need of the industrial communities, as well as the thickly populated slum sections, for economic and engineering help is both more pressing and more difficult to meet than that of the city single-family group. Present-day technical knowledge and experience can and will make better and lower-cost housing for the minimum-income groups. The same operation would help the economic position of the whole country.

CHAPTER III

The Annual Cost of Shelter

I N the early days of man, the capital cost of his shelter was defined by the time and labor expended by him and his associates in building the home. The annual cost was represented only by the labor spent in repairs and maintenance, among primitive peoples a very small item. Today in the existing primitive cultures, such as that of the Australian aborigines, the home-dweller is both landlord and tenant and the capital and annual cost of shelter are represented solely by the labor of the householder. Such peoples are perhaps fortunate in being independent of others in the provision of their homes, but they lack the wide variety of home comforts and services resulting from the complex cooperative life of an advanced modern civilization.

The cost of shelter to the house-builder of the present is also measured by the time and labor, both manual and mental, devoted to its construction. But in this case time and labor are those of the whole group cooperating under the principles and the influences of a complex economic structure. Money has evolved as the measure of such cooperative work and its product; throughout the modern world it is the only measure of economic value and the only medium of exchange. It measures the wealth and productivity of the nation and of each individual. It is only too obvious that our various national currencies are functioning poorly in today's economic turmoil; it is equally obvious that these changing money standards must serve us to evaluate, analyze, and define the cost of shelter and the elements of which it is composed.

In a primitive society the cost of shelter and the individual's rights and obligations involved therein are easy to evaluate; in a complex group of an advanced economic structure such evaluation becomes increasingly difficult. From our earlier consideration of the place of shelter in national economics we know of its great importance in the wealth of all nations: it is an essential part of the economic structure. The annual returns therefrom, both direct and indirect, also comprise a large factor in the national income, whether as income to the owner or expense to the occupant in the form of rent.

THE PHILANTHROPIC ATTITUDE

Study of the cost of shelter leads almost inevitably to the conception of eleemosynary assistance. When one finds what it costs to build and maintain or to rent a home, however modest, one inevitably sympathizes with owner or tenant, particularly if the home involved be small. Why is it that such philanthropic thoughts arise?

There are many reasons. We are the descendants of ancestors to whom the conceptions of feudalism and slavery were familiar. In both these institutions there existed an inescapable obligation upon the part of the overlord to house and protect and often to feed his dependents, even though the obligations of the dependents were also heavy. This responsibility has descended to us, so that we feel that housing for the economic under-dog should be provided free or at less than cost. In the southern cotton-mill villages it is usual to supply operatives with housing, rent-free in part at least, in lieu of additional wages — a tangible expression of this tradition.

But tradition is by no means the only factor. Shelter is the only capital item of importance with which the poor man has to deal. It is a problem that confronts him in youth, before he is ready to grapple with it. The philanthropic philosophy arises in part from sympathy with his difficulties.

High standards are often set by welfare workers for the housing of the lower classes. As ideals they are excellent; as practical expedients they are wide of the mark. The establishment of a standard that the economic condition of a people forbids necessarily leads to philanthropic conceptions. The eager striving towards a higher standard of living, expressed in physical rather than spiritual values, inevitably causes the slighting of a basic need like housing.

Eleemosynary ideas are naturally engendered by study of the slums, where measures for the provision of proper housing have become secondary to other interests; the inertia or helplessness of the owners leads perforce to social intervention. The slum dramatically recalls our past errors in housing and the consequent waste, so that we view the housing problem from the standpoint of philanthropy. The extension of this philosophy from slum clearance to large-scale housing provision appears to the welfare worker to be only one of degree. Finally, it may be that our entire economic structure rests on a false foundation; that in pursuit of individualism we have failed to remember the obligations of man to man.

Probably all these factors are responsible to some degree for the eleemosynary viewpoint. Where there is smoke there must be fire; when so much is said about the cost of housing to the individual as compared with his other needs, we must infer that it is not being provided with the same degree of efficiency. The situation demands not philanthropy, easily aroused and easily expressed, but industrial and engineering skill, which is much more difficult to secure.

One of the stock arguments of the welfare worker revolves about the annual cost of shelter. We shall therefore first present the facts concerning it, and then consider the oft-heard assertion that a considerable proportion of the population of the United States cannot afford an economic rent for the home they need.[1]

---

[1] This contention always carries the corollary that people should be provided by state or private donation with the house they cannot afford.

DISTRIBUTION OF THE FAMILY BUDGET

We can best approach this matter through the medium of cost-of-living studies. At the outset it must be emphasized that the distribution of the family budget is strongly influenced by the family income. In countries of an advanced economic status food represents from 40 to 55 per cent of the annual family outlay and shelter from 15 to 20 per cent. In the case of families with very high incomes, however, the outlay for food, while large in amount, is small in relation to that income.

The distribution presented in Chart 19 of family budgets of different income groups demonstrates a radical difference between the distributions for wage-earners and for people with relatively large incomes, as evidenced chiefly in the items of food, clothing, fuel and light, and sundries.

Many years ago Engel, a pioneer in cost-of-living studies, laid down the rule that the proportion of family income expended for rent remains constant regardless of the amount of income. While that rule is discredited by Engel's own statistics and by practically every major cost-of-living study made since his time, the proportion of family income expended for rent shows less variation as between different income classes and even as between different countries than do the proportions for food and other major divisions of the family budget.

Our analysis is chiefly concerned with representative averages, not with the expenditures of higher-income families, since averages are largely controlled by the expenditures of wage-earning and other moderate-income groups — the only ones, indeed, for which extensive budget data are available.

The most comprehensive and most recent of such studies are those made by the United States Bureau of Labor Statistics. They indicate that rent (or the cost of shelter) represented 15.1 per cent of the total family expenditure in 1891, 18.1 per cent in 1901, and 13.4 per cent in 1918 (see Table 19 and Chart 20). The 1918 study was made under abnormal conditions incident to the World War; the percentage of the

— CHART 19 —

PERCENTAGE DISTRIBUTION OF WAGE-EARNERS' FAMILY BUDGETS COMPARED WITH THOSE FOR HIGHER-INCOME GROUPS IN THE UNITED STATES

Data for Wage-Earners' Families from United States Bureau of Labor Statistics 1901 Cost-of-Living Study; based on 11,156 "normal" families

Data for Higher Income Groups from National Bureau of Economic Research Report: "Income in the United States"; based on a few cases

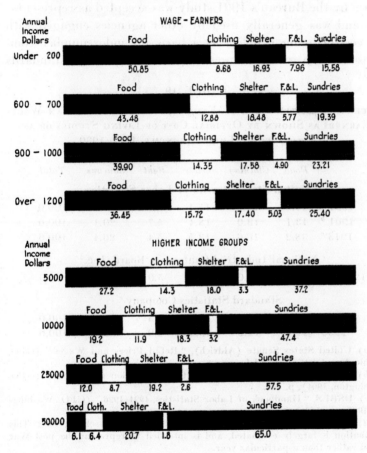

Notes:— F.&L., Fuel and Light

budget devoted to rent at that time was unduly low, for prices of food and clothing were exceptionally high, whereas rents had only just commenced to advance; the index number [2] for food in December, 1918, was 187 and that for clothing 205, while the rent index (which later rose to 168) was only 109.

The 1918 distribution of the budget, therefore, cannot be considered representative. For a long time the distribution shown by the Bureau's 1901 study was accepted as representative and was generally used by other agencies engaged with the cost-of-living problem as a basis for index-number comparisons. The great changes in prices, wages, and standards

TABLE 19

PERCENTAGE DISTRIBUTION OF FAMILY BUDGETS OF AMERICAN WAGE-
EARNERS AS SHOWN BY OFFICIAL COST-OF-LIVING STUDIES OR AS
ESTIMATED BY THREE AGENCIES, 1891–1930

	Food	Clothing	Shelter	Fuel and light	Miscellaneous	Total
United States Bureau of Labor Statistics						
1891 [a]	41.0	15.3	15.1	5.9	22.7	100.0
1901 [b]	43.1	13.0	18.1	5.7	20.1	100.0
1918 [c]	38.2	16.6	13.4	5.4	26.4	100.0
National Industrial Conference Board, Inc.[d]						
1923–30	33.0	12.0	20.0	5.0	30.0	100.0
Standard Statistics Company [e]						
1929	39.0	12.0	19.0	5.5	24.5	100.0
1930	41.5	12.0	19.5	6.0	21.0	100.0

(a) United States Senate (Aldrich), "Retail Prices and Wages" (GPO, Washington, 1892), Vol. XLI.

(b) USDL, "18th Annual Report of the Commissioner of Labor" (GPO, Washington, 1904), p. 101.

(c) USBLS, "Handbook of Labor Statistics, 1924–1926" (GPO, Washington, 1927), p. 119.

(d) "The Service Letter on Industrial Relations," March 30, 1932. This distribution is largely estimated, and is intended to represent the post-War period rather than a particular year.

(e) "Standard Trade & Securities (Bulletin)," October 15, 1930. These figures are estimated, and do not include agricultural and governmental workers.

2 Based on 1913 as 100.

— CHART 20 —

PERCENTAGE DISTRIBUTION OF EXPENDITURES OF WAGE-EARNERS' FAMILIES IN THE UNITED STATES IN VARIOUS YEARS

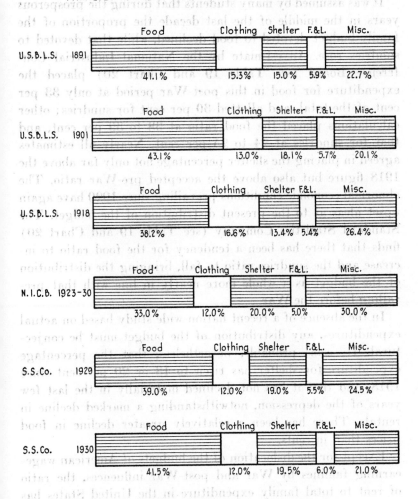

U.S.B.L.S. - United States Bureau of Labor Statistics: Based on Cost-of-
Living surveys.
N.I.C.B. - National Industrial Conference Board: This Distribution is
largely estimated.
S.S.Co. - Standard Statistics Company: Figures are estimated.
Agricultural and Governmental workers excluded.
F.&L. - Fuel and Light

of living since the War, however, caused serious doubt as to whether these 1901 percentages were still applicable.

It was assumed by many students that during the prosperous years in the middle of the last decade the proportion of the family budget devoted to food declined, while that devoted to sundries rose. An estimate by the National Industrial Conference Board (see Table 19 and Chart 20) placed the expenditure for food in this post-War period at only 33 per cent of the total, and allotted 30 per cent for sundries; other calculations placed the food ratio at 38 to 39 per cent, and that for sundries at 24 to 25 per cent. Nearly all estimates agreed in placing the shelter percentage not only far above the 1918 figure but also above the accepted pre-War ratio. The abnormal economic conditions prevailing since 1929 have again upset ideas as to the present distribution of the budget. The Standard Statistics Company (see Table 19 and Chart 20) finds that there has been a tendency for the food ratio to increase and the sundries ratio to fall, bringing the distribution of the budget as a whole more nearly in line with that prevailing before the War.

In the absence of a recent nation-wide study based on actual expenditures, any distribution of the budget must be conjectural. It seems probable, nevertheless, that the percentage expenditure for shelter has risen to 18 or 20 per cent since 1918, and that it has not declined materially in the last few years of the depression, notwithstanding a marked decline in rentals. There has been a relatively greater decline in food prices than in rents.

Except for the dislocation of the budgets of American wage-earning families by War and post-War influences, the ratio of rent to total family expenditure in the United States has for half a century been fairly steady. This will be apparent from Table 20. When allowance is made for the fact that these studies were conducted by different agencies and cover in some cases a few families and in other cases many thousands, and further that the period covered included such exceptional con-

TABLE 20

PROPORTION OF FAMILY BUDGET EXPENDED FOR RENT IN THE UNITED STATES
AS SHOWN BY VARIOUS COST-OF-LIVING STUDIES, 1874–1930

Year (Approx.)	Source of Study	Per cent
1874	United States Bureau of Statistics	19.18 [a]
1875	Massachusetts Bureau of Statistics	17.00
1883	Same	19.74
1884	Illinois Bureau of Labor Statistics	17.42
1887	Kansas Bureau of Labor (704 Kansas budgets)	18.30
1890	Missouri Bureau of Labor (St. Louis budgets)	15.38
1890	Same (Kansas City budgets)	16.63
1890	United States Department of Labor (2561 families in United States)	15.06
1890	Same (192 "normal" families with incomes of $700 to $800)	15.60
1890	United States Senate Report 986 (232 budgets)	19.99
1890	Same (72 "normal" families included in preceding report)	22.04
1901	Massachusetts Bureau of Statistics (families with incomes of $600 to $700)	17.27
1901	United States Bureau of Labor Statistics (25,440 United States families)	18.12
1904	Mrs. L. B. More (group of 200 New York City families)	19.40
1907	R. C. Chapin (New York City families with incomes of $800 to $900)	20.70
1908	John R. Howard (100 Buffalo families)	15.00
1911	British Board of Trade (1036 U. S. families with incomes of $14.60 to $19.47 per week)	16.66
1915	U. S. R. R. Commission (265 families)	20.00
1917	United States Bureau of Labor Statistics (608 New York City families)	12.91 [b]
1917	Philadelphia Bureau of Municipal Research (260 families)	14.10
1917	United States Bureau of Labor Statistics (512 Philadelphia families)	12.04 [c]
1917	Dallas (Texas) Wage Commission (50 families)	14.51
1918	United States Bureau of Labor Statistics (12,096 families)	13.40 [c]
1923	New York State Commission on Housing and Regional Planning (3841 N. Y. C. families with various incomes)	18.30
	Same (3036 N. Y. C. families with incomes under $2500)	20.20
1924	Leila Houghteling (301 Chicago families of unskilled wage-earners)	15.30 [d]
1926	Heller Committee of University of California (25 professional families with an expenditure of $6500)	20.70 [e]
1929	East Side Chamber of Commerce (252 middle-class families on lower East Side of New York) (by Joseph Platzker)	19.00
1930	United States Bureau of Labor Statistics (100 families of Ford Company workers earning approximately $7 per day)	22.60 [f]

(a) Simple average computed by the authors.
(b) The disparity between this figure and those of Mr. Chapin and Mrs. More may be due in part to the influence of War conditions.
(c) Relatively low figure apparently due to War conditions.
(d) Percentage of family funds.

ditions as those attending the World War, the rent ratio shows a marked degree of uniformity. The trend is on the whole slightly upward; this is brought out more clearly by comparisons covering a longer period such as those given in Table 21, which shows estimated distributions of the family

TABLE 21

PERCENTAGE DISTRIBUTION OF THE AMERICAN FAMILY BUDGET BY MAJOR ITEMS, 1775–1931 [a]

Year	Rent	Food	Clothing	Fuel and light	Sundries	Total
1775	12	56	16	8	8	100
1800	12	54	16	9	9	100
1810	12	55	15	8	10	100
1820	12	56	14	8	10	100
1830	14	52	14	9	11	100
1840	14	52	14	8	12	100
1850	15	52	14	7	12	100
1860	16	49	14	8	13	100
1865	18	51	13	6	12	100
1875	20	49	16	5	10	100
1880	15	46	16	5	18	100
1890	15	45	15	6	19	100
1901	18	43	13	5	21	100
1913	18	42	14	6	20	100
1918	14	38	17	5	26	100
1929	19	36	13	6	26	100
1931	19	38	13	6	24	100

(a) Owing to a lack of data, especially in the earlier years, these distributions are necessarily arbitrary, although based on what seems an adequate amount of research.

budget at intervals since 1775 (the changes are shown graphically in Chart 21). Broadly speaking, the indications of this table are as follows:

The percentage expenditure for food has steadily decreased; that for clothing has varied but shows a relative decline; that

(e) Not a rent percentage, as these families were assumed to own their homes, but apparently comparable with other figures here given.

(f) For 68 families renting their homes.

— CHART 21 —

PERCENTAGE DISTRIBUTION OF EXPENDITURES OF WAGE-EARNERS' FAMILIES IN THE UNITED STATES (ESTIMATED): 1775-1930

Note:- F.&L., Fuel and Light ; S., Sundries

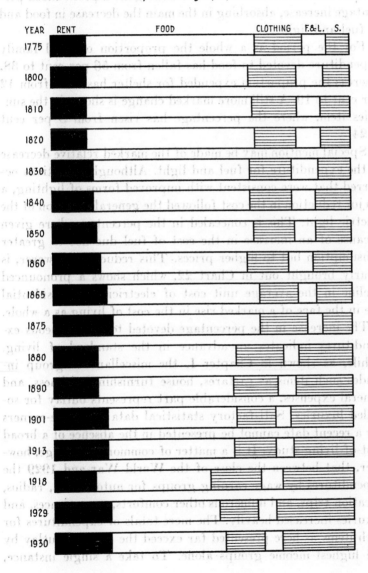

for rent, while fluctuating, has gone distinctly upward, and in 1930 was relatively higher than in any other year except 1875; that for fuel and light has shown a significant relative decrease; and that for sundries has undergone a pronounced percentage increase, absorbing in the main the decrease in food and in fuel and light.

For the period as a whole the proportion of total family expenditure devoted to food has fallen from 56 per cent to 38, whereas the proportion expended for shelter has risen from 12 per cent to 19. A still more marked change is shown in the sundries item, where the percentage has risen from 8 per cent to 24.

Special mention may be made of the marked relative decrease in the expenditure for fuel and light. Although reductions occurred that were consistent with improved forms of lighting, a major reduction in the cost followed the general adoption of the electric light. This is concealed in the percentages here given because of an increase in the cost of fuel due not to greater consumption but to higher prices. This reduction, however, is clearly brought out in Chart 22, which shows a pronounced decline in the average unit cost of electricity for residential use in the face of a marked rise in the cost of living as a whole.

The increase in the percentage devoted to miscellaneous expenditures indicates an advance in the standard of living. While, as shown in Chapter I, the miscellaneous group includes such items as carfares, house furnishing, sickness, and funeral expenses, a considerable part represents outlay for so-called luxuries. Satisfactory statistical data for wage-earners for a recent date cannot be presented in the absence of a broad cost-of-living study. It is a matter of common knowledge, however, that between the close of the World War and 1929 the expenditures by wage-earning groups for automobiles, radios, vacation trips, and numerous other comforts, conveniences, and luxuries increased heavily. The mere totals of expenditures for such items as here presented far exceed the possible outlay by the highest-income groups alone. To take a single instance,

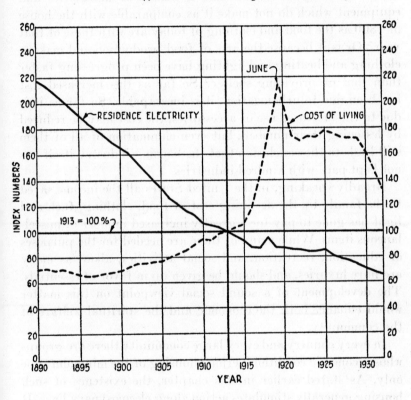

— CHART 22 —

COMPARISON OF INDEX NUMBERS OF PRICES OF ELECTRICITY FOR DOMESTIC USE AND OF COST OF LIVING IN THE UNITED STATES: 1890-1932

Charted from Data of the National Electric Light Association
in Statistical Supplement of the Electric Light and Power Industry

Note:- Chart is plotted from December values for each year

it is obvious that with 20,000,000 passenger automobiles in the United States a high proportion of wage-earning and low-income groups must own one.[3]

It thus appears that the cost of housing in the United States has been steadily increasing in relation to that of other essentials. Is this because of increasing urbanization? Is it because the present-day house contains a wealth of accessories and equipment which do not make it as comparable with the house of 1800 as the food and clothing of today are with those of that year? Or is it because the arts of food production and making clothing and heating and lighting have been progressing faster than that of providing shelter? So far as this increased cost has been due to urbanization, it is inescapable. So far as it is due to the increased use of accessories, the cost may be reduced by lessening their number; but even elimination of all of them still leads to the conclusion that the housing industry itself has not kept pace with kindred industries.

Broadly speaking, in the United States all the income saved to the family by the declining cost of food, clothing, fuel, and light has gone to pay for a greatly increased number of miscellaneous items. While many of these are needed for the purposes of education, recreation, and social activities, about as many are pure luxuries, and should be given up in favor of essentials. The development of a sound social viewpoint on this matter would enhance both the economic and the spiritual welfare of the community.

In every country and every large community there are groups whose economic condition permits housing of the minimum type only. As stated earlier in this chapter, the existence of such housing generally stimulates action along eleemosynary lines. It

[3] The National Bureau of Economic Research states "The figures of production and registration alone are sufficient evidence that the purchase and use of automobiles is participated in by all classes of the population. . . .

"It is clear that a large proportion of the current purchases of passenger automobiles is made by the members of the wage-earning and lower-salaried groups." (National Bureau of Economic Research, Inc., "Recent Economic Changes" [McGraw-Hill Book Company, Inc., New York, 1929], Vol. I, pp. 59–60.)

has been asserted that one-third of our population is unable to pay an economic rental for the housing which modern standards of decency demand. The present depression suggests that we should attribute this to our recent high standard of spending rather than to a high standard of living. Be that as it may, the pressing question now is how to raise simultaneously the general average and the minimum of our housing standards. Perhaps if we turn our attention to the causes of the unsatisfactory housing of the lowest economic group, we may unravel a clue to its improvement.

High ideals are helpful but to require for a group standards too high for its economic ability is futile. In a varied society such as that of the United States there are many levels of economic status within even the simplest classifications. To apply to all sections and population groups such minimum standards as those set forth by the President's Conference and by certain welfare groups is impracticable. Rather should purchasing power be increased, either by increasing income or by decreasing housing costs.

The average budget of the American family in recent years has included a number of miscellaneous luxury items the total expenditure for which approximates that for shelter. The man of average income is in a position to improve upon his home by cutting down on his luxuries; this applies with even greater force to the preponderant medium-income group, and to those of still higher income. It applies but slightly to those of the lowest-income group. By the same token, the well-meant demand of social welfare agencies for minimum living standards should not be made for the poor; for such standards involve a cost of new house construction that does not harmonize with other features of the family budget. Food, clothing, fuel, light, automobiles, and amusements are all relatively cheaper than a new house.

Percentage distributions of family budgets in various countries, in nearly all cases based upon pre-War allocations, are shown in Table 22. In some cases these figures cover only limited

TABLE 22

PERCENTAGE DISTRIBUTION OF FAMILY BUDGETS IN SELECTED
COUNTRIES, PRE-WAR PERIOD [a]

	Food	Clothing	Housing	Fuel and light	Miscellaneous
Canada	35.0	14.3	22.6	9.1	19.0
Great Britain [b]	60.0	12.0	16.0	8.0	4.0
France (Paris only)	60.0	15.0	12.0	5.0	8.0
Germany (Federal Statistical Office)	55.0	10.0	20.0	6.0	9.0
Netherlands (Amsterdam only)	44.8	8.8	13.4	6.7	26.3
Denmark	41.7	11.2	12.4	4.0	30.7
Norway					
Wage-earners	48.0	12.7	15.6	5.4	18.3
Public officials	39.4	15.1	15.6	4.7	25.2
Sweden	42.8	11.9	15.0	4.1	26.2
Finland	61.9	13.0	13.3	4.6	7.2
South Africa	39.7	10.6	22.6	4.4	22.7
Australia	34.8	23.2	23.7	— [c]	18.3
New Zealand	39.0	15.8	23.2	5.9	15.9
Egypt	51.9	16.7	11.7	— [d]	19.7

(a) "The Cost of Living in Foreign Countries" (NICB, New York, 1927), p. 392.

(b) The distribution given in reference 4 below is more generally applicable.

(c) Included under Miscellaneous.

(d) Included under Food.

areas or certain types of families, and other studies show results
differing from those given here, notably in the case of Great
Britain [4] and Sweden. The great change in economic conditions
since the World War has doubtless affected the distribution
of family budgets in some countries to an important degree.
Distributions for selected countries compiled from various
sources are shown in Chart 23.[5] Both the chart and the table
show that the proportion for shelter of 22 to 23 per cent is

[4] The following allocation is more generally applicable to Great Britain:
food 54 per cent, clothing 12 per cent, shelter 16 per cent, fuel and light 7 per
cent, sundries 11 per cent.

[5] For more detailed information concerning family budgets in foreign
countries, see the Appendix, p. 528.

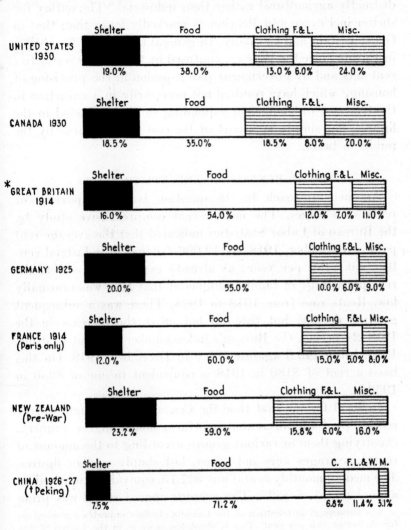

—— CHART 23 ——

PERCENTAGE DISTRIBUTION OF EXPENDITURES OF WAGE-EARNERS' FAMILIES
OR OTHER MODEST-INCOME GROUPS IN VARIOUS COUNTRIES IN SPECIFIED YEARS

UNITED STATES 1930
Shelter — Food — Clothing — F.&L. — Misc.
19.0% — 38.0% — 13.0% — 6.0% — 24.0%

CANADA 1930
Shelter — Food — Clothing — F.&L. — Misc.
18.5% — 35.0% — 18.5% — 8.0% — 20.0%

*GREAT BRITAIN 1914
Shelter — Food — Clothing — F.&L. — Misc.
16.0% — 54.0% — 12.0% — 7.0% — 11.0%

GERMANY 1925
Shelter — Food — Clothing — F.&L. — Misc.
20.0% — 55.0% — 10.0% — 6.0% — 9.0%

FRANCE 1914 (Paris only)
Shelter — Food — Clothing — F.&L. — Misc.
12.0% — 60.0% — 15.0% — 5.0% — 8.0%

NEW ZEALAND (Pre-War)
Shelter — Food — Clothing — F.&L. — Misc.
23.2% — 39.0% — 15.8% — 6.0% — 16.0%

CHINA 1926-27 (†Peking)
Shelter — Food — C. — F.L.&W. — M.
7.5% — 71.2% — 6.8% — 11.4% — 3.1%

Notes:- F.&L., Fuel and Light
F.L.&W., Fuel, Light and Water
C., Clothing ; M., Miscellaneous
† Budget for 48 working-class families
*Estimated

characteristic of Canada, Australia, New Zealand, and South Africa, which though of an advanced type of civilization are distinctly agricultural rather than industrial.[6] The outlay for shelter in France and Belgium is markedly lower than that in Great Britain and Germany. In general the figures for shelter in Europe since the War are confused by the various restrictive rent acts and by government participation in the provision of housing,[7] which have resulted not necessarily in a reduction in the true cost of shelter corresponding to that indicated in the figures, but simply in a part of the cost's being borne by the public in taxes.

ACTUAL RENTALS IN THE UNITED STATES

Another approach to the question is by comparison of rents with wages. The most recent comprehensive study by the Bureau of Labor Statistics indicated that the average rent paid in December, 1918, by 12,096 families in industrial centers was $180 per year; as already explained, however, the rent percentage in family budgets at that time was unusually low. Rents rose from 1918 to 1924. There was a subsequent gradual decline, but this did not offset the increase in the 1918–24 period, the Bureau's index number for rent in June, 1930, being 149.6 against 109.2 in December, 1918. On this basis a rent of $180 in 1918 is equivalent to one of $250 in 1930.[8]

In 1930 for the first time the Census gathered data on the rentals paid for all rented non-farm homes in the country, classifying them in various groups according to the amount of rental; averages were not given, but simply median figures. The median monthly rental was $27.15, equivalent to a median annual rental of $325. The *average* annual rental was prob-

[6] A subsequent distribution of the Canadian budget indicates a percentage for shelter of 18.5 per cent. This is about the same as in the United States. See the Appendix, p. 528.   [7] See Chapter XI.

[8] Prior to the Census of 1930 almost the only information on this point was contained in the cost-of-living studies made by the Bureau, by certain state boards or commissions, and by such private agencies as the National Industrial Conference Board, colleges, and individuals.

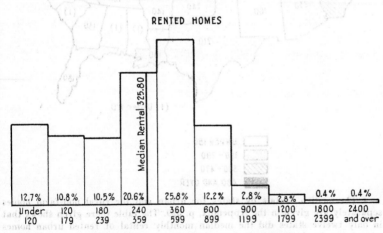

—— CHART 24 ——

—— CHART 24 ——

DISTRIBUTION OF NON-FARM HOMES IN THE UNITED STATES
BY VALUE AND BY RENTAL GROUPS: 1930

OWNED HOMES

Median Value 4778

| 7.6% | 5.4% | 5.1% | 11.1% | 22.3% | 21.9% | 9.4% | 8.6% | 3.2% | 3.4% |

| Under 1000 | 1000 1499 | 1500 1999 | 2000 2999 | 3000 4999 | 5000 7499 | 7500 9999 | 10000 14999 | 15000 19999 | 20000 and over |

GROUPING BY DOLLAR HOME VALUE

RENTED HOMES

Median Rental 325.80

| 12.7% | 10.8% | 10.5% | 20.6% | 25.8% | 12.2% | 2.8% | 2.8% | 0.4% | 0.4% |

| Under 120 | 120 179 | 180 239 | 240 359 | 360 599 | 600 899 | 900 1199 | 1200 1799 | 1800 2399 | 2400 and over |

GROUPING BY ANNUAL DOLLAR RENTAL

ably somewhat higher, about $350 to $375. (See Charts 24, 25, and 26.)[9]

Since this median rental of $325 per year is influenced to some extent by homes in the highest rental groups, we may assume the median for wage-earning groups alone to be sub-

—— CHART 25 ——

MEDIAN ANNUAL RENTALS IN THE STATES OF THE UNITED STATES: 1930

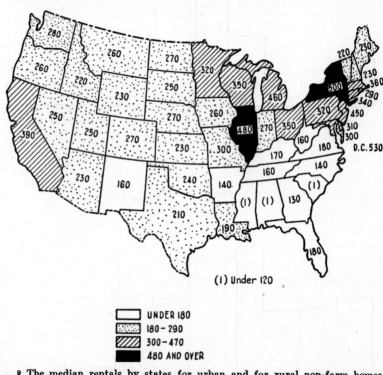

(1) Under 120

	UNDER 180
	180 – 290
	300 – 470
	480 AND OVER

[9] The median rentals by states for urban and for rural non-farm homes separately are given in the Appendix, p. 529. The table there given shows that in only twelve states did the median monthly rental of rented urban homes exceed $30. In three states — New York, Michigan, and Illinois — it was more than $40. In twenty-seven states it was between $20 and $30, while in nine southern states it was below $20. Much lower figures were shown for the group of rural homes; in thirteen states the median monthly rental of these was less than $10.

stantially less. It is also possible that the *average* rental for
wage-earning families was less than the Census median of $325
for all renting families — a conclusion which is supported by
various data. For example, the Bureau of Labor Statistics in-

— CHART 26 —

DISTRIBUTION OF HOMES RENTING FOR LESS THAN $20 PER MONTH
IN THE UNITED STATES BY PERCENTAGE GROUPS : 1930

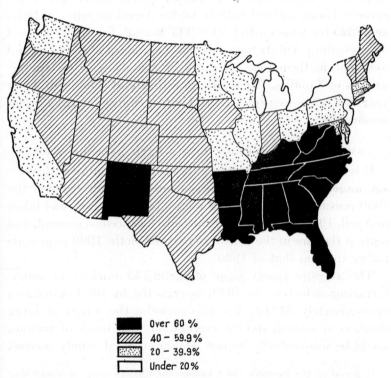

■ Over 60 %
▨ 40 − 59.9%
▦ 20 − 39.9%
□ Under 20%

dex numbers just cited indicate an average annual rental for
wage-earning groups in 1930 of $250; a survey of the living
expenses of 301 families of unskilled workers in Chicago in
1924 showed an average annual rental of $283.[10] Assuming

    [10] Houghteling, Leila, " The Income and Standards of Living of Unskilled
Laborers in Chicago " (University of Chicago Press, Chicago, 1927), p. 115.

that this declined in accordance with the decline of the Bureau's index number of rents in the country at large, the average rent paid by this group in the early part of 1930 would have been $255.[11] This was, however, a rather low-income group; other evidence suggests that the average rent paid by wage-earning groups in the United States in 1930 was somewhat less than $300.[12]

A report of the National Industrial Conference Board gives $240 as a representative minimum yearly rental for wage-earners' homes without bath in twelve American cities in 1927, and $325 for homes with bath.[13] The Board's figures were based on prevailing rentals for an assumed standard of housing, and were not mathematical averages of rentals paid by specific groups of families. All in all, an estimate of $300 rental per year for wage-earners in the United States in 1929 seems reasonable.

COMPARISON OF AVERAGE RENTS WITH AVERAGE WAGES

It is illuminating to compare these average rentals with average wages paid. This comparison must be made between the 1930 census rentals and 1929 wages, for the Census was taken in April, 1930, before wage reductions had become general, and rents at the time of the Census were based on the 1929 wage scale rather than on that of 1930.

The average yearly wage of 8,838,743 workers in manufacturing industries in 1929, as reported by the Census, was approximately $1310; but this includes the wages of large numbers of women, and the average for male heads of families would be substantially higher. Moreover, total family income,

[11] Based on the Bureau's index number for Chicago alone, it would have been about $240.

[12] The average rent paid by a group of sixty-eight workers in the Ford Motor Company in 1930 as shown by a government survey was $391 yearly, but as the wages of these workers were approximately $7 per day the rents paid by them may safely be regarded as much above the general average (Monthly Labor Review, June, 1930, p. 38).

[13] NICB, " The Cost of Living in Twelve Industrial Cities " (New York, 1928), p. 30.

which is the proper basis for comparison with rents paid, substantially exceeds the earnings of the husband alone. In 1918, according to the Bureau's cost-of-living study, the average family income was 12 per cent greater than the earnings of the husband alone, other statistics confirm this ratio.

The average family income for workers in manufacturing industries in 1929 was therefore considerably in excess of the average census wage of $1310. Average family income may be placed at over $1600; in 1918, according to the Bureau of Labor Statistics, it was $1513. Hourly wages were considerably higher in 1929 than in 1918, and while there had been some reduction in the number of hours per week, it is possible that the average family income of wage-earners in manufacturing industry in 1929 was as much as $1800. The average compensation of employees of Class I railroads from 1926–30, as reported by the Interstate Commerce Commission, was about $1700 per year;[14] that of workers in the construction industry in 1929 was $1771.[15] Family incomes in each group were presumably somewhat higher. The average earnings of some other groups doubtless were lower.

Taking $1600 as a 1929 basis of wage-earners' family income, an average rental of $300 per year would be about 19 per cent of the family income. If the latter were as high as $1800, an average rent of $300 would be about 17 per cent of it; while it is impossible to determine the proportion positively, this ratio seems low. With the census median of $325 as a basis, this would represent a little more than 20 per cent on an income of $1600 and about 18 per cent on an income of $1800. These percentages, although based on a rental apparently in excess of that actually paid, agree closely with those allotted to rent in recent years in Table 21.

14 USDC, "Statistical Abstract of the United States," 1932, p. 371.
15 USC, "Census of the Construction Industry" (GPO, Washington, 1933), p. 36, Table XVI.

THE QUESTION OF ECONOMIC RENT

Authorities have often contended that a large majority of families in the United States cannot afford an economic rent for suitable homes. This statement is applied sometimes to new homes, but frequently to all those of a reasonably decent standard. One prominent writer, Edith Elmer Wood, has stated:

"The housing problem, here as elsewhere, is fundamentally economic. The distribution of income and cost of building are such that only a third of the population can afford to buy or rent a new home. . . . Taking the country as a whole, about a third of our families have incomes of $2,000 and over. The middle third range from $1,200 to $2,000. The lowest third have less than $1,200. The top third are well housed; the middle third only fairly; the lowest third badly. Their health, morals, efficiency and family life are being seriously damaged. Only the top third can control their environment without help." [16]

Elsewhere Mrs. Wood has written:

"Building costs are such, not simply now, but on a basis of pre-war prices, as to make it an economic impossibility to build a house of acceptable standards and rent it at a price which the un-skilled wage-earner can pay, and produce a commercial return on the capital invested. It simply cannot be done. . . . The only solution, therefore, is the elimination of commercial profit, and this can only be done by the Government." [17]

Mrs. Wood is by no means alone in taking this position. The Reconstruction Commission of the State of New York said some years ago:

"Houses for the lowest paid wage-earners have *never* been built in the State of New York. The poorer paid worker takes the house

[16] "Government-aided Housing" in "Housing Problems in America" (National Housing Association, New York, 1929), Vol. X, p. 59.

[17] "Government Housing" in "Housing Problems in America," Vol. VII, p. 292.

that is abandoned by the better paid earner. Private venture has never built houses for the low-paid wage-earner; it never will." [18]

The New York State Commission of Housing and Regional Planning has likewise asserted that " at all times and in all places private enterprise has been unable to supply adequate housing to meet the needs of the underlying population." [19] Numerous similar statements could be cited, and their persistence warrants careful study of the facts.

These very general and sweeping statements seem to criticize both our economic structure and our social standards. They imply that physical housing standards are too low for decent living, that the income of the masses is insufficient to cover present-day housing and other basic necessities. The cause given is inefficiency on the part of private initiative; and the remedy, the provision of housing by government.

It seems likely that the standards advanced as essential by these theorists are too high for those who are necessarily limited to minimum housing. Excellent as ideals, these standards have not yet been obtainable through the existing economy. But decent living depends more on spiritual ideals than on physical.

Furthermore, one doubts whether the income of the masses is actually insufficient when one learns the relative expenditures of our people for shelter, automobiles, and luxuries (see Table 3). One quarter of the amount spent on the two latter is nearly half the item for shelter. It is fair to ask those who claim they cannot pay an economic rent: " Are you wasting income on non-essentials to the detriment of your home, and if so, should society pay for that wastage? "

The suggested remedy of government provision of housing will be taken up later. The known inefficiency of government in business and the problematic nature of accumulating taxation burdens may be casually adduced here to meet these casual proposals.

[18] State of New York, Legislative Document No. 78, 1920, p. 55.
[19] Legislative Document No. 91, 1925, p. 28.

Yet the statements quoted do raise very pointedly the question of economic rent. Without attempting to prove anything about that question we must consider some data upon it.

The term " economic rent " is used to define such a yearly rental of gross income from housing as would defray all costs and provide a net return to the owner equal to that obtainable from other comparable investments.

The major cost items covered by such " rental," other than interest, are taxes, maintenance, insurance, administration in the case of rented houses (the renting business), depreciation and obsolescence. The amounts and proportions of such items may vary widely between different times, communities and individual houses.

TABLE 23

Elements Constituting an Economic Rent of Single-Family Urban Dwellings and of Apartment-Houses in the United States, 1930

(Average percentage on total investment [a])

| | Single-family Dwellings | | Apartments | |
	Brick	Frame	" Walk-up "	With elevator and other services
Taxes	2.5	2.5	2.5	2.5
Maintenance	1.5	2.0	2.5	2.5
Administration and service [b]	0.6	0.6	1.0	4.0
Vacancies and bad accounts [b]	0.7	0.7	1.5	1.0
Insurance	0.2	0.2	0.2	0.2
Depreciation and obsolescence	1.0	2.0	2.5	2.0
	6.5	8.0	10.2	12.2
Net return (assumed) [c] ..	6.0	6.0	6.0	6.0
Total economic rent	12.5	14.0	16.2	18.2

(a) Allowing for the fact that certain items do not apply to the value of the land.

(b) Not applicable in the case of an occupying owner; see p. 128.

(c) Figure most commonly used. In some localities it might approximate the first-mortgage rate, but in any case it must be largely empirical. Obviously, to the extent that 6 per cent is above or below a reasonable net return, the total economic rent would be reduced or increased.

Table 23 and Chart 27 give the percentages for these items for single-family dwellings and apartments in the United States in 1930. With the exception of administration and services of

—— CHART 27 ——

ELEMENTS CONSTITUTING AN ECONOMIC RENT FOR SINGLE–FAMILY URBAN DWELLINGS AND FOR APARTMENTS IN THE UNITED STATES: 1930

	INTEREST	TAXES	M.	D.	A.	V.	I.
SINGLE–FAMILY BRICK	6.0	2.5	1.5	1.0	.6	.7	.2

TOTAL 12.5%

	INTEREST	TAXES	M.	D.	A.	V.	I.
SINGLE–FAMILY FRAME	6.0	2.5	2.0	2.0	.6	.7	.2

TOTAL 14.0%

	INTEREST	TAXES	M.	D.	A.	V.	I.
WALK–UP APARTMENT	6.0	2.5	2.5	2.5	1.0	1.5	.2

TOTAL 16.2%

	INTEREST	TAXES	M.	D.	A.	V.	I.
HIGH GRADE APARTMENT	6.0	2.5	2.5	2.0	4.0	1.0	.2

TOTAL 18.2%

M. MAINTENANCE
D. DEPRECIATION AND OBSOLESCENCE
A. ADMINISTRATION AND SERVICE
V. VACANCIES AND BAD ACCOUNTS
I. INSURANCE

high-rental apartments and depreciation and obsolescence, on which point several variations must be noted, the percentages have a firm statistical basis. Slight variations due to a more or less efficient landlord, more or less migratory tenants, higher and lower demands in services,[20] do not materially affect the figures.

Certain items in Table 23, specifically the allowances for vacancies and bad debts, may be disregarded by the occupying owner. This is also true to a large extent of the charge for administration. Whether or not it may cost less per year to own or rent the house one occupies is not clear. For identical homes it should cost less to own, if only by the landlord's net administration expenses.

There is not sufficient information from which to determine the cost of administration and services in high-class apartments where various expensive services are included as part of the rent. The allowance of 4 per cent for these items is arbitrary but apparently not excessive.

The allowances for depreciation and obsolescence are necessarily somewhat arbitrary. Physical depreciation is different from obsolescence which involves the general public attitude toward different features or aspects — site, surroundings, or merely lighting fixtures may condemn a dwelling as undesirable. The very extensive blighted areas of our cities and the stigma attaching to " second-hand houses " positively prove that values have been lost. Present rapid changes in the equipment of buildings, particularly in the direction of air conditioning and other new types of heating and ventilating, plus the change in lighting methods likely to come soon, will probably result in even more rapid obsolescence than has been the case in the past. When business intrudes into a residential district there is rapid obsolescence in houses, usually not offset by an increase in site values. Mere fashion may render obsolete dwellings that from a physical standpoint are not seriously depreciated.

We have already noted that in Great Britain economic rents are estimated at a considerably lower rate than in this country. One reason is the more homogeneous masonry construction used

---

[20] The cost of fuel is an important item for many apartment-house owners, but should not be considered in this connection unless it is also included in the figures for a single-family dwelling.

which requires less annual repair and smaller amounts for depreciation; the houses moreover are generally built with simpler accessories.

The "probable useful" life of a well constructed single-family frame dwelling is usually estimated by students of building depreciation at twenty-five to forty years, and that of a brick building at fifty years; for low-cost apartments it is considerably shorter.[21] Based on a life of thirty-three and one-third years, the "straight-line" depreciation would be 3 per cent per year; on a fifty-year life, 2 per cent. On the assumption that the amount set aside for depreciation and obsolescence is invested in a sinking fund, however, a smaller charge would amortize the investment. It might seem, therefore, that the allowances given in Table 23 are too high but this overlooks the great importance of obsolescence.

For this reason the percentages here used for depreciation and obsolescence are believed to be justified. They are less than those frequently used in similar calculations of operating costs by real-estate experts. The United States Housing Corporation in 1919, after a survey made in connection with the National Association of Real Estate Boards, placed this allowance for single-family dwellings in that year at 3 per cent and for moderate-rental apartments at 3.5 per cent; it calculated the "justified," or economic, rental of single-family dwellings at 15.6 per cent and that of apartments at 20.2 per cent. Labor and material costs are now lower than in 1919; taxes, on the other hand, are much higher.[22]

It is debatable whether depreciation and obsolescence should be figured on land values. While it is true that land often depreciates, on the other hand it frequently appreciates, especially in growing communities; it seems reasonable, therefore, to compute these charges only on the value of the improve-

[21] For certain estimates by the United States Bureau of Internal Revenue, see the Appendix, p. 531.

[22] "United States Housing Corporation Report" (GPO, Washington, 1920), Vol. I, p. 47. The computations of the Corporation will be found in the Appendix, p. 532.

ments. In Table 23 they are related to the total investment for convenience but are somewhat lower than they would be if based on the value of the improvements alone. Since the bare land is usually but a small percentage of the total cost of a home, the difference is not important. Depreciation is properly to be charged against the various utilities such as sewer and water connections which normally represent a much larger investment than the land alone.[23]

To sum up, the economic rental of a single-family frame dwelling in the United States in an urban or suburban community where the house is of good construction may be reckoned at 14 per cent per year on the total investment. The economic rental of a similar house of brick is a little less, while that of tenements and low-cost apartments runs considerably higher. The annual cost of a home to the owner-occupant may be nearer 12.5 per cent. All these allowances are subject to considerable variation in location, character of construction, and general economic conditions.[24]

How far do rentals actually paid represent an economic rent? In the absence of information on the value of rented homes in the United States, it is impossible to give a definite answer, and the conclusions presented below must be interpreted broadly.

Probably considerable residential property does not yield an economic rent. By reference to the compilations of the United States Housing Corporation, given in the Appendix, p. 532, it will be seen that from 1913 to 1918 the rentals reported for single-family residences and apartments often fell far below the estimated economic yield. This, however, was a period of rising real estate values but of relatively low rents, and the data are not sufficiently established to warrant positive deductions. An analysis of thirty-one apartment-houses in New York City in 1931 indicated the following gross and net yield percentages: [25]

23 See Chapter VII.
24 Data for a British cottage home are given in the Appendix, p. 533.
25 Kerby, C. K., " Gross and Net: What Return on Apartment Invest-

	Gross income	Net return
5 apartment buildings on Fifth Avenue .	15.0	5.0
7 apartment buildings on Park Avenue .	13.8	4.3
5 apartment buildings on other avenues .	14.1	4.3
14 apartment buildings on side streets ..	14.3	4.1

Some of the large cooperative apartment-house projects erected in New York City in recent years under the limited-dividend housing legislation of 1926 also report a somewhat similar yield. The report of the North Carolina Tax Commission for 1927 gave the gross rental of 584 residences in that state with an aggregate " fair value " of $2,940,000 as 9.1 per cent, and the net rent as only 3.2 per cent.[26] Such instances are obviously not conclusive, but they suggest that actual rentals are frequently less than the estimated economic return.

In the case of industrial or company housing, which reaches significant proportions in some localities, notably in the mill villages of southern cotton-manufacturing centers, frequently no attempt is made to collect an economic rent. Instead, the rent is often a more or less nominal figure, and the difference between it and an economic rent is absorbed by the manufacturing company which owns and rents the houses; it is in effect a part of the wage payment. An instance of this follows: [27]

Total cost of home per room, including land	$600.00
Annual rental per room	17.56
Loss per room, including interest	60.18
Total indicated economic rent per room	77.74 [28]

In the case of some other " company housing," the rental actually obtained may come much nearer to an economic rental

ments? " (Building Investment, November, 1930), pp. 12–14. The percentages here given may not represent a normal condition.

[26] " Report of the Fox Commission to Governor McLean " (Raleigh, 1929), p. 219.

[27] Data furnished by Lockwood Greene Engineers, Inc., New York.

[28] It is interesting to note that the indicated economic rent of $77.74 is equivalent to approximately 13 per cent on the cost of $600 per room, or only a little less than the computed economic rent of 14 per cent for single-family frame houses given in Table 23.

than in the case cited; nevertheless it is a common practice for the employing corporation to fix the rental for such housing at substantially less than an economic return.

Circumstantial evidence that much residential property in the United States does not carry an economic rent is found in the rule of thumb cited in real-estate circles that a house is worth ten times its actual rental; [29] or, to state the rule conversely, that the annual rental is only 10 per cent of the value instead of 14 per cent as computed in Table 23. But with taxes ranging around 2.5 per cent, not to mention depreciation and other factors, a 10 per cent gross annual rental is not an economic return; as a matter of fact, many real-estate interests assume that the proper ratio is 100 times the monthly rental, which places the economic rent at 12 per cent.

The annual rent bill of the American people in 1928 (including the rental value of owned homes) was estimated in Table 3 at $11,000,000,000; by 1930 rents had fallen about 8 per cent, but in the meantime several hundred thousand new dwellings had been erected, so that the total expenditure in 1930 may be estimated at $10,500,000,000. If this be compared with the estimate of $90,000,000,000 as the value of all dwelling-house property (including land), as noted on page 50, the indicated gross yield is a little over 11.6 per cent, or somewhat below our estimate of the economic rental in Table 23.

Suppose that the median rental value of rented homes, $325 per year, reported by the Census in 1930 be compared with the estimated value of such rented homes. Applied to approximately 12,500,000 rented non-farm homes in 1930, this median rental gives an aggregate rental of $4,000,000,000. On the basis of a $90,000,000,000 value of all homes the value of rented non-farm homes may be estimated as $37,080,000,000. On this basis the aggregate rental would be equivalent to 10.8

---

[29] This rough formula dates back at least 300 years. However, in view of the great change in the character of the house in recent times and of the increase in taxes, it is no longer generally applicable.

per cent. However, as suggested on pages 118–19, it is believed that the average rental of rented non-farm homes in 1930 was somewhat in excess of the median. If this average be placed at $350 per year, the aggregate rental for this group of homes would be $4,375,000,000 and the percentage return on the estimated value of $37,080,000,000 would be nearly 11.8 per cent.

If limited to *new* houses in industrial communities constructed at the costs prevailing since the World War, the contention that many families cannot afford an economic rent may be substantially correct. On the basis of an economic rental of 14 per cent, families which are able to pay only $275 to $300 yearly for rent require homes costing or worth not more than $2000 to $2200. Comparatively few homes have been supplied at any such costs in recent years in urban communities, to which the average rentals here used apply. As shown on page 281, the average cost in recent years of new houses in 257 cities of the United States has been over $4000, exclusive of the site. Even in Philadelphia, noted for its moderate-priced homes, the average cost of new, single-family, two-story houses — again exclusive of the site — was in every year from 1926 to 1930, inclusive, in excess of $4000 (in 1920 it was $6800). In the great industrial centers of the United States comparatively few homes have been provided in recent years at a cost of less than $3000. Bureau of Labor Statistics figures covering ten cities show that nearly 80 per cent of new dwellings projected in 1929 and nearly 75 per cent of those projected in 1931 cost $3000 or more, exclusive of site cost; about 40 per cent cost from $4000 to $7000. Nearly all the houses costing less than $3000 were in one or two cities.[30]

Doubtless many houses were constructed in some communities at lower cost, certainly those in rural districts, but in comparing costs with rentals it is necessary to relate both factors to the same type of community. Wages and rentals in Detroit or Chicago are not properly comparable with home values in rural Mississippi or even with those in southern cities.

[30] Monthly Labor Review, December, 1932, pp. 1389–1390.

It may be conceded, therefore, that average rentals paid by wage-earning or other relatively low-income groups in 1930 frequently did not represent an economic return on *new* housing constructed in the same industrial communities in recent years. However, the period since the War has been one of extremely high building costs. The index number of construction costs in 1920 was more than two and a half times the level of 1913, and despite a sharp decline it was in 1930 nearly twice the 1913 average; the average cost of a two-story house in Philadelphia in recent years, as already stated, has been above $4000, while in 1914 it was $2020. Clearly, costs in such a period do not afford a fair basis for judging the ability of low-income groups to pay an economic rent under normal conditions.

Since 1930 there has been a further marked decline in building costs, and we may assume that they will continue to be brought more nearly in line with economic rents. The experience of Great Britain, described on page 299, supports such an assumption. In that country building costs rose even much more sharply after the World War than they did in the United States, and government aid to building was extended on an unprecedented scale. By the end of 1932, however, the Government held that except in the case of a very small section of the population building costs had receded to a point where private enterprise was able to supply houses on a commercial basis.

The foregoing consideration substantiates our estimate of what an economic rent for American housing should be, somewhere between 14 per cent and the indicated actual rental of 12 per cent (this for the single-family urban home, which is three-eighths of American housing). It also intimates that actual rentals may equal the returns on other investments. It brings out the difficulty of getting an economic rent for new housing. In that point may lie such reason as can be allowed to the school of thought represented by Mrs. Wood. That school seems to assume that a second-hand house is analogous to second-hand clothes, a patent absurdity. If a house is structurally sound, clean and comfortable, it is fit for its occupants whether they are its first, second, or fifteenth.

The casual suggestion by many critics that government should supplement or displace private initiative in housing will be thoroughly discussed in Chapter XI. But before leaving the matter of economic rent we may do well to note what effects government intervention would probably have upon the items composing it.

Taxes clearly would be increased even if the intervention were only in the form of tax remission on particular housing developments. The items for maintenance, insurance and depreciation are normally influenced by government's definition of construction standards through building codes, a service in which great improvement may be effected. City planning is a means by which government may properly function to reduce losses by obsolescence. That the hand of government on the renting business ultimately increases rents will be demonstrated later in Chapter X, where we assign a place to government aid in housing finance, and discuss the bearing of mortgage measures on interest rates, which here have been included somewhat obscurely in " net return " in Table 23.

There remains the question of housing provision, the sheer cost of the house itself, on which all the other items are figured. More information must be presented before we can properly meet the very grave question of the function of government here. Our point of view, however, is that such intervention is fraught with danger to the whole economic structure.

The first proposition of this chapter, that the cost of shelter is high, has been established by our examination of its place in the national and family budgets and of its trend relative to other costs. The second proposition remains a question rather than an assertion. It is whether a large part of the population can or cannot afford an economic rent for suitable homes. Too many variables are involved in this question to allow of definite analysis. Certainly, however, the evidence accumulates on the point of cost. New housing costs too much, whether for high-, medium-, or low-income groups. Standards properly set for new houses are unattainable only because of excessive building costs. For the same reason rentals are handicapped in competing with other items in the budget. Clearly there must be defects in the process by which this over-costly necessity is produced.

CHAPTER IV

Disabilities in the Housing Industry

WHY does housing cost so much? The answer requires a look into the disabilities which hamper the industry. A doctor must know anatomy in order to diagnose a case, but the patient relates symptoms first of all. We shall first rehearse the disabilities of the industry, then analyze its organization and compare its efficiency with that of other comparable industries.

From all directions come complaints that the means for providing shelter for modern man are unsatisfactory, and such criticism has been steadily increasing during the last ten years. While much of it is ill-considered and without focus, there must be a reason for its extent. For the present, it will suffice to enumerate the disabilities which form the object of such criticism.[1]

The life of every organism involves a continuous interplay between the ever-changing elements of which it is composed. Environment alters, and the body within it must also change or die. To this end the abilities within the body which are in harmony with the new conditions fight against its disabilities; the greater the environmental change and the more complex the organism, the more intense and longer will be the conflict. Functional disability is inertia working against too rapid changes; increasing disability bespeaks great bodily changes; evolution

---

[1] In the Appendix, p. 534, appear quotations from various sources. They have been condensed, and perhaps do scant justice to their authors, but are intended to give a picture of conditions in the housing industry as current comment paints them.

signifies new life. Functional ability of an element within the body is relative to all its other elements, and the body itself has ever-changing functional abilities related to all other bodies in time and space. Under this infinite interplay of forces mankind and the universe evolve.

Dr. Walter B. Cannon recently drew an enlightening comparison between the functioning of the human body and the economic structure. His " biocracy " makes clear the good and bad of " technocracy " and the working of economic forces; showing how the human body functions normally, it clarifies by extension evolutionary forces, social as well as physical. Something happens to the environment of an organism; whether this be normal or abnormal, the functional abilities of the elements within that environment come into action; that action continues until a normal balance between the elements concerned has been effected. This happens in the digestive process, with a cut or burn, or in sickness. The same thing occurs when some new thought or increase in knowledge or advance in technique comes into a social environment: the elements affected try to absorb the unusual factor in the normal way. If it be congenial to their abilities, normal balance between them is soon and easily renewed; if it is obnoxious to them, the renewal of balance may be a long and difficult process.

In every city of India the sewing machine may be found in the street-side shops. In the midst of an ancient civilization this new-found instrument has disabled the hand of the sewer who would use the needle — a curious but significant phenomenon. But back in the country the ancient needle still stitches away, filling the small but varied household needs. Disabilities are indeed relative.

In the case of industries a similar evolution has taken place. Some have developed slowly and consistently and retained their age-old importance; others have failed to develop and have disappeared; just as among animals a new type has often appeared, so new industries have developed which bear little or no relation to those already existing, and have supplied new and hitherto unknown wants.

The forces of evolution have moved irresistibly if obscurely in the industrial realm. Movements so immensely complex cannot be described simply. Human wills are part of the interplay; improvements in technique and knowledge sometimes have preserved, sometimes disposed of wants and desires that earlier seemed essential. The history of any branch of manufacture, whether it be long or short, simple or complex, is bound to record the adaptation of function to environment, the elimination of disabilities, the survival of the fittest.

Nearly all our leading industries have a long history. Textiles, and beautiful ones, were woven thousands of years ago in many places and under widely diverse conditions. Shoes in some form have been made for ages. Ceramics have been burned almost from time immemorial. Agriculture is one of the oldest businesses of man. The provision of shelter reaches back into the dimmest past. From the day of the early civilizations down to the Industrial Revolution, the development of those industries was gradual. Changes, however, were germinating. Thousands of years went by with little change in productive processes; then, two hundred years ago, began an incredible transformation. Stimulated by improved technique of production, increased scientific knowledge, and its application to group effort, the disabilities of traditional methods gave way in increasing numbers and extent to the forces of evolution. First to do so were methods and processes which were the simplest or most concrete, or which most readily adopted the new technique — as the boat and the loom, for example, adopted mechanical power.

Among major industries the building industry has been the slowest in this development; it has accumulated far more disabilities than the others, and these have been — and still are — highly resistant to progress. In enumerating them we shall not attempt to apportion the responsibility for their existence, although we shall examine management, finance, labor, the law, and the owner. To a large extent the evils which affect the industry are the result of long-continued customs for which no one interest is responsible. All along the line the industry has been handicapped by conditions, rules, practices, laws, and customs that reduce its efficiency and add to the cost of its product.

The disabilities of the building industry may be classified as (1) general, (2) architectural, (3) constructional, (4) managerial, (5) labor, (6) financial, (7) legislative, (8) consumer, and (9) miscellaneous.

(1) General Disabilities

a. Local nature. A fundamental handicap upon the building industry is its local nature. Until recently it has been taken for granted that a house must be fabricated, or " manufactured," on the spot. The construction of a dwelling, say, in Chicago to be shipped to St. Louis or Cleveland was hardly to be thought of.[2] Notwithstanding some development of factory production, it is still the almost universal practice to assemble the various materials on the site. This limits competition, and thus acts as a brake upon initiative and efficiency. Benn states that it " sets a premium on laziness and dilatory methods in the building trade the world over." [3]

b. Lack of organization. A second handicap is lack of organization. As pointed out in Chapter V, the industry is not a definite, clear-cut entity, but an agglomeration of a large number of more or less related industries.

c. Excessive plant capacity. Like many other industries, building suffers from excessive plant capacity, unadjusted to major fluctuations in demand. As far back as 1922 Herbert Hoover, at that time Secretary of Commerce, estimated that the capacity for the production of leading building materials was 30 per cent greater than would be needed under a uniform distribution of demand. In boom times, on the other hand, the in-

[2] It is interesting, however, to note that even in Colonial days ready-framed houses were sometimes shipped from New England and Louisiana to the English and French Islands. (Clark, V. S., " History of Manufactures in the United States 1607–1860 " [The Carnegie Institution of Washington, 1916], Vol. I, p. 18.)

[3] Benn, Ernest J. P., " The Return to Laissez Faire " (D. Appleton and Company, New York, 1929), p. 145.

dustry finds its facilities overtaxed and the entire series of operations congested.

d. Seasonal production. Such fluctuations in demand are not peculiar to the building industry. But in addition, building is

—— CHART 28 ——

AVERAGE VOLUME OF BUILDING CONSTRUCTION AS SHOWN BY MONTHLY CONTRACTS AWARDED IN 36 STATES OF THE UNITED STATES:1920-1929

In Millions of Square Feet, Charted from data compiled by the
Standard Statistics Company from Records of the F.W.Dodge Corporation.

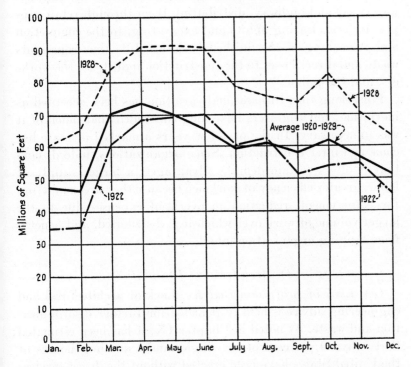

subject to a pronounced seasonal fluctuation which has resulted in a high degree of disorganization, affecting every affiliated interest.[4] It is generally attributed to the impracticability of

[4] "The construction industry is subject to greater seasonal fluctuations than any other of the major industries of the country." (Watkins, Ralph J., "The Construction Industry in Ohio," p. 30.)

building operations in cold weather; construction charts almost invariably show a relatively low volume of work in winter, followed by a decided rise (see Chart 28). The inevitable result of these seasonal fluctuations is an increase in the cost of production. The Committee of the President's Conference on Unemployment has said: [5] " Construction costs are high in part because of the seasonal hazard, which affects each step of the construction process from felling timber, quarrying rock, manufacturing brick, cement, tile, plaster, and a hundred and one other commodities, transporting these materials by railway, waterway, and highway, distributing them through retail supply dealers, clearing of site and excavating, to the completion and furnishing of the finished building. Idle time represents waste and direct losses to the construction industries, the workers, and the public."

For a long time this seasonal variation has been accepted as inevitable; but engineers have long contended that much of it was unnecessary. In the past few years a marked increase has come in winter construction. Some organizations, indeed, hold that it offers certain definite advantages: a larger supply of labor, greater efficiency of workmen because they are competing for employment, reduction in overhead expenses due to the larger volume of work over which it is distributed, and benefits from keeping organization intact.

(2) Architectural Disabilities

(a) Lack of professional advice. Lack of architectural and engineering advice is held responsible for further disorganization and waste. As noted in Chapter IX, it has been estimated that fully 80 per cent of the single-family dwelling houses of the United States have been erected without the direct services of an architect; builders have used rough sketches adapted from some general plan, often producing a creditable result. Yet even the employment of architects has not prevented a large

[5] "Committee Report — Seasonal Operations in the Construction Industries " (McGraw-Hill Book Co., Inc., New York, 1924), p. XI.

amount of inferior design and construction. One explanation is the greater attractiveness to architects of large undertakings, which are more profitable and more stimulating to the imagination. Yet in the aggregate dwelling-house construction exceeds in value all other forms of building combined.

(b) *Tradition and lack of standard specifications.* A complaint frequently lodged against architects is that they are too closely bound by tradition not only as to design but as to the use of materials, and especially that they are averse to standardization and mass production. As a result, it is held, their plans call for an excessive number of individual items and special sizes, many of which could be eliminated if standard sizes and forms were generally adopted.

(c) *Unnecessary estimates.* Another architectural handicap is the great expense involved in estimates. The common practice of asking for a large number of bids involves heavy engineering and drafting expense. Studies made in New York and Chicago reveal that 3 per cent of the total cost of construction is so consumed.[6] This experience relates to large construction projects rather than to dwelling-houses, but applies in varying degree to the latter, as well as to cases where direct architectural service is employed.[7] It is often a serious matter even for the small builder, who may prepare estimates on several jobs for every contract that he secures. A familiar story is that of the contractor who said, " I figure and figure on estimates, and occasionally make a mistake and get the contract." A partial remedy is limitation of the number of bidders on a particular job and the making of quantity surveys the results of which shall be available to all competitors.

[6] Haber, William, " Industrial Relations in the Building Industry," pp. 69–70. Haber cites one instance where seven general bids, costing $150,000, were prepared for a 3500-room hotel, and another where an architectural competition for a semi-public building involved a total cost for plans of over $1,000,000.

[7] In dwelling-house construction the architect often knows a reliable builder whom he engages without asking for estimates from others.

(3) Constructional Disabilities

(a) *Lack of integration.* The integration which characterizes the iron and steel industry, where a single organization controls all phases of production from the mining of ore and coal to the manufacture of the finished product, finds no counterpart in the building industry.

(b) *Work on site.* An even more serious handicap is inefficient assembling of materials and mechanical equipment; the disadvantage of bringing materials in unfinished condition to the site for fabrication there requires no demonstration. If making an automobile meant that all of its many parts were produced in numerous plants belonging to a large number of different companies, and delivered at the buyer's garage for further manufacture, assembling, and final finishing by local mechanics working with their own portable tools, the process would be considered intolerable. Yet this is a more or less accurate picture of what happens in building. It is difficult to conceive of an automobile industry or a railroad-equipment industry conducted on such lines.

(c) *Antiquated assembling methods.* There is a far more serious loss due to the fact that the work of assembling involves a great waste of labor and is really hand manufacture; the fabrication of dwellings is conducted by the same laborious methods that have been employed for centuries, involving an immense waste of time in handling, cutting, and fitting of materials.

(d) *Custom work.* Not only is the dwelling a hand-made product, but often it is largely custom-made. While scores of other articles, from automobiles to shoes, are turned out in great numbers according to standard specifications, the dwelling-house is in many cases still made according to individual plans. The architect who designs a small house ordinarily calculates on stock sizes of numerous items such as door and window frames, and many kinds of lumber, but there is a large amount of custom work on such parts as mantels, stairs, and paneling.

Even a slight variation in dimensions from a general average necessitates much individual cutting and fitting. Estimates of the loss from lack of standardization run as high as $2,000,-000,000 yearly; [8] yet standardization of parts (which does not mean standardization of *houses*) would not prevent a wide variety in the finished product.

(4) *Managerial Disabilities*

(*a*) *Small operators.* The large number of minor operators in this industry introduces various complexities; this " small-shop " characteristic of the industry imposes obvious limits upon efficiency. Many contractors are of the " shoe-string " type, without sufficient resources or experience to carry through a large project; the speculative builder too often is of this class, and injects a highly disturbing element into the industry.

(*b*) *Failure to use labor-saving devices and modern methods.* A further difficulty is that many contractors cannot afford modern labor-saving devices; too often this is owing to inefficiency rather than lack of capital. The average dwelling-house builder fails to use many simple machine tools such as the power-saw, although several of these are readily adaptable to small jobs without undue expense.[9] The house is still fabricated in much the same way as it was one hundred, two hundred, or three hundred years ago. Accessories, which represent from one-fifth to one-quarter of the cost of an American home, frequently require a wasteful amount of cutting and fitting and finishing. Masonry and carpentry are torn away to make room for piping and, worse, the design of the house in many cases is not adapted to these facilities.

Considerable progress has been made, however, in the use of machine methods and factory production for certain features of the house. Doors, sash, blinds, and stair treads have for many

---

8 New York Trust Company, " Index," October, 1931, p. 223.

9 On the other hand, it is sometimes contended that the use of such a tool as the power-saw involves waste, since a carpenter often spends more time going from and back to his task than would be required to cut the particular piece of material on the spot with a hand-saw.

years been produced in factories, with large saving over the old hand methods; more recently, machine methods have been applied to trim and finish. Many accessories such as plumbing fixtures, heating plants, mantels, kitchen cabinets, and refrigerators are produced by great manufacturing companies under modern methods.

(*c*) *Lack of ability.* A large number of contractors, being really carpenters or other artisans, lack the necessary experience and ability.[10] The industry has been called an " open door for small producers to try their luck," [11] and this may be one explanation of its high rate of bankruptcies. These incapable contractors produce a large amount of unsound and shoddy construction. The general complaint on this score is indicated by the following extract from an engineering source:

" It is no secret that the average house today is a shoddy affair, of high first cost, and soon reduced to a condition requiring constant maintenance; that it is built as it was a great many years ago, by hand methods, with every piece cut in the field by men whose horizon is limited to the locality in which they live, whose training is of a sort that makes them impervious to the adaptation of new methods, whose financial capacity does not permit of modern research or study, in case they do recognize their value, and who themselves often are the victims of profiteering material dealers. Today there are available better automobiles, better furniture and even better office buildings than were available only ten years ago, and they cost less. But the average house not only costs more today than it did in the days of our fathers and grandfathers, but it is an inferior product." [12]

(*d*) *Bad practices.* Management has been held responsible by labor for many practices which interfere with the efficiency of production and which virtually amount to a restriction of

[10] In this connection, it may be noted that of one group of sixty-eight builders, eight had been contractors, twenty-six had been carpenters, and six others building-trade employees. (USDC, " Causes of Commercial Bankruptcies," GPO, Washington, 1932, p. 47.)

[11] Haber, William, " Industrial Relations in the Building Industry," p. 5.

[12] " A House-Building Industry " (Engineering News-Record, June 12, 1930).

output. Various complaints on this score from trade-union sources were collected by the committee of the Federated American Engineering Societies some years ago.[13] Among such criticisms were the following:

Contractors fail to have materials on hand when men arrive on the job;
Use inferior materials;
Fail to train apprentices properly;
Make mistakes in estimating;
Make changes after work is completed;
Use poor materials and unsatisfactory tools;
Use cement mortar instead of lime mortar, reducing productivity of masons;
Provide insufficient scaffolding;
Wastefully handle breakable material, such as brick, with breakage and extra cost in laying broken brick;
Fail to provide shop work for mechanics in bad weather.

Labor itself may be held partly responsible for some of these mistakes, as for example inadequate training of apprentices.

(5) Labor Disabilities

Some of the most disorganizing influences in the building industry arise out of labor relationships. Among them are the following:

(a) *Excessive number of crafts and jurisdiction.* It is safe to say that building-trade labor, though strongly organized, is not efficiently organized. One criticism is that the number of crafts is excessive,[14] and certainly this kind of division of labor adds heavily to cost. It is the outcome of the evolutionary division of labor. But its application is to an ancient process (itinerant manufacture) which is more and more giving way

---

13 Federated American Engineering Societies, "Waste in Industry" (McGraw-Hill Book Company, Inc., New York, 1921, pp. 84–85).

14 ". . . All told there are 52 crafts in the building trades. These, in my opinion, could be reduced to some 8 or 10. . . ." Marshall, Gen. R. C., Jr., "How Labor Can Reduce the Cost of Houses" in "Housing Problems in America," 1923, Vol. IX, p. 18.

to new methods in the shop. It has outlived its usefulness in single-house construction both because of the wastefulness of hand methods of manufacture in the field and the difficulty of organizing and coordinating so many separate working factors for each individual job. It may be helpful in the great office building but not so in the small house. The insistence on " jurisdiction " often means the employment of highly-paid skilled labor for work that could be done equally well by common laborers. There is, for example, a rule in various plumbers' unions that the moving of plumbing equipment above the first floor shall be done by union plumbers and, of course, at plumbers' wages. The following instances are representative of complaints on this score:

" Carpenters' helpers are prohibited from using carpenter tools, requiring carpenters to do such work as stripping forms from concrete. Experience shows that helpers can do this more economically and as well.

" Brick masons insist on washing down and pointing brick work when laborers could do it more economically.

" Structural steel workers under certain rules must bring the steel from the unloading point to the building site, thus doing laborers' work at high cost.

" Structural steel men place reinforcing steel for concrete, whereas experience has proved conclusively that properly trained laborers can do it to as good advantage, and at greatly lowered cost.

" Structural steel men claim the rigging on a job. For a small derrick used in footing excavation, the bucket cable had to be guided by hand and the hoisting engineer signalled by a skilled iron worker.

" Hoisting engineers claim the right to run all types of engines, including small gas-driven pumps which require no skill. On one job a contractor had to hire a union engineer at $8.00 per day simply to start a pump in the morning, oil it occasionally, and stop it at night. . . ." [15]

[15] Federated American Engineering Societies, " Waste in Industry," pp. 82–83.

The losses thus caused are exceeded by those arising from interruptions to work. There are frequent clashes between rival unions as to which has jurisdiction over a particular operation. Such disputes, incidental to almost every major building undertaking, need no detailed discussion. They have occasioned losses running into hundreds of millions of dollars, and have time and again brought ruin to the contractor, although he was in no way responsible for them and did not care which craft performed the work if only it could be done promptly and properly. Many instances of the inciting of such trouble by walking delegates and racketeers could be cited.

These disputes have been termed the bane of the building industry. But numerous contractors and investigating commissions condemn them no more bitterly than do the leaders of organized labor. Samuel Gompers, for instance, said at the 1902 convention of the American Federation of Labor:

" Beyond doubt the greatest problem, the danger which above all others most threatens not only the success but the very existence of the American Federation of Labor, is the question of jurisdiction. No combination of Labor's enemies need cause us the apprehension which this fratricidal strife does in the claims made by the unions for the extension of their trade jurisdiction." [16]

A delegate to an American Federation of Labor convention asserted that " often the disputes are of such a trivial nature that we ought to hide our heads in shame."

(b) *Strikes*. Heavy losses have been suffered because of widespread and prolonged strikes. In recent years there have been comparatively few major strikes in the industry, and the number of jurisdictional disputes appears to have declined. The building trades, nevertheless, still head the list in this respect. Chart 29 gives comparisons for the period 1916–30.

(c) *Restriction of output*. A charge frequently lodged against building-trade labor is that it deliberately practices restriction of output. It is outside the scope of this book to pass

[16] Haber, William, "Industrial Relations in the Building Industry," pp. 154–155.

upon so controversial a subject. Years ago it was not an un-common practice for building-trade unions to set a definite limit on the amount of work which its members might perform in a day; such rules are now the rare exception. It is true that output of these workers shows marked periodical differences, but these are due more to fluctuations in demand for labor than to union rules. The use of a standard wage rate without regard to differences in efficiency tends indirectly to restrict output. Inevitably production per man will be less when employers are outbidding one another for labor than in times of general unem-ployment. Recent complaints of restriction of output blame unions for insistence upon skilled labor for unskilled work and opposition to labor-saving machinery and improved methods and materials, rather than for agreements or rules to limit pro-duction. It is only fair to add that labor has, on the other hand, held management responsible for indirect restriction of output and for a large amount of waste.

(*d*) *High wage scales.* As will be shown in Chapter VII, rates of wages in the building industry are far higher than in most other occupations, and this cannot be attributed solely to sea-sonal unemployment. Other reasons are the local nature of the industry, already mentioned, which gives labor as well as man-agement a monopoly in a given area, the high degree of union-ization, and the competition for labor by employers.

Wage rates have been widely held responsible for the high cost of building since the World War, and for much of the curtailment in building construction in recent years. A special complaint is that increases in wage schedules have not been ac-companied by any corresponding increase in productive effi-ciency (see Chapter VI).

That the great increase in wages in recent years has directly contributed to the higher cost of building can hardly be dis-puted. That there are other factors is evident from the fact, stated in Chapter VII, that direct labor costs often represent less than one-third of the total cost of the home.

(*e*) *Labor* vs. *management.* In presenting these comments

—— CHART 29 ——

COMPARISON OF YEARLY NUMBER OF DISPUTES IN THE BUILDING INDUSTRY
AND IN OTHER LEADING INDUSTRIES IN THE UNITED STATES: 1916-1930

Charted from data in Monthly Labor Review, June 1931.

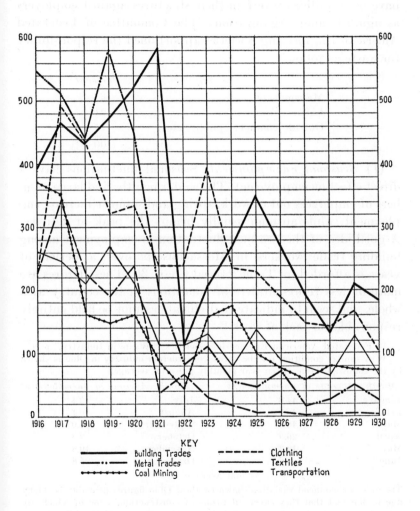

KEY
—————— Building Trades   - - - - - - Clothing
—··—··— Metal Trades   —————— Textiles
•••••••• Coal Mining   ——— ——— Transportation

upon trade-union conditions and practices, we have no desire to make labor the scapegoat for the various ills from which the building industry suffers. To a large extent the situation is a natural outgrowth of the much simpler industrialism of earlier times prolonged into this highly industrialized period.

Official commissions which have investigated the industry have been quite as severe in their strictures against employers as against labor organizations. The Committee of Federated American Engineering Societies apportioned the responsibility for waste as follows: [17]

	Per cent
Management	65
Labor	21
Outside contacts (public, etc.)	14
	100

(f) *Seasonal unemployment.* Seasonal fluctuations have a direct effect on employment. The winter months find large numbers of employees out of work, spring and summer increase employment, while autumn usually brings the peak of activity. A good idea of this seasonal fluctuation in employment among building-trade workers in Massachusetts over a period of years is afforded by Table 24 and Chart 30. These figures are more or less representative of conditions in the country as a whole, and seem to indicate that climate cannot be held entirely responsible for lack of work.[18]

[17] Federated American Engineering Societies, "Waste in Industry," p. 9.

[18] A similar condition for the entire construction industry in Ohio is shown by the following table of ten-year monthly per cent averages:

Month	Average of unemployment	Month	Average of unemployment
January	44.3	July	3.4
February	46.4	August	0.1
March	40.4	September	0.0
April	26.9	October	2.8
May	18.3	November	10.8
June	8.6	December	25.8

Annual average 19.0

The more pronounced variation shown by these Ohio figures probably is chiefly due to the fact that they cover all forms of construction, some of which are subject to even more violent seasonal changes than those in the building indus-

—— CHART 30 ——

PERCENTAGES OF BUILDING-TRADES WORKERS EMPLOYED ON THE
FIRST OF EACH MONTH IN MASSACHUSETTS: 1928 AND 1929

Charted from reports of the Massachusetts Department of
Labor and Industries.

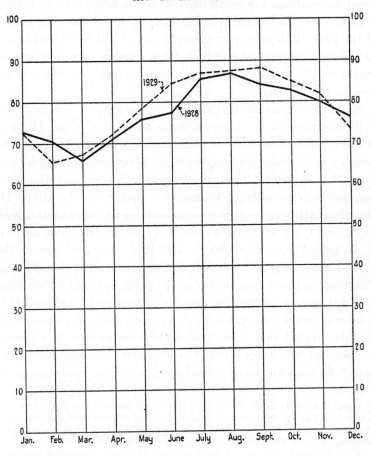

Such seasonal unemployment is, indeed, a world-wide characteristic of the building industry. Table 25 gives a comparison by quarterly intervals for building and construction in Canada in the years 1928–29, figures for manufacturing and for all occupations combined also being shown. Similar experience could be shown for numerous European countries.[19]

While characteristic of all building-trade occupations, seasonal fluctuations are much more severe in some than in others, and moreover do not occur in all occupations at the same period of the year. This is clearly brought out in Table 26 and Chart 31. The occupation of painters shows notable variation and an exceptionally high degree of unemployment in the earlier months of the year.

Seasonal variation in employment means, of course, that building-trade workers lose a large amount of time. Herbert Hoover, when Secretary of Commerce, estimated that for the country as a whole building-trade workers were employed " not over 65 per cent of their possible time." Probably the most comprehensive unofficial estimate is that made by Paul H. Douglas. After reviewing the statistics of Massachusetts, New York, and Ohio, and various unofficial studies, Douglas arrived at an estimate of time lost by building-trade workers in the United States as a whole. His figures given in Table 27 and Chart 32, indicate that on the average 22 per cent of working time was lost; estimates for manufacturing and transportation industries combined are added for purposes of comparison. Douglas stated that it is " admittedly hazardous to estimate the amount of unemployment upon such a scanty statistical basis." In the absence of official data, however, these conserva-

---

try itself, and partly to the fact that in this case it was assumed that there was no unemployment in the month of greatest activity (September), whereas it is extremely probable that even in that month some workers were unemployed. (Watkins, R. J., " The Construction Industry in Ohio," p. 84.)

[19] An extended summary of the experience of various European countries on seasonal fluctuations in employment in the building trades can be found in the International Labour Review, January, February, and March, 1929.

tive percentages may be regarded as approximating actual conditions.

This irregularity and consequent loss has a direct bearing upon wage scales. It has afforded building-trade workers their

TABLE 24

PERCENTAGE OF UNION BUILDING-TRADE WORKERS IN MASSACHUSETTS
UNEMPLOYED AT THE END OF EACH QUARTER, 1908–1923, AND
AT THE FIRST OF EACH QUARTER, 1927–1929 [a]

Quarter Ending

Years	March 31	June 30	September 30	December 31	Average
1908	25.2	18.3	9.3	21.2	18.5
1909	18.5	5.0	3.1	17.8	11.1
1910	8.9	4.2	4.5	18.0	8.9
1911	19.3	6.4	5.0	20.9	12.9
1912	17.0	2.7	2.5	14.9	9.3
1913	13.4	7.9	9.2	23.9	13.6
1914	29.7	12.4	13.8	33.8	22.4
1915	26.3	13.2	8.5	17.6	16.4
1916	22.0	7.6	3.7	11.0	11.1
1917	16.0	5.8	6.2	18.5	11.6
1918	16.3	4.5	4.8	12.2	9.4
1919	21.0	5.5	4.8	6.3	9.4
1920	11.7	7.9	5.3	26.4	12.8
1921	55.6	32.7	27.0	31.2	36.6
1922	19.9	7.0	4.3	17.5	12.2
1923	14.7	3.4	3.7	14.1	9.0
1927 [b]	27.4	17.2	13.5	27.3	21.3
1928 [b]	28.9	14.6	17.2	27.5	22.0
1929 [b]	27.9	12.9	14.9	26.2 [c]	20.5
Simple average	22.1	10.0	8.5	20.3	15.2

(a) Data gathered by Massachusetts Department of Labor and Industries. Records were not kept from December, 1923, to April, 1927, nor since December, 1929.

(b) For quarters beginning April 1, July 1, etc.

(c) As of December 2, 1929, the last reported figure.

TABLE 25

PERCENTAGE OF UNEMPLOYMENT AMONG TRADE-UNION WORKERS IN
BUILDING AND CONSTRUCTION, MANUFACTURING, AND ALL INDUS-
TRIES COMBINED, IN CANADA, IN SPECIFIED MONTHS IN
1928 AND 1929 [a]

Month and year	Building and construction	Manufacturing	All occupations
1928			
January	23.2	8.2	6.8
April	13.6	4.5	5.2
July	3.3	3.8	2.5
October	5.1	4.5	3.1
1929			
January	19.0	5.6	6.3
April	11.3	7.0	5.5
July	7.0	3.6	3.0
October	10.4	7.8	6.0

(a) Canadian Labour Gazette, April, 1929, p. 423; April, 1930, p. 432.

TABLE 26

PERCENTAGE OF UNION WORKERS IN SELECTED BRANCHES OF THE
BUILDING TRADES IN MASSACHUSETTS REPORTED AS UNEMPLOYED
IN EACH MONTH IN 1928 [a]

Date	All occupations	Bricklayers, masons, plasterers	Carpenters	Painters, decorators, paperhangers	Plumbers, gas- and steamfitters
Jan. 3	27.2	23.1	25.8	42.4	17.1
Feb. 1	29.4	31.8	27.4	46.9	21.6
Mar. 1	34.1	35.0	31.6	48.6	30.7
April 2	28.9	29.4	24.4	36.4	37.5
May 1	24.1	17.9	20.8	23.0	30.6
June 1	22.9	17.1	20.0	17.7	29.0
July 2	14.6	9.2	17.1	21.4	23.8
Aug. 1	13.2	11.0	16.8	14.1	16.3
Sept. 4	15.8	11.9	16.8	18.0	13.1
Oct. 1	17.2	14.1	16.8	17.4	8.1
Nov. 1	20.1	16.8	17.6	20.9	8.3
Dec. 3	23.7	23.0	22.8	27.6	11.2

(a) Computed from data published by the Massachusetts Department of
Labor and Industries.

—— CHART 31 ——

PERCENTAGES OF UNION WORKERS IN SELECTED BUILDING TRADES
EMPLOYED IN MASSACHUSETTS ON THE FIRST DAY OF EACH MONTH: 1928

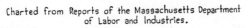

Charted from Reports of the Massachusetts Department
of Labor and Industries.

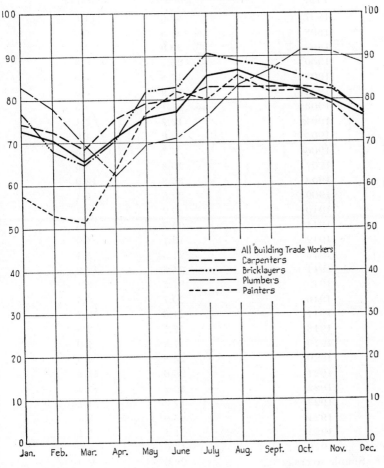

TABLE 27

AVERAGE PERCENTAGE OF TIME LOST BY BUILDING-TRADE WORKERS
AND BY WORKERS IN MANUFACTURING AND TRANSPORTATION
INDUSTRIES COMBINED, IN THE UNITED STATES,
1897–1926 [a]

Year	Building trade workers	Manufacturing and transportation workers
1897	32.0	14.5
1898	28.3	13.9
1899	20.9	7.7
1900	26.7	6.3
1901	17.8	4.5
1902	15.9	3.5
1903	21.1	3.5
1904	17.7	7.1
1905	12.0	4.0
1906	8.7	3.5
1907	20.8	3.5
1908	35.8	12.0
1909	22.5	5.1
1910	20.2	3.7
1911	25.7	5.6
1912	18.1	4.0
1913	21.5	5.4
1914	34.6	12.9
1915	31.5	12.4
1916	20.7	3.5
1917	21.6	3.5
1918	17.7	3.5
1919	17.5	4.0
1920	23.8	4.3
1921	26.6	21.2
1922	19.2	15.4
1923	17.2	4.4
1924	25.9	8.3
1925	21.4	5.1
1926	17.6	4.5
Simple average [b]	22.0	7.0

(a) Douglas, Paul H., "Real Wages in the United States, 1890–1926,"
Published by The Pollak Foundation, Newton, Massachusetts, pp. 445 and 451.
(b) Computed from Douglas' data.

chief justification for the relatively high wage scale they have attained. The question may fairly be raised, however, whether a part of this lost time is not attributable to demands for higher wages.

—— CHART 32 ——

PERCENTAGE OF UNEMPLOYMENT AMONG WORKERS IN BUILDING TRADES, AND IN MANUFACTURING AND TRANSPORTATION IN THE UNITED STATES (ESTIMATED):1897–1926

Charted from Data in Paul H. Douglas' "Real Wages in the United States, 1890–1926": published by the Pollak Foundation, Newton, Mass.

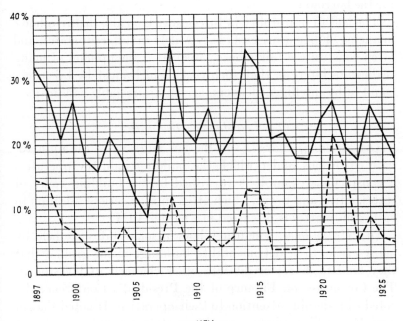

KEY
—— Building Trades
---- Manufacturing and Transportation

(6) Financial Disabilities

The outstanding difficulties encountered by the home owner with respect to financing are set forth in Chapter X; they are aggravated by the fact that he is to an unusual degree dependent upon credit. A specific complaint is that lenders do not discriminate sufficiently on the ground of quality, so that they indirectly encourage shoddy construction.

Numerous other conditions incident to financing add to the complexities of building. For example, a mortgage frequently contains several thousand words and recording fees often are based upon the length, whereas a uniform act proposed several years ago by the National Conference of Commissioners on Uniform Laws and endorsed by the American Bar Association contained only 160 words.[20] Perhaps more important than any saving on fees would be the clarification of mortgage provisions for the borrower.

The lack of uniformity in foreclosure laws also disturbs home financing. Foreclosure costs vary widely in different states, and often constitute a fairly heavy item. It is the opinion of many real-estate interests that such costs, which must be taken account of by intelligent lenders, are an appreciable handicap.

(7) Legislative Disabilities

(a) *Building codes.* Even the law aggravates the unfortunate conditions under which the building industry operates; a conspicuous example is furnished by the building codes of states, cities, and towns, which often entail a serious addition to cost. This matter is discussed in Chapter VIII.

(b) *Usury laws.* The usury laws of some states are held by many critics to be detrimental to building, on the ground that they tend to divert credit into other channels of investment. The Committee on Finance of the President's Conference devoted considerable attention to their operation. It noted that in New Hampshire, where a maximum statutory rate of interest had been in effect for over one hundred years, money flowed out of the state in 1921 " at such a rapid rate that the Legislature rescinded the statutory maximum and has not found it

---

[20] The President's Conference on Home Building and Home Ownership, Vol. II, p. 11.

necessary to restore it since then." [21] The Committee urged a study of usury and maximum interest rates as related to mortgages and the rescinding of usury laws in relation to second mortgages, with proper safeguards in the public interest, expressing the opinion that such action would tend to bring additional money into the second-mortgage market.

Usury legislation has been widely condemned by conservative real-estate interests on this ground, and because it increases the cost of credit to the home owner. A prominent authority on second-mortgage financing has said:

" It is clear, therefore, that statutory maximums do not provide money at that rate, but, instead, hamper the investment borrowers of second mortgages and land contracts and compel them to resort to indirection often unlawful in itself or to pay the high costs of usury penalty hazards. . . .

" Thus has usury legislation in investment loans made the second mortgage and land contract business a discount business with added cost to the borrower and no more profits for the lender, since the additional cost goes to the middleman." [22]

(c) *Tax legislation*. Tax legislation imposes a further burden upon building. Since taxes are an important factor in rentals, it is evident that unduly heavy taxation on real estate operates directly to discourage speculative building or the construction of dwellings to rent.

It has long been complained that an unfairly large proportion of the state and local tax burden has been placed upon real estate. In many states from 60 to 90 per cent of state and local taxes are so derived. Thus, in 1930 nearly 69 per cent of the total tax bill of the State of New York, amounting to $1,141,-000,000, was derived from real property, notwithstanding the fact that New York has many franchise and other special taxes, such as the inheritance tax and the stock transfer tax, which

21 The President's Conference on Home Building and Home Ownership, Vol. II, p. 41.

22 Reep, S. N., " Second Mortgages and Land Contracts in Real Estate Financing," (Prentice-Hall, Inc., New York, 1928), pp. 72–73.

yield a substantial revenue. The proportion of *local* taxes in New York State derived from real estate is much larger, averaging about 90 per cent in recent years. This is brought out by Table 28.

In Massachusetts in 1931 more than 64 per cent of all direct taxes for state, county, and municipal purposes were derived from real estate. In Rhode Island, more than 75 per cent of the local taxes are so obtained, and in Connecticut real property is credited with bearing 60 per cent of the cost of government. In Iowa, real estate, while contributing only 26 per cent of the total yearly income of the residents, pays nearly 90 per cent of all local and state taxes.[23] These instances are more or less indicative of conditions in the country as a whole.

The North Carolina Tax Commission found, in the case of 584 parcels of residential property, that taxes absorbed 34½ per cent of the rent, before taxes. The percentages of the rental thus absorbed by taxes on urban property in certain states are reported by one investigator as follows:[24]

	Years	*Per cent*
Arkansas	1923–25	17.1
Colorado	1926	27.1
Indiana	1922–23	30.6
Iowa	1927	31.3
North Carolina	1927	29.5
Pennsylvania	1924–25	20.9
South Dakota	1922–26	29.9
Virginia	1926	16.0
Washington	1924–26	31.7

This heavy burden has in recent years received increasing comment and attention from real estate and other organizations and from public authorities; the messages of state governors

[23] Message of Governor Turner to Iowa Legislature (United States Daily, Supplement, February 16, 1931).

[24] Coombs, Whitney, "Taxes on Farm Property." Quoted from "The President's Conference on Home Building and Home Ownership," Vol. II, p. 104.

have particularly emphasized it, and in 1931 those of at least a dozen governors did so.[25]

(8) Consumer Disabilities

Some of the most unsettling conditions in the building industry are chargeable to the owner himself. In the last analysis

TABLE 28

PROPORTION OF LOCAL TAXES IN THE STATE OF NEW YORK RAISED FROM THE GENERAL PROPERTY TAX,[a] 1913–1930

	Total local tax	Raised through general property tax	Per cent raised through general property tax [b]
	(Millions of Dollars)		
1913	284	268	94
1914	240	225	94
1915	258	243	94
1916	266	251	94
1917	301	284	94
1918	325	300	92
1919	348	315	91
1920	390	347	89
1921	454	409	90
1922	470	430	91
1923	503	458	91
1924	537	488	91
1925	577	520	90
1926	630	567	90
1927	688	632	92
1928	764	696	91
1929	820	741	90
1930	884	796	90

(a) State of New York, "Annual Report of the State Tax Commission, 1930" (J. B. Lyon Company, Albany, 1931), pp. 60–63.

(b) The general property tax covers both real property and tangible personal property, but in recent years personal property has yielded less than 1½ per cent of the total taxes provided under the general property tax.

The decline in the ratio of general property taxes to total is explained by the imposition of new taxes, such as excise taxes, or by increased revenue from some of these other forms of taxation.

[25] National Real Estate Journal, March 16, 1931, p. 14.

he determines the character of the house and to a large extent its cost.

(*a*) *Lack of knowledge.* A fundamental difficulty is that too often the purchaser knows very little about his problem. Although the home in many cases represents the largest single investment he ever makes, he ordinarily buys or builds but once, and has little opportunity to master details. Too often he bases his decision on some feature that makes a superficial appeal. It is a proverb in the real-estate business that " a $75 gadget sells a $7500 house." A breakfast nook, a laundry chute, or some other novelty outweighs such fundamental considerations as sound construction or proper insulation.

" Men are lured, by what seems attractive, to make important decisions, and live to regret their choice. . . . Many families would be better satisfied with their houses if they used more dis-crimination in picking out good ones, and did not ' fall ' for showy features — or, in effect, demand them, even when they may have been provided at the expense of items they later find they really need, or of shoddy structures that quickly deteriorate and multiply the owner's repair bills.[26] . . .

" The things that catch the eye, the things that other people are having, the black-tiled bathroom, the electric refrigeration, the new types of equipment in dining-room and pantry and elsewhere — these are the things that the average home buyer and home builder thinks about and on which he — or rather she — places emphasis. These are things that cost money — as we have seen, from 40% to 50% of the cost of the house is not in the building itself but in the things that go into that building." [27]

(*b*) *Insistence on individuality.* Despite his lack of knowl-edge, the owner-builder frequently demands an individuality of design that is unknown in the case of many products. He accepts an automobile or a radio exactly like his neighbor's, and buys his clothing and shoes ready-made; but he insists on expressing his personal ideas in the construction of his dwelling.

[26] Taylor, J. S., " Address before the N. A. R. E. B.," p. 3.
[27] Housing, December, 1930, p. 264.

Such insistence should not be condemned, but it is sometimes carried to absurd lengths. A striking example is found in the multiplicity of sizes and styles of many items which could easily be standardized, although the bulk of the demand is for a comparatively limited number. Until recently there were nearly 600 styles and sizes of window sash,[28] 125 varieties of metal lath, 480 sizes of paint brushes, and 1012 different sizes and varieties of plumbing traps. Much has been accomplished through the Division of Simplified Practice of the Department of Commerce in inducing manufacturers to cut down the number of such items. In some cases the reductions have been drastic. Selected instances are given in Table 29.

Practically all authorities declare that the buyer's insistence upon individuality and variety is one of the major disabilities in the building industry. It does not seem, on the whole, very formidable; such insistence would quickly disappear if a house were a truly modern product, handled as the automobile is handled; it is the present condition of the industry that permits, if it does not enforce, individuality. Yet individuality in the home is not to be lost or even impaired in the future; rather the individual choice of the owner, now applied to design and construction, will be transferred to other things, such as his library or his garden or other features expressive of his spiritual ideals. Individuality will and should remain the predominating factor.

(*c*) *Insistence on speed.* The owner's insistence on speed has been held responsible for a vast amount of poor construction; it directly encourages unreasonable demands by labor upon the contractor.[29]

(*d*) *Concentration of leasing dates.* A highly disorganizing influence, more far-reaching than is generally recognized, is the widespread concentration of leasing dates into one or two periods or even one or two single days of the year. The desig-

28 Gries, John M., " New Materials, Processes and Standardization," in " Housing Problems in America," 1923, Vol. IX, p. 57.

29 Haber, William, " Industrial Relations in the Building Industry," p. 51.

TABLE 29

REDUCTION IN NUMBER OF TYPES OR VARIETIES OF VARIOUS BUILD-
ING MATERIALS AS A RESULT OF SIMPLIFIED PRACTICE
RECOMMENDATIONS [a]

	Reduction in Number of Varieties		Per cent reduction
	From	To	
Common brick	44	1	98
Vitrified paving brick	66	6	91
Rough and smooth face brick	75	2	97
Concrete building units	115	14	88
Structural slate for plumbing and sanitary purposes	827	138	83
Roofing slate	98	49	50
Iron and steel roofing	292	179	39
Metal lath	125	29	76
Brass lavatory and sink traps	1,114	76	93
Range boilers and expansion tanks ..	130	13	90
Wrought-iron and wrought-steel pipes, valves, and pipe fittings			
Sizes of valves and fittings	20,000	19,238	4
Sizes of pipes	62	49	21

(a) Division of Simplified Practice, Bureau of Standards, USDC. In many cases these figures appear to represent acceptances of the Division's recommendations rather than permanent achievement. Bulletin, October 1, 1930.

nation of May 1st or October 1st as " moving day " is common in many large cities. Many persons associate this custom merely with the difficulty of securing a moving van or with the extra cost of moving on these particular days. As a matter of fact, these aspects, while important to the individual, are in the aggregate almost insignificant as compared with the broader effects. The custom of wholesale moving on a given day disorganizes the entire industry, from the building contractor and the landlord to the sawmill operator, and involves not only producers of raw materials, but labor, architects, and even the bankers who finance the home. Its effects are aggravated since it necessitates rush work on painting, papering, and repairs just when there is an active demand for labor for new con-

—— CHART 33 ——

EFFECTS OF UNIFORM LEASING DATES ON ELECTRIC AND TELEPHONE INSTALLATIONS IN THE UNITED STATES, IN SELECTED YEARS

Redrawn from report of Committee of President's Conference on
Unemployment: Seasonal Operation in Construction Industry

NUMBER OF CONTRACTS SIGNED WEEKLY FOR ELECTRIC SERVICE IN CHICAGO
WITH THE COMMONWEALTH EDISON COMPANY, FOR YEARS 1922 AND 1923

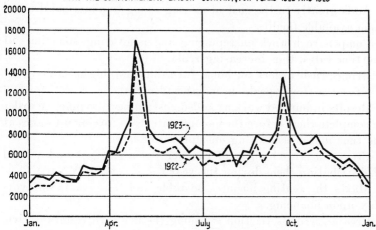

NUMBER OF SUBSCRIBERS IN RICHMOND, VA. HAVING
TELEPHONES MOVED MONTHLY 1921, 1922 AND 1923

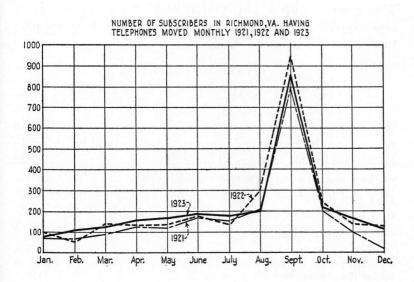

struction. It puts a particular strain upon telephone companies and electric light and other public service agencies. (See Chart 33.)

Some of the injurious effects of such concentration of leasing dates have been described by one agency as follows: [30]

Adds greatly to the cost of moving owing to abnormal demand upon available facilities.

Compels rush work on repairing and renovating, sometimes at overtime rates, thus increasing rents.

Brings rush orders on home furnishing establishments.

Causes seasonal peaks in maintenance costs.

Results in hurried work at added cost on new dwellings in order to complete them before the moving date, thus forcing up wages at the time and accentuating unemployment later.

Creates a large number of vacancies at a single period instead of distributing them during the year.

Makes the renting business unstable and thus reacts unfavorably upon financing.

Creates needless friction all along the line with resultant civic disadvantages.

This concentration is partly attributable to school and vacation schedules, which makes it more difficult to reduce this particular confusion and waste.

MISCELLANEOUS DISABILITIES

The accident hazard, extremely high in frequency and severity (see Table 30), is partly chargeable against management, but in view of the emphasis placed on accident prevention in recent years by employers' organizations, it would be unfair to lay the major blame there. The indifference or carelessness of workers may be equally responsible. While the attendant injury and loss of life are of first importance, a significant addition to the cost of construction is also involved. Under workmen's compensation laws, this risk must be provided against

[30] Chicago Homes Economic Council, various leaflets. The Council was organized for the special purpose of securing a more uniform distribution of leasing dates throughout the year.

TABLE 30

ACCIDENT RATES, FREQUENCY AND SEVERITY, BY INDUSTRIES, 1929 [a]

Industry	Frequency [b]	Severity [c]
Mining	74.43	9.99
Meat packing	55.94	1.47
Construction	50.41	4.62
Refrigeration	43.35	3.04
Tanning and leather	31.35	1.60
Foundry	30.30	1.73
Electric railways	29.75	1.93
Metal forming	29.71	1.67
Ceramic	28.93	1.07
Paper and pulp	28.43	1.77
Petroleum	26.78	2.49
Quarry	26.71	6.11
Non-ferrous milling and smelting	23.16	2.71
Public utilities	22.58	3.13
Automobile	22.17	0.97
Railway car and equipment	21.88	2.20
Food	21.07	1.50
Machinery	18.91	1.11
Steel	18.13	2.75
Glass products	17.70	0.80
Chemical	17.50	1.72
Laundry	12.78	1.53
Printing and publishing	12.23	0.67
Textile	11.82	0.58

(a) "Accident Facts — 1930" (National Safety Council, Chicago, 1930), p. 56.

(b) Accident frequency rate is the number of lost-time accidents per one million man-hours worked.

(c) Accident severity rate is the number of days lost per one thousand man-hours worked.

by insurance. In 1920 the total premiums paid by construction interests to insurance companies for compensation and liability insurance were estimated at $30,000,000, and the total economic loss from this hazard, insured and uninsured, at $120,-000,000.[31] One authority has estimated that the cost of insur-

31 Federation of American Engineering Societies, "Waste in Industry," p. 23.

ance of all kinds represents 7 per cent of the total cost of construction.[32] The ratio for dwelling-houses is doubtless considerably less.[33]

The complex problems described in this chapter are not peculiar to the United States, but prevail the world over. A British architect [34] estimates that of a total normal annual expenditure of £300,000,000 on building, £30,000,000, is wasted by bad management, lack of system, and out-of-date methods. He asserts that in his country there is too often a hit-or-miss policy, and cites as an illustration the common practice of furnishing original drawings to a contractor without detailed specifications, e.g. for piping; the result is that a contractor goes ahead, only to find later that he must cut away masonry in order to make provision for piping — a wasteful process that sometimes adds as much as 30 per cent to the cost of brickwork.

Conditions in Great Britain are frequently so represented as to make those in the United States appear favorable by comparison. The architect just quoted contended that "in the more spacious and less trammeled air of Canada and the United States, where experiment is the rule and ' stand pat ' the exception, the building industry has known little or nothing of the discouragement and waste that are the product of rigid and obsolete regulations." He stressed the great economies that have resulted from standardization in the United States and Canada, where he pictured building operations as proceeding with almost time-table smoothness and expedition.

---

[32] Marshall, Gen. R. C., Jr., "Housing Problems in America," 1923, Vol. IX, p. 15.

[33] As an illustration of the heavy cost of insurance on certain classes of construction, the following premium rates may be cited:

4 per cent of payroll in building chimneys in Ohio.

7.8 per cent of payroll for structural ironwork in Ohio.

33 per cent of payroll for structural ironwork in New York City.

Rates on demolition work sometimes run even higher. (Stewart, Ethelbert, U. S. Commissioner of Labor Statistics, "Accidents in the Construction Industry," address before the Twelfth Annual Industrial Safety Congress, Syracuse, 1929, pp. 1–2.)

[34] Bossom, Alfred C., "Wasting £30,000,000 a Year" (The National Review, September, 1931, pp. 330–337).

The comparison with American construction may have been intended to apply to large projects like office buildings or great apartment-houses, where highly efficient methods of construction have been attained. So far as ordinary dwelling-houses are concerned it is safe to say that most American building authorities would discount this comparison as flattery. It suggests the old proverb that the sails on the distant boat seem white and trim while those on our own are dirty and torn.

CHAPTER V

The Organization of the Building Industry

THE evolution of the building art is a fascinating part of the study of anthropology and archaeology. In foraging and hunting, man came into most intimate touch with all vegetable and animal growth, the physical properties of wood and grasses, of the skins and hair and bones of animals; stone and mineral substances surrounded him. Thus came almost by intuition his knowledge of the strength of materials and of how to combine them for the shelter which he sought. Naturally, too, his technique of tools began in cutting and shaping wood and stone to fit into his prospective house. One of the most startling things which archaeology brings to our attention is the similarity of the ancient wood-working and masonry tools to those still in use in building construction today.

Since man's first tools were adapted to the handling of tractable material only, it is perfectly natural that his early constructions were of wood. Since then, except for the earliest abodes, the cave, the leaf-woven tree house, and the simplest forked-stick tent, his construction has developed along two lines, timber framing and masonry. Although there have been some large edifices of wood, the larger building construction has in general developed in masonry and substitutes, while timber has become more and more the material of domestic use only.

Early wooden houses are represented by the hut of the Ba Venda, the Long House of the Iroquois, the slab house of the Puget Sound Indians or the Maori, and the cruck house of the

Saxons. There is great similarity between these and present-day wooden houses. The Ba Venda, for example, build a framework, both structural and lathing, of suitable sizes of trees and branches. Fastenings are made with available materials, principally vegetable thongs. A plaster of mud forms the finish. The construction principle is largely that of post and lintel in a concealed form. In spite of the domelike shape of the hut, the branches forming the dome act only as arched beams. The same was true of the Iroquois Long House. When man was able to shape heavier pieces of timber, he used his wood in what was more strictly beam construction. Thus the planks of the Puget Sound Indians spanned relatively long spaces. Thus, too, the cruck frames of the Saxons supported purlins and rafters. Fastenings were still crude. A little later man learned to notch timbers, drill holes, and make wooden pegs, and in this stage of development we may put the early American wooden houses of relatively heavy framing and the contemporary Japanese houses, relatively light. From these to the nailed wooden frame of today is but a short step. Half-timbering represents no departure. It is merely another way of applying the old mud plaster of the Ba Venda. Today we use Portland cement stucco or gypsum or lime plaster to replace mud but the change is not radical — we have only found a more effective substitute material. Wood framing itself has shown remarkably little change over a long period.

As soon as we consider a great civilization, we find masonry. The plains of Mesopotamia and the region of the Nile afforded the means for the manufacture of sun-dried brick; the earliest masonry houses, for instance, were of the adobe type. Bricks were laid dry and gradually coalesced by action of the elements, the result being not very different from that of the rammed-earth house. Even when natural brick became common, few peoples were so poor in wood that floor construction was not still of timber framing. When wood was too rare, a corbelled arch was used, a cumbersome structural method involving much waste space and material. Unfortunately, wood disintegrates to such an extent that we are unable to say whether the many roofless houses of archaeological research were framed with wooden or with corbelled ceilings.

From sun-dried to artificially burned brick was but a step. But burned brick had new properties of hardness and glaze that did not allow nature to fuse the masonry. So man supplied mortar, and the house of brick with mortar joints, usually with wooden floors, became almost as common as the wooden house. This development, though later than the completely evolved wooden frame, like it, has changed relatively little for many centuries.

Meanwhile, methods for constructing much larger buildings steadily developed and improved. While here and there stone was used as a domestic building material, it has rather been the material of larger buildings whose importance and permanence warranted the effort of masonry. Up to the time of the Romans, the builders in stone employed the principles of wooden construction, and the only principle they knew was that of the post and lintel, although sometimes a corbelled or false arch was employed. Stone used as post and lintel has definite spanning limits of around twelve feet. Even the Greeks, with all their subtlety of design based on modules and entasis, were unable to pass the barrier of the limiting span of stone; thus Greek rooms were perforce relatively small or else full of columns.

The development of the dome by the Romans permitted a new use of stone and the provision of wide interior spaces. This engineering idea and that of the arch were perhaps the greatest construction achievements of all time. From them spring directly the barrel vault of the basilica, the simple Romanesque vault, and finally the lofty and complex vaulting of the Gothic. After the Gothic period construction stood still for centuries until a new material, steel, permitted the revival of post-and-lintel construction on a much more flexible basis of span, and another material, concrete, permitted new arches, domes, and vaults of a kind unknown to the Gothic builders. The Romans had known concrete, but the principle of reinforcing this concrete with steel rods added the new and required flexibility.

None of these great construction achievements had much effect on the construction of the house. Roman houses were not often domed nor Gothic houses usually vaulted. Man pursued his domestic arts in the old, old ways. In our own day there have been efforts to frame houses like skyscrapers, and serious attempts to take advantage of the alluring properties of reinforced concrete. They have not progressed far enough to make any serious differences in the traditional methods. If we rightly read the past, we may conclude that mankind is unlikely to improve the building of the detached house with ideas drawn from the construction of great churches, castles, or other public edifices. If we are to improve upon the home of our predecessors, we must forget large projects of masonry and great carrying strength and apply ourselves to the special problem of the multitude of small homes, each with its own unique opportunity to the occupant for expressing his individual spirit.

While developments in materials and methods were taking place in the building industry, there were necessarily concomitant changes in technique. Primitive peoples built their houses communally and on the whole easily. There were traditions, skilled trades, even jurisdiction. Thus for religious reasons women were not permitted to work on the roof, or required to. Among many African tribes all craft work in connection with the house was reserved for special groups of males. But the materials were cut near at hand and expeditiously put together with a minimum of labor. Primitive man always scorns to do any more labor than he must.

With the first advances of civilization, slavery became common. Captives were impressed in droves into the building operations. Slavery did not require a particularly efficient organization of the task, but it did afford sufficient labor for the work to progress unceasingly. Slavery was later superseded by the religious building guilds who organized the labor, and still later the building-trades guilds took over this organization with the motive of improving their lot as well as their product. Each new type of construction brought more complicated problems of management — the use of materials from a wider region necessitating more routing of them to the site, the need for men of varying skills and hence craft. In the Middle Ages these requirements might be met inefficiently without serious effect on the underlying economic philosophy. Economic organization of today cannot brook such inefficiency; if it exists, it is a cancer on the public weal.

In our own day the problems of building are perhaps more complex than they have ever been before. There are in general two different types of problems, one of which we have solved reasonably well and the other of which lies unsolved and a challenge to every serious engineer. The first applies to the large building. This in most cases, as in apartments, schools, and office buildings, houses a large number of units within a single building shell. The second applies to the individual small house or other building. Both types involve the coordination of a large volume and diversity of materials; but the first assembles these materials into large numbers of single units which together comprise one large integral building unit, while the second assembles the same materials into a multiplicity of small structures. Naturally the second problem is the more difficult. Small wonder that it has not been solved as readily as the first; small wonder, too, that less thought has been given it. The profits from a single large enterprise are apparent, those from a scattered grouping of small units less obvious. But all this does not palliate the failure to cope with the situation.

The problem of organization relative to the large building has been solved with a fair degree of success, although continued research is needed in materials, planning, routing, and relations with labor. The solution has come about in a natural way; standardization, at least within the unit large enough to warrant it, has inevitably resulted from economical engineering and architectural design. But the same development in connection with the construction and architectural design of houses has been long delayed. All over the land are houses — scattered, small, individual homes — and the complicated problem of what they ought to be seems to have been nobody's job. No particular person or agency has here effected the standardization ever more pressingly demanded.

Through all the ages of which we have any historical record, the building industry seems to have accounted for about the same proportion of the general group organization and effort, though obviously varying somewhat with the seasons, climate, and social development. A tenth to a fifth of man's time has, roughly speaking, been devoted to the prosecution of this important art. Statistical studies of the industry reveal its present size, but in other regards it has developed strangely little.

As we have already seen, the present-day structure of the homes of America and countries of similar civilization has changed but slightly for centuries; it is still a complex of many different materials, cut, shaped, and otherwise manufactured from the rough, mostly upon the building site — and fitted together as of old by the cut-try-and-cut-again method. Similarly, the organization of the industry harks back to the guilds of the Middle Ages for its general form and character, this notwithstanding our greatly increased knowledge of raw materials, the markedly altered housing demands of our increasing group living, and the sweeping changes which have occurred in the technique and organization of most other industries during the past two hundred years.

Let us now scrutinize more carefully the technique and organization of this industry. This will not be easy, because the " building industry " does not represent a clear-cut entity like cotton goods manufacturing or steel making, where all operations are handled by a single establishment; instead, it is a heterogenous aggregation of a large number of more or less related industries. It has, indeed, been called the most disorganized industry in the country next to agriculture.[1]

Building is essentially a fabricating industry; the builder

1 See p. 535.

"manufactures" the house. But building is sharply distinguished from most other manufacturing industries. In the first place, the manufacturing process is not conducted by a permanent labor force at great central plants, from which the finished product is shipped out in large quantities to its destination. The average manufacturer ships a finished product from his factory to the consumer, or at least to a wholesaler or retailer; the builder has no factory. He dumps his raw materials on the site and there employs a number of workmen, who bring their own tools,[2] to form and place the materials by hand. In this respect he has far more in common with the itinerant scissors grinder than with the manufacturer of cotton goods or of automobiles. His steam shovels, concrete mixers, wheelbarrows, ladders, and various other equipment all have to be shifted from one location to another, and likewise his materials. Not only is there enormous waste of time and effort, but a considerable part of his equipment, such as concrete forms, staging, and similar items, is scrapped at the end of each piece of work.

Many builders have no stable labor force at all comparable with the force in a cotton mill or a boot and shoe factory. They frequently recruit their workers, or a large proportion of them, for each job. Furthermore, in most building construction the work is not handled by modern large-scale efficient methods, where different operations are planned and coordinated, but is instead a "small-shop," hit-or-miss affair.

In the erection of great office structures or large apartment-houses the work is often planned and routed with precision. In the construction of a great New York skyscraper, for instance, every detail of the work is arranged far in advance; practically every piece of material has a designated place; materials are delivered with clocklike regularity; the equipment is modern and the methods of erection are efficient. In some large-scale construction of single houses the builder likewise has a more or less permanent organization and the work is care-

---

[2] The contractor may, of course, supply a few larger tools, such as a concrete mixer.

fully planned. But even where a great number of dwellings are produced by a single builder in one development, each structure is really a separate job, and its manufacture cannot fairly be compared to that of standardized units characteristic of many factory-made products.

Large-scale operations in dwelling-house construction, furthermore, provide only a minor part of the country's housing.[3] A high proportion of builders erect only a single house, or at

TABLE 31

CLASSIFICATION OF BUILDING CONTRACTORS, AND OF ALL SUBCONTRACTORS, HANDLING MORE THAN $25,000 OF BUSINESS EACH IN 1929, BY SIZE [a]

Volume of business	Building contractors [b]	Per cent	Sub-contractors [c]	Per cent
$25,000 — $ 49,999	2,929	26.9	6,169	40.9
50,000 — 99,999	3,078	28.2	4,620	30.6
100,000 — 199,999	2,263	20.8	2,480	16.5
200,000 — 499,999	1,614	14.8	1,334	8.8
500,000 — 999,999	569	5.3	314	2.1
1,000,000 and over	428	4.0	164	1.1
Totals	10,881	100	15,081	100

(a) "Construction Industry — Summary for the United States," p. 70.
(b) Includes operative builders.
(c) Apparently most of these subcontractors were engaged in building construction.

best a very few houses, at any one time in any one neighborhood. A survey of the construction industry of the United States made for the first time by the Bureau of the Census in 1930 showed that of 10,881 contractors doing a business of more than $25,000 in 1929, more than 6000, or 55 per cent, reported a volume of less than $100,000. The average volume reported by 2455 of the contractors engaged in residential construction exclusively was almost exactly $100,000. For 5484 building

[3] The Committee on large-scale operations of the President's Conference held that "mass production has become the typical method in present-day house building." This conclusion hardly seems in line with the large number of small contractors reported by the Census. (The President's Conference on Home Building and Home Ownership, Vol. III, p. 68.)

contractors doing a business of less than $25,000 in 1929 (this number representing only 20 per cent of the number of active contractors in this size group) the average value of the output was only $10,971.[4] Table 31 presents a classification of larger concerns by volume of business done; Chart 34 gives a distribution by states. Data gathered by the United States Bureau of Labor Statistics in 1932 covering approximately 10,000 establishments engaged in building construction showed an average of only 8 employees per establishment.[5] As a further indication of the small size of many contracting or subcontracting establishments, Table 32 shows the number of employees per firm in certain branches of building in Ohio.

Building, as we have said, is distinctly a non-integrated industry. Instead of there being single organizations to purchase the land, manufacture the materials, handle the financing, and attend to the construction, these operations are divided among different sub-groups which are often as disorganized as the work of construction itself. A special difficulty arises from the fact that these sub-groups, instead of working together to produce the best house practically obtainable at minimum cost, are interested primarily in promoting the use of their own particular products or services. This " sub-group consciousness," as it has been called, is one of the outstanding ills of the industry.

In brief, instead of great central establishments at the top, coordinating the other branches and producing the final product in quantity and ready for delivery to the consumer, we have a local builder who is often the final agent, conducting what may be termed a retail business of erecting a few houses annually.

The difference in this respect between the building industry and others of comparable size may be seen in Chart 35, which shows for each of a number of important industries, first, the number of establishments, and second, the annual value of the output per establishment. In the case of residential building as

---

[4] USDC, Bureau of the Census, " Construction Industry — Summary for the United States " (GPO, Washington, 1933), pp. 70 and 168.

[5] USBLS, " Trend of Employment, July, 1933," p. 22.

—— CHART 34 ——

NUMBER OF CONTRACTORS PER 100,000 POPULATION REPORTING
CONSTRUCTION WORK VALUED AT $ 25,000 OR MORE IN THE
VARIOUS STATES OF THE UNITED STATES: 1929

Redrawn from Chart by Bureau of the Census

KEY

NUMBER OF CONTRACTORS

	5 to 16
	17 to 28
	29 to 40
	41 to 53

TABLE 32

AVERAGE NUMBER OF EMPLOYEES PER CONTRACTING FIRM IN CERTAIN
BRANCHES OF THE BUILDING INDUSTRY OF OHIO [a]

Year	General contracting [b]	Plastering and lathing	Plumbing and steam-fitting	Painting and decorating
1914	18.3	12.2	10.2	9.7
1915	16.3	9.1	9.7	6.7
1916	30.8	11.1	9.6	6.7
1917	21.3	8.5	9.0	6.3
1918	17.9	17.3	7.6	5.7
1919	14.6	5.1	7.9	6.1
1920	17.7	7.0	8.2	5.6
1921	11.2	6.9	7.5	5.0
1922	12.2	7.1	7.9	5.7
1923	12.3	7.8	9.1	5.3
1924	10.6	7.3	8.2	4.1

(a) Watkins, Ralph J., "The Construction Industry in Ohio." (Published
by the Ohio State University Bureau of Business Research, 1926), Table VI,
opp. p. 10.

(b) This may include general contractors in other classes of construction.

an industry there are so many establishments which do less than
$25,000 worth of work per year that these are shown plotted in
dotted lines above the actual number of establishments doing
more than $25,000 each, which appear in solid lines. The an-
nual value per establishment in the building industry has been
based only on establishments doing more than $25,000 worth of
work annually; if that value were to be computed on *all* establishments, including those doing less than $25,000 per year,
the ordinate would be almost invisible.

The materials are often delivered half-finished, with a consequent excessive waste in handling and re-handling; the use of
labor-saving devices is the exception.

This method of itinerant manufacture on the spot, with more
or less itinerant labor, and with materials only partially
prepared for incorporation into the process of construction,
sharply differentiates the dwelling-house industry from most of
the other major manufacturing industries of the country. It is

—— CHART 35 ——

NUMBER OF ESTABLISHMENTS AND ANNUAL VALUE OF PRODUCT PER ESTABLISHMENT IN SELECTED INDUSTRIES IN THE UNITED STATES:1929

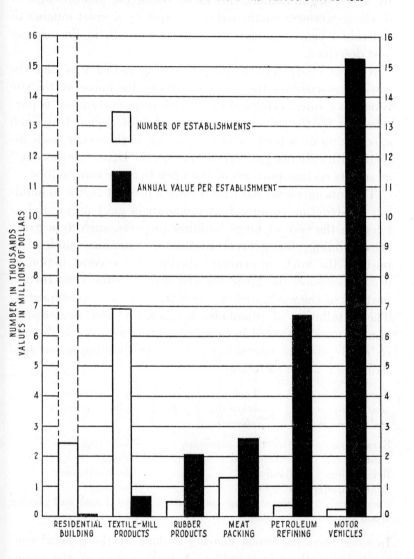

a fundamental distinction, the disadvantages of which may be traced through the entire process of construction. In recent years factory-made or " ready-cut " houses have been produced by a few organizations, but in the main the manufacture of dwelling-houses is conducted on the spot by a great number of individual concerns, most of which are small, in the manner just described.

Another characteristic of the building industry is that the work of assembling the various parts of the house at the site is not, as a rule, performed by a single organization but is parceled out by the owner among a number of contractors, each specializing on a particular feature; or, if the owner deals directly with only one general contractor, the latter " farms out " or sublets certain portions of the work to other contractors.

The subcontractor has thus become a distinct factor in building construction to an extent unknown in most major industries. In the case of large building projects, such as a great office-building, the general contractor sometimes sublets all parts of the work; in ordinary dwelling-house construction he usually engages the labor for and directly supervises certain portions of the work, such as excavation and rough carpentry. The installation of plumbing, heating, and electrical equipment is usually turned over to subcontractors. While there is no rigid rule, the prevailing practice in dwelling-house construction is about as follows:

Work ordinarily done by the general contractor	*Work usually done by other contractors, either directly for the owner or under subcontract*	
Excavation	Structural iron work	Plastering
Foundations	Ornamental iron work	Tiling
Bricklaying	Roofing	Electrical work
Stone masonry	Plumbing	Painting
Carpentry	Steamfitting and heating	Metal sash and glazing
Wood finish	Lathing	Shades and screens

In some cases hardwood flooring is done by the general contractor; in others it is sublet. A further idea of the variation in practice is afforded by Chart 36. This is by no means a complete exposition of a complicated procedure, and there are wide variations in different sections of the country.

The employment of subcontractors also shows considerable variation as between different types of work. In the District of Columbia in 1929, according to the Census, plumbing contractors did between 20 and 25 per cent of their work directly for owners, whereas contractors engaged in electric and elevator installation did approximately 97 per cent of it under subcontract.

Special mention should be made of the speculative, or, as he is often called, "operative" builder, who erects buildings without orders from a specific purchaser; a large amount of dwelling-house construction is so handled. Such building is often connected with the promotion of development schemes, and too often results in housing of a distinctly low standard.[6]

Operative builders, like general contractors, may sublet portions of the work, although in many cases they directly conduct the greater part of it; they are much more important in some sections of the country than in others. Thus they represent a substantial percentage of the total number of builders in the District of Columbia, and in several central states, whereas in certain New England states and several South Atlantic ones none was reported by the Census survey;[7] of 30,597 establishments doing a construction business of more than $25,000 in

---

[6] The Census treats the terms "operative builder" and "speculative builder" as practically synonymous. The Committee on Construction of the President's Conference, however, considers an operative builder as one who purchases and develops an entire tract of land, installing the various utilities as well as building the houses, allowing the home purchaser some choice in the design and construction, whereas it defines a speculative builder as one who "usually constructs a number of houses as a finished product," the purchaser being compelled to accept the builder's ideas except perhaps for certain portions of the interior decoration. (The President's Conference on Home Building and Home Ownership, Vol. V, p. 88.)

[7] The Census definition of an operative builder may not agree with that commonly used. In any case speculative building certainly represents much more than the indicated 2.5 per cent of the total volume.

1929, only 750, or 2.5 per cent, were classed as operative builders.[8]

What lack of organization and a multiplicity of agencies mean in construction is shown from actual experience on a recent job: the numerous steps that must be taken, the miscellaneous equipment that must be provided and brought to the site, the great number of materials that must be purchased, and the different negotiations that must be carried on.

This job was the construction of a suburban residence costing about $22,500. It was undertaken by a skilled general contractor of long experience. He handled the excavation, installation of water, sewer, and gas and electric connections, the steel framing, wood framing, and rough and finish carpentry. Before starting actual work, he had to arrange for workmen's liability insurance, secure a building permit, file plans and specifications, and make applications to the several proper authorities for installation of the various utilities. A temporary telephone service and a temporary water-supply had to be provided, also temporary electric current for light and for operation of power units. A temporary heating service was later required for drying out plaster; if building had been done in cold weather such a service would have been needed while painting and papering were in progress. Again, before starting construction work the general contractor had to provide a large amount of equipment outside of materials actually used in construction.[9]

For the various parts of the work the general contractor had to purchase a large variety of materials (ordinarily he would not have these in stock but would " shop around " in order to get the lowest prices possible [10]). The contractor purchased a considerable part of these materials in small quantities as needed

---

8 While these figures covered all classes of construction, presumably nearly all of the operative builders were engaged in building construction.

9 The more important tools and materials of this sort are given in the Appendix, p. 551; most of them are regularly carried as part of the general contractor's general equipment but have to be transported to each job.

10 A list of materials is given in the Appendix, p. 553.

in the course of the work. Such purchases necessitated frequent trips to or telephone calls on various dealers. The list for two selected months presented in Table 33 gives a fair idea of the variety and small size of such purchases, all of which of course had to be kept account of. In the great majority of cases each item represents a purchase from a separate dealer. On this job eighteen subcontractors were engaged.[11]

TABLE 33

List of Miscellaneous Purchases Made in Two Selected Months by General Contractor in Building a Single-Family House

December

5	15 bbls. cement	$32.25
	Copper wire nails	1.70
8	Reinforcing rods	6.91
9	6 d. cut finish nails	5.40
	65 lbs. 8 d. nails	2.93
	Miscellaneous	1.50
10	30 bags cement	16.13
	2 steel sash	7.00
	20 bags cement	10.75
11	100 cu. ft. insulation ..	20.00
12	Lead, oil, turpentine ..	9.53
	6 joist hangers	5.30
	5 brushes	1.95
	23 ft. lead pipe	8.80
	5 rolls Bermico	6.25
	2 rolls insulating paper	4.50
	35 ft. asbestos paper ..	2.80
	10 lbs. roofing cement ..	1.25
	2 kegs 8 d. com. nails ..	7.60
	1 keg 20 d. nails	3.50
	2 thermometers	1.60
15	20 ft. spruce	1.29
	Pipe and bends for drains	2.67
16	Lead flashing	.90
17	Pipe and drain bends .	9.33

December

18	1 roll insulating paper	2.25
	3 rolls Bermico	3.75
	16 lts. wire glass	2.58
	12½ lbs. putty	.69
	Express	.56
	1 keg 8 d. com. nails ..	4.00
	Paint pot	.25
	Copper flashing	1.88
	Sheet lead	.88
	Coupling	1.43
20	30 cement blocks	$ 4.20
26	Wallboard and boards .	23.65
30	Lumber	30.31
	Boards	170.00

March

1	200 gal. fuel oil	15.00
3	lag screws	.52
6	Nails	8.75
10	1 brush	.35
	250 gal. fuel oil	18.75
11	Drawer pulls and bolts	5.65
	7 rolls Bermico	8.75
	Sandpaper	.73
20	1 lt. wire glass	.25
23	1 angle iron	1.50
	2 bags lime	.90
	1 bundle lath	1.12
24	Miscellaneous	1.97
	7½ bbls. cement	16.14
27	1 push button	2.00
28	Bermico paper	1.00
	Cesspool grate and ring	7.50
31	Pipe, bends and cement	19.22
	8 tons Blue Dust	24.00
	2 sets sash balances ...	4.28

[11] See the Appendix, p. 555.

The general contractor is responsible for all subcontracting operations included in his contract. This necessitates a good deal of work on his part, as, for instance, the making of written contracts with subcontractors and arrangements for payments, and providing subcontractors with all necessary data, plans, specifications, and other details, not only of the particular subcontractor's work but of related work. The general contractor furthermore has to prepare a time schedule of the job and to notify the subcontractors a reasonable period in advance when to start their part of the work. If for any reason the subcontractors do not appear at the proper time, he must look them up. Moreover, the general contractor must check the work of subcontractors to see if it is according to specifications. In particular he must determine whether there is any interference between their work and his own later work, for instance the existence of pipes projecting too far from the wall to permit paneling to be placed over them. He must also supervise at all times the making of the necessary alterations or cuttings for the installation of piping and other utilities, and must make sure that the subcontractors have the necessary permits and that their work is inspected by the proper authorities. The general contractor furthermore must aim to protect the subcontractors' work from damage by the work of other subcontractors or his own general contract work. Among minor responsibilities of the general contractor is the provision of storage room for the subcontractors' material and seeing that subcontractors do not overload floors with their own materials.

It will be seen that the general contractor has a large number of miscellaneous responsibilities even in the case of subcontract work. His task in this respect is made more difficult because of interference due to weather conditions, accidents, and delays of one sort or another. For instance, in excavation work a steam shovel may damage some of the batter-boards, or over Sunday a foot of water may have accumulated at the bottom of the cellar, necessitating getting pumps into action; or the same rain may have resulted in a cave-in of one side of the excavated area, requiring the bringing in of laborers to shovel out the accumulated earth. During the course of a day, a brief shower may come up which necessitates calling the men hurriedly together to cover cement and concrete work; the same shower may have saturated the sand so thoroughly that the general contractor will have to change his concrete mixture for the time being.

Yet again, the architect or the owner may suddenly demand some change in design; such as the arrangement of a window, which necessitates undoing work already completed or studying plans and specifications to be sure that the change will not conflict with some other part of the structure. For example, the owner may decide to run a steel beam across his garage ceiling which necessitates a change in the hanging of the garage doors or in the arrangement of heating pipes. Ordinarily there is a good deal of cutting and fitting of doors, and not infrequently some major change or correction which compels a carpenter to make special measurements.

No such interference with production at the whim of the purchaser is, or could be, tolerated in the manufacture of automobiles, shoes, cotton goods, or any other standardized factory product. Under modern factory methods various preliminary stages of planning the numerous specific operations are coordinated to such an extent that there is, or should be, an even flow of work through the factory with a minimum of interruption and delay. It would be intolerable in the manufacture of boots and shoes if the routing of the work should be held up while the employer rushed out to buy a gross of eyelets or linings. Yet in the erection of an ordinary dwelling it is an almost daily occurrence for a workman to wait around while the contractor hurries to the hardware store for a box of screws of a given size or to the lumber yard for a few extra pieces of lumber.

The effect of such lack of organization on the ultimate consumer is shown in Charts 37 and 38, which illustrate in diagrammatic form the process by which a consumer in a relatively small community might obtain in the one instance a house, and in the other instance an automobile. In each case the number of potential sources of supply has been limited to a comparable number, and labor groups have been brought together in broad classifications according to whether or not they must be treated with independently. In Chart 37 we see that the owner in this small community may go to one of two architects, through whom in turn he may deal with one of five general contractors; or he may go directly to the general contractors. Each of the five general contractors in turn may deal with one of several subcontractors in every required trade, only the most important ones being listed. Both these subcontractors and the general contractors have labor employment options and in some cases both will draw from the same group. Materials finally are obtained principally by the subcontractors but also in some cases by the general contractors. In this chart a line has been drawn connecting every square between which there might be a contact, and the result is like a complicated spider's web. Yet this is by no means a complete picture of the complicated nature of the organization required to furnish the owner with his house.

In the purchase of an automobile, on the other hand, the owner is confronted with five different sales organizations each of which represents one manufacturer, the total number corresponding to the number of general contractors in Chart 37. Having placed his order for a car with one of these sales departments, the order is sent to the factory of the manufacturer who has made the sale. This factory employs its own labor which is not employed in the factory of any other manufacturer. It may obtain five basic parts of the car from five materials manufacturers, corresponding to the five dealers shown on the building chart. The reader will realize that in many cases even some of these materials are prepared by the factory in question. The simplicity of the car-purchase chart [12] compared with the house-purchase chart is obvious.

[12] Of course there are more parts to an automobile than shown on this chart, but the simplification made is no greater than that made in the building chart, and that in the latter was required in order that the entire diagram might not be a welter of undecipherable lines.

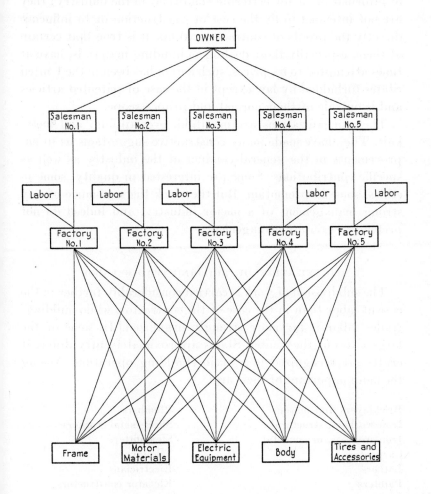

— CHART 38 —

DIAGRAMMATIC CHART OF METHOD OF PROVIDING
A PURCHASER WITH AN AUTOMOBILE

EMPLOYERS' ORGANIZATIONS

Employers in the building trades are associated in various kinds of organizations.[13] The important point is that these are non-profit associations, organized primarily for the exchange of information or for bettering conditions in the industry; they are not intended to fix the cost of construction or to influence directly the profits of contractors. While it is true that certain of them, especially those dealing in building materials, have at times attempted to fix prices, such action has been in the United States forbidden by law except in the case of patented articles and is outside of their normal and proper scope.

These organizations are manifold, overlapping, and loose-knit. They have made many constructive suggestions as to improvements in the general conduct of the industry as well as specific contributions. Some are interested in quality, some in ethics, some in promotion. But they lack the semblance of any strong management of a major industry, and indeed do not pretend to exercise management.

ORGANIZATION OF BUILDING-TRADES LABOR

The subdivision of work is carried considerably farther in the case of labor than in the case of the contractor, while building-trades labor is far more strongly organized. In some of the large cities of the United States approximately fifty different crafts are recognized in a major building operation. Among the more important of these are:

Bricklayers and masons	Plumbers
Iron workers, structural	Sheet-metal workers
Iron workers, ornamental	Steamfitters
Carpenters	Tile layers
Lathers	Electricians
Painters	Elevator constructors
Plasterers	Roofers

[13] Several of these are briefly described in the Appendix, pp. 557–561.

In the case of a simple dwelling, at least the following crafts ordinarily participate in the construction:

Carpenters	Lathers
Bricklayers and masons	Plasterers
Roofers	Painters
Floor layers	Paperhangers
Plumbers	Electricians
Steamfitters	Linoleum layers
Sheet-metal workers	Laborers
Tile layers	

Some results of this marked degree of specialization of building-trades labor are discussed elsewhere.[14]

Labor organizations in the building trades are in sharp contrast with the loosely-bound, non-profit organizations of employers above described; they are essentially militant, having been created for the specific purpose of securing pecuniary benefit through maintenance of wage scales and of obtaining favorable hours of work and other advantages.

The basic organization is the local union, covering a given craft in a given community or area. These unions are usually grouped as central or state organizations, and again as national unions, and finally are brought together with similar organizations in other industries into the American Federation of Labor. The latter, as the name suggests, is a federation and its component organizations reserve, and more or less frequently exercise, the right to secede; they insist on maintaining a high degree of local authority. The organizations in the building trades have been particularly independent in this respect, and there has been more or less constant friction with the American Federation of Labor.[15] Building-trades unions are sometimes called the " aristocracy of labor."

[14] See p. 147.

[15] The character of the Federation, it may be noted, is almost the opposite of that of the Knights of Labor which preceded it. Apparently the failure of the Knights of Labor to obtain its ends through industrial unionism and political methods determined the policy of the American Federation of Labor in adopting the trade union as a basis and relying upon direct action, such as the strike.

While an organization of house carpenters is reported to have been formed in Philadelphia in 1724, and a strike of building-trades workers occurred in that city in 1791,[16] it is generally agreed that modern trade unionism in the United States did not begin until 1825; some writers place the date still later.[17] Moreover, while many building-trades unions with modern features were formed in the next ten years, most of them were disrupted by the panic of 1837. Practically no national labor organization now in existence dates back of the Civil War.

A national organization of bricklayers was effected in 1865. The dates of national organization of some of the other building trades were as follows: [18]

Carpenters	1881
Plumbers	1882
Painters	1887
Stone cutters	1887
Electricians	1891
Tile layers	1897
Wood and metal lathers	1899
Elevator workers	1901
Marble workers	1901
Hod carriers and building laborers	1903

The largest national building-trade labor organizations in the United States in 1929, with their approximate membership

[16] In Europe, strikes in the building trades are reported to have occurred several centuries earlier.

[17] "If a labor movement be defined as a continuous organization of wage earners or of industrial workers, the American labor movement cannot be said to have begun much before 1880. It is true, of course, that there existed as early as 1800 organized wage earners who conducted their activities in much the same way as does organized labor today. These groups, however, showed but slight continuity. The labor movement before 1880, except for a few national unions like the Bricklayers, Molders, Iron and Steel workers, was no more than the rise and fall of organizations, stimulated by favorable economic conditions and disintegrated by industrial depressions or by internal dissension over conflicting social programs." (Wolman, Leo, "An Outline of the American Labor Movement" [Workers Education Bureau of America, New York, 1923], p. 12.)

[18] Hollander and Barnett, "Studies in American Trade Unionism" (Henry Holt and Company, New York, 1906), p. 296.

as indicated by the reports of the American Federation of Labor, are the following: [19]

	Approximate membership
United Brotherhood of Carpenters and Joiners of America	300,000
Bricklayers', Masons', and Plasterers' International Union of America (1927)	80,000
International Brotherhood of Electrical Workers [20]	142,000
Brotherhood of Painters, Decorators and Paperhangers of America	108,197
Operative Plasterers and Cement Finishers International Association of America	39,631
International Hod-Carriers, Building and Common Laborers Union of America	78,950
United Association of Journeymen Plumbers and Steamfitters of the United States and Canada	45,000

The total membership of the Building Trades Department of the American Federation of Labor has varied greatly depending chiefly on whether some important national union was " in " or " out." For instance, in 1927, when the carpenters and joiners with 300,000 members had seceded, the total member-

---

[19] " Report of the Proceedings of the 24th Annual Convention of the Building Trades Department of the American Federation of Labor," p. 61. The 1929 figures for organization of the building trades are regarded by the authors as more strictly comparable with normal conditions than similar figures for 1932 or later. It may be of interest, however, to compare the figures given with corresponding figures for 1932 issued by The Brookings Institution in its publication " The American Federation of Labor," by Lewis L. Lorwin (Washington, 1933), pp. 476–479:

United Brotherhood of Carpenters and Joiners of America	290,000
Bricklayers, Masons, and Plasterers' International Union of America	56,700
International Brotherhood of Electrical Workers of America	139,900
Brotherhood of Painters, Decorators and Paperhangers of America..	79,600
Operative Plasterers' International Association of the United States and Canada	35,300
International Hod-Carriers, Building, and Common Laborers' Union of America	90,000
United Association of Plumbers and Steamfitters of the United States and Canada	45,000

It should be noted that the figures for 1929 quoted by The Brookings Institution are not identical with those given here though very nearly the same.

[20] A large part of these workers are outside of the building industry.

ship of the department was 600,500. In 1928, when the carpenters had temporarily returned but the national organization of bricklayers, masons, and plasterers with 80,000 members had seceded, it was 837,000.[21]

In 1920 the membership of this department was approximately 890,000. On the basis of 2,250,000 workers [22] in the building trades, this might suggest that building-trades labor in that year was about 40 per cent organized. Such a statement, however, would be inaccurate, since not all members of the Building Trades Department are engaged in the building industry. A study of trade unionism by the National Bureau of Economic Research placed the ratio of organization in 1920 at 25½ per cent [23] — a relatively high proportion, exceeded in only two major industries, mining and transportation, and in the clothing industry. Comparisons for certain major industrial groups and also for a few selected key industries are given in Table 34. Certain of these, with estimates for the year 1927, are also shown in Chart 39.

For some specific occupations the percentage of organization runs much higher. For example, the report just cited showed the ratios of Table 34.

If comparison be made for certain occupations in specific localities, the ratios are higher still; according to the same report, in 1920 nearly 80 per cent of the brick and stone masons in Chicago, Baltimore, and Cleveland were included in trade unions; in Boston the proportion was almost 96 per cent.

Accurate information as to the extent of organization of building-trades workers since 1920 is not available.[24] The National Bureau of Economic Research estimated that in 1927 about 50 per cent of building-trades workers were organized

[21] American Federation of Labor, Building Trades Department, "Report of the Twenty-second Annual Convention" (Allied Printing Trades Council, New Orleans, 1928), pp. 57–58.

[22] See p. 212.

[23] Wolman, Leo, "The Growth of American Trade Unions, 1880–1923," p. 86.

[24] In 1933 the membership increased sharply.

—— CHART 39 ——

RELATIVE EXTENT OF ORGANIZATION OF LABOR IN SELECTED
INDUSTRIES IN THE UNITED STATES: 1910, 1920, AND 1927

Charted from data in Report of the National Bureau of Economic Research
    Growth of American Trade Unions, by Leo Wolman.
    Recent Economic Changes.

All Industries
Exclusive of
Agriculture
- 1910 — 10.9 %
- 1920 — 20.8 %
- 1927 — 20 %

All Manufacturing
- 1910 — 11.6 %
- 1920 — 23.2 %
- 1927 — 16 %

Extraction of
Minerals
- 1910 — 27.3 %
- 1920 — 41 %
- 1927 — 33 %

Building Trades
- 1910 — 16.4 %
- 1920 — 25.5 %
- 1927 — 40 %

Transportation
- 1910 — 17.1 %
- 1920 — 37.3 %
- 1927 — 45 %

Food and
Kindred Products
- 1910 — 7.6 %
- 1920 — 19.4 %
- 1927 — Estimated

Clothing
- 1910 — 16.9 %
- 1920 — 57.8 %
- 1927 — 47.8 %

Note:- Percentages for 1927 largely estimated.

TABLE 34

PERCENTAGE OF ORGANIZATION AMONG BUILDING-TRADE WORKERS
AND CERTAIN OTHER WAGE-EARNERS IN THE UNITED STATES,
1910 AND 1920 [a]

Group	Per Cent Organized 1910	1920
All wage-earners	9.4	18.7
All wage-earners except in agriculture	10.9	20.8
By major divisions of industry:		
Extraction of minerals	27.3	41.0
Transportation	17.1	37.3
Building trades	16.4	25.5
Manufacturing industries	11.6	23.2
Stationary firemen	9.6	19.9
Stationary engineers	4.6	12.4
Professional service	4.6	5.4
Public service	2.5	7.3
Domestic and personal service	2.0	3.8
Clerical occupations	1.8	8.3
Trade	1.0	1.1
In selected industries		
Clothing	16.9	57.8
Leather	14.6	29.4
Lumber	10.3	18.1
Food and kindred products	7.6	19.4
Textiles	3.7	15.0
Brick and stone masons	39.1	50.0
Carpenters and joiners	20.8	40.5
Painters, etc.	17.6	29.1
Plasterers	32.0	46.6
Plumbers and gas fitters	20.7	33.5

(a) Wolman, Leo, "The Growth of American Trade Unions, 1880–1923" (National Bureau of Economic Research, Inc., New York, 1924), pp. 85 and 88.

and placed the number of such union workers at 1,014,000.[25] This ratio seems too high. Indeed, this is indicated by the Bureau's own figures of the actual number of union members, since it seems reasonably certain that the number of workers in

[25] National Bureau of Economic Research, Inc., "Recent Economic Changes," Vol. II, p. 480.

the industry was greater than in 1920, when, as shown on page 213, it was placed by the Bureau at about 2,400,000. If there were no more than 2,500,000 workers in the industry in 1927, and this figure seems too low, a union membership of 1,014,000 would indicate that only 40 per cent were organized — a liberal estimate. The pronounced recession in building operations since 1929 presumably has resulted in the withdrawal of many building-trades workers from local unions, if only to avoid payment of dues, so that the ratio in 1932 may have been considerably less than 40 per cent.

SIZE OF THE BUILDING INDUSTRY

Building ranks as one of the major industries of the country. The " construction " industry, which, as already pointed out, includes much more than building construction, is frequently accorded second place, being exceeded only by agriculture; [26] but to attain this rating it must include highway and street construction, water-power development, public works and utilities, subway construction, and other classes of work.[27]

Such comparisons obviously depend upon what is included under a given industry. For example, the textile industry may be considered as covering only the operations of textile mills or as including such related industries as clothing manufacture. In view of the fact that the term " construction " covers so many lines of work, it seems proper to make comparisons on a broad basis. In Table 35 there is given such a comparison, showing the total number of wage-earners and the total value of output in 1929 for certain major divisions of industry and for the construction industry as reported by the Census. It will be seen that construction, instead of taking second place, ranks ninth with respect to the value of output in 1929, and fifth with respect to the number of employees. However, the number of employees here given, although based upon a Census report, is far

---

[26] The relative importance of the " construction " industry as measured by Evans Clark on the basis of number of workers employed and value of product is shown in the Appendix, p. 558.

[27] In this connection see Table 36, p. 204.

below the total number of workers in the building industry as reported by the Census under occupations. Thus for the year 1930 the census of occupations, as shown on page 213, reported approximately 2,600,000 workers in the building industry.

TABLE 35

RANK OF MAJOR INDUSTRIES AS INDICATED BY VALUE OF PRODUCT AND NUMBER OF WAGE-EARNERS, 1929 [a]

Industry	Value of products	Number of wage-earners	Value of product per wage-earner
Agriculture	$16,052,400,000	10,471,998 [b]	$ 1,530
Food and kindred products	12,023,589,000	753,247	16,000
Meat packing (wholesale) ..	3,434,654,000	122,505	27,920
Textiles	9,243,303,000	1,707,798	5,410
Mill products ...	5,043,171,000	1,096,163	4,610
Wearing apparel	3,536,041,000	536,561	6,590
Iron and steel	7,137,928,000	880,882	8,100
Machinery	7,043,380,000	1,091,269	6,460
Railroads	6,373,005,000 [c]	1,694,042	3,760
Transportation equipment ...	6,047,209,000	583,355	10,370
Mining	5,887,300,000	806,418	7,310
Mineral fuels ...	3,190,527,000	726,885 [d]	4,390
Construction	5,830,000,000	1,008,000	5,785
Building construction ..	4,100,000,000	650,000 [e]	6,310
Residential construction only .	1,640,000,000 [e]	328,000 [e]	5,000
Motor vehicles [f] ...	3,722,793,000	226,116	16,460
Chemicals	3,759,405,000	280,868	13,400
Forest products ..	3,591,765,000	876,383	4,100
Electric light and power [g]	1,802,655,000 [c]	49,269 [h]	36,600

(a) Based on USC data except figures for railroads, which are from Interstate Commerce Commission.

(b) Includes all gainful workers over 10 years of age.

(c) Income.

(d) Census figure for coal mine and oil and gas well operatives.

(e) Estimated. Census does not show figures for building separately.

(f) Not including motor-vehicle bodies and parts, and motorcycles.

(g) 1927.

(h) Operatives only, 1930.

Such discrepancies have been characteristic of nearly all discussions of the construction industry and have never been satisfactorily reconciled. If the larger total number of workers be accepted, then construction would indeed rank second to agriculture. But whether construction ranks second or ninth among the nation's industries is not significant; either rank points clearly to its great importance.

ANNUAL INVESTMENT IN NEW

BUILDING CONSTRUCTION IN THE UNITED STATES

Prior to the Census of the Construction Industry for the year 1929, made by the Bureau of the Census in 1930 and published in summary form early in 1933, there were no comprehensive official figures on the value of construction work in the United States. Various private agencies [28] concerned with the compilation of statistics relating to building placed the annual investment in new construction of all kinds, exclusive of public works, in several active years, in the neighborhood of $7,000,000,000. The figures of the Copper and Brass Research Association from 1921 to 1931 are given below: [29]

1921	$3,185,300,000
1922	4,666,200,000
1923	4,953,800,000
1924	5,587,700,000
1925	7,339,600,000
1926	7,484,400,000
1927	7,199,500,000
1928	7,555,500,000
1929	6,436,500,000
1930	4,509,000,000
1931	2,909,000,000 [a]

Average (computed from above data) 5,620,600,000

(a) Based on data for 11 months.

The Census report just referred to placed the gross volume of construction of all kinds, including public works, in 1929 at $7,285,720,000. But it stated that approximately $1,507,000,-

[28] Notably the F. W. Dodge Corporation and the Copper and Brass Research Association.

[29] Shown graphically in Chart 40.

—— CHART 40 ——

ANNUAL EXPENDITURES FOR BUILDING CONSTRUCTION,
INCLUDING REPAIRS, IN THE UNITED STATES : 1921–1931

Charted from data furnished by Copper and Brass Research Association.

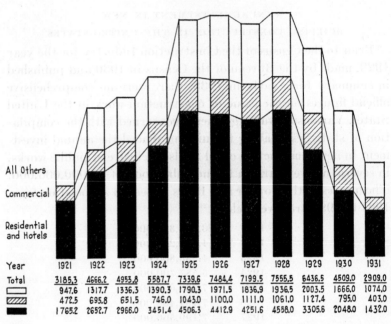

Year	1921	1922	1923	1924	1925	1926	1927	1928	1929	1930	1931
Total	3185.3	4666.2	4953.8	5587.7	7339.6	7484.4	7199.5	7555.5	6436.5	4509.0	2909.0
☐	947.6	1317.7	1336.3	1390.3	1790.3	1971.5	1836.9	1936.5	2003.5	1666.0	1074.0
▨	472.5	695.8	651.5	746.0	1043.0	1100.0	1111.0	1061.0	1127.4	795.0	403.0
■	1765.2	2652.7	2966.0	3451.4	4506.3	4412.9	4251.6	4558.0	3305.6	2048.0	1432.0

Millions of Dollars

000 of this amount represented duplication of the reports of
contractors and subcontractors, and placed the actual net total
of all " construction " work done in 1929 at $5,778,453,000,
as follows : [30]

By establishments doing a business of over $25,000 . . $4,794,772,000
By establishments doing a business of less than
     $25,000   983,681,000
                    Total $5,778,453,000

[30] USC, " Construction Industry — Summary for the United States," p. 24.

Of this total approximately 70 per cent, or $4,000,000,000, was building construction. An exact computation cannot be made, since the Census returns for establishments doing a business of less than $25,000 cover only about 20 per cent of such establishments. For a total of $4,911,767,000 of work done " under general contract or directly for owner " [31] by establishments reporting more than $25,000 worth of work in 1929 the distribution was as shown in Table 36.

It will be noted from Table 36 that the Census placed the net total value of building work handled by contractors and subcontractors doing a business of over $25,000 each in 1929 at $3,270,648,000. Of this amount, $2,779,102,000, or 85 per cent, was handled by general contractors and $491,546,000, or 15 per cent, by subcontractors working directly for owners. Subcontractors did a much larger amount of work than this, but such subcontract work done for general contractors is included in the total for the latter group.

The volume of building construction handled by establishments doing less than $25,000 is not stated by the Census, but may be conservatively estimated at $800,000,000. The addition of this sum to the total of $3,270,648,000 for larger concerns gives a grand total of upwards of $4,000,000,000.

The value of all construction work reached a peak in 1928. In 1929, the year covered by the census data, it was from 85 per cent to 87.5 per cent of the 1928 total.[32] On the basis of the lower figure a net total of $5,778,500,000 in 1929 would indicate a peak figure of about $6,800,000,000. As this covers all forms of construction, these Census data are considerably below the private estimates of $7,000,000,000 for building construction alone. Whether the difference is to be explained by a difference in the basis and methods used is not important for the present purpose. In any case, the private estimates covered a

---

[31] The Census states that this item " represents approximately the actual amount of construction work," and that it is sufficiently accurate for general purposes to use this approximation.

[32] This percentage is based upon returns of private agencies covering a period of years.

TABLE 36

VALUE OF EACH CLASS OF CONSTRUCTION WORK IN THE UNITED STATES
HANDLED UNDER GENERAL CONTRACT OR DIRECTLY FOR
OWNERS IN 1929 [a]

(By establishments handling more than $25,000 of work in 1929)
(000's omitted)

	All establishments	General contractors	Subcontractors [b]
Building	$3,270,648	$2,779,102	$491,546
Highway and street ...	721,431	714,995	6,436
Water-power development	23,286	22,673	612
Railroad and car-line ..	90,178	87,513	2,665
Public works and utilities	644,096	599,006	45,090
Air transport work	6,835	6,528	307
Subway, other than buildings	71,912	71,912	—
Miscellaneous	83,381	43,676	39,705
Total	$4,911,767	$4,325,405	$586,361

	Per cent	Per cent	Per cent
Building	66.6	64.3	83.8
Highway and street	14.7	16.5	1.1
Water-power development	0.5	0.5	0.1
Railroad and car-line	1.8	2.0	0.5
Public works and utilities	13.1	13.9	7.7
Air transport work	0.1	0.1	0.1
Subway, other than buildings	1.5	1.7	—
Miscellaneous	1.7	1.0	6.7
	100	100	100

(a) "Construction Industry," p. 42.

(b) This is the amount of subcontract work handled directly for owners. A large amount of work done by subcontractors for general contractors is included in the totals for the latter.

period of extraordinary activity in building and therefore should not be taken as representing a normal condition. Averaging the lean years with the boom years of the past decade, we may reasonably place the value of all construction over an extended period at $6,000,000,000 yearly and that of building alone at $4,500,000,000.

The amount of residential construction in 1929 cannot be stated accurately from the Census returns. For establishments doing a business of over $25,000 a distribution of the value of building construction by type of establishment, with an estimate for smaller concerns, is given in Table 37.

TABLE 37

APPROXIMATE VALUE OF BUILDING CONSTRUCTION WORK IN THE UNITED STATES IN 1929 BY TYPE OF ESTABLISHMENT [a]

	Number	Value
General contractors (over $25,000)		
Residential building only	2,455	$245,200,000
Commercial building only	539	132,500,000
Manufacturing building only	75	93,800,000
Building not specialized	7,062	2,139,900,000
Total	10,131	$2,611,400,000
Operative builders	750	153,500,000
Subcontractors (over $25,000) [b]	—	550,000,000
Contractors (less than $25,000) [c]	—	800,000,000
Total (approximate)		$4,114,900,000

(a) "Construction Industry," p. 69. Since some of the figures are estimated this should not be taken as a Census table.

(b) Not including work done for general contractors or operative builders. Figures are partly estimated since the Census does not show such subcontract work for building separately.

(c) Estimated, on assumption that most of work done by smaller contractors was building construction.

It is impossible from this table to compute the total value of residential construction separately. It will be noted that establishments engaged exclusively in such construction contributed only about 10 per cent of all building construction handled by the larger concerns. However, a much larger volume of residential work doubtless is included in the figures for the group " building not specialized." Most of the work done by the group of contractors doing less than $25,000 business each in 1929 presumably was residential.

For the total of $3,270,000,000 of building construction by the larger contractors and larger subcontractors, working directly for owners, the Census made a distribution by types of building as shown in Table 38. This places the ratio of residential construction by this group at 27.6 per cent of the total; or including hotels, 30.9 per cent. If it be assumed that $750,-000,000 of work by small contractors was residential construction, then the ratio for this type of work would be raised to over 40 per cent.[33]

This percentage relates only to a single year when residence construction was well below normal. It is much lower than the

TABLE 38

PERCENTAGE DISTRIBUTION OF VALUE OF BUILDING CONSTRUCTION IN UNITED STATES IN 1929 BY CLASS OF BUILDING [a]

(For establishments reporting a business of more than $25,000 in 1929)

	General contractors	Sub-contractors [c]	Total
		Per cent	
Residential	26.2	35.5	27.6
Hotel	3.5	2.1	3.3
Commercial	29.4	18.7	27.8
Manufacturing	12.8	15.6	13.2
Educational	10.3	8.5	10.1
Hospital and institutional	5.0	3.8	4.8
Public [b]	2.7	1.3	2.4
Religious and memorial	3.3	2.0	3.1
Social and recreational	2.8	1.8	2.6
All other	4.1	10.7	5.1
	100 [d]	100	100

(a) USC, " Construction Industry: Summary for the United States," p. 43.
(b) Including Military and Naval.
(c) Sub-contractors working directly for owners.
(d) Census gives 100 but actually adds to 100.1.

average credited to residential construction by most other agencies. For example, the average distribution over a period of eleven years, as computed from the data of the Copper and Brass Research Association, was as follows:

[33] " Census of the Construction Industry," p. 43.

Per cent

Residential (exclusive of hotels)	54.6	
Hotels	2.7	
Total residential		57.3
Commercial	14.8	
Industrial	10.0	
Educational	7.6	
Hospitals and institutions	2.7	
Public	1.7	
Religious	2.4	
Social and recreational	3.5	
Total non-residential		42.7
Grand total		100.0

Residential construction in 1929 was far below peak levels. While figures for the entire country are not available, in 257 identical cities the numbers of families provided for by new dwelling-house construction, as reported by the United States Bureau of Labor Statistics, were as follows in the years 1921–32: [34]

1921	224,545		1927	406,095
1922	377,305		1928	388,678
1923	453,673		1929	244,394
1924	442,919		1930	125,322
1925	491,222		1931	98,178
1926	462,214		1932	27,381

It will be seen, therefore, that in these cities the number of families provided with new dwellings in 1929 was somewhat less than half the number for 1925. In view of this fact, it is believed that the higher ratios for residential construction to total arrived at by using data of the Copper and Brass Research Association and the United States Bureau of Labor Statistics, covering as they do a considerable period of years, are more representative than those of the Census for the single year 1929. Indeed, it is certain that over a period of years residential construction comprises more than half of all building work. Build-

[34] Monthly Labor Review, April, 1933, p. 846.

TABLE 39

Percentage Distribution of Estimated Annual Cost of New Building Construction, for Cities Covered by United States Bureau of Labor Statistics, by Type of Building, 1922–1931 [a]

	Ten-year average [b] *1922–1931*
Residential buildings	
One-family dwellings	25.3
Two-family dwellings	7.0
One-family and two-family dwellings with stores combined	1.1
Multi-family dwellings	18.4
Multi-family dwellings with stores combined	1.8
Hotels	3.6
Lodging-houses	— [c]
All other	1.1
Total	58.3
Non-residential Buildings	
Amusement buildings	2.6
Churches	1.7
Factories and workshops	5.1
Public garages	1.9
Private garages	2.4
Service stations	0.5
Institutions	2.3
Office-buildings	7.7
Public buildings	2.7
Public works and utilities	1.7
Schools and libraries	5.7
Sheds	0.2
Stables and barns	— [c]
Stores and warehouses	6.9
All other	0.3
Total	41.7
Grand total	100.0

(a) Percentages for each year will be found in the Appendix, p. 560.
(b) These are simple averages of the yearly percentages.
(c) Less than 1/10 of 1 per cent.

ing permit records of the City of Philadelphia over a period of thirty-two years indicate that residential construction, excluding hotels, constituted 55 per cent of all buildings for that period. Such other limited data as are available indicate clearly that residential construction represents well over half the total.

If, then, the volume of building in a normal year be taken at $4,500,000,000 and 55 per cent of this be credited to residential construction (exclusive of hotels), the total for this class of work would be approximately $2,500,000,000. Of this amount, it appears that approximately $1,500,000,000 may be credited to new dwellings and the balance to repairs, remodeling, and similar work. This figure is necessarily an approximation.[35]

In Chapter I (Table 11), it was estimated that dwellings represented about 60 per cent of the total value of all buildings in the United States in 1930. Apparently there is no conflict between this percentage and the somewhat lower percentages above shown for new construction in recent years. During the past three decades there has been a relative increase in the erection of elaborate office structures and public buildings, such as banking houses, schools, hospitals, and other institutions, while certain new types of non-residential construction, such as garages and motion-picture houses, have appeared. Although the cost of dwellings erected also has increased, it seems reasonably certain that non-residential construction has increased in relative importance. This would mean, conversely, that dwelling-houses constitute a larger proportion of the value

[35] In this connection, it may be noted that on the basis of 244,394 new dwellings in 257 cities, as shown on p. 207, the total number of new dwellings provided in the entire country in 1929 may be estimated at 350,000. For a normal year, it probably would be safer to estimate the number of new dwellings required at 425,000. As a matter of fact, an estimate of about this number or slightly more has been made by some housing authorities. If the average cost per dwelling, exclusive of land, be taken at $3500, the total expenditure would be $1,500,000,000. On the basis of a total value of $70,000,000,000 as shown in Table 1, an allowance of 2 per cent for maintenance and repairs would call for an annual expenditure of $1,400,000,000 of which perhaps $1,000,000,000 could be charged to repairs and the balance to such work as care of yards, cleaning, etc., which would not strictly be classed as repairs. It is probable that actual expenditure for repairs falls short of the amount indicated.

of all buildings standing than they do of new construction alone in recent years. Such a conclusion appears to be borne out by a study of the tax returns of the few states for which valuations of different classes of buildings are obtainable.

Taking the results of the Census of the Construction Industry in 1929 as a basis, therefore, the normal yearly building bill of this country may be placed at about $4,500,000,000, of which more than half, say $2,500,000,000, is for dwellings, exclusive of hotels. This is considerably more than half the " ordinary " expenses of the Federal Government in recent years, and over three times the amount of such expenses in the years just preceding the World War. It is more than twice the valuation placed on all the buildings of Boston in 1930, including commercial structures, schools, hospitals and churches.[36] It is practically seven times the cost of the Panama Canal, exclusive of military features; yet the Panama Canal is reckoned almost as one of the wonders of the world, whereas this annual task of constructing new dwellings is regarded more or less as a matter of course.

In Great Britain, prior to the World War, dwelling-houses represented a somewhat lower percentage of total building than in the United States. The elaborate program of housing [37] adopted by Great Britain after the close of the War, however, resulted in a marked increase in the ratio, which in several recent years has run well in excess of 60 per cent. This is brought out by Table 40. The percentages for dwelling-houses there shown, it should be noted, are not directly comparable with those already given for the United States since they exclude the outlay for alterations. Similar data for 146 British towns for the years 1925–27 showed the following ratios of costs of dwelling-house construction to total:

[36] The total valuation placed on assessed buildings in Boston in 1930 was $937,862,400, and on exempt buildings of all classes, $206,132,100. (" Annual Report of the Assessing Department," City of Boston, 1930, pp. 6 and 7.)
[37] See Chapter XI.

Year	Per cent
1925 [38]	68.2
1926 [38]	68.4
1927 [38]	62.1
1928 [39]	59.5
1929 [39]	60.5
1930 [39]	62.6

The total value of residential construction in Canada for the period 1921–30, based on contracts awarded, was a little more than $1,000,000,000. This represents 28 per cent of the value of all construction contracts for this period, including engineering works. Excluding engineering works, the ratio of residential to total was 40 per cent.[40]

NUMBER OF WORKERS IN THE BUILDING INDUSTRY

It might seem a very simple matter to ascertain accurately from the Census statistics of occupations the number of workers in the building industry; as a matter of fact, estimates by various statisticians and, indeed, even by the same agency, run all the way from less than a million to several millions. One reason for this is that the classification may cover many individuals who are not engaged directly in building work. For example, of the large number of electrical workers reported by the Census only a portion are engaged in building. Again, the enumeration of carpenters may include ship carpenters or carpenters in woodworking shops, some of whom are not connected with the building industry. As an illustration of the difficulty in using Census data, while the Census reported 869,478 laborers in the building trades in 1910, and 623,203 in 1920, it placed the number in 1930 at 419,802 and in repeating its 1920 classification omitted any figures for this group (see Table 41). Even the basis of this classification has been questioned. Finally, it

[38] Ministry of Labour (Great Britain), "Nineteenth Abstract of Labour Statistics of the United Kingdom" (His Majesty's Stationery Office, London, 1928), p. 215.

[39] "Twentieth Abstract," 1931, p. 200.

[40] MacLean Building Reports, Ltd. In the Monthly Commercial Letter, Canadian Bank of Commerce, July, 1931.

is impossible from available data to show the number of workers engaged in dwelling-house construction separately.

The most reliable calculations indicate that in 1920 approximately two and one-quarter millions of workers were included in the building industry proper. A study for the National Bureau of Economic Research based on Census data placed the

TABLE 40

PERCENTAGE DISTRIBUTION OF ESTIMATED COST OF BUILDINGS FOR WHICH PLANS WERE APPROVED IN 78 TOWNS IN GREAT BRITAIN, 1911–1927 [a]

Year	Dwelling-houses	Factories and workshops	Shops, offices, warehouses, and other business premises	Churches, schools and public buildings	Other buildings and additions and alterations	Total
1911	46	13	10	18	13	100
1912	39	22	9	15	15	100
1913	38	20	10	17	15	100
1914	41	18	11	15	15	100
1915	27	37	10	10	16	100
1916	12	51	9	4	24	100
1917	5	63	6	2	24	100
1918	4	53	8	2	33	100
1919	26	34	11	10	19	100
1920	49	23	7	7	14	100
1921	44	11	9	16	20	100
1922 [b]	—	—	—	—	—	—
1923	59	7	8	8	18	100
1924	64	8	6	7	15	100
1925	66	8	6	6	14	100
1926	69	6	6	8	11	100
1927	61	8	8	9	14	100
1928	59	7	9	10	15	100
1929	59	8	8	11	14	100
1930	59	6	8	13	14	100

(a) Ministry of Labour (Great Britain), "Twentieth Abstract of Labour Statistics of the United Kingdom" (His Majesty's Stationery Office, London, 1931), p. 199.

(b) No information collected for this year.

total in that year at 2,400,000.[41] Another writer, apparently having the assistance of the United States Census and the United States Bureau of Labor Statistics, arrived at a total of 2,162,000.[42] Employers were excluded in both cases.

In 1930 the total was somewhat higher. Using the Census returns of occupational statistics as a basis and estimating the numbers in certain occupations where not all workers reported by the Census could be considered as belonging to the building industry, a total of roughly 2,600,000 in 1930 was reached, as shown in Table 41, which also gives comparative figures for 1920. The percentage distribution for 1930 is also shown in Chart 41.

The ratio of workers in the building trades to total population appears to have been fairly constant over a long period of time, at least with respect to skilled workers. An even greater uniformity is shown in Great Britain.[43]

This comparative steadiness of the ratio of building-trade workers to population in the United States is in contrast with experience in agriculture and in manufacturing industries. In agriculture the ratio has declined sharply since 1870, while in manufacturing it has shown a very pronounced increase. This is brought out by Table 43, which compares the number of skilled workers in the building industry per million of population with the numbers in agriculture and in the manufacturing, mining and railroad industries.

While the total number of workers in the building industry shows a fairly constant ratio to population in recent census returns, the numbers engaged in different occupations show wide changes during the period covered. This is to be expected in view of the changing character of buildings, as, for instance, the very general introduction of plumbing and electrical equip-

---

[41] Wolman, Leo, "The Growth of American Trade Unions, 1880–1923," p. 130.

[42] Haber, William, "Industrial Relations in the Building Industry," p. 8.

[43] Thus for England and Wales the ratio of building-trades workers to population from 1851 to 1921 (census years only) ranged only from 2.36 per cent to 2.93 per cent.

ment. There were more than twelve times as many plumbers and steam- and gasfitters in 1930 as in 1880 — an increase of over 1100 per cent — whereas the number of carpenters increased only about 140 per cent. The differences as between occupa-

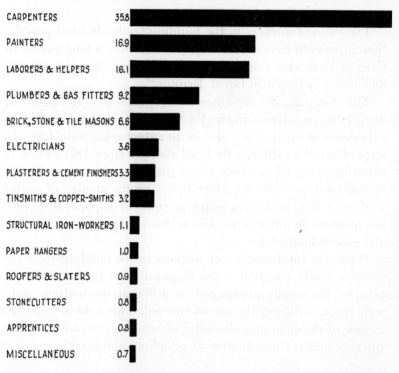

——— CHART 41 ———

PERCENTAGE DISTRIBUTION OF WORKERS IN THE BUILDING TRADES IN THE UNITED STATES: 1930

Charted from data of the United States Bureau of the Census

CARPENTERS	35.8
PAINTERS	16.9
LABORERS & HELPERS	16.1
PLUMBERS & GAS FITTERS	9.2
BRICK, STONE & TILE MASONS	6.6
ELECTRICIANS	3.6
PLASTERERS & CEMENT FINISHERS	3.3
TINSMITHS & COPPER-SMITHS	3.2
STRUCTURAL IRON-WORKERS	1.1
PAPER HANGERS	1.0
ROOFERS & SLATERS	0.9
STONECUTTERS	0.8
APPRENTICES	0.8
MISCELLANEOUS	0.7

tional groups, for skilled workers, are brought out by Table 42.[44] Some of these changes are shown graphically in Chart 42, which compares the number of workers in certain building-trade occupations per million of population.

[44] The classification in 1930 is not the same in all cases as in early years.

TABLE 41

NUMBER OF WORKERS IN THE BUILDING INDUSTRY IN THE UNITED
STATES, 1920 AND 1930 [a]

	1920	1930	
Builders and contractors	90,109	167,512	
Employees			*Per cent*
Brick and stone-masons, and tile-			*1930*
layers	131,264	170,903	6.6
Carpenters	887,379	929,426	35.8
Electricians (1/3 of total)	70,988	93,439	3.6
Painters	248,497	430,105	16.6
Paperhangers	18,746	28,328	1.1
Plasterers and cement finishers ..	45,876	85,480	3.3
Plumbers and gas-fitters	206,718	237,814	9.2
Roofers and slaters	11,378	23,636	0.9
Stone-cutters	22,099	22,888	0.9
Structural iron-workers	18,836	28,966	1.1
Tinsmiths and coppersmiths	74,968	83,427	3.2
Laborers and helpers	——[b]	419,802	16.2
Operators, not otherwise specified	7,003	18,442	0.7
Apprentices [c]	23,449	22,140	0.8
	1,767,201[d]	2,594,796[e]	100.0
Laborers as reported in 1920	623,203		

(a) USC, " Occupation Statistics," 1930 (GPO, Washington, 1932), Table 3.
(b) No comparable figure given by Census in 1930.
(c) Including only 1/3 of electricians' apprentices.
(d) Exclusive of laborers.
(e) This total probably overstates the actual number of workers engaged
in the building industry proper. See p. 211.

William Haber, in his " Industrial Relations in the Building Industry," assumed that 83 per cent of carpenters were engaged in building. If this ratio be
applied to the 1930 figures for carpenters in 1930, the grand total for that year
would be reduced to roughly 2,425,000. Some further reductions probably should
be made in some of the other items, but these would be relatively small and
might be offset by the inclusion of certain workers not given above. Thus
Dr. Haber in getting up figures for 1920 included certain crane men and hoist-
men and mechanics.

In its preliminary report on gainful workers in the United States in 1930
the Census reported the number engaged in the building industry at 2,561,541,
but gave no exact distribution of this total.

TABLE 42

NUMBER OF WORKERS IN CERTAIN SKILLED OCCUPATIONS IN THE BUILDING TRADES
IN THE UNITED STATES, BY DECADES, 1880–1930 [a]

Occupations	Total Number of Workers					
	1880	1890	1900	1910	1920	1930 [h]
Carpenters and joiners	390,595 [b]	618,242 [c]	600,252	830,322	900,335 [d]	929,426
Marble and stone cutters	32,842	61,070	54,460	48,356	30,911 [d]	22,888
Masons (brick and stone)	102,473 [f]	160,845	160,805	204,174	157,599	170,903
Mechanics (not otherwise specified)	7,858	15,485	9,378	26,208	— [e]	18,442
Painters, glaziers, and varnishers	130,319 [f]	222,233	277,541	340,513	324,648	430,105
Paperhangers	5,013 [f]	12,369 [f]	21,990	26,384	19,174 [d]	28,328
Plasterers	22,083 [f]	39,002 [f]	35,694	50,533	40,391	70,053
Plumbers and gas- and steam-fitters	19,383 [f]	61,231	97,785	167,849	227,048 [d]	237,814
Roofers and slaters	4,026 [f]	7,043 [f]	9,067	15,111	12,214 [d]	23,636
Total	714,592	1,197,520	1,266,972	1,709,450	1,702,320	1,931,615

Percentage Distribution [g]

Occupations	1880	1890	1900	1910	1920	1930
Carpenters and joiners	54.7	51.6	47.4	48.6	52.6	48.1
Marble and stone cutters	4.6	5.2	4.3	2.8	1.8	1.2
Masons (brick and stone)	14.3	13.4	12.7	11.9	9.2	8.8
Mechanics (not otherwise specified)	1.1	1.3	.8	1.5	—	1.0
Painters, glaziers, and varnishers	18.2	18.5	21.9	20.0	19.0	22.3
Paperhangers	.7	1.0	1.7	1.5	1.1	3.6
Plasterers	3.1	3.3	2.8	3.0	2.3	1.5
Plumbers and gas- and steam-fitters	2.7	5.1	7.7	9.8	13.3	12.3
Roofers and slaters	0.6	0.6	0.7	0.9	0.7	1.2
Total	100	100	100	100	100	100

NOTE. Since this table excludes unskilled workers and some other groups,
these percentages do not indicate the ratios which these various groups bear
to the *total* number of workers in the industry.

(*a*) Figures from 1880–1920 furnished directly by the Census.

TABLE 43

WAGE-EARNERS IN VARIOUS INDUSTRIES IN THE UNITED STATES PER
MILLION OF POPULATION, 1850–1930 [a]

Year	All gainful occupations	Manufacturing and mechanical industries	Agri-culture	Mine operatives Coal	Mine operatives All others	Steam rail-roads	Building trades (skilled workers)
1850	231,546	41,252	101,895	3,336		——	13,204
1860	263,918	41,759	102,534	4,705		——	12,987
1870	323,988	65,733	153,432	4,292		——	16,053
1880	347,841	71,754	153,409	4,987		——	14,246
1890	372,494	90,710	146,141	3,331	2,854	11,969	19,131
1900	382,542	93,237	136,602	4,530	2,983	13,390	16,673
1910	414,862	115,530	136,608	6,673	3,380	18,472	18,582
1920	393,701	121,272	103,625	6,943	2,227	19,639	16,195
1930	397,679	116,592	85,361	5,631	2,179	12,353	15,068 [b]

(a) Based on Census data.
(b) Census figures for 1930 are not on a strictly comparable basis.

DEPENDENCE OF OTHER INDUSTRIES UPON BUILDING

Some of the industries affiliated with building are themselves
ranked among the major industries of the country. The lumber industry was credited with an output in 1925 of nearly
$1,500,000,000 for basic products, this figure excluding the
furniture, box and container, and certain other lines of manufacture.[45] The output of cement in an active year is in excess
of $250,000,000; a considerable part of this, however, is for

---

(b) Include ship calkers, riggers, and smiths, combined in 1880 with ship
carpenters, but does not include apprentices.

(c) Does not include ship carpenters, classified in 1890 with ship and boat
builders.

(d) Figures for 1920 approximate only.

(e) Comparable figures for 1920 not available.

(f) Does not include apprentices.

(g) Computed from census data given above.

(h) The classifications in 1930 were not always identical with those of earlier
years. It may be noted that the figures for 1920 given here, which were furnished by the Census, do not agree with others which were taken directly
from a census bulletin. These discrepancies illustrate the lack of precise
information.

45 "Commerce Year Book, 1931," Vol. I, p. 345. (The output of the lumber
industry in all branches was over $3,500,000,000 yearly, on the average, in 1923,
1925, and 1927.)

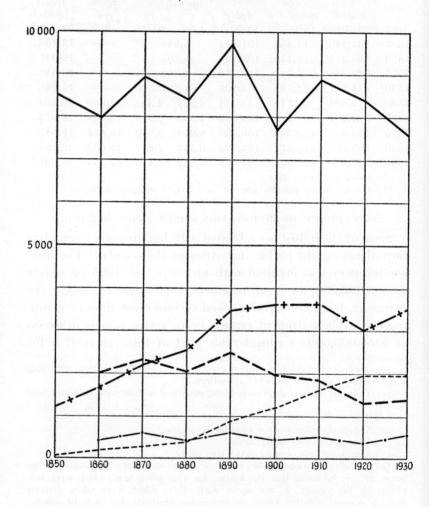

— CHART 42 —

NUMBER OF SKILLED WORKERS IN VARIOUS BUILDING TRADES, PER MILLION OF POPULATION, IN THE UNITED STATES:1850-1930

Data from 1850 to 1920 inclusive are from United States
Bureau of Labor Statistics;Handbook of 1924-26. Data
for 1930 were computed from Census returns

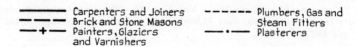

——————— Carpenters and Joiners   – – – – – Plumbers, Gas and
– – – – Brick and Stone Masons   Steam Fitters
–+– Painters, Glaziers   –·– Plasterers
and Varnishers

highway and uses other than building.[46] About one-seventh of the country's output of steel is used in building construction.[47] The value of brick and similar building materials exceeded $300,000,000 annually in several years prior to 1930,[48] and the value of building stone was well in excess of $150,000,000 yearly.[49]

While the values of such basic products which were used in building alone cannot be precisely stated, it is safe to say that they exceeded $2,000,000,000 in some years when construction was active. To this must be added the outlay for such items as glass and hardware, and a long list of other products which, though individually representing a much smaller expenditure, make up an important total.

It is probably correct to charge more than one-half this expenditure to dwelling-house construction. If to these products directly related to actual construction there be added those contributing to the furnishing of the home, such as carpets, furniture, kitchenware, and a hundred or more incidentals, representing an aggregate outlay of $2,000,000,000 to $3,000,-000,000 yearly under normal conditions, some idea of the wide extent of the building industry can be obtained.

The bare figures given in this chapter afford only an inadequate idea of the importance of the building industry. Through its far-flung ramifications it evidently exerts a vital influence on general business and on business cycles; it has been called the " balance-wheel " of industry, although in view of the fact that cyclical changes in building are more pronounced than general business cycles this statement is open to challenge.[50]

But at least building is capable of exerting a far-reaching effect upon trends in general industry. The boom which followed the depression of 1921 was inaugurated by a phenomenal

[46] " Commerce Year Book, 1931," Vol. I, p. 359.
[47] *Ibid.*, p. 379.
[48] *Ibid.*, p. 363.　　　　　　　　[49] *Ibid.*, p. 367.
[50] For a very brief but suggestive review of building cycles in the United States, see an article by John R. Riggleman of the Division of Building and Housing, USDC, in the Journal of the American Statistical Association, June, 1933, pp. 174–183.

increase in building to make up the great shortage which resulted from the World War. In 1928–29 a sharp curtailment in building clearly foreshadowed a decline in general business activity. It would be unsafe to regard building as the major controlling factor in general cyclical changes in business, but that there is a definite connection between the two cannot be doubted. As one writer has said:

"No analysis of business conditions in this country can at any time be complete or authoritative that fails to take building conditions into account. It is not at all likely that this country can enjoy a real prosperity at any time when its construction industry is employed at anything much less than full capacity. It is always one of the most important contributors to general prosperity as well as one of the largest recipients of the accumulated surpluses that result from prosperity." [51]

In the opinion of some students of building problems it should be possible so to arrange major building operations as to mitigate the severity of alternate peaks and depressions to which industry has been subject in the past. This is a matter outside of the scope of this work, but the fact that conditions in a great key industry like building are of vital importance to all industry should require no proof.

Indeed, the entire nation has an important stake in the prosperity of the construction industry. According to some students, nearly 10,000,000 persons in the United States are dependent on the building industry for a living. Including such affiliated industries as lumber, cement, brick, and glass manufacturing, the number is much greater. Dr. Julius Klein, at that time Assistant Secretary of Commerce, in a radio address in April, 1930, said:

"At least one-quarter of the entire population of the United States receives directly or indirectly a substantial part of all of its income from construction. In other words, the livelihood of at

[51] Holden, Thomas S., "Building Contracts and Business Movements." Address at 1926 meeting of the American Statistical Association. Quoted by Haber in "Industrial Relations in the Building Industry," p. 10.

least one out of every four of you — including men, women
and children — depends upon construction to maintain American
standards of living."

So high a proportion, it should be emphasized, is for the construction industry as a whole, and includes many industries but
loosely affiliated with the building industry proper. Nevertheless, the statement clearly emphasizes the vital interest of the
nation in the prosperity of the building industry.

SUMMARY

The building industry, as we have shown, is the second or
third largest in the nation; it employs two and one-half million
men; its output in recent years has averaged $5,000,000,000.
Nevertheless it is a loose organization of small units in which
the individual entrepreneur has little capital and employs few
men; the work is done in a hit-or-miss fashion; employers' organizations are weak; while those of employees are strong and
active.

These conditions are most marked in the housing industry,
which comprises more than one-half of all building construction, so that the housing industry is of the same stature as the
steel, oil, clothing, and meat industries. Its annual production
in the last decade, worth three billion dollars, has equaled the
average normal post-War yearly expenditures of the Federal
Government. Yet, compared with other industries of similar
size, like steel or cotton manufacturing, the housing industry
is lacking in efficiency. It is a heterogeneous mass of small industries, and these are subdivided into other very small units.
The nucleus of the mass is the building contractor, sometimes
technically aided in defining his product by an architect or
engineer. Around him are grouped numberless units of all sizes
and kinds whose function it is to supply him with the wide
variety of materials he may want and the labor for fashioning
and combining them into a house. The average contractor is engaged in relatively very small operations and very small quan-

tity purchases. He has limited credit and limited capital. Normally he cannot save in his actual construction operations by discounting his bills for materials nor in financing through ample funds. Less than 25 per cent of the building contractors in the United States handle business of $25,000 a year or more; 75 per cent handle less. The subcontractor, who is an essential part of the industry as now organized, averages still lower.

Employers' organizations exist, but they are necessarily loose and non-profit-making, and are but little concerned with management problems; being generally occupied with broad principles and policies. Often when they have endeavored to cooperate along specific lines they have been unable to do so effectively.

The workers in the building trades, on the other hand, are highly organized into unions, which have repeatedly obtained increased wage scales out of harmony with those of other industries. The building-trades unions are among the most independent of all. They have frequently resigned from and rejoined the American Federation of Labor, which does not seem to exercise appreciable control over them. The degree of organization varies with the locality and with the exact trade involved, but only transport and clothing workers and miners are more highly organized. In general the unions may be credited with one-quarter of those engaged in the industry.

The organization of the building trades in this and other countries presents a curious mixture of socially constructive purposes and economically destructive acts. Though the reason for this disharmony probably is less the fault of labor unionism than of our present social structure, nevertheless some dire influence certainly distorts the generally meritorious purposes on which labor unionism is founded. While society suffers from this slip 'twixt the cup and the lip, labor itself suffers most.

Various writers critical of conditions in the building industry have often blamed its non-integrated condition upon the trades unions. Such a charge cannot be substantiated. As a matter of fact, the trades unions may more properly be praised for such integration as exists than blamed because there is so little.

Present-day building construction involves a wide variety of work whose very special character is but poorly defined by any generally recognized and expressible standards; and the work must be done mostly in the field by hand implements and under insufficient supervision. In some large cities about fifty crafts are used in building construction. High efficiency may be developed in such an organization as that required for a large office-building or factory; but in small dwelling-house construction, with perhaps fifteen specialized trades working on a job under nearly as many subcontracts, no such efficiency seems possible. It is a converting and fabricating process. Each building is a special order differing from every other, and involving a large and entirely different bill of materials; a normal project may involve a thousand or more such separate retail items. For each job a special system of field management and labor organization is set up. The only constant factor is the technique of the general contractor in charge of the job. No wonder the home construction process usually resembles the last days of the Tower of Babel.

Far from being an exaggeration, this is a conservative statement of conditions in the housing industry. Anyone who has experienced the process recalls it as a morass in which he floundered, uncertain where he stood at every point, overclouded by legalities and financial, physical, and industrial complications. The house which probably represents to the average home-buyer the largest single purchase of his life, requiring one-sixth to one-fifth of his income to maintain, should be a tangible, clearly defined project; the ways and means of purchase should be equally defined and easy. But emphatically they are not. The prospective owner is at the mercy of forces and conditions beyond his control and beyond his ken. His effort to acquire a home calls for the coordinated work of a large number of men, each of them not permanently related to his colleagues but working for his own interest. This is not to say that the steamfitter, for instance, preys upon the innocent owner, but he does deal as an expert with a novice. Perhaps the owner trusts all to his architect, but the architect is undertaking a really impossible job — to coordinate, regulate, and control contractors and subcontractors, materials, methods, specifications, and costs. Genuine efforts to guide the owner are being made by the building and loan associations, by architects' associations, and by sundry publications. But the situation of the man who would build a house remains a pitiable one.

It does not appear that particular blame attaches to any individual or any particular group in the industry for this chaotic condition. Features of the present industry are good or bad simply as they compare with features of other industries. Individuals in the building industry are similar in psychology and in ability to those in other industries. The conditions which we criticize are evolutionary in their character; in so far as they are relatively bad, they indicate that the building industry has not followed so far along the path of evolution as have other industries.

From the evidence offered in this chapter, two facts emerge as clear as crystal. This enormous industry is a loose, heterogeneous aggregation of numerous interrelated sub-industries and crafts. It is out of date in point of organization and technique.

CHAPTER VI

Relative Efficiency of the Building Industry

ALL of the disabilities enumerated earlier result in waste, the one universal and ever-present characteristic of the building industry. Wasteful methods of lumber manufacture, wasteful labor regulations, wasteful legislative restrictions, and wasteful demands of the owner reduce the efficiency of construction and result in a cost that makes home-ownership unnecessarily expensive for all and impossible for many. Mention has already been made of the loss involved in the duplication of builders' estimates, and in the heavy cost of accident insurance; yet these wastes, which can be definitely estimated, are small as compared with those due to such intangible factors as failure to adopt modern methods and large-scale production, inefficient planning, and interruptions to work. A Committee of the Federated American Engineering Societies estimated that 53 per cent of building operations represented waste.[1] If the annual building bill of the country be taken at $4,500,000,000, this would mean a total of $2,250,000,000. This may be an exaggeration, but the evidence presented thus far shows that waste reaches a staggering total.

Needless waste means reduced efficiency. In most major industries such losses have been eliminated or reduced and the by-products utilized to an extent that has made their efficiency a byword.

As a result of such reduction of waste and of changes in methods, including the development of power machinery,

[1] Federated American Engineering Societies, "Waste in Industry," p. 9.

standardization, and routing systems, there has been a pronounced increase in productivity per worker in many major industries.

The public is familiar with the assembly platform of the Ford Motor Company, where each worker stands at a certain point and performs only a single operation as the material passes him, until at the end of the line the finished automobile is ready for use. This method is no longer unique, but is typical of the process utilized in every automobile plant producing cars in large numbers. Some such change in production methods has occurred in the case of almost every article entering into the family budget, from food to cosmetics, with the important exception of shelter.

Productive efficiency is usually expressed in terms of labor output but increases in output per worker are often due largely to changes in equipment, methods, and organization for which the worker himself has little responsibility. The change in individual output is thus a measure of the efficiency of an industry or plant as a whole and not of any single factor. Nor is such gain in output a complete measure of changes in efficiency; in many cases it has been accomplished only by a decided increase in plant investment, so that production must be maintained on a strictly large-scale basis if the advantage of increased per-capita output is not to be offset by an increase in overhead expense.

A broad comparison of hand methods of a century ago with modern machine methods shows a phenomenal increase in output per worker — often 20, 30, or 50 times as much; in some instances more than 100 times. In the case of staple agricultural crops, data compiled by the United States Bureau of Labor Statistics indicate that in seventy-five or eighty years production per worker has increased under modern methods by amounts ranging from 100 per cent to more than 10,000 per cent. Thus, as against 62.4 man-hours per acre required for the production of wheat in 1850, only 1.6 man-hours were needed in 1924; this is equivalent to a gain of 3800 per cent in output per worker. The corresponding gain for production of corn was over 500 per cent, for cotton 273 per cent, and for potatoes 118 per cent. For harvesting of hay the increase was recorded as 1217 per cent. The average increase in productivity for the four crops was 1185 per cent.[2]

This, of course, applied only where modern methods were used. No such increase occurred for the entire production of the country.

For the specific operations of harvesting and threshing of wheat, still greater percentage increases were shown by this study, amounting in the case of California to 12,000 per cent, or 120 times, where the work was done by the modern " combine " as compared with the old-fashioned sickle or scythe and mattock and flail.

A pamphlet issued by the International Harvester Company [3] gives the following comparative costs of preparing an acre of ground by different methods; some of the figures are evidently approximate.

With primitive tools	$160.00
With a spade	40.00
With a plow and one horse or mule	6.50
With a plow and four horses	3.60
With a 15 horse-power machine	1.23

This shows a reduction of 99 per cent in cost. Of the estimated cost of $1.23 by machine, 33 cents was allocated to man labor and 90 cents to interest, depreciation, repairs, and other operating costs. In the shelling of corn a modern power sheller operated by one man can shell 720 bushels in a twelve-hour day. This is approximately ninety times the output per man under the old hand methods of long ago.[4]

Even greater increases are shown in some other industries. The time required for carding cotton under the old-fashioned methods of 150 years ago, a government report states,[5] was more than 4000 times that required under the machine methods

---

[2] Monthly Labor Review, October, 1931, pp. 1–36.

[3] International Harvester Company, " Muscles or Motors," p. 9.

[4] Monthly Labor Review, October, 1931, p. 19.

[5] United States Commissioner of Labor, " Thirteenth Annual Report, 1898 " (GPO, Washington, 1899), pp. 40–41, 217.

of the late Nineties; and where under the old hand methods 3117 hours of labor were required to produce 100 pounds of No. 12 cotton yarn, only nineteen hours were required under the machine methods of 1896, and since then there has been a further reduction.

A writer who has made a special study of industrial evolution in the United States estimates that under the hand spinning methods of 1800 a single worker could produce 4 skeins of yarn per day. In 1815 a mill spinner could tend 90 spindles with a total daily output of 180 skeins. " Ten years later each operative served more spindles and each spindle produced 5 skeins of yarn. Within another decade spinners operated nearly 200 spindles and each of these produced a still larger product." [6] Today, a single spinner often tends from 1500 to 2000 spindles. Exact comparisons with hand methods are difficult, but the gain in output has been sensational. The per-man-per-hour output of a modern factory spindle is estimated at 108 times that of the *charkha* of India (the hand-operated spinning wheel of that country) when the latter is operated with greatest skill, and 206 times when it is operated with ordinary skill. [7]

Again, take the case of the common nail. In early Colonial days the manufacture of nails was largely a home industry; [8] they were so expensive that settlers in moving from one community to another sometimes burned their cabins to save the nails, [9] while wooden pegs were very extensively used. Today

[6] Clark, V. S., " History of Manufactures in the United States, 1607–1860," Vol. I, p. 432.

[7] Gregg, Richard B., " Economics of Khaddar " (S. Ganesan, Triplicane, Madras, India, 1928), p. 37.

[8] In Birmingham, England, alone, 60,000 persons were at one time engaged in making nails by hand. (Chamberlain, J. F., " How We Are Sheltered " [The Macmillan Company, New York, 1911], p. 143.)

[9] " Small landowners, in deserting their homes with a view to making a settlement elsewhere on more fertile soil, were in the habit of burning their cabins when abandoned, in order to secure the nails by which the planks were held together, and so general did this habit become that in 1644–45 it was provided by law, as a means of destroying the motive for setting the houses on fire, that each planter, when he gave up his dwelling, should be allowed, at public expense, as many nails as two impartial men should calculate to be in the frame of the deserted residence." (Bruce, Philip A., " Economic History of Virginia

a hot iron rod is passed through a series of machines at high speed, and the finished product is turned out so economically that its factory value per pound is only a little more than that of the steel from which it is made. It is not worth a carpenter's time now to pick up nails dropped in the course of work.

When friction matches were first invented they were dipped by hand. No statistics are available as to the output under the hand method, but the efficiency of modern match-making machinery is so much greater that statistical comparisons would be almost incredible. The same would be true of many types of glass manufacture.

In making these comparisons it is necessary to bear in mind that the character of the product often has undergone considerable change, so that all ratios are approximate. For example, a modern shoe with its eyelets, linings, trimmings, etc., is a very different article from the shoe of 150 years ago. In most cases comparisons for identical products, if data were available, would show even greater ratios of increase than those already given.[10]

Even if comparisons be made with the machine methods of fifty, seventy-five, or a hundred years ago, they often show pronounced increases in per-capita output. In many branches of cotton manufacture, for example, the output per worker

---

in the Seventeenth Century." Quoted from Monthly Labor Review, January, 1930, p. 14.)

[10] In this connection the following extract from the report of the Commissioner of Labor, already referred to, is pertinent: " At first thought one would naturally suppose, in comparing the old hand-work system with that of the modern factory, after the method that had been set forth in the preceding pages, that articles of the two periods exactly alike would be selected for the purpose. This would have been done had it been possible to find them. The truth is that scarcely an article now in use is the exact counterpart of the one serving the same purpose forty or fifty years ago. The one in use today will usually be found superior to the one used in days gone by. . . . The fact that the plow made today is stronger, more durable, and better in all ways simply emphasizes the advance that has been made in the manufacture of one of the farmer's most important implements. Were it possible to express this added value in figures, the superiority of the modern over that of the past would be strikingly shown and the advantage for the plow of today exhibited in the figures of time and cost in the detailed table would be greatly magnified." (Commissioner of Labor, " Thirteenth Annual Report," pp. 15–16.)

today is several times that of a century ago. When textiles first became a factory industry, it was common practice for an operative to tend only one or two looms, and this average still holds in certain foreign countries. In the United States the number of looms per operative has steadily increased until at the present time a single weaver working on print cloth and sheetings sometimes tends from 72 to 84 looms. For certain special products, in exceptional instances, a single operative tends more than 100 looms. Such looms, although automatic in their operation and upkeep, require some supplementary labor by other operatives not required in the case of the common looms of earlier days. Nevertheless, the increased per-capita production of a modern American weaving plant compared to that of a mill with American equipment of one hundred years ago, running on similar goods and in each case counting all the employees engaged in the weaving department, may be estimated at fivefold to sevenfold.

Because most cotton mills change frequently from one product to another, and make radical changes in the character of their products, it is exceedingly difficult to secure comparable data over long periods of time. The author was fortunate enough to obtain from the Nashua Manufacturing Company a comparison covering nearly a hundred years; the figures, given in Table 44, show an increase of over 650 per cent per operative on the basis of pounds woven, and of 600 per cent on the basis of yardage. Despite the marked improvements in cotton manufacturing machinery, only a small part of this increase is attributable to a larger output per machine, the gain being chiefly due to the increased number of spindles or looms tended by a single operative. This in turn is due to the automatic character of machinery, which has steadily reduced the amount of manual labor required.[11] Table 45 gives com-

---

[11] The Thirteenth Report of the United States Commissioner of Labor, already referred to, showed that whereas in 1835 it required 5130 man hours to produce 500 yards of gingham stripes, in 1895 the time had been reduced to 119 hours. In 1870 it required 1440 hours to produce 12 dozen pairs of cotton-age trousers; in 1895 less than 150 hours. These figures were averages for several

parisons for certain specific cotton manufacturing operations for 1892–1932.

The gain in productivity in cotton manufacturing shown by these figures is supported by evidence compiled by a British cotton-trade authority for the principal spinning and manufacturing centers of the Lancashire (England) cotton district. According to this study, the average output in spinning rose

TABLE 44

PER-HOUR PRODUCTION PER SPINDLE, PER LOOM, AND PER OPERATIVE
IN A LARGE COTTON MILL MAKING SHEETINGS, 1838, 1876 AND 1932 [a]

Pounds woven	*1838*	*1876*	*1932* [b]	*Per cent increase 1838–1932*
Per spindle	0.042	0.041	0.067	59.5
Per loom	1.264	1.242	2.000	58.2
Per operative	0.983	2.244	7.375 [c]	650.2
Yards woven				
Per spindle	0.124	0.120	0.183	47.6
Per loom	3.729	3.642	5.490	47.2
Per operative	2.898	6.580	20.266 [c]	599.3

(a) Data furnished by W. H. Cadwell, Agent of the Jackson Mills, Nashua Manufacturing Company.

(b) For seven full weeks ending February 20.

(c) In some types of modern spinning the per-man output is as much as 15 to 26 pounds, while weaving varies from 17 to 24 pounds.

from 968 pounds of yarn per worker in 1819–21 to 5520 pounds in 1880–82, an increase of 470 per cent, while the average output of woven cotton goods increased during the same period from 342 pounds per worker to 4039 pounds, a gain of nearly 1100 per cent. The average output per spindle in these British mills rose only from 15.2 pounds to 31.5 pounds, or a little over 100 per cent; the average output per loom

plants. Figures for selected individual plants and for specific operations showed that the time spent in producing a given unit or product under the old-fashioned machine methods of the earlier periods frequently was thirty, forty, fifty, or more times that required under the machine methods of 1895–98, (pp. 38–41).

TABLE 45

PER-HOUR PRODUCTION PER OPERATIVE IN CERTAIN OCCUPATIONS IN A
LARGE COTTON MILL MAKING SHEETINGS, 1892 AND 1932 [a]

	Pounds		Per cent	Yards		Per cent
	1892	1932	increase	1892	1932	increase
Roving spinners .	50.43	105.2	108.6	145.6	289.0	98.4
Other card-room hands	25.90	48.9	88.8	74.8	134.5	79.8
All	17.11	33.4	95.2	49.4	91.8	85.8
Yarn spinners ...	39.83	131.9	231.1	115.0	361.9	214.6
Other spinning-room hands .	30.46	45.2	48.3	87.8	124.1	41.5
All	17.26	33.6	94.6	49.9	92.4	85.1
All dressing hands	32.90	78.7	139.2	95.0	216.3	127.6
Weavers	8.04	91.6	1,039.3	23.2	251.9	985.7
Other weave-room hands	74.80	37.6	dec.	216.0	103.3	dec.
All	7.26	26.7	267.7	21.0	73.3	249.0
Total of above ...	3.51	9.1	159.2	10.2	25.0	145.0
All cloth-room hands	78.90	98.8	25.2	227.9	271.0	18.9
Shops, yard	44.30	64.1	44.7	128.0	176.1	37.5
Entire mill	3.13	7.4	136.4	9.0	20.2	124.4

(a) Data furnished by W. H. Cadwell, Agent of the Jackson Mills, Nashua Manufacturing Company. (Overseers and office force not included.)

increased from 335 pounds to 1806 pounds, or about 440 per cent.[12]

A much greater increase in production per worker is shown in the iron and steel industry over a seventy-five-year period. A comparison prepared by the United States Bureau of Labor Statistics indicates that between 1850 and 1925 the output per man per year in blast-furnace production increased from 25 long tons to 1257 long tons, or almost fifty times.[13]

[12] Ellison, Thomas, "The Cotton Trade of Great Britain." Quoted by Jacob Schoenhof in "A History of Money and Prices" (G. P. Putnam Sons, New York, 1896), pp. 224–225.

[13] Monthly Labor Review, June, 1928, p. 29. In some recent discussions it has been claimed that output in recent years is 650 times that of fifty years ago. The actual ratio for this period appears to be a little over twenty times.

This great increase has been largely due to the development of machinery and plants with capacities undreamed of a hundred years ago. To take only one illustration: the total annual output of the 804 blast furnaces in the United States in 1840 is estimated at about 283,000 tons.[14] Today a single modern blast furnace has a capacity of almost exactly this total.[15]

The boot and shoe industry affords a striking example of the change which has occurred in production methods and productive efficiency. Shoemaking, which was essentially a hand-work operation in the early part of the nineteenth century, is now almost exclusively a factory industry, and its machinery, division of labor, and especially routing of work have been developed to an exceptional degree, almost comparable with the operation of a modern railway system. The result of these changes has been a marked increase in output per worker. According to the United States Bureau of Labor Statistics, whereas in 1863 it required 1832 hours of labor time to produce 100 pairs of shoes, in 1923 it required only 107 hours. This shows a relative increase in productivity per hour from 7.8 to 133.5, or of about sixteen times, during the sixty-year period.[16] Doubtless the per-man output in 1863 was much higher than it was under the hand methods of a century earlier.[17]

In railroad transportation, the tractive power of locomotives has almost doubled during the present century, and the average capacity of freight cars has increased by 50 per cent. These

14 Clark, Victor S., "History of Manufactures in the United States, 1607–1860," Vol. I, p. 500.

15 The total annual capacity of the 18 completed blast furnaces in Indiana on December 31, 1931, was 5,054,700 tons or an average of over 280,000 tons. The aggregate annual capacity of 25 furnaces in Illinois on the same date was 5,537,200 or an average of about 220,000 tons per furnace. (American Iron & Steel Institute, "Annual Statistical Report, 1931" [New York, 1932], p. 20.)

16 Monthly Labor Review, January, 1927, p. 42.

17 It took a shoemaker in ancient Rome five and a half days to make a pair of shoes. Today the per-capita output in a modern shoe plant would be about seventy times as great. (Raymond, Allen, "What is Technocracy?" [McGraw-Hill Book Company, New York and London, 1933] p. 39.)

changes were accompanied by a decided increase in the average train-load, which rose from 184 tons in 1891–95 to 706 tons in 1928.[18] In the mining of bituminous coal, where machine processes have been developed on an extensive scale, the output per man per day increased during the period 1890 to 1930 by nearly 100 per cent.[19]

COMPARISONS COVERING RECENT PERIODS

Even during the past twenty-five or thirty years the development of machinery and of manufacturing methods has progressed so rapidly that there has been a further pronounced gain in per-capita output in most major industries. For the four major divisions of industry, *viz.* agriculture, mining, manufacturing, and transportation, the average increase in per-capita output during the first quarter of the present century is estimated at 60 to 75 per cent; in mining alone the per-capita output has more than doubled. Comparisons by the United States Department of Commerce and the National

TABLE 46

PERCENTAGE INCREASES IN PER-MAN OUTPUT IN FOUR MAJOR DIVISIONS OF INDUSTRY IN THE FIRST QUARTER OF THE PRESENT CENTURY

Industry	Per Cent Increase USDC [a]	NBER [b]
Agriculture	61	53
Mining	118	99
Manufacturing	$48\frac{1}{2}$	$42\frac{1}{2}$
Transportation	$63\frac{1}{2}$	56
Average	$58\frac{1}{2}$ [c]	76

(a) "Commerce Year Book, 1930," Vol. I, p. 28. The base year is 1899 and the period covered 1899–1927.

(b) National Bureau of Economic Research, Inc., "Recent Economic Changes," Vol. II, p. 452. The base period is 1898–1900 and the period is from then to 1924–26.

(c) Weighted by the number of workers in 1899; if weighted by the value of products in that year, the average increase would be 87 per cent.

[18] Statistical Abstract of the United States, 1932, pp. 369 and 376.

[19] Monthly Labor Review, December, 1930, p. 42, and February, 1933, p. 261.

Bureau of Economic Research are given in Table 46. For the group of manufacturing industries collectively the yearly changes in per-man output from 1899 to 1927 are shown in Table 47. It will be seen that the greater part of the gain in this period was made after the close of the World War.

TABLE 47

INDEX NUMBERS OF PER-MAN OUTPUT IN MANUFACTURING
INDUSTRIES, 1899–1927

(1899 = 100)

	NBER [a] index		NBER [a] index
1899	100	1914	108.5
1900	96.2	1915	117.5
1901	101.8	1916	119.2
1902	103.4	1917	109.8
1903	100.7	1918	104.7
1904	104.0	1919	104.5
1905	113.3	1920	107.9
1906	114.0	1921	107.3
1907	108.5	1922	128.5
1908	101.5	1923	132.5
1909	109.6	1924	133.0
1910	108.7	1925	145.4
1911	103.4	1926	148.7
1912	114.6	1927	149.5
1913	116.3		

(a) National Bureau of Economic Research, Inc., "Recent Economic Changes," Vol. II, p. 454.

In individual industries the percentage increase has been very much greater. The United States Bureau of Labor Statistics has from time to time compiled index numbers for eleven selected industries. For the period 1914–27, as shown in Table 48, these studies show an increase ranging from 24 per cent in the case of boot and shoe manufacture to 178 per cent for automobiles and 292 per cent for rubber tires.

The automobile industry is a classic example of increased per-capita production. From 1.56 vehicles per wage-earner

TABLE 48

PERCENTAGE INCREASES IN OUTPUT PER MAN PER HOUR IN ELEVEN SELECTED INDUSTRIES, 1914–1927 [a]

Industry	Per cent increase
Rubber tires	292
Automobiles	178
Petroleum refining	82
Flour milling	59
All industry	55
Cement manufacturing	54
Leather tanning	41
Paper and pulp	40
Cane sugar refining	33
Slaughtering and meat packing	26
Boot and shoe manufacturing	24

(a) Monthly Labor Review, March, 1930, p. 2.

NOTE. These percentages do not measure the relative efficiency of production in different industries. Thus in the boot and shoe industry, which stands at the bottom of this list, mass-production methods had been carried to an advanced stage prior to 1914.

per year in 1899 the output rose to 9.76 in 1925, or more than 500 per cent, largely because in 1899 the industry was in its infancy. After the industry became stabilized the rate of increase was much slower. Thus in 1919 the output was 5.52 vehicles per wage-earner, in 1921 it was 7.53, and in 1923 9.64; in the following two years it rose only to 9.76, and in the next two years the index of per-man-hour productivity declined (see Table 49).

Turning from manufacturing industries to a radically different field — road construction — it is reported that " a typical gang for constructing a concrete road, consisting, under methods in use before 1919, of about 74 men, would construct up to 350 feet of pavement per day; in 1928 a gang of 45 men would often construct 800 feet of pavement per day. Accepting these estimates, which have been judged reasonable by several competent engineers, the daily output per man increased from 4.7 to 17.7 lineal feet of road surfacing. Accompanying the changes in methods, contractors have had to increase the amount of equipment required for road building, and its value now commonly amounts to from 35 to 50 per cent of the value of the season's contract." [20]

In the case of ditch-digging, some modern machines do the work of fifty men.

TABLE 49

INDEX OF PRODUCTIVITY OF FOURTEEN TYPES OF MACHINE TOOLS EXTENSIVELY USED IN MODERN PLANTS [a]

(1902 = 100)

Year	Index of productivity	Year	Index of productivity
1904	110	1918	220
1906	130	1920	230
1908	150	1922	260
1910	155	1924	360
1912	170	1926	460
1914	200	1928	570
1916	210	1930	700

(a) Ernst and Ernst, "Weekly Bulletin," June 2, 1931.

The instances here given afford an idea of the changes which have occurred in productivity in some of the country's major industries. They may not be altogether typical but at least they show beyond a doubt that in many major lines of industry there have been revolutionary changes in methods of manufacturing, largely due to the introduction and perfection of power machinery, which have resulted in tremendous increases in the output per worker. Whether the increase has been 100 per cent, 500 per cent, or 1000 per cent is not vital for the present purpose.[21] The point is that they have been of the order of hundreds of per cent.

[20] National Bureau of Economic Research, Inc., "Recent Economic Changes," Vol. I, p. 248.

[21] In recent discussions on technocracy claims have been made that output under present machine methods is in some cases many thousand times that under hand methods of earlier periods or even under that of machine methods of comparatively recent times. Many of these claims have been shown to be ridiculous exaggerations. For example, in one case an increased output of about 9000 times was claimed for the manufacture of electric light bulbs by a certain new machine. The editor of the Iron Age placed the ratio at not over sixteen times and held that if all collateral conditions were taken into account it might be only four times. (Raymond, Allen, "What is Technocracy?" pp. 155–156.)

PRODUCTIVITY OF DWELLING-HOUSE CONSTRUCTION

Experience in building construction, at least in the dwelling-house branch, is in sharp contrast with the conditions just described. Precise comparisons are not available, but the evidence is clear that there has been no increase in the efficiency of dwelling-house construction at all comparable with the gains in the production of wheat, pig iron, cotton goods, and shoes. The output per worker in some building trades is said to be less than it was fifty or a hundred years ago.[22] There have been no such revolutionary changes from hand to machine methods as have occurred in many manufacturing industries. " Bricks are still laid in the same way as they were in the time of Moses." [23]

In the plastering trade the workmen's tools are almost identical with those of a century ago. It is true that in the manufacture of many building materials, bricks, cement, hardware, and numerous other items, large-scale production has been done with a marked increase in productivity per worker. Again, in the case of certain items such as blinds, window sash, doors, and window and door frames, where the manufacture has been transferred from the hand shop to the factory, an important gain in per-capita output has been achieved. But when it comes to the manufacture of these elements into a house, a very different situation is presented. Instead of a smoothly functioning arrangement of different processes, such as that already noted in automobile and shoe manufacture, we find the time-honored disorganization, frequent delays, waste of material, tearing down of work to correct mistakes or to make room for some accessory, and a score of other wasteful practices. There has been during the last twenty-five years some gain in productivity per worker in building construction,

[22] See p. 541.

[23] A permissible exaggeration. Egyptian sun-dried bricks were, it is true, laid in the familiar " English bond " but the bedding was of Nile mud with alfa grass, often plaited, as reinforcement. True mortars are not to be found until the period when bricks were burned, but the Sassanians, the Saracens, and the builders of the late Middle Ages all produced brickwork containing all the features of present-day masonry and actually superior to it.

but this is insignificant compared with the increases in manufacturing industries where mass-production methods have been
brought to a high degree of perfection.

Immediately after the World War productivity in building construction fell off sharply. In 1920 bricklayers on ordinary wall work laid only about 500 bricks per day against an
average of 1200 to 1500 a day prior to the World War.[24] This
may be due partly to the disorganization of working forces
and management incident to the prosecution of the War; in considerable measure it is due to the severe shortage of building-
trade labor immediately after the War and to the intense competition of employers in reconstituting their working forces.
Whether consciously or not, a let-down on the part of building-
trades workers resulted, and the output per worker decreased
from 30 to 50 per cent.

This condition was temporary, and with the recovery of the
industry from war disorganization and an increase in the supply of workers the per-man output steadily improved, and in
a few years was back at the pre-War level. In recent years, when
the volume of construction and the demand for labor have been
sharply curtailed, there has been a decided increase. From data
gathered from contractors in thirty-six cities, the Engineering
News-Record concluded that there was a gain of 19 per cent
in the productivity of building-trade labor between 1926 and
the early part of 1932. It estimated that from 1926–29 the
gain was 6 per cent, that in 1929 there was a gain of 9 per
cent and in 1931 a further gain of 3 per cent, making a cumu-
lative total of 19 per cent over 1913. Table 50 gives the data
by individual cities,[25] and indicates that the most pronounced
gain in efficiency occurred in New York City. These figures
cover general building and not merely dwelling-house construction; they may be chiefly controlled by large-scale operations.
Nevertheless it is reasonable to assume that dwelling-house con-

[24] In the British building trade, as shown on p. 460, output fell off even
more sharply.

[25] "Construction Costs," p. 8. In this table the average increase from 1926
to 1929 is shown as 5 per cent.

TABLE 50

INDEX NUMBERS OF ESTIMATED PRODUCTIVITY OF BUILDING-TRADES
LABOR IN VARIOUS CITIES, 1927–1932.[a] (1926 = 100)

	1927	1928	1929	1930	1931	1932
Amarillo, Tex.	—	—	—	—	—	115
Anderson, Ind.	100	100	110	120	120	—
Auburndale, Mass.	80	75	71	105	108	—
Babylon, N. Y.	98	97	98	108	110	—
Bethlehem, Pa.	110	110	100	90	90	—
Birmingham	—	—	—	—	—	133
Bloomington, Ill.	100	100	110½	125	137	—
Boston, Mass.	100	100	120	120	120	—
Canton, Ohio	100	100	125	125	130	—
Chapel Hill, N. C.	90	92	95	100	105	—
Chattanooga	100	110	120	130	135	—
Chicago	100	100	105	120	125	—
Cincinnati	105	110	115	120	120	—
Cleveland	—	—	—	—	—	125
Cumberland, Md.	100	105	105	110	120	—
Duluth	100	100	105	110	120	—
Greensboro, N. C.	100	—	—	—	105–110	—
Knoxville, Tenn.	100	100	100	120	120	110
Lincoln, Neb.	100	100	100	110	125	—
Milwaukee	100	100	110	110	110	130
Montgomery, Ala.	95	90	85	100	110	120
New Britain, Conn.	—	—	—	—	—	115
New York	100	104	108	125	125	140
Oklahoma City	—	—	—	—	—	120
Roanoke	—	—	—	—	—	130
Rock Island	—	—	—	—	—	110
Rockford, Ill.	100	92	92	100	100	—
St. Louis	100	95	90	105	115	118
Salt Lake City	—	—	—	—	—	115
San Antonio	—	—	—	—	—	115
San Francisco	100	100	125	125	125	—
Seattle	100	100	117	119	122	—
Sioux City	100	100	105	105	115	105
Syracuse	100	100	90	110	110	—
Trenton	100	100	100	100	105	112
Wichita, Kan.	100	—	—	—	—	110
AVERAGE	100	100	105	114	118	119

(a) Engineering News-Record, "Construction Costs," 1932, p. 8.

NOTE. Apparently the productivity of labor includes any gain in efficiency

struction shared in the improvement; how much of the gain is attributable to better management and equipment and how much to labor alone cannot be stated.

Table 51 gives a private estimate for construction in New York City from 1913 to 1931. Since much of the construction

TABLE 51

INDEX NUMBERS OF ESTIMATED PRODUCTIVITY OF BUILDING-TRADES LABOR IN NEW YORK CITY, 1913–1931 [a]

	(1913 = 100)	(1926 = 100)
1913	100	90
1914	105	95
1915	111	100
1916	111	100
1917	111	100
1918	105	95
1919	100	90
1920	89	80
1921	111	100
1922	111	100
1923	111	100
1924	111	100
1925	111	100
1926	111	100
1927	111	100
1928	116	104
1929	120	108
1930	139	125
1931	139	125

(a) Engineering News-Record, " Construction Costs," 1932, p. 8.

in New York is of large buildings, where modern methods are extensively employed, it is doubtful whether there has been a corresponding gain in the case of dwelling-house construction.

Such statistical evidence is corroborated by statements of prominent builders and by research studies. The Associated General Contractors of America, while unable to furnish statistical data, held in October, 1930, that with certain ex-

---

of management methods and other factors. As these figures were published in April, 1932, figures for 1932 presumably represent conditions obtaining rather early in the year.

ceptions, notably bricklaying and plastering, there had been a general improvement in efficiency, attributed to improved management and methods, and a general increase in production per man per day. In this connection it was stated:

" In order to make a comparison of the efficiency of today with other years, consideration must be given to a number of factors. A modern structure is relatively a more complex one than that of former years, and considerable investigation would be necessary to determine the relative weight to be given each of these factors in order that the picture be not distorted. However, inasmuch as building costs are not as high as material and labor costs would indicate in comparison with former years, which can only be accounted for because of a greater general efficiency, I believe that we are safe in assuming that generally this efficiency carries on down through the organization to the productivity of the tradesmen." [26]

A pronounced increase in productivity since 1913 for certain groups of building-trades workers was reported by one large construction company, as indicated by Chart 43; this comparison was for commercial construction and may not reflect conditions in residential building. It was the opinion of this company that there had been a further increase in productivity since 1929.

In some building operations substantial progress has been made in the development of labor-saving devices. Thus, the use of a steam shovel in excavating the cellar of a house is no longer unusual, while in carpentry work new tools have been introduced which have greatly shortened the time required for a given operation. Among these are electric hand-saws, electric planes, hammers, screw-drivers, floor-nailers, mortisers, drills, grinders, and polishers, not to mention others. Similar progress is reported in the European building industry. Thus, according to one writer,[27]

[26] Foreman, H. E., Engineer, The Associated General Contractors of America, Inc.

[27] Méquet, G., " Housing Problems and the Depression " (International Labour Review, February, 1933, pp. 1–81).

" In recent years there has been an enormous advance in mechanization and standardization in the building trade. This improvement is quite general, and present-day building undertakings are so equipped as to be able to build much more rapidly than some twenty years ago and with fewer workers. An example cited in a report of the International Federation of Building Operatives shows that a large building firm in Berlin which had only some 20 machines in 1913 had nearly 200 in 1928. In particular, the num-

—— CHART 43 ——

AVERAGE MAN-HOUR PRODUCTION OF CARPENTERS, STRIPPERS, CONCRETE LABORERS, MECHANICS, AND LABORERS ON REINFORCEMENT IN THE UNITED STATES: 1913-1929

Redrawn from Chart of H.H.Fox, vice-president of Turner Construction Company, in Engineering News-Record, November 7, 1929.

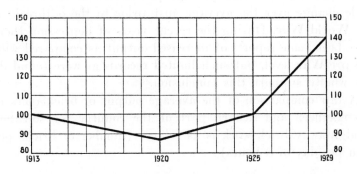

Note: This Chart apparently relates to large commercial Buildings; not to dwellings.

ber of concrete mixing machines rose from 2 to 30 and of electric motors from none to 90, while the firm also now possesses excavators, works locomotives, and many other machines which were not in use by it twenty years ago."

Unfortunately the adoption of such devices on small construction jobs has not become general in the United States, and a vast amount of work is still done in the old-fashioned, laborious, costly, and wasteful manner. It is true that some of the modern machines and tools are expensive; on the other hand, many of them are well adapted to use on small jobs.

There is, then, considerable evidence of an appreciable gain in efficiency of production in building trades in recent years; but complaint is still general that in some occupations, notably bricklaying, the output per man per day is no greater, and perhaps less, than it was before the War. For some time prior to the World War an average of 1200 to 1500 bricks per man per day on such straightaway work as a tenement-house party wall, without windows, was commonly obtained. In 1923 a special study by the United States Bureau of Labor Statistics [28] revealed that the average number of bricks laid per eight-hour day in fifteen cities was 1360; excluding three cities with the lowest averages, that of the remaining twelve was 1490 (see Table 52).

The average per-man per-day production in 1923 showed little change over the average just prior to the outbreak of the World War. During the recent years of depression there have been some reports of increased output as compared with the pre-War level, but such limited records as were found do not wholly support this conclusion. [29]

A fair comparison of the average output of bricklayers in the northern and eastern part of the country for so-called straightaway brick work is as follows (number of bricks per man per day of 8 hours):

Pre-War — For ten years prior to 1914, bricklayers on tenement houses, party walls, using ordinary mortar, laid about 1200 to 1500.

1920 — Various estimates place the average at about 550 to 800.

1923 — A government study gives a simple average for nine northern cities of 1100.

1923 — The Metropolitan Life Insurance Company reported for its extensive building project on Long Island 1200 to 1600.

[28] Monthly Labor Review, November, 1924, p. 2. As an illustration of the lack of data it may be noted that the Commissioner of Labor Statistics in describing this study stated that his staff " was unable to find a single building contractor, superintendent, or foreman who had a record of work done per man hour on the jobs in progress or upon any former job." The Bureau thereupon undertook to compile statistics from observations on work then in progress but the difficulties of doing this in the case of carpentry work were from the outset so great that the task for this occupation was abandoned and the study practically resolved itself into a report on bricklaying.

[29] See p. 248.

1930–31 — Several estimates place the average at about the pre-War level, or approximately 1400 to 1500.

Considerably higher averages are reported in some southern and western sections of the country.

TABLE 52

AVERAGE NUMBER OF BRICKS LAID PER HOUR AND PER DAY OF EIGHT HOURS IN 15 CITIES IN 1923 [a]

	Number of Bricks Laid	
	Per hour	Per day of 8 hours
Atlanta, Ga.	185	1,482
Birmingham, Ala.	241	1,928
Chattanooga, Tenn.	226	1,809
New Orleans, La.	204	1,628
Norfolk, Va.	232	1,854
Boston, Mass.	98	782
New York, N. Y.	158	1,261
Philadelphia, Pa.	123	986
Chicago, Ill.	157	1,254
Cincinnati, Ohio	132	1,052
Cleveland, Ohio	148	1,182
Denver, Colo.	212	1,699
Detroit, Mich.	154	1,232
Indianapolis, Ind.	96	766
Minneapolis and St. Paul, Minn.	193	1,546
Simple Average, 15 cities		1,364
Simple Average, excluding 3 lowest cities [b]		1,494

(a) Monthly Labor Review, November, 1924, p. 2. Based on observations made by the United States Bureau of Labor Statistics. The number of bricks laid per day is sharply affected by the thickness of wall, number of openings, type of bond, and various other factors. The Bureau stated that its averages were for "straightforward" work and that it made special effort to secure data that would be fairly comparable.

(b) i.e., exclusive of Boston, Philadelphia, and Indianapolis.

A firm of Boston builders has submitted data from their records, having endeavored to select types of work that were fairly comparable. Unfortunately most of the data were for jobs taken in recent years, while in cases where earlier figures were available the number of jobs was often too limited to warrant definite conclusions.

Table 53 gives comparisons for certain general bricklaying work; Table 54 gives similar comparisons for face-brick work. It should be understood that the two tables cover very different types of work. The laying of face-brick is a much more particular and slower operation than the laying of common brick. Table 53 bears out the contention already referred to that the output per man per day was much smaller in 1920 than before the War. Table 54, as far as it goes, tends to show a somewhat larger number of face-brick laid per man per day in 1929 and 1930 than before the War, but the number of jobs covered is not large enough to warrant this as a statistical conclusion. It was the opinion of this builder in 1930 that there had been a marked increase in bricklaying output in the preceding year or two and that the average was substantially in excess of that obtained before the World War.

Data for various other operations were furnished by this builder, but in most cases they covered only a few recent years, so that no conclusions as to trend were possible. In the few cases where the records extended back over a period of years, frequently only a single job that appeared to be comparable was located. It seems inadvisable to submit comparisons having so narrow a basis. In general, evidence of any marked change in output as compared with the pre-War period was lacking. There was considerable indication of a moderate improvement since 1928, but even here the results were not uniform.

While the various data here presented do not permit of the construction of index numbers which would be precisely comparable with those prepared by the United States Bureau of Labor Statistics on a much broader base for manufacturing industries, they may serve as a basis for approximate comparisons. In Chart 44, therefore, an approximated curve for per-man output for dwelling-house construction has been entered in comparison with the index numbers of the Bureau of Labor Statistics for selected manufacturing industries.

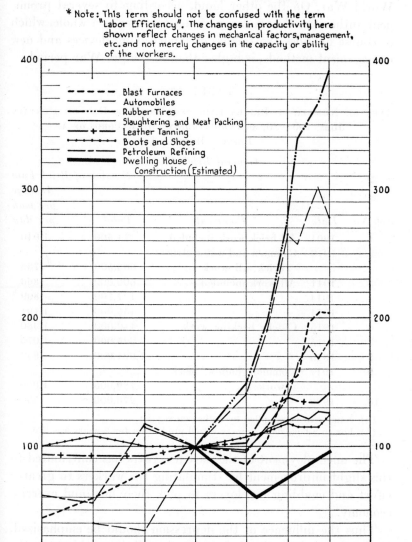

— CHART 44 —

INDEX NUMBERS OF MAN-HOUR PRODUCTIVITY OF LABOR IN
CERTAIN MAJOR INDUSTRIES IN THE UNITED STATES: 1899-1931

Charted from Monthly Labor Review, March 1930.

* Note: This term should not be confused with the term
"Labor Efficiency". The changes in productivity here
shown reflect changes in mechanical factors, management,
etc. and not merely changes in the capacity or ability
of the workers.

Blast Furnaces
Automobiles
Rubber Tires
Slaughtering and Meat Packing
Leather Tanning
Boots and Shoes
Petroleum Refining
Dwelling House
Construction (Estimated)

The data presented in the preceding pages suggest that the efficiency of labor *per se* in some major building trades is practically the same as in the period immediately preceding the World War. On the other hand, according to several prominent authorities the efficiency of construction as a whole, which of course includes the factors of labor-saving devices and new management methods, is higher than in the pre-War period.

TABLE 53

AVERAGE NUMBER OF BRICKS LAID PER MAN PER DAY ON CERTAIN JOBS, 1904–20, AS INDICATED BY THE RECORDS OF A BOSTON BUILDER [a]

General Brick Work

Job No.	Date	Comment	Total	Number of Brick Laid Average per man per day
1	1904	All brick work included .	774,500	1,040
2	1910	Common and water-struck brick, all work	603,500	732
3	1911	All work included	600,000	863
4	1914		127,700	809 [b]
5	1914		455,000	1,191
6	1915	Chiefly backing work ...	440,000	1,380
7	1915		225,000	1,075
8	1916		1,924,000	852
9	1917	Common hollow brick work	789,000	1,009
10	1920		276,000	536

(*a*) Name will be supplied by author on request.
(*b*) For an 8-hour day: average actual production for 9 hours was 910.

The unemployment of the past few years has contributed to this slight improvement by stimulating the workers to greater effort and enabling employers to pick their men and exercise economy.

Thus the influence of the depression should be emphasized. In those manufacturing industries where " the machine sets the pace," this factor is of far less significance than in the building trades where the bearing of employment conditions on productivity of labor has long been recognized. Even the modest increase in production in the building trades reported under the abnormal industrial conditions since 1929 does not indicate a permanent gain in efficiency. In any event, the gain thus far

TABLE 54

AVERAGE NUMBER OF BRICKS LAID PER MAN PER DAY ON CERTAIN JOBS, 1904–30, AS INDICATED BY THE RECORDS OF A BOSTON BUILDER [a]

Face-brick Work

Job No.	Date	Comment	Total	Number of Brick Laid Average per man per day
1	1904	Kittanning face-brick ...	112,000	444
2	1915	Water-struck brick	81,000	600
3	1915		73,360	344
4	1917	Kittanning face-brick ...	136,000	337
5	1925	Sand lime brick, running bond; header every fifth course	90,200	335
6	1925–6	Same as above, except header every fourth course	33,600	205
7	1925–6	Water-struck brick; header every fourth course	148,500	317
8	1929	Water-struck brick, running bond; header every sixth course	48,000	403
9	1929	Ditto	3,700	293
10	1930	Running bond; Flemish header every sixth course	45,500	516
11	1930	Water-struck brick; Flemish bond; header every sixth course	42,000	486
12	1930	Water-struck brick	38,000	483

(a) Name will be supplied by author on request.

reported is insignificant as compared with the advances which have been made in many of the country's major industries.

The house-building industry is often referred to as an assembling process. This is not a proper term. It is rather a true manufacturing process in which materials are cut and fitted and nailed and cemented into the final product.

The major materials of a house have remained unchanged for many years, and so have the processes by which they are put together. The arts of carpentry, brick work, plastering, even painting, are ages old. They were practiced, and well, in Egypt, Greece, and Rome. By the time of the Middle Ages the craftsmanship displayed in them had reached a pitch from which present craftsmanship may quite properly be said to have receded.

Meanwhile, the methods of manufacturing everything else have progressed and developed amazingly. Increases of productive efficiency of 500 per cent during the past hundred years are taken for granted. It requires an increase of thousands per cent to be regarded as sensational.

It is quite true that individual building materials — nails, cement, steel, bricks, shingles — have reached manufacturing efficiencies comparable to those in most of our major industries. But the process of further manufacturing and building these materials into a house has lagged behind, has not reacted to the stimulus of the Industrial Revolution. Hence the process of manufacturing a house is still subject to the manifold disabilities which we have indicated above.

For the past two centuries this struggle between the group productive forces and the building industry has been going on, until now the Babel's Tower of disabilities is about to fall. And on its site will be started a new tower of up-to-date construction. Once started, it will rise rapidly and in a decade, or certainly a generation, it will quite likely overtop all other structures.

Finally, and obviously, these disabilities force and demand a regeneration of the industry. The means to that end is necessarily a new conception of building structure based upon present-day industrial, commercial, and social conditions.

CHAPTER VII

Analysis of the Cost of the Home

IN primitive conditions as in primitive times the cost of a house cannot be measured exactly. It is a matter of human effort and convenient materials. It is simple but vague — no subject for statistics. Often the obligation of the community to assist, a moral obligation entirely, plays a large part. Gradually, as civilization advances and functions specialize these vague values are drawn into focus and the medium we call money enables us to estimate costs. The improvements in the industrial arts, the increase of wealth, the tendency toward urbanization are reflected in the increasing cost of the home. That it does increase with civilization, gradually but surely, we can declare, without assigning definite values until practically modern times. We cannot turn the searchlight of statistics upon the various forms of human effort that were involved in the building of an Inca's palace or a home in Knossos, but we can analyze closely the cost of the modern urban dwelling.

With the development of community and city life the house has come more and more to depend upon the cooperation of the group,[1] and has grown farther and farther away from the occupant's control. Of all the budgetary items for the citizens of a modern state, shelter is the least understood. To the owner, the purchase of a modern house is usually the largest single investment of his life; to the tenant, the field of selection seems unjustifiably limited and the price of what he wants excessive and beyond his means.

[1] Although, as shown in Volume I, the communal building of a house is common among primitive peoples and this is an obvious example of group cooperation, on the whole the cooperation required in the advanced state is far greater although much less apparent.

Men in primitive conditions provide themselves with shelter directly, naturally, and easily; but men in advanced countries find the problem complicated and largely one of "take it or leave it." Even in country sections, at least in the United States, the would-be owner is becoming more and more dependent upon the local contractor, specialized labor, the lumber yard, and the finish mill, and less upon his own labor and ingenuity in providing materials and putting them together.

As a result of increasing complexity of the house mechanism, new elements of cost have assumed increasing importance. Housing has become one of the foremost elements of capital wealth in all advanced countries. At the same time the site, once almost valueless, has now become an important factor. The problem of financing, unknown in early times, is today of primary importance; and financing charges often constitute a substantial item in the total cost. Fees for architectural service, insurance premiums on construction, and other incidental charges count more than one might think. No analysis of the high cost of housing can be effective without determining what proportion must be allotted to each of the major items — some of which are likely to be overlooked by the average buyer, who wonders why he gets so little for his housing dollar.

ELEMENTS IN THE COST OF THE HOME

These proportions are evidently quite variable. They depend upon the type of dwelling, the character of the community, the materials of construction, the method by which the house is acquired. The distribution of costs in an apartment-house will differ from that in a single-family dwelling. The relative and actual cost of land on a farm or in the country will naturally be lower than in a city or suburb, while the improvements also will cost much less, many of them, such as paving, curbing, sewers, water mains, and other utilities, perhaps being absent altogether. The relationship of elements of construction may be quite other in a brick house than in a frame house of the same general type. Moreover, the ratios where the owner has the house built to his order will be quite different from those where a speculative builder has purchased the land and builds for the market, with an overhead and profit necessarily calculated on all elements of cost and not merely on the building. Finally, even among comparable houses there may be wide variations: labor costs differ throughout the nation; financing costs show divergence, depending both on geography and on the financial status of the purchaser.

Nevertheless, despite these local variations, there is a broad relationship between the component cost elements. For example, while land is subject to a wide range of unit values, there is a more or less natural relationship between its cost and the cost of the building erected upon it. Normally one does not find a $15,000 house on a $1000 site, or conversely a $2500 dwelling on a $5000 lot. Even in the case of apartment-houses, where the cost of land may be distributed over a large number of dwellings, the land cost per apartment approximates that in the case of a single-family home. Again, the cost of modern mechanical devices, such as plumbing, heating, and electrical equipment, bears a rather constant relationship to the total cost of the home.

It would be a tremendous task to differentiate between all the various types of construction; in the overwhelming mass of statistics the wood might not be seen for the trees. Moreover, the results would probably be both unconvincing and inaccurate. For the purposes of this work, it will suffice to consider the distribution of cost in the normal home. While the composite American home is not a specific thing, the urban single-family home, comprising 37 per cent of our homes and representing half the nation's capital home investment, is definite enough to be fairly representative; analysis of its cost with side references to other types will give us the salient features in the cost of the American home.

For such an urban home, built for the owner, the major elements entering into the cost to the purchaser may conveniently be grouped under five main heads, as follows:

1. Land
2. Street improvements, utilities, etc.
3. The building
     a. Structure
          (1) Materials
          (2) Labor
     b. Finish
     c. Accessories
     d. Builder's overhead and profit [2]
4. Financing
     a. Interest during construction
     b. Discounts on loans, commissions, etc.
     c. Recording and miscellaneous fees
5. Architect's fees (absent in the majority of cases)

COST OF LAND AND IMPROVEMENTS

An important factor in housing costs is that the value of the raw land represents only a small proportion of the total cost of the home, or indeed that of the site alone. The so-called "lot" improvements — grading, landscaping, and shrubbery — and the "street" improvements — paving, curbing, sewers, water and gas mains, and other utilities — often cost much more than the land itself. While this may not hold in the case of certain residential sections in large cities, it may be accepted as broadly true. In many cases these improvements represent from four to five times the cost of the bare land, the ratio depending upon the type of community and the density of housing.

The experience of the City Housing Corporation (Table 55) offers a concrete instance, although it does not show a typical condition, and although the costs include park and lot allowances which do not fall under the technical head of "improvements." The table demonstrates that the cost of raw land in the form of the building lot and the cost of the lot as finally improved are quite different matters, the raw land being valued by this company at only 12 per cent of its final improved lot value.

In connection with this table, the following comment by Dr.

[2] This item, after its discussion as a separate unit, will be considered under the headings of structure, finish, and accessories.

TABLE 55

ESTIMATED COST OF IMPROVING RESIDENTIAL LAND IN SUPERBLOCK
SUBDIVISION — BERGEN COUNTY, NEW JERSEY [a]

Item	Explanation	Cost per sq.ft. of salable lot	Cost per salable lot (4000 sq.ft.)	Per cent
Land cost of lot	Purchase price of unsubdivided gross land area, including title and title survey expenses, averaging $2500 an acre	$ .06	$240	12
Land cost of beds of street and park areas	Land area devoted to streets and parks, 40 per cent of gross land area, leaving 60 per cent as net usable or salable area — consequently add 40 ÷ 60 per cent, or ⅔, to above amount, making $4000 an acre	.04	160	8
Improvement cost	Cost of grading streets, installing storm sewers, sanitary sewers, concrete paving, curbs, sidewalks, street trees, street lights (electricity, gas, and water being installed gratis)	.20	800	40
Landscaping cost	Includes the extra costs of a garden community: (a) Park development, park walks, lights, grading, top soil, shrubs, benches, play equipment	.06	240	12
	(b) Private lot development or yard planting work. (This item is usually not included as part of the cost of real estate and is either omitted or considered in construction cost.)	.09	360	18
Overhead cost	Engineering and architectural fees and expenses for planning of the above and supervising, plus interest and taxes on the land during construction only .	.05	200	10
Total improved cost		$ .50	$2,000	100

(a) Compiled by the City Housing Corporation for its Radburn (New

R. T. Ely, who has devoted a large amount of study to land and public-utility economics, is worthy of attention:

"It has frequently been argued that land is a ' gift of nature.' Writers who take this position forget how much of man's toil goes into bringing land into use. Recent studies in land economics have shown that land is one form of capital, in the sense that capital is ' stored up effort.' Making land utilizable involves real costs and heavy expenditures. It is probable that less ' unearned increment ' accrues to the holders of land than to the owners of any other agent of production." [3]

Inasmuch as some writers take the ground that the housing problem is almost exclusively a land problem, and that if the speculative feature of land values could be eliminated the problem would largely be solved,[4] the figures from Radburn are striking in the force they lend to Dr. Ely's statement.

It has come to be a rule of thumb in the building industry that in urban communities the cost of land with lot and street improvements should be about 20 per cent of the cost of the completed single-family home; in communities where land is much cheaper and where few street improvements are added, the ratio may be nearer 10 per cent. In the case of farm homes, where so-called street improvements are often absent, the cost of the site may be an insignificant fraction of the total cost.

The broad rule on this point as laid down by experts of the United States Department of Commerce is as follows:

"Where streets, curbing, sidewalks, water, electric, gas, and sewerage improvements have not been made, a lot may sometimes be obtained for less than 5 per cent of the total cost of the house and lot, and 10 per cent should probably be the upper limit. If all im-

---

Jersey) development. See the Annals of the American Academy of Political and Social Science, March, 1930, p. 168. (Article by Richard T. Ely, "Taxing Land Values and Taxing Building Values.")

[3] The Annals of the American Academy of Political and Social Science, March, 1930, pp. 167–168.

[4] See for example, Whitaker, Charles Harris, "The Joke about Housing" (Marshall Jones Co., Boston, 1920).

provements have been made, the cost of the lot frequently runs up to 20 per cent, but it should rarely exceed 25 per cent." [5]

The Veterans' Welfare Board of California reported that of the cost of veterans' homes, 22 per cent on the average was charged against the lot, and that " the lot, unless under exceptional circumstances, should represent from 20 to 25 per cent of the total cost of the home." [6]

These estimates find confirmation in statistical evidence gathered by Robert Whitten.[7] This information, secured from builders in twenty-five cities, indicated an average ratio of improved lot cost to total cost of house and lot of 20.2 per cent, ranging from 17.7 per cent in cities with 50,000 to 100,000 population to 25.7 per cent in those with 500,000 to 1,000,000. The writer just cited also obtained estimates from subdividers and officials of real-estate boards. Replies from sixty-four cities of varying size gave a general average ratio of 18.1 per cent between the cost of the improved lot and the total cost of house and lot. For cities of 500,000 and over the average ratio was 20.2 per cent, from 16.7 per cent in Detroit to 25 per cent in Los Angeles. These ratios related to houses costing from $6000 to $9000. Broadly speaking, therefore, the value of the site with improvements represents about 20 per cent of the cost of a new single-family home in urban or suburban communities, frequently a little more.

In the case of apartment-houses, the cost of the site represents a lower proportion, since the cost of the land is distributed over a number of homes. But even in apartment-house construction land values are often so high that although an apartment-house may contain several hundred apartments, the prorated

5 Gries, John M., and Taylor, James S., " How to Own Your Home " (USDC, 1925), p. 12.
6 Veterans' Welfare Board of California, " Annual Report, 1928 " (California State Printing Office, Sacramento, 1928), p. 33.
7 Whitten, Robert, and Adams, Thomas, " Neighborhoods of Small Homes; Economic Density of Low-Cost Housing in America and England " (Published by Harvard University School of City Planning, Harvard University Press, Cambridge, 1931), pp. 34–35, 155–157.

share of the site cost still represents a major fraction of the total cost per apartment. Such data as were obtained indicate an average allowance of 15 per cent for the cost of the site in the case of apartment-houses as a fair one.[8]

COST OF THE BUILDING

The cost of the building, exclusive of overhead and builder's profit, is the largest single item in the cost of a home. While it varies from less than 50 per cent to more than 80 per cent, a range of 60 to 70 per cent holds true in a large amount of housing, especially where cellars are required.[9]

COST OF FINANCING

Original financing costs, which include interest during construction, discounts, and commissions on borrowed funds, as well as fees, vary according to the financial status of the buyer. The purchaser of a home who is not compelled to borrow finds his initial financing charges, other than a few fees, practically measured by the loss of interest during the period of construction. But the great majority of home purchasers are not in this position; borrowing on first mortgage is general, and the second mortgage is employed in a large number, perhaps a major-

[8] For eleven apartment-house projects in various sections of New York City, erected under the New York State Housing Law (Report of New York State Board of Housing, Legislative Document [1932] No. 84 [J. B. Lyon Co., Printers, Albany, 1932], p. 69), which provides for tax exemption of the building over a term of years, the ratio of land cost (which included a considerable part of the cost of street improvements) to total cost is closely in line with that for single-family dwellings. Following are totals and average percentages:

	Amount	Per cent
Land	$1,733,065	17.1
Improvements, including financing	8,428,009	82.9
Total	$10,161,074	100.0

A study covering thirty-one apartment-houses in the Borough of Manhattan indicated land costs ranging from 27 per cent on side streets to 39 per cent on Park Avenue. Conditions in such sections, of course, are not typical. Kerby, C. K., "Gross and Net: What Return on Apartment Investments?" (Building Investment, November, 1930), pp. 12 and 14.

[9] The Committee on Design of the President's Conference placed the range at 65 to 75 per cent (The President's Conference on Home Building and Home Ownership, Vol. V, p. 17).

ity,[10] of cases. In highly speculative dwelling-house construction, third mortgages often are resorted to, but these are exceptional among home owners.

In the case of purchasers who borrow extensively and have to resort to junior financing, discounts or commissions on borrowed funds represent an appreciable addition to the capital cost.[11] It may be noted here that a discount of 15 per cent on a three-year second mortgage is a common occurrence; if this mortgage represents 25 per cent of the cost of the home, the discount alone constitutes nearly 4 per cent of the total initial cost, while commissions and other fees add 1 or 2 per cent or more. If a commission is also paid for first-mortgage money, the total of these original financing costs may easily amount to 7½ per cent of the purchase price; frequently they are as much as 10 per cent. In highly speculative building such financing costs may run still higher; one writer, evidently discussing building of this character, placed promotion and financing costs at 27 per cent of the total cost, land and improvements at 21½ per cent, and the building at only 51½ per cent.[12]

COST OF ARCHITECTURAL SERVICE

It has been estimated that 80 per cent of the single-family dwellings in the United States have been built without employing an architect. In recent years a large number of moderate-priced homes have been built from architects' plans, but these plans have often been purchased ready-made from home-service bureaus or other agencies, so that the total expense on this account is insignificant as compared with the total cost of the home. A similar low cost may be achieved where a single company builds a large number of houses from the same plan. Where an architect is employed to prepare an original design with specifications and also to supervise the construction of the

10 See p. 347.
11 This matter is taken up in detail in Chapter X.
12 Holden, Arthur C., "Speculating in Homes" (The Atlantic Monthly, February, 1928, p. 246).

house, the proportion of total cost represented by his charges becomes significant — frequently 4 per cent for the plans and specifications and a further 2 per cent for supervision.

Practically no authoritative statistical evidence concerning builder's overhead and profit is available. It is generally conceded that the average building contractor operates on a low profit margin. As a general rule, an allowance of 12.5 per cent for overhead and profit combined is fairly representative. Where the builder does not provide the site this must be computed on the basis of the cost of the building only. Offhand there would seem to be no reason at all for including " builder's overhead and profit " as a separate item. It should be merged with the cost of the building and distributed perhaps between its different elements. The overhead and profit of the furniture dealer, the butcher, baker and candlestick maker are not matters of the buyer's concern. But most of the statistical analyses of building costs include this separation.

If the building represents 65 per cent of the total cost, builder's overhead and profit at 12.5 per cent would add 8 per cent of the total cost, bringing the entire cost of the building up to 73 per cent. An architect's fee of 6 per cent on the cost of the building would add 4 per cent more, making the total 77 per cent. Initial financing costs vary widely, from almost nothing up to 10 per cent or more. If the average be taken at 5 per cent of the cost of the building, this would increase the ratio of building cost to total cost to slightly over 80 per cent, leaving the established 20 per cent for land and improvements.

This computation may profitably be tabulated: [13]

[13] This broad division is closely checked by experience in post-War construction in Great Britain. Figures collected by Whitten and Adams ("Neighborhoods of Small Homes," p. 168) for certain classes of British cottages show:

	Grade A house	Grade B house	Grade C house
	Per cent		
Land	3.2	2.8	2.4
Street and utility improvements	16.5	14.8	12.9
Building, including architects' fees and builders' profit	80.3	82.4	84.7
	100.0	100.0	100.0

	Per cent		Per cent
Land	5		
Improvements	14	Land and improvements	19
Building	65		
Builder's overhead and profit (12.5x65)	8	Building, including overhead and profit and architect's fee	77
Architect's fee (6x73) .	4		
Financing (5x73)	4	Financing	4
	100		100

Clearly the cost of the house itself is by far the largest item, twice as large as all the others put together; and many of these other items vary with the cost of the house. It is obvious that if major savings are to be made in the cost of the whole home, the chief place to make them is in the house itself; this leads us to further analysis of the cost of the building.

ANALYSIS OF THE COST OF THE BUILDING

A. On the Basis of Structure, Finish, and Accessories

The cost of the building may conveniently be divided into structure, finish, and accessories.

Structure includes such items as foundation and cellar work, the frame, roof, exterior boarding and clapboarding, shingles, stucco or brick covering, stair work, and exterior doors and windows.

The term " finish " is ordinarily used to include finish carpentry such as finish floors, interior door and window frames, interior doors, miscellaneous mill work, part or all of the lathing and plastering, painting, both exterior and interior, paperhanging, and tile work.

The term " accessories " as here used includes the major types of mechanical equipment discussed in Chapter II, i.e., plumbing, heating, and various electrical installations, and also a number of miscellaneous items such as screens, shades, gas ranges, and kitchen stoves, where the stove is not used as the main source of heat for the house.

The following distribution is in line with general practice in the industry:

Structure [14]	Finish	Accessories
Excavation	Finish carpentry and	Plumbing
Stone masonry	mill work	Heating
Brick masonry	Lathing and	Electric wiring
Rough carpentry	plastering	Lighting fixtures
Cement work	Painting	Range
Stair work	Tile work	Gas water heater
Structural steel	Cabinet work	Refrigerator
Roofing	Hardware — finish	Radio and telephone,
Labor — general	Paper hanging	screens and shades
Sheet-metal work		
Hardware — rough		
Glazing		

Such a classification should not be interpreted rigidly. Items like excavation, masonry, concrete, and roofing, while chiefly structure, may include ornamental or other features which could properly be placed under finish. Carpentry appears in both fields. Lathing might be regarded as preparatory to finishing and is sometimes classed under finish, but the strength added to an ordinary stud wall by lath and plaster cannot be disregarded, and a part of this item should be allocated to structure. Painting is ordinarily classed under finish, yet a priming coat, at least, is essential to the preservation of the structure. A certain amount of roofing is required to keep out the weather and is certainly structure, but practically every roofing has certain decorative qualities which have been attained at increased cost and which must be classed as finish.

Taking the distribution of major operations given in the first column of Table 56 as a basis, the following division by percentage between structure and finish may be a reasonable approximation:

[14] These items, of course, may include certain portions of finish.

	Structure	Finish	Total Including accessories	Excluding accessories
Excavation and grading .	1.0	0.3	1.3	1.8
Masonry	13.7	1.1	14.8	20.2
Carpentry and hardware	15.0	12.3	27.3	37.1
Concrete	11.7	—	11.7	16.0
Roofing	1.8	—	1.8	2.5
Plaster, tiles, etc.	4.0	7.7	11.7	16.0
Painting and glazing ...	0.2	4.0	4.2	5.7
Papering	—	0.5	0.5	0.7
Accessories			26.7	
	47.4	25.9	100.0	100.0

The small allowance for finish in masonry is intended to represent decorative brick work not really essential to the structure. An allowance of 55 per cent of carpentry work to represent structure seems fair.[15]

Such major accessories as plumbing, heating, and electrical equipment constitute 15 per cent, 20 per cent, or even more of the total cost of construction. Including still more recent equipment such as electric or gas refrigerators and oil-burning plants, the proportion would be even higher.

A general idea of the importance of major accessories is afforded by the distributions in Table 56 as reported by various agencies, the other items entering into construction work also being given. Chart 45 shows these distributions graphically with special emphasis on the major accessories. It will be seen that the cost of the major accessories in these cases represented from 17 to 23 per cent of the total cost of the building, averaging 21 per cent. If to these there be added the cost of miscellaneous accessories, the proportion may be raised to 25

---

[15] A distribution based on the cost of constructing a typical house of six rooms and bath in Philadelphia in 1914, 1920, and 1921 is given in the Appendix, p. 563. This indicates that items which could be classed as finish represented approximately 30 per cent of the total construction cost, but this proportion might be reduced somewhat by allotting part of the lathing and plastering to structure.

per cent. The relative cost of accessory equipment has steadily been increasing in recent years, and with the prospect of further new features, such as mechanism for air conditioning, it promises to increase still further.

TABLE 56

VARIOUS DISTRIBUTIONS OF DIRECT CONSTRUCTION COSTS IN RESIDENTIAL BUILDING IN THE UNITED STATES AS REPORTED BY CERTAIN AGENCIES

Operation	United States Bureau Labor Statistics a 1931–32	War Industries Board 1915 b	Copper and Brass Research Ass'n c	American Brass Company d	Average e
Excavation and grading	1.3	4.4	2.2	5.6 f	3.4
Masonry	14.8	12.7	11.5	⎧	13.0 g
Concrete	11.7	—	—	⎨ 23.1	—
Plaster, lathing, tile and stucco h	11.7	14.4	13.0	⎩	13.0
Carpentry	27.3	44.9 i	35.9 i	34.6	35.6
Roofing	1.8	2.7	6.6	6.2	4.3
Painting and glazing	4.2	3.1	5.5	5.2	4.5
Papering	0.5	—	—	—	—
Accessories					
⎧ Plumbing	10.1	6.9 ⎫	11.4 ⎫	11.3 ⎫	9.9 ⎫
⎨ Heating and ventilating	6.6 ⎬ 21.2	8.3 ⎬ 17.0	8.6 ⎬ 23.3	8.1 ⎬ 23.0	7.9 ⎬ 21.1
⎩ Wiring and fixtures	4.5 ⎭	1.8 ⎭	3.3 ⎭	3.6 ⎭	3.3 ⎭
Miscellaneous	5.5	0.8	2.0	2.3	2.6
Total	100	100	100	100	

(a) Average based on construction in fifteen cities (Monthly Labor Review, October, 1932, p. 768).

(b) Estimates for a twelve-room two-family wood-frame and stucco house ("Economics of the Construction Industry" (USDC, GPO, 1919, p. 89).

(c) Based on actual construction costs of nine houses varying in price from $9000 to $23,000 ("A Real Home" [Copper and Brass Research Association, New York, 1927], p. 43).

(d) Covering labor and materials cost of an "average rust-proofed house."

(e) This is merely a simple average of the percentages here given. Data for a true average were not available.

(f) Includes landscaping.

(g) Omitting American Brass Company.

(h) Stucco specifically mentioned only in Copper and Brass Research Association report.

(i) Includes cost of hardware.

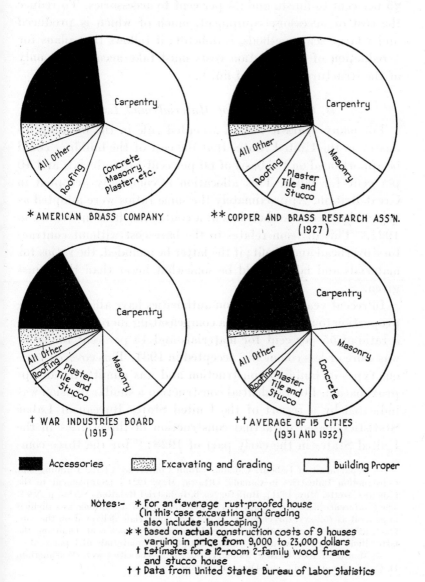

— CHART 45 —

VARIOUS DISTRIBUTIONS OF THE TOTAL LABOR AND MATERIALS COST OF
RESIDENTIAL CONSTRUCTION IN THE UNITED STATES

*AMERICAN BRASS COMPANY

**COPPER AND BRASS RESEARCH ASS'N.
(1927)

† WAR INDUSTRIES BOARD
(1915)

††AVERAGE OF 15 CITIES
(1931 AND 1932)

■ Accessories   ▨ Excavating and Grading   □ Building Proper

Notes:- * For an "average rust-proofed house
          (In this case excavating and Grading
          also includes landscaping)
        ** Based on actual construction costs of 9 houses
           varying in price from 9,000 to 23,000 dollars
         † Estimates for a 12-room 2-family wood frame
           and stucco house
        †† Data from United States Bureau of Labor Statistics

To sum up, then, in the case of a representative suburban home with modern equipment, 45 to 50 per cent of the cost of the building may perhaps fairly be assigned to structure, 30 to 25 per cent to finish, and 25 per cent to accessories. To reduce the cost of accessory equipment, much of which is produced under large-scale methods, is difficult; it follows that plans for a reduction of construction costs must take account not only of the structure but also of finish.

B. On the Basis of Materials and Labor

For many years it was an accepted rule in the building industry in the United States that the cost of the building could be apportioned on the basis of 60 per cent for materials and 40 per cent for labor. This allocation is commonly accepted in Great Britain. Approximately the same ratios were adopted as typical by Canadian builders at a conference held in Ottawa in 1921.[16] This division relates to the bare cost without contractors' overhead and profit; if the latter be included, the ratios for materials and labor would be somewhat lower than those just given.

In recent years construction authorities have allotted a lower proportion to materials with a compensating increase for labor; a ratio of 55 per cent for materials and 45 per cent for labor was more or less commonly accepted in 1931. This covered various types of building construction and was admittedly an approximation. For residential construction a similar division was indicated by a report of the United States Bureau of Labor Statistics, based on actual construction in three cities in the United States in the early part of 1928;[17] for the three com-

[16] Department of Labour, Canada, "Joint Conference of the Building and Construction Industries in Canada, Ottawa, May, 1921" (Supplement to the Labour Gazette, May, 1921), Bulletin No. 3, Industrial Relations Series, p. XVI. The Conference declared its agreement that the cost of a building was divided in general as follows: direct labor, 35 per cent; materials delivered on the contract, 55 per cent; contractors' overhead and profit, 10 per cent. Omitting the latter item, the ratios would be: labor 38.9 per cent, materials 61.1 per cent.

[17] Monthly Labor Review, January, 1929, p. 2. The cities were Washington, D. C., Cincinnati, Ohio, and Decatur, Illinois.

—— CHART 46 ——

PERCENTAGE DISTRIBUTION OF COST OF CONSTRUCTION, BETWEEN LABOR AND MATERIALS, IN CERTAIN RESIDENTIAL AND NON–RESIDENTIAL CONSTRUCTION IN SPECIFIED CITIES OF THE UNITED STATES: 1928

Redrawn from Chart of United States Bureau of Labor Statistics.

■ Labor   ☐ Materials

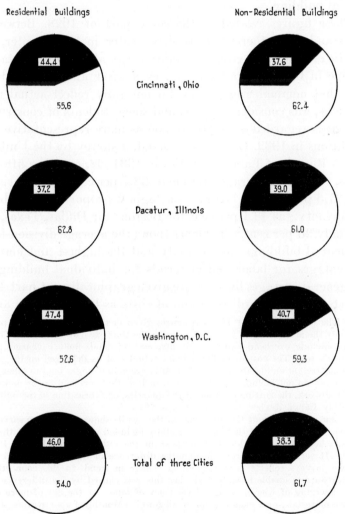

Residential Buildings

Non–Residential Buildings

Cincinnati , Ohio

Dacatur, Illinois

Washington , D.C.

Total of three Cities

bined, the cost of materials represented 54 per cent of the total and labor 46 per cent. The survey covered several types of residential building in each city, and included both frame and brick construction; there was a considerable range in the average percentages as between different cities. Chart 46 gives the distribution by cities, and for non-residential as well as residential building.

These figures related to the early part of 1928. Between 1928 and 1932 there was, as shown later in this chapter, a drastic decline in the cost of building materials. The percentage decline in building-trades wages, even after allowing for the fact that nominal wage scales did not fully reflect actual reductions, was considerably less, and some students of construction costs regarded a 50–50 division as more representative of conditions in 1932. On the other hand, a survey by the United States Bureau of Labor Statistics in 1931–32, covering fifteen cities, showed an average division of 62.7 per cent for materials and 37.3 per cent for labor; [18] the highest proportion for labor for any city was 43.1 per cent for Boston; for Dallas, Texas, it was only 26 per cent.[19] Table 57 shows the average division for residential buildings for each city and the highest and lowest percentages for labor and materials for individual buildings; the general averages by cities are given graphically in Chart 47. Chart 48 shows the distribution of costs as between labor and

[18] The Bureau stated: " The cost figures given in the present article represent only the actual cost of the building from the time excavation started. They do not include overhead expenses, profits, cost of land, finance charges, or architect's fees. The cost of material is its actual cost as delivered on the job, including freight and hauling. The labor costs are actual wages paid to labor on the job and do not include any shop labor, such as that involved in the making up of millwork, the cutting of stone at the quarries, or fabrication in the mills." (Monthly Labor Review, October, 1932, p. 763.)

[19] One explanation of the difference in the results shown by the two surveys may be found in the fact that the latter study included seven cities in southern states, where wages are lower than those in the cities covered by the 1928 survey. It seems hardly probable that the difference in the results shown by the two surveys reflects a corresponding change in trend. In this connection the Bureau was unable to state " whether this was caused by the difference in cities, lowering of wages, increased efficiency of labor, or the use of more expensive materials, or a combination of all four." (Monthly Labor Review, October, 1932, p. 765.)

—— CHART 47 ——

PERCENTAGE DISTRIBUTION OF COST OF CONSTRUCTION, BETWEEN MATERIALS AND LABOR, FOR CERTAIN RESIDENTIAL BUILDING IN SPECIFIED CITIES OF THE UNITED STATES: 1931-1932

Charted from data of United States Bureau of Labor
Statistics in Monthly Labor Review of October 1932

☐ MATERIAL   ▦ LABOR

City	Material
WEIGHTED AVERAGE	62.7
BOSTON	56.9
SEATTLE	57.5
TRENTON	59.0
NEW YORK	59.6
INDIANAPOLIS	59.7
ST. LOUIS	63.0
ROANOKE	64.1
CHICAGO	65.1
SALT LAKE CITY	65.6
DULUTH	66.3
SAGINAW	66.5
LITTLE ROCK	67.7
NEW ORLEANS	69.4
ATLANTA	70.1
DALLAS	74.0

materials for different operations for residential building in the fifteen cities combined.

A census report on the construction industry in 1929 showed that for approximately $3,500,000,000 of building construction of all classes, including subcontract work, by establish-

TABLE 57

PERCENTAGE DISTRIBUTION OF COST OF CONSTRUCTION BETWEEN MATERIALS AND LABOR FOR RESIDENTIAL CONSTRUCTION IN FIFTEEN SPECIFIED CITIES, 1931–1932 [a]

| | Averages by Cities | | Range in Individual Buildings | | | |
| | | | Material | | Labor | |
	Material	Labor	High	Low	High	Low
Atlanta, Ga.	70.1	29.9	73.8	63.5	36.5	26.2
Boston, Mass.	56.9	43.1	60.9	43.8	56.2	39.1
Chicago, Ill.	65.1	34.9	65.9	60.3	39.7	34.1
Dallas, Tex.	74.0	26.0	80.2	68.8	31.2	19.8
Duluth, Minn.	66.3	33.7	70.1	62.3	37.7	29.9
Indianapolis, Ind. .	59.7	40.3	72.3	56.3	43.7	27.7
Little Rock, Ark. ..	67.7	32.3	71.2	62.3	37.7	28.8
New Orleans, La. ..	69.4	30.6	73.1	60.8	39.2	26.9
New York, N. Y. ...	59.6	40.4	67.8	57.2	42.8	32.2
Roanoke, Va.	64.1	35.9	69.3	59.6	40.4	30.7
Saginaw, Mich. ...	66.5	33.5	67.8	54.1	45.9	32.2
St. Louis, Mo.	63.0	37.0	70.4	55.7	44.3	29.6
Salt Lake City, Utah	65.6	34.4	67.9	61.8	38.2	32.1
Seattle, Wash.	57.5	42.5	68.5	55.5	44.5	31.5
Trenton, N. J.	59.0	41.0	62.7	52.4	47.6	37.3
Weighted average, 15 cities	62.7	37.3				

(a) Monthly Labor Review, October, 1932, pp. 764–765.

ments doing a business of more than $25,000 each, the ratios were 58.3 per cent for materials and 41.7 per cent for labor.

All in all, then, there is firm ground for accepting the traditional 60–40 division, albeit in some sections or communities the ratios may depart considerably from this average. Chart 49 is a graphic presentation of the relative cost of the principal

— CHART 48 —

PERCENTAGE DISTRIBUTION OF LABOR AND MATERIALS COST FOR CERTAIN RESIDENTIAL BUILDING IN FIFTEEN CITIES OF THE UNITED STATES BY MAJOR OPERATIONS:1931-1932

Redrawn from Chart of United States Bureau of Labor Statistics

▨ LABOR   ▢ MATERIALS

	COMBINED COST	LABOR	MATERIALS
EXCAVATING AND GRADING	1.3	98.5%	1.5%
BRICKWORK	14.8	41.6%	58.4%
CARPENTER WORK	27.3	32.9%	67.1%
TILE WORK	3.5	44.0%	56.0%
CONCRETE WORK	11.7	36.5%	63.5%
ELECTRIC WIRING AND FIXTURES	4.5	36.0%	64.0%
HEATING AND VENTILATING	6.6	24.7%	75.3%
PLUMBING	10.1	20.3%	79.7%
PLASTERING AND LATHING	8.2	66.6%	33.4%
PAINTING	4.2	61.5%	38.5%
PAPERING	0.5	55.4%	44.6%
ROOFING	1.8	32.3%	67.7%
MISCELLANEOUS	5.5	24.8%	75.2%
	100.0%	TOTAL 37.3%	62.7%

items in the cost of a home on the 60–40 basis. The upper bar shows the cost of the building only; in the next bars the items for labor and materials contain an allowance for builder's over-

—— CHART 49 ——

PERCENTAGE DISTRIBUTION OF COST OF LABOR AND MATERIALS AND OTHER MAJOR ITEMS COMPOSING COST OF AN URBAN OR SUBURBAN HOME IN THE UNITED STATES (APPROXIMATE):1930

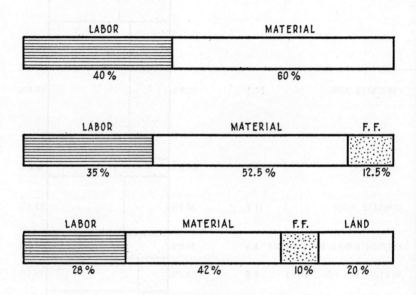

NOTE :- F.F., Fees, Financing, etc.

head and profit; in the second bar there is an allowance for financing cost, while in the last bar the cost of the site is included.[20]

[20] This is in accordance with the arrangement of items given on p. 254, and assumes that the builder did not provide the land. If the home is purchased from a speculative builder, the latter would expect to make a profit on the land and other items, and the percentages for other items in the final bar of the chart would be correspondingly less.

The inclusion of these additional items means that labor and materials constitute a much smaller proportion of the cost of the complete home than they do of the cost of the building alone. Whereas cost of materials represents 60 per cent of the latter, it represents only 36 per cent of the former. Similarly, the cost of labor, which was 40 per cent of the building cost, constitutes only 24 per cent of the home cost. This statement refers to what may be termed construction labor only. As already indicated, a considerable part of the final land cost really is labor cost.[21] [22]

We have thus seen that from the viewpoint of the building contractor the total cost of the house is divided between the 60 per cent cost of materials and the 40 per cent labor of construction and installation. This ratio has persisted to an unusual degree in different periods and regions, even though materials have been sometimes up and sometimes down; in different sections and in houses of different plan and type there is a variation in the ratio, but only a slight one.

From the viewpoint of the owner, more significant ratios are those between the three major factors of structure, finish, and accessories (heating, lighting fixtures, and similar requirements); 40 to 50 per cent of the total cost is required for structure, 35 to 25 per cent for finish, and 25 per cent for accessories. Again, it is extraordinary how these percentages persist, both in the modern urban and rural single dwelling and in the

[21] It is obvious that in the last analysis nearly all the cost is that of labor, since the cost of materials is largely made up of the labor cost of fabricating them.

[22] A table in the Appendix (p. 564) gives the average distribution of the costs for residential building in the fifteen cities referred to on p. 270, first by major operations, such as excavation, brick work, carpentry work and plumbing, and then for each of these operations as between cost of material and labor cost. There is naturally much variation in these proportions. For example, in excavation, plastering, painting, and papering, labor costs run considerably in excess of the cost of materials, whereas in carpentry, electric wiring and fixtures, plumbing, and heating equipment the reverse is ordinarily true. The lower part of this table gives similar distributions for a British cottage.

A distribution of the total cost of materials and of labor, respectively, for a frame house and for a brick house, as computed by the USDC in 1922 is shown in tabular form in the Appendix, p. 565; this table also gives a similar distribution for the British cottage.

large city apartment-house, notwithstanding that the last two
centuries have shown a growing percentage for accessories and
a consequent decreasing one for structure and finish.

COURSE OF BUILDING COSTS

Broadly speaking, the trend of wholesale prices of commodities in the United States during the past 130 years has
been downward. Although this movement has been violently interrupted in three great war periods — the Napoleonic Wars,
the American Civil War, and the World War, the average level
in 1930 was lower than it was in 1800.

The course of dwelling-house costs has by contrast been almost steadily upward; but we must allow for the fact that the
dwelling of 1930 was a very different thing from that of 1800.
It included not only such expensive accessories as bathrooms
and central heating plants but a large number of other features
which were absent or unknown in earlier years. This may seem
to invalidate the comparison; yet to a greater or less degree
similar qualifications apply to most other products. The modern mowing machine and even the plow, for instance, are very
different articles from the early models; the latest steel rail
is almost as far removed from the first flat iron rail as from
a stick of oak timber; there is probably a greater difference between the first automobile and present-day models than between
the house of 1800 and the house of today. Yet, while many of
these other improved products cost less than they formerly did,
the dwelling-house costs more. We shall first consider this upward course of costs in terms of absolute " current " dollars,
and then develop such information as is available regarding index numbers for the cost of dwelling-house construction.

Currency fluctuations introduce difficulties into these comparisons. While in many economic studies index numbers are
corrected to allow for them, no attempt has been made to do so
here; on account of the long period covered this would involve
an undue amount of labor, while in many cases satisfactory data
for such correction are not available.

In the Colonial period, when lumber was almost the sole building material and a supply was to be had practically at the doorstep of the home builder, and wages were low, the cost of shelter was small. Early records contain frequent references to the sale of houses, often with considerable land, for £20, £15, or even less. In 1664 the total value of ninety-five log houses in Dedham was placed as low as £691; only four were valued as high as £20 each.[23] The average sale price of houses changing hands in Plymouth Colony in about 1650 was less than £25, the prevailing value of a bullock was about £6, and that of a cow about £5, and judging from these and other commodity prices houses " quoted at £25 and less were very simple and primitive." [24]

More than a hundred years later, in 1767, a valuation of the town of Haverhill, Massachusetts, listed 281 houses at only £5 each.[25] It seems certain that these valuations were often nominal, but the fragmentary evidence at hand leaves no doubt that the cost of a modest house in those days was but a small fraction of what it is now. Even at this time, however, there were many dwellings rated at much higher values than those cited; a Dutch writer is quoted as recording that in 1681 the City of New York contained 500 houses built with Dutch bricks, " the meanest not valued at less than £100." [26]

In connection with these figures it should be kept in mind that wages in early days were far below those of recent years. In the Colonial period common laborers frequently received only 30 or 40 cents a day, and carpenters in Massachusetts were paid about 75 cents.[27] By 1800 the wages of carpenters were $1 to

[23] Weeden, W. B., " Economic and Social History of New England, 1620–1789 " (Houghton Mifflin Co., Boston, 1890), Vol. I, p. 283.

[24] Whipple, Sherman L., and Waters, Thomas Franklin, " Puritan Homes " (Ipswich Historical Society, Publication No. XXVII, Salem, Massachusetts, 1929), p. 18.

[25] Weeden, W. B., " Economic and Social History of New England, 1620–1789," Vol. II, p. 730.

[26] Quoted by J. L. Bishop in " History of American Manufactures from 1608 to 1860 " (Edward Young & Co., Philadelphia, 1864), Vol. I, p. 224.

[27] In 1630 a Colonial court in Massachusetts ordered that carpenters and certain other building-tradesmen should not receive more than 2 shillings (48.6

$1.25 a day, but the average wages of all workers, even excluding farm labor, were well under $1. Nevertheless, while the low costs of dwellings in the early periods under discussion were partly due to low wages paid building-trades workers — an important factor — and partly to the limitations on purchasing power imposed by wages in general, the pronounced rise in building costs since then reflects many other influences, such as the change in the value of the dollar and in the character of the dwelling, already described.

From the limited information obtainable it is impossible to define a general average of costs for the Colonial period. But with the close of the eighteenth century we can begin to make generalizations. The census of dwelling-houses taken in connection with the federal direct tax of 1798 [28] showed an average value of $508 for 276,695 homes (including the sites) ; [29] since homes valued at $100 and less were excluded, this average must exceed that of all buildings then standing. We may assume that the latter average in 1798 was only about one-half this figure, or $250. Yet there were at this time many homes valued at thousands of dollars each, and the legislation calling for this direct tax provided for graduated rates of taxation for homes worth $30,000 and over.[30]

Such an average valuation may seem low, and it is possible that assessors then underrated, as they have since frequently underrated, the going sale value. There is, nevertheless, plenty of evidence that a modest house could be built in the eastern United States at the close of the Eighteenth Century for a few hundred dollars. It was said of dwellings in Philadelphia in 1793 that "houses of wood are cheaply built. A

---

cents) per day, but owing to a scarcity of such labor the rate actually paid was considerably higher (USBLS, "History of Wages in the United States from Colonial Times to 1928" [GPO, Washington, 1929], p. 47).

[28] See p. 14.

[29] A census of real estate was taken in connection with the direct tax of 1813, but the value of houses was not shown separately from the value of land.

[30] A carefully itemized report of this census for the City of Boston shows many houses valued at several thousand dollars each.

house of two stories, six yards by four, will cost about £50 Sterling." [31]

Tench Coxe, at one time Assistant Secretary of the Treasury, outlined a scheme for creating a market town in Pennsylvania about the year 1790 in which he suggested the erection of 794 brick and stone houses at an estimated cost as follows: [32]

No. of houses	Valuation [a]	
510	$ 300 each	$153,000
220	500 each	110,000
50	800 each	40,000
10	2,000 each	20,000
4	650 each	2,600
794		$325,600
	Average	$410

(a) Inclusive of the value of the lots.

This estimate indicates that a modest dwelling could be obtained at that time for about $300.

In 1840 the Census reported the number of new dwellings erected in the United States; the indicated average cost was approximately $774,[33] ranging from $220 in North Carolina to over $3157 in Louisiana.[34]

Building costs rose sharply after the Civil War, reaching a peak in the Seventies. After a fairly sharp decline they rose gradually during the remainder of the century. In 1900 the average cost was about $1300.

From 1900 to the outbreak of the World War, average costs showed a further gradual increase; after the War an extraordinary rise in costs occurred. This is clearly indicated by Table 58, which shows the annual average cost, exclusive of site, of a

[31] Cooper, Thomas, "Some Information Respecting America" (J. Johnson, London, 1794), p. 95.

[32] Coxe, Tench, "A View of the United States of America" (William Hall and Wrigley and Berriman, Philadelphia, 1794), p. 387.

[33] Apparently this is the only occasion that such information was gathered by the Census. The averages by states are given in the Appendix, p. 567.

[34] Presumably the high average for the latter state was due to the erection of a large number of mansions, since the Massachusetts average was $1759 and that for New York only $1130.

two-story house in Philadelphia and that of apartments and tenements in New York City over a period of years, as indicated by building-permit data.

Since 1920 the United States Bureau of Labor Statistics has regularly collected data on the per-family cost of housing in leading cities, as indicated by building-permit records.[35] The Bureau's averages, shown in Table 59, which do not include the site or the builder's profit, indicate that in these urban communities the average per-family cost of housing of all types since 1921, except in 1932, has been over $4000.

Including rural and farm dwellings, the cost of which cannot be stated, the average would naturally be substantially less. A sample questionnaire study by the President's Conference showed an average cost of $3146 for 1546 such houses for the period 1926–30.[36] For 312 village houses the average was $3912, and for 264 other rural (non-farm) houses $3556. The average cost of 970 farm houses was $2789, but considerable labor performed by farmers and their families was not included.

Following is an approximate estimate of the per-family *cost* of new housing, exclusive of the site, for the entire country, based on scattered data of the miscellaneous character just described. Chart 50 gives the same data in graphic form.

1800	$ 300	1910	1,600
1840	750	1920	4,750
1860	800	1930	3,700
1880	1,100	1932	3,100 [37]
1900	1,300		

[35] Since plans may be amended after they are originally filed, such building-permit data afford only a closely approximate idea of the cost.

[36] The President's Conference on Home Building and Home Ownership, Vol. VII, p. 148. Apparently a majority of these houses were built in the latter half of this five-year period, the highest percentage being for the year 1930. A precise statement cannot be made, since for 20 per cent of these houses the year of construction was not reported.

[37] The average for 1932 here given is decidedly higher than that indicated by the use of index numbers of building costs discussed later. Construction in 1932 was at an abnormally low level, and it seems probable that persons erecting houses in that year had capital or incomes well in excess of the average, and that had building been more active the averages for 1932 would agree more closely with those suggested by the use of index numbers.

TABLE 58

Estimated Average Cost of Two-Story Single-Family Brick Dwellings
in Philadelphia and of All Tenements (Including Apartments)[a] in New York City, 1900–1930

(Based on building-permit data; costs are exclusive of land)[b]

Year	2-story dwellings, Philadelphia	All tenements, New York City
1900	$1,710	
1901	1,640	
1902	1,730	$2,072
1903	1,820	2,111
1904	1,980	2,083
1905	1,930	1,950
1906	1,900	1,881
1907	1,820	1,959
1908	1,920	2,393
1909	1,910	2,693
1910	1,990	2,688
1911	2,090	2,515
1912	2,250	2,359
1913	2,250	2,497
1914	2,020	2,352
1915	2,080	2,091
1916	2,460	2,423
1917	2,650	2,580
1918	3,260	3,053
1919	4,800	2,543
1920	6,820	3,568
1921	4,800	5,574
1922	4,730	4,561
1923	5,570	4,394
1924	5,440	4,525
1925	5,180	4,957
1926	4,640	4,671
1927	4,270	4,314
1928	4,160	4,405
1929	4,220	4,967
1930	4,140	5,656 [c]

(a) The term "tenement" in New York City covers all structures housing three families or more where cooking is done on the premises, whether the cheapest tenement-house or a Park Avenue apartment-house.

(b) The figures for Philadelphia were furnished by the Philadelphia Housing Association; those for New York City were furnished by the Tenement House Commission.

(c) The rise in this year was probably due to exceptional circumstances.

The figures on page 278 are in " current " dollars at time stated. It will be understood that a large part of the marked increase in cost since 1910 is due to the change in the value of

——— CHART 50 ———

COSTS OF HOUSING PER FAMILY, FOR THE BUILDING ONLY (EXCLUSIVE OF THE SITE), IN THE UNITED STATES(APPROXIMATE):1800-1932

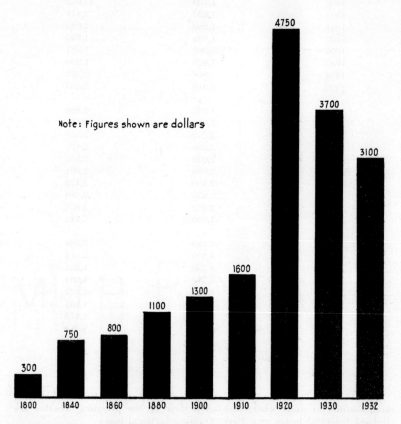

Note: Figures shown are dollars

the dollar as reflected in prices of building materials and in wages. While the more general inclusion of modern accessory equipment since the World War was a factor, this accounts for only a slight proportion of the increase.

TABLE 59

AVERAGE COSTS OF NEW DWELLINGS PER FAMILY IN THE SAME 257
CITIES, 1921–1932 [a]

	One-family	Two-family [b]	Multi-family [c]	All classes
1921	$3,972	$3,762	$4,019	$3,947
1922	4,134	3,801	3,880	4,005
1923	4,203	4,159	4,001	4,127
1924	4,317	4,336	4,418	4,352
1925	4,618	4,421	4,289	4,464
1926	4,725	4,480	4,095	4,422
1927	4,830	4,368	4,170	4,449
1928	4,937	4,064	4,129	4,407
1929	4,915	4,020	4,402	4,566
1930	4,993	3,924	3,857	4,385
1931	4,834	3,607	3,644	4,225
1932	3,943	3,250	3,011	3,705

(a) Monthly Labor Review, April, 1933, p. 845. The Bureau states that
"these costs refer to the cost of the buildings only, and do not include land
costs or profit or loss to the seller or the speculative builder."

(b) Includes one-family and two-family dwellings with stores.

(c) Includes multi-family dwellings with stores.

INDEX-NUMBER COMPARISONS OF FACTORS ENTERING INTO BUILDING COSTS

So far as known, there is no index number for dwelling-house
construction costs. Several index numbers of commercial and
industrial building are available, however, and it is believed
that the index for the latter, especially for frame construction,
reflects fairly well the general course of dwelling-house construction costs; in any case, it is the best measure obtainable.
One such index number [38] is given in Chart 51, which also shows
the course of general wholesale prices, building-material prices,
and building-trade wage rates. The last two index numbers
were constructed on an arbitrary basis, but agree reasonably
well with the results obtained by other agencies using different

[38] That of the American Appraisal Company for industrial construction,
frame type, in eastern cities, going back to 1852. For this extended period
costs for eastern cities were used as being more representative and as more
nearly comparable with the wage data.

methods. Owing to the extreme changes since 1913, index numbers from 1913 to 1932 on a somewhat larger scale are shown separately in Chart 52.[39]

Despite considerable irregularity in the course of building costs as shown by the curves in Charts 51 and 52, the general trend over the entire period was upward, and the index in 1932, even after a marked decline from the peak reached in 1920, was more than two and a half times that for 1852. The index number of general wholesale prices, on the other hand, which was far above that for building costs in 1852, declined steadily from 1855 to 1897 except during the Civil War period. From 1897 it went gradually upward, and under the abnormal conditions incident to the World War later advanced rapidly to a peak nearly three times the level in 1850. This rise was followed by a severe decline in 1921, and after some irregularity there was a precipitate drop in 1931 which brought the curve back approximately to the 1850 level. This decline was continued during 1932, the index in December of that year dropping below 90. While the building-material cost index in Chart 51, broadly speaking, reflected the changes in general wholesale prices, in 1932 it was far above the level of 1850.[40]

The course of building-material prices since the World War, as weighted and averaged by the Division of Building and Housing of the United States Department of Commerce, according to the importance of each in a six-room frame house and a six-room brick house, is shown in Table 60.

From 1850 to 1920 the course of building-trade wage rates, as given in Charts 51 and 52, showed a fair degree of conformity to the course of building-material prices and building costs, although the upward trend of wages was more consistent.[41] Since 1922 the course of building-trade wage rates has

[39] For supporting data for these charts, together with a brief statement of the method of compiling certain of the index numbers, see the Appendix, p. 564 ff.

[40] The trend of costs of building materials as a group is perhaps sufficiently indicated by the charts. The movements of individual items composing this index show considerable differences. See Appendix, p. 564.

[41] This trend of wages alone is more clearly brought out by Chart 53.

— CHART 51 —

INDEX NUMBERS OF WAGES IN THE BUILDING TRADES, BUILDING COSTS
FOR AN INDUSTRIAL BUILDING, BUILDING-MATERIAL PRICES, AND GENERAL
WHOLESALE PRICES IN THE UNITED STATES: 1850-1932

1913 = 100

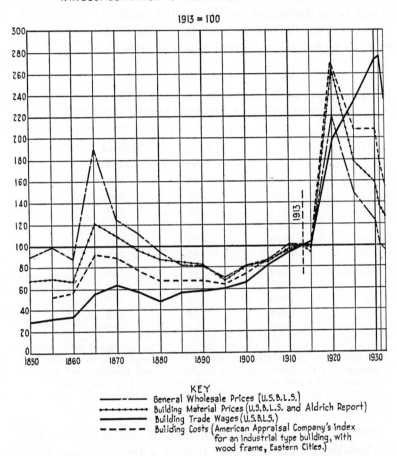

KEY
———·——— General Wholesale Prices (U.S.B.L.S.)
·······•······· Building Material Prices (U.S.B.L.S. and Aldrich Report)
——————— Building Trade Wages (U.S.B.L.S.)
— — — — — Building Costs (American Appraisal Company's index
                                for an industrial type building, with
                                wood frame, Eastern Cities.)

shown marked divergence from that of the three other curves,
advancing to the highest point on record in the face of an abrupt
decline in wholesale prices, building-material prices, and building costs. In 1932 the wage curve declined, but its fall was much
less severe than the drop in the other curves.

The wage curves shown in the charts are based on nominal

hourly rates, which in many cases in 1931 and 1932 were considerably in excess of the rates actually paid; some students estimate that in 1931 actual rates were fully 20 per cent under the nominal rates. In 1932 the situation was recognized to some extent by a downward revision of the nominal rates, but the wage curve for that year, shown in the charts, does not fully reflect the decline that occurred in actual rates.

TABLE 60

INDEX NUMBERS OF PRICES OF BUILDING MATERIALS ENTERING INTO CONSTRUCTION OF A SIX-ROOM HOUSE,[a] 1922–1932

(1913 = 100)

	Frame house	Brick house
1922	182	186
1923	207	209
1924	201	203
1925	196	197
1926	195	195
1927	187	188
1928	178	183
1929	177	182
1930	173	177
1931	158	165
1932	151	157

(a) USDC, "Survey of Current Business." (Annual Supplement, 1932, pp. 36–37, and February, 1932, p. 25). These indices, compiled by the United States Department of Commerce, Division of Building and Housing, and Bureau of the Census, are based upon prices paid for material by contractors in some sixty cities in the United States. The prices are weighted by the relative importance of each commodity in the construction of a six-room house.

Owing to the extensive unemployment among building-trade workers since 1929 it may be that their total earnings fell off quite as sharply as did wholesale prices. This matter of annual earnings is referred to later. It should be emphasized, however, that *for the builder or the home owner the hourly rate is the important figure since it determines the actual cost of construction so far as labor is concerned.*

—— CHART 52 ——

INDEX NUMBERS OF WAGES IN THE BUILDING TRADES, BUILDING COSTS FOR AN INDUSTRIAL BUILDING, BUILDING-MATERIAL PRICES, AND GENERAL WHOLESALE PRICES IN THE UNITED STATES: 1913-1932

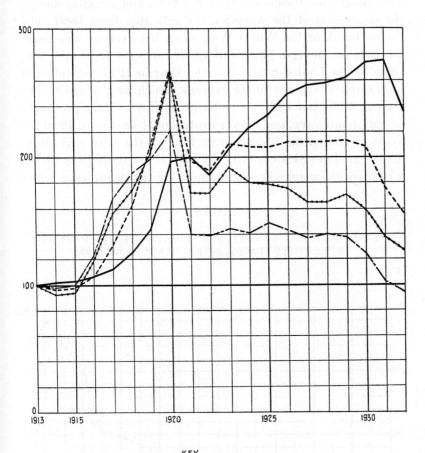

KEY

— — — General Wholesale Prices (U.S.B.L.S.)
•••••••••• Building Material Prices (U.S.B.L.S. and Aldrich Report)
———— Building Trade Wages (U.S.B.L.S.)
— — — — Building Costs (American Appraisal Company's index
for an industrial type building, with
wood frame, Eastern Cities.)

From Chart 53 it will be seen that the average hourly rate of building-trades workers in 1930 was approximately ten times that in 1840; by far the greater part of this advance occurred after 1913. From 1840 to 1849 the combined hourly rate for various trades was fairly steady at around 15 cents. After a sharp advance incident to the Civil War, and a decline during the depression of the seventies, the rate rose from 1880 until the outbreak of the World War, when the average was about 53 cents per hour, or three and a half times the 1840 rate. The entry of the United States into the War in 1917 was followed by a fairly sharp rise in the average, which went above $1 per hour in 1920 and 1921. A moderate decline in 1922 proved to be only temporary, and in every subsequent year until 1932 the average showed an advance over that of the year preceding, finally reaching $1.43 in 1931; by 1933 it had declined to $1.20. These are the nominal rates as shown by the union wage scales

— CHART 53 —

AVERAGE HOURLY RATES OF WAGES OF BUILDING-TRADES WORKERS
IN THE UNITED STATES (APPROXIMATE): 1840-1932

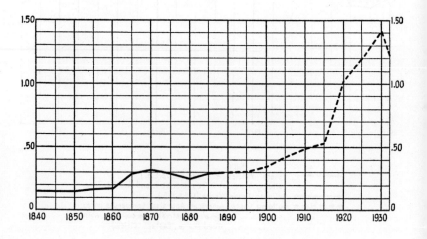

collected by the United States Bureau of Labor Statistics. As just stated, in many cases there was considerable cutting of these rates in 1930 and 1931, and it is probable that the open reduction in 1933 did not adequately represent the actual decline.

This discussion throws into high relief the importance of building-trades wages and indicates some dislocation. A superficial effort to blame high costs of building upon wages solely would have no place in this real effort to establish and arrange facts. But we are brought squarely to the consideration of the difficult question of wages in the building trades.

HOURLY AND ANNUAL EARNINGS OF BUILDING-TRADE AND OTHER WORKERS

A general comparison of hourly rates in the building industry and in manufacturing industries collectively is given in Table 61. It will be seen that whereas rates for unskilled labor showed only a small difference between the two groups, the rates of skilled workers in the building industry were in many years about double those in manufacturing industries. Chart 54 [42] shows that while the wages of all groups increased sharply from 1890 to 1926, the greatest actual increase was in the building trades.

A comparison of hourly rates as between different groups may be misleading because of differences in working conditions; in the building trades in particular, the exceptional amount of seasonal unemployment must be taken into account.[43] It is generally agreed that the best basis for income comparisons as between occupational groups is the total amount of wages actually received in the course of a year. On the other hand, as

[42] Douglas, Paul H., "Real Wages in the United States, 1890–1926." The Pollak Foundation, Newton, Massachusetts. Corresponding figures will be found in Appendix Table X, p. 572.

[43] This matter is referred to in Chapter IV, where it is shown that building-trade workers in the United States on the average lose more than 20 per cent of potential working time. Some estimates run much higher.

—— CHART 54 ——

AVERAGE HOURLY EARNINGS OF WORKERS IN VARIOUS INDUSTRIES
IN THE UNITED STATES (ESTIMATED) : 1890-1926

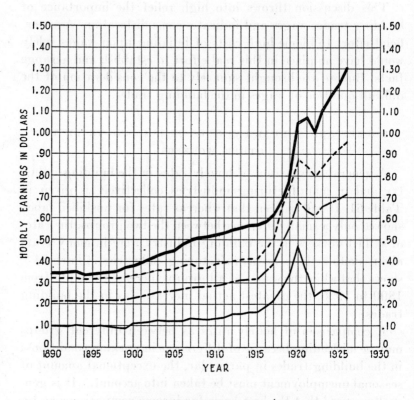

BUILDING TRADES (Based on Union Rates)
METAL TRADES (Based on Union Rates)
COTTON MANUFACTURING (Based on Payrolls)
ALL INDUSTRIES

already pointed out, from the standpoint of the home builder
and owner the hourly rate is the significant thing.

Such a comparison of annual earnings is given in Table 62.
It indicates that even after allowing for unemployment, the
annual earnings of building-trade workers were in excess of
those for any other group in every year with the exception of

1918 and 1919, when they were exceeded slightly by those of workers in the iron and steel industry.

TABLE 61

COMPARISON OF HOURLY WAGE RATES IN THE BUILDING TRADES AND IN MANUFACTURING INDUSTRIES, 1910–1931 [a]

Wage Rates per Hour

| | Building (Engineering News-Record) | | Manufacturing (National Industrial Conference Board) | |
	Skilled	Unskilled	Skilled	Unskilled
1910	$0.525	$0.179	—	—
1911	.534	.179	—	—
1912	.542	.182	—	—
1913	.555	.19	—	—
1914	.565	.177	—	—
1915	.57	.182	—	—
1916	.58	.192	—	—
1917	.61	.281	—	—
1918	.68	.38	—	—
1919	.78	.466	—	—
1920	1.05	.579	$0.692	$0.548
1921	1.06	.54	.594	.446
1922	1.00	.442	.562	.409
1923	1.10	.518	.616	.451
1924	1.19	.555	.638	.473
1925	1.22	.538	.641	.469
1926	1.26	.548	.647	.477
1927	1.32	.554	.652	.490
1928	1.35	.5558	.658	.494
1929	1.36	.5465	.670	.503
1930	1.38	.5607	.667	.495
1931	1.27	.5002	.634	.461

(a) "Construction Costs, 1932" (Engineering News-Record, New York, 1932), p. 17.

In Table 63 and Chart 55 these annual averages for building-trade workers [44] are compared with combined averages for workers "attached to" the manufacturing, transportation, and coal-mining industries.[45]

[44] Douglas, Paul H., "Real Wages in the United States, 1890–1926." The Pollak Foundation, Newton, Massachusetts.

[45] Workers "attached to" the industry include those who would normally be eligible to employment but some of whom are unemployed for a considerable

TABLE 62

Estimated Average Annual Earnings in Various Industries in the
United States, 1890–1926 [a]

Year	Building industry [b]	Iron and steel industry	Cotton goods [c]	Boots and shoes [c]	All mfg.	Unskilled labor [b]	All industry exclusive of farm labor
1890		$556	$307	$461	$439		$486
1891		567	311	457	442		489
1892		559	312	466	446		497
1893		532	338	441	420		483
1894		481	278	447	386		457
1895		519	294	428	416		478
1896		491	291	422	406		472
1897	$598	493	278	413	408	$367	474
1898	631	515	268	402	412	374	482
1899	713	529	286	412	426	405	493
1900	673	538	312	409	435	410	503
1901	778	553	310	428	456	436	518
1902	828	575	330	435	473	445	530
1903	812	588	334	463	486	456	548
1904	858	566	305	461	477	443	546
1905	939	588	305	486	494	466	559
1906	1,029	617	336	494	506	484	571
1907	916	636	377	511	522	495	593
1908	754	569	372	495	475	442	564
1909	919	629	351	499	518	496	594
1910	956	651	350	519	558	506	627
1911	906	652	348	528	537	496	624
1912	1,023	665	374	537	550	521	638

(a) Douglas, Paul H., "Real Wages in the United States, 1890–1926" (Published by Houghton Mifflin Co., Boston, for the Pollak Foundation, Newton, Massachusetts, 1930), pp. 271, 258, 287, 246, 472, 477, 391.

(b) It should be noted that Douglas' averages for building-trade workers allow for unemployment. Apparently the other averages allow for unemployment among workers *employed* in the industries, but not among all workers *attached* to the industry.

(c) The Douglas averages for these items are partly explained by the fact that they include earnings of women and minors.

---

part of the time. The amount of unemployment among this group would therefore be greater and the average annual earnings somewhat less than for the group considered as actually engaged in the industry.

TABLE 62 (*continued*)

Year	Building industry [b]	Iron and steel industry	Cotton goods [c]	Boots and shoes [c]	All mfg.	Unskilled labor [b]	All industry exclusive of farm labor
1913	1,000	700	394	566	578	536	666
1914	845	711	387	552	580	492	673
1915	890	684	401	538	568	515	672
1916	1,056	820	456	601	651	625	748
1917	1,108	1,012	548	657	774	754	866
1918	1,266	1,324	726	800	980	1,039	1,088
1919	1,444	1,487	825	999	1,158	1,128	1,245
1920	1,791	1,725	1,026	1,144	1,358	1,207	1,459
1921	1,764	1,331	797	1,117	1,180	780	1,321
1922	1,816	1,290	750	1,081	1,149	807	1,291
1923	2,052	1,533	841	1,108	1,254	1,030	1,379
1924	1,966	1,514	770	1,073	1,240	996	1,375
1925	2,163	1,569	793	1,091	1,280	1,065	1,409
1926	2,417 [d]	1,604	792	1,086	1,309	1,095	1,444

(*d*) As noted in connection with Table 64, Douglas' average of $2417 for building-trade workers in 1926 seems too high. This is suggested by an analysis of other wage data covering a limited section of the country.

After allowing for the difficulties involved in computations of this sort, the data just presented show clearly that both the hourly rates of wages and the annual earnings of building-trade workers in the United States have been in varying degrees in excess of those in the other important industrial groups covered. They also show clearly that the relatively high rates in the building trades are not to be explained solely by seasonal unemployment or time lost from other causes.

While the high wages paid building-trade workers does not necessarily result in a proportionately higher purchasing power, it certainly raises the cost of their product to other workers, who are prevented from purchasing the product; this in turn leads to unemployment of the very people who have obtained the wage. Other workers who do buy the housing product are debarred from purchasing other things, owing to the excessive cost of the house, and this in turn reacts on the demand for products of other industries and the resulting employment.

TABLE 63

Estimated Average Annual Earnings of Building-Trades Workers and of Workers in Manufacturing, Transportation, and Coal Mining Combined, after Allowance for Unemployment, United States, 1897–1926 [a]

Year	A [b] Building-trades workers	B Workers "attached" to mfg., transportation, and coal mining	Per cent A of B [c]
1897	$598	$363	164
1898	631	370	171
1899	713	412	173
1900	673	427	157
1901	778	453	172
1902	828	471	176
1903	812	492	165
1904	858	469	183
1905	939	495	189
1906	1,029	511	201
1907	916	537	171
1908	754	454	166
1909	919	516	178
1910	956	561	170
1911	906	541	168
1912	1,023	566	181
1913	1,000	587	171
1914	845	544	155
1915	890	544	163
1916	1,056	671	157
1917	1,108	795	139
1918	1,266	1,027	123
1919	1,444	1,167	124
1920	1,791	1,379	129
1921	1,764	1,008	175
1922	1,816	1,027	177
1923	2,052	1,256	163
1924	1,966	1,196	164
1925	2,163	1,262	171
1926	2,417 [d]	1,304	185

(a) Douglas, Paul H., "Real Wages in the United States, 1890–1926," pp. 468, 472. The Pollak Foundation, Newton, Massachusetts.

(b) Douglas states that since these figures are based on *union* rates and

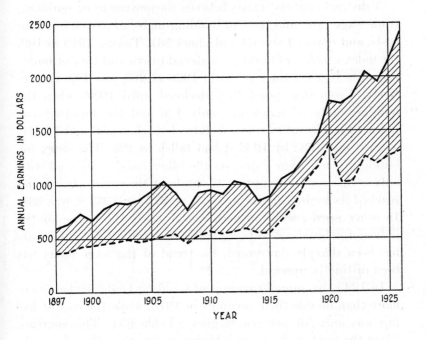

—— CHART 55 ——

AVERAGE ANNUAL EARNINGS OF BUILDING-TRADES WORKERS AND OF
WORKERS IN MANUFACTURING, TRANSPORTATION, AND COAL-
MINING COMBINED, IN THE UNITED STATES(ESTIMATED): 1897-1926

Charted from Paul H. Douglas', "Real Wages in the United
States 1890 –1926," published by the Pollak Foundation, Newton, Mass.

KEY
—— Building Trade Workers
– – – – Manufacturing, Transportation and Coal-Mining Workers
Shaded area between curves shows excess of Building
Trade Workers over Industrial Workers

To be economically justifiable, high wages for the building
trades would have to be a result of increased efficiency of the
industry, lowering the cost of the product, and making it avail-

do not take account of brief periods of broken time, they are "undoubtedly
too high." He considers the relative change from year to year fairly accurate.
  (c) Computed from Douglas' data.
  (d) This figure is apparently too high.

able to more people. In this event the high wages would be real and not fictitious and would actually add to the purchasing power of the group and hence to the national wealth.

COMPARISON OF BUILDING-TRADE WAGES, RENTS, AND COST OF LIVING IN THE UNITED STATES

A distinct contrast exists between the movement of building-trade wage rates and those of building-material prices, building costs, and rents (Table 64 and Chart 56). Taking 1913 as 100, the index number of building-material prices and that of building costs reached their peaks in 1920 at 265 and 269, respectively. From that point they declined until 1932, when the building-material index was only 126 and the building-cost index 145. The index for rent did not reach a peak until 1924, when it was 168; by 1932 it had fallen to 123. The index for building-trade wage rates, on the other hand, advanced with only occasional interruption throughout the entire period and reached its highest figure in 1931, at 276; in 1932 it was 235. In other words, while in most recent years the course of the indices for building costs, building-material prices, and rents has been sharply downward, the trend of the wage index has been distinctly upward.

In 1925 the annual earnings of building-trade workers were more than double their earnings in 1913, while the cost of living was only 76 per cent higher (Table 65). This increase lifted the workers to a much higher status than they formerly enjoyed as measured by the cost of living, and apparently raised their income status relative to that of industrial workers in general. It will be recalled, moreover, that the *hourly* rate of building-trade wages, which rather than the annual earnings is of importance in the cost of rent, advanced even more sharply than did the annual earnings of building-trade workers.

A general average of annual earnings of building-trade workers since 1926 is not available.[46] Owing to the abnormal amount

[46] For 1929 the report of the Census upon the construction industry gave the average wages paid on all classes of work as $1771. This figure is not

TABLE 64

COMPARISON OF INDEX NUMBERS OF WHOLESALE PRICES OF BUILDING
MATERIALS, HOURLY WAGES IN THE BUILDING TRADES, COST OF
BUILDING, AND RENTS IN THE UNITED STATES,
1913–1932

	Building-material [a] prices	Hourly [b] wage-rate in building trades	Building [c] costs	Rents [d]
1913	100	100	100	100
1914	93	101.9	96.7	100
1915	94	102.8	98.5	101.5
1916	119	106.2	109.3	102.3
1917	156	112.8	133.7	100.1
1918	174	125.2	164.3	109.2
1919	204	145.4	212.1	119.7
1920	265	196.8	268.7	143.0
1921	172	200.3	195.9	160.1
1922	172	187.5	189.6	161.2
1923	192	207.3	208.9	164.1
1924	180	224.0	204.8	167.8
1925	179	232.7	202.0	167.2
1926	176	248.0	203.8	164.8
1927	167	256.7	204.3	161.1
1928	166	258.1	203.5	156.7
1929	168	261.6	204.3	152.8
1930	159	272.8	195.4	148.0
1931	140	276.3	165.6	139.1
1932	126	235.0	145.1	122.9

(a) Monthly Labor Review, February, 1933, p. 424.

(b) Ibid., November, 1932, p. 1153.

(c) Industrial frame building, for *the entire country* (The American Appraisal Co., "Clients Service Bulletin," Vol. X, No. 1).

(d) The index for rent is for the month of December from 1914 to 1918 inclusive, and the average of such monthly figures (two or more) as were given for later years (Monthly Labor Review, February, 1933, pp. 430–431).

directly comparable with those of Mr. Douglas, but seems to support the view that his average for 1926 was too high (" Census of the Construction Industry," p. 38).

— CHART 56 —

COMPARISONS OF INDEX NUMBERS OF WHOLESALE PRICES OF BUILDING MATERIALS, HOURLY WAGES IN THE BUILDING TRADES, COST OF BUILDINGS, AND RENTS, IN THE UNITED STATES: 1913-1932

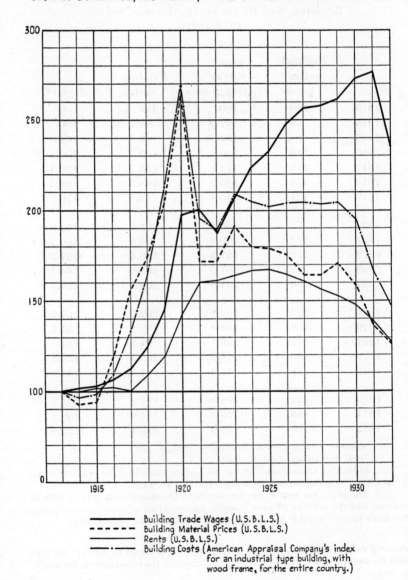

——————— Building Trade Wages (U.S.B.L.S.)
– – – – – Building Material Prices (U.S.B.L.S.)
——————— Rents (U.S.B.L.S.)
—·—·— Building Costs (American Appraisal Company's index
        for an industrial type building, with
        wood frame, for the entire country.)

of unemployment since 1929, such figures, even if obtainable, would have little significance. The cost-of-living index continued to decline, reaching 134 in 1932. Annual earnings, as a

TABLE 65

COMPARISON OF ESTIMATED ANNUAL EARNINGS OF BUILDING-TRADE WORKERS IN THE UNITED STATES WITH INDEX FOR COST OF LIVING, 1913–1926

	Annual earnings of building-trade workers [a]	Index number	Cost-of-living index [b]
1913	$1,000	100	100
1914	845	85	103
1915	890	89	105
1916	1,056	106	118
1917	1,108	111	142
1918	1,266	127	174
1919	1,444	144	188
1920	1,791	179	208
1921	1,764	176	177
1922	1,816	182	167
1923	2,052	205	171
1924	1,966	197	171
1925	2,163	216	176
1926	2,417 [c]	242	175

(a) As computed by Paul H. Douglas, " Real Wages in the United States, 1890–1926." Published by The Pollak Foundation, Newton, Massachusetts. See Table 63, p. 292. Douglas' computations did not extend beyond 1926. In view of the unusual conditions prevailing since 1928, figures of annual earnings would be of little significance.

(b) USBLS, Monthly Labor Review, February, 1932, p. 465. Figures from 1914 to 1918 are for the month of December; for subsequent years they are averages of two to four monthly figures.

(c) This figure is apparently too high.

result of widespread unemployment, doubtless fell sharply and possibly faster than the cost of living. To some extent the lack of employment in the building trades may have been due to the high rates of wages demanded.

HOURS OF WORK IN THE BUILDING TRADES AND OTHER
INDUSTRIES

Workers in the building trades, as the public is aware, have much shorter working hours than do most wage-earning groups; this advantage or differential has existed for more than forty years. From 1840 to 1885 the hours of work in the building trades were practically the same as those of railroad workers, ten per day. Although substantially less than those of textile workers, they were only slightly under those of workers in twenty-one representative industries combined. From 1885 to 1900 the work day was shortened more rapidly in the building industry than in other leading industries. Since 1900 there has been a shortening of the work week in industry in general. The building trades, however, continued to enjoy shorter hours than any other major group. The fairly rapid spread of the five-day week in these trades in recent years has brought the average hours of building-trade workers in a large number of communities down to forty per week, whereas the standard hours in manufacturing industry as a whole are approximately fifty per week.[47]

This decline in the average working hours for building-trade workers is in line with the general tendency of mass production. Unfortunately, in this case the decline is not paralleled by an increased efficiency or other benefits of mass production, and the result is a product more costly and less available.

[47] United States Senate (Aldrich), " Wholesale Prices, Wages, and Transportation " (GPO, Washington, 1893), pp. 178–179. For manufacturing industries in the United States the average or usual hours of work in selected years were computed by the National Industrial Conference Board from census and other official data as follows:

Year	Hours	Year	Hours
1899	59.6	1919	50.8
1904	57.9	1921	50.3
1909	56.8	1923	50.4
1914	55.1	1929	50.6

(NICB, " Service Letter on Industrial Relations," October 30, 1932, p. 462).

The hours discussed in the above paragraph take no account of the shortening of working time recently effected under the National Recovery Act.

BUILDING COSTS IN GREAT BRITAIN AND OTHER COUNTRIES

No satisfactory index of building costs in Great Britain, for any such extended period as was covered in Charts 51 and 52 for the United States, was located. For a period of forty years prior to the World War prices of certain important building materials in Great Britain showed a marked downward tendency. The course of building-trade wages, however, was almost steadily upward.

TABLE 66

APPROXIMATE SQUARE-FOOT COSTS OF CONSTRUCTION FOR GOVERN-
MENT-AIDED HOUSES IN GREAT BRITAIN, 1914–1927 [a]

	Cost per square foot (Pence)	Index numbers
1914 (pre-War)	66	100
1919, May to July	195	295
1920, June to August	238	361
1920, October to December	229	347
1921	150	227
1922	99	150
1923	119	180
1924	131	198
1925	132	200
1926	133	202
1927	121	183

(a) Unwin, Sir Raymond, " House Building Costs in England and Wales " (International Housing and Town Planning Congress Report, Paris, 1928), p. 123.

The close of the World War was followed in Great Britain by a pronounced rise in building-material prices, wages, and building costs. In 1920 the cost of building was more than three and a half times the cost before the War. This is shown in Table 66, which gives the course of square-foot costs for government-aided houses under British subsidy schemes since the War.[48] Chart 57 shows the index numbers for these square-foot

[48] Unwin, Sir Raymond, " House Building Costs in England and Wales," p. 123.

costs since the War, together with a very rough estimate of the
course of costs for a considerable period before it, based on the
costs of brick and lumber and building-trade wages. While this
does not give an accurate statement of building costs in any
year, it indicates the general trend.

The course of wholesale prices of building materials in Great
Britain since the War shows a general correspondence with

—— CHART 57 ——

COURSE OF BUILDING COSTS IN GREAT BRITAIN (APPROXIMATE)
1871-1932

Estimated from index numbers of Building Material prices,
Building Trade wages and Building costs as compiled by
various official sources, except that from 1927 they are based
on unofficial data.

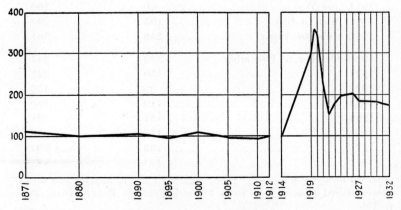

changes in the United States. The movement of building-trade
wages in the two countries, however, discloses a sharp contrast.

In Great Britain, as in the United States, there was a pronounced rise in building-trade wages immediately after the
War, but whereas in the United States a brief recession after
1920 was followed by a renewed upward movement, continuing
until 1931, in Great Britain the peak of wages was reached in
1920 and was followed by a substantial decline in the next two
years, after which the rates remained almost stationary with,

indeed, a slight downward tendency. The result is that while in the United States the average hourly rate in 1932 was 130 per cent above the 1914 level, that in Great Britain was only 92 per cent higher.[49] A table in the Appendix (p. 575) gives the

—— CHART 58 ——

AVERAGE HOURLY RATES OF WAGES IN THE BUILDING TRADES
IN THE UNITED STATES AND IN GREAT BRITAIN: 1914-1932

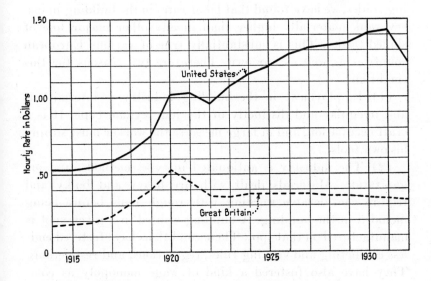

Note:- United States averages are from National Bureau of Economic Research and United States Bureau of Labor Statistics. British averages are from various official sources. They are the rates prevailing on December 31 of each year for large Towns. In converting from pence to cents one penny was taken as equal to two cents in all years irrespective of fluctuations in Sterling Exchange. The purpose of this Chart is to bring out the divergence in trend for the period.

hourly rates of the principal groups of workers in the building trades of Great Britain on selected dates. The comparative movement of hourly building-trade wages in the two countries is shown in Chart 58.

[49] The British rates are weighted averages for seven occupations groups in the industry. The actual rates, by occupations, will be found in the Appendix, p. 576.

In almost all European countries there were pronounced increases in wholesale prices, building-material prices, wage rates, and building costs after the War; neither space nor available data permit of an extended comparison. In nearly all countries there have been substantial declines from the peak figures, but in most of them building costs are still well above those of the pre-War era.

Reverting for a moment to the question of wages in the building trades, we have found that labor rates in the building industry rank materially higher than in any other major line of skilled trades. This is substantially true of various European countries as well as our own. There are two reasons for this condition:

(1) Employment in the building industry is intermittent and irregular and distinctly of the journeyman type. It is a craft occupation, and in large measure the worker must supply his own tools.

(2) The industry is antiquated in type, methods, and organization. Materials dealt with are heavy and bulky and require considerable working with rough tools before being included in the building. A building wanted in a given spot is manufactured on that spot. These conditions have fostered endless conflicting and varying rules, regulations, and restrictions. They have also fostered a kind of wage monopoly as compared with other skilled labor working under more favorable conditions.

The condition resulting from the first cause (a lower number of possible working hours through the year) seems to be a perfectly reasonable one. Obviously, if the conditions are unfavorable to continuous work, society should pay higher rates than in occupations where weather and other conditions are more favorable. Yet our information indicates that actual yearly earnings in the building trades are normally more than in other skilled trades, though not in the same proportion as wage rates. It seems clear, therefore, that not only are the rates of wages substantially higher in the building trades than in other comparable occupations, but annual earnings as well. The cost of this excess naturally falls most heavily upon those occupied at the lowest rates of pay or at the lowest annual earnings — the common laborers and the skilled laborers who are on the lower end of the wage scale and earnings, and in recent years a large number of the so-called " white-collar " class.

A much improved economic condition, i.e., a better general business condition, would result in the country as a whole if the higher and lower rates of pay and earnings in the skilled trades could be more nearly harmonized. It is not clear just how this can be brought about; it does seem certain that if the low rates could be moved up toward the average there would be a distinct economic improvement, and increased buying power would be given to a mass of people; recent technological improvement in the textile industry appears to justify such an increase. Perhaps if the top wage rates in the building industry were to be lowered toward those of the average skilled workman, the increase in work both as to quantity and as to duration which might result would mean no diminution in annual earnings but a lower cost of building to everybody else. A more satisfactory solution would be for the industry to develop an efficiency which would justify the present high wages and result in a cheaper product, regardless of the high wage, which would then no longer be synonymous with high labor costs; the general business situation would improve, to the benefit of all. The obsolete organization of the building industry is the chief cause of the current building wage scales. No great harmonizing in labor costs between this industry and others can be expected while such inefficiency lasts; nor can the bad social and hygienic conditions incident to slums be permanently prevented.

As long as the building industry remains thus backward, wage rates will probably be high, individual employment and earnings unsatisfactory, and total employment and the total wage bill in the industry distinctly low. Were the building process and organization to be brought up to date, however, building work and the total yearly wage bill would doubtless increase, especially if wage rates were to drop to a level comparable to the median wage line of other skilled occupations. The industry is clearly standing in the way of its own progress.

Whether or not the higher wage rates current in the building industry are earned, the owner or buyer of a home has to meet them. If by new building methods the efficiency of production could be increased and continuity of employment assured to the laborer, both the owner and the wage-earner would profit. Great reductions have been effected in the labor cost of production in other things with concurrent improvement in employment conditions, and changes in building methods might bring similar results. One obviously desirable change is from craft methods applied in the field to more precise and better coordinated methods applied in the shop. If houses could be produced largely in factories, it would mean more continuous employment under better conditions, and lower housing costs.

No practical method, however, has thus far been proposed for doing satisfactorily in the shop the work of manufacturing now done in the field. Some authorities assert that for various reasons it cannot be done; others believe that it can be accomplished with general advantage to home production. Savings in this field call for a more homogeneous structure, better adapted to production in the shop, and simpler, more positive field methods of erection.

This same conclusion was reached in Chapter II, in which the actual character of the present-day house was considered. Integration of structure and finish is needed, and from the data presented in this chapter it is evident that savings would undoubtedly be effected by changes in that direction.

In the cost of the house, we find that the 60 per cent for the cost of materials is the largest factor, the remaining 40 per cent being labor for field manufacture and erection. If some of the structure could serve as finish and some of the finish as structure, and if that combination could partly provide for accessories, the design would be simpler and the building more homogeneous. In some materials such a combination could be effected almost perfectly, in other materials only partially. Yet if this integration could be accomplished one quarter of the present cost of the house might be saved, perhaps more.

The saving effected by these means would include its proportion of the total labor cost, that is, 40 per cent of the whole. A further reduction in the labor item might be made through changes in methods in the actual technique of building. A quarter of the total labor expense amounting to one-tenth of the entire present cost of the house might well be saved in this latter way.

Putting this one-tenth together with the 25 per cent saved through materials and design we have a total of 35 per cent. This estimate seems conservative. It is roughly one-third of the cost of the house. Applied to the cost of an average suburban home which includes land and improvements it would approach a quarter.

In other countries of comparable, if lesser, industrial development houses are for the most part without cellars and of a more homogeneous and simple structure. Bricks or other masonry are used to a greater extent for the exterior walls. The extent of possible savings would be less because of the greater simplicity of the house. Even in such countries, however, new structural design, new methods of construction, and especially new materials may confidently be expected substantially to reduce housing costs and improve quality.

Perhaps future savings cannot be mathematically calculated from data based on traditional methods. Nevertheless, a broad and comprehensive view of the entire problem assures us that one-third of the present cost of housing in this country can be saved when this industry is modernized, as most of the others have been.

CHAPTER VIII

Government Restrictions on Building

WHATEVER the form of power controlling group life, it has always imposed regulations and restrictions on building materials and methods. The earliest of these were enforced to gratify the whims or convenience of the " old man," the chief, or other ruler. But beginning 2000 years before the Christian era, as we trace the Greek and Roman records and the various succeeding civilizations of Western Europe, we find such regulations directed increasingly toward the public welfare.

Present-day government exercises a strict control over building construction. Such control has to do primarily with mass welfare, for instance protection from conflagrations, of which the Middle Ages in Europe provide numerous examples. Regard for health has resulted, in more recent times, in sanitary and hygienic regulations. The management and use of the public services involved an increasing network of regulatory measures having to do both with practical business and engineering and with the health of the users of such services. Beginning almost with earliest recorded history, we find measures of control dealing with the strength of materials, and the methods by which they shall be built into the structure, in order that collapse and injury may not result. There are also regulations directed to beauty, defense, and other social purposes, not unlike modern zoning laws.

Since the ideal and objective of all such measures is the general good of the group, there has developed an increasing complexity of social, economic, technical, scientific, political, and spiritual considerations. It is not strange that the influence of such motives upon governmental action should result in strangely thwarting the basic purposes of its regulatory measures. Legislation often defeats the very purposes for which it is devised.

Government of all kinds and in all ages is likely to be ultraconservative, dilatory, and slow-moving, especially democratic government. However expert and able may be its chief administrative officers and staff, its law-making bodies are for the most part submerged by the wide variety of matters upon which they must act, and by the seemingly infinite detail with which each is surrounded. Furthermore, legislation involving distinctly scientific and technical features is much too often influenced by the ignorance of the masses and by the political intrigue of their representatives.

Thus we are likely to find the laws that regulate building construction poorly directed, not so fully representative of the best scientific and technical thought as they might be, and constantly tending to obsolescence and the waste incident to the playing of politics. With the divided, subdivided, and subsubdivided organization of the building industry preventing concerted action, with the rapid changes in housing demands incident to our intensified urbanization, and with the great changes and improvements made in building materials, it is small wonder that our building laws are out of date. The extent to which they are so can be made clear in a few pages.

In all civilized countries, governments intervene in methods of building construction for these purposes:

(1) To promote safety; to ensure sound construction, protection against fire, etc.

(2) To promote health, by requiring certain standards of ventilation, sanitation, etc.

(3) To promote sound social growth by zoning and city planning.

All these regulations have generally been upheld by the

courts as a legitimate exercise of public authority, either in the form of police powers or otherwise. The prospective builder ordinarily is required to obtain a " building permit " before commencing construction.

Of such regulatory legislation, that contained in building codes is the most extensive and perhaps the most important. It was shown in Volume I that such building code legislation dates back many centuries and has been enacted in many countries. At the cost of repetition a few instances may be noted.

As far back as 2000 B.C. the civil code of King Khammurabi of Babylon contained a provision that in case a house collapsed and caused the death of the owner its builder should be put to death.[1] In Rome there is evidence of extensive public welfare regulation of building, at least as far back as the beginning of the Christian era.

" So much depended upon the excellence of the building in Rome, and upon the materials and methods employed, that building laws or municipal regulations were enacted in the ancient city, prescribing kind and quality of material, thickness of walls, maximum height of buildings, minimum width of streets, and many other provisions quite similar to those enacted in our modern cities." [2]

In the time of Augustus Caesar because of the construction of high apartment-houses an ordinance was passed limiting the height of buildings to 70 feet.[1]

In England public regulation of building construction dates at least before the year 1200. An " assize of buildings " passed in 1189 at the instance of the first Lord Mayor of London, following a serious fire,[3] provided that party walls must be of

[1] Burton, Frank, " A History of Building Codes " (Quarterly of the National Fire Protection Association, April, 1930, pp. 365–367).

[2] Burr, W. H., " Ancient and Modern Engineering and the Isthmian Canal " (John Wiley and Sons, London, 1902), p. 27.

[3] While building codes today are quite as much concerned with considerations of structural safety as with fire risks, in early times they were more occupied with the problem of protection against fire, and their modification often was brought about by a serious conflagration.

According to one writer, in King Alfred's reign it was the custom in England to cover up all fires at a fixed hour. William the Conqueror found

stone and 3 feet in thickness. In 1212 an ordinance stated that roofs could not be covered with thatch but must be tiled.[4] Considerable difficulty was encountered in attempting to enforce these provisions. In 1619 a proclamation issued by King James I prohibited the construction of houses with stories overhanging each other and ordered that in future walls should be built straight from the foundation to the parapet. Twelve years later another proclamation was issued regulating the height of rooms, the size and shape of windows, and other details of construction.[5] After the Great London Fire in 1666, Sir Christopher Wren urged in vain a comprehensive scheme for rebuilding, with provision for wide streets and parks. A law of 1667, providing for rebuilding the city, had certain resemblances to a modern building code; it established the height of ceilings and the thickness of walls, and contained detailed specifications for the construction of chimneys and the size of timber for certain purposes; district surveyors were appointed to enforce the law.[4] In 1670 a fee of 6s. 8d. was established for a building permit; [4] this was to go to the surveyor and included his fee for staking out foundations. Whether this was the beginning of the permit system is not known. Gradually the codes of various countries were expanded and elaborated, until today practically every leading nation has a large body of laws, ordinances, or other regulations covering the construction of buildings.

In the United States building codes are in the main confined to urban and suburban communities. Usually they are in the form of local ordinances, designed to meet the broad requirements of state legislation. The Federal Government does not legislate on building except for the District of Columbia;

---

this custom useful and ordained that it should be rigidly carried out upon the ringing of a bell. The Norman for covering fire was "couvre feu," whence the English word curfew (Gamble, S. G., "A Practical Treatise on Outbreaks of Fire" [Charles Griffin and Company, Limited, London, 1926], pp. 2–3).

4 Burton, Frank, "A History of Building Codes," pp. 369 and 374–375.

5 Bernan, Walter (Meikleham, R.), "On the History and Art of Warming and Ventilating Rooms and Buildings" (George Belt, London, 1845), Vol. I, Essay VII.

certain departments of the government, notably the Department of Commerce, have, however, done a good deal of educational work looking toward the improvement of the building-code legislation of the various states.

The grounds of safety on which local governing bodies interpose their authority relate principally to loading requirements, to quality and strength of materials, to design elements such as thickness of walls and strength of members, and to fire protection. For example, building codes almost invariably provide that floors shall be capable of sustaining certain loads and that walls and roofs shall be able to withstand certain wind pressures, and that the quality of materials shall not be below stated standards. Likewise, steel, concrete, timber, and other materials must be capable of sustaining specified stresses.

With respect to design, there are provisions regulating the ratio between height and thickness of walls, the bracing of structural work, the spacing of girders, and the minimum dimensions and weights of certain materials, as well as allowable stresses. In the matter of fire protection most codes contain elaborate provisions — permissible height of building, permissible area between partitions, protection of steel by incombustible covering, requirements for standpipes, the arrangement, number, and width of stairways, and other means of ready egress. It is evident that such codes exert an important influence upon the structure of the house; they not only determine the material which may be used but have a definite bearing upon design.

Health and sanitary regulations control the character of plumbing with a view to reasonable accommodation and the protection of health. Rules for ventilation deal not only with the number and size of windows but also with their arrangement. Minimum heights of rooms are often prescribed, as well as vent shafts for toilets, kitchenettes, public halls, and stairways. Such regulations frequently insist upon certain distances between detached buildings and depths of backyards, and specify the proportions of the building lot. Like building-code regulations, they have a definite effect upon the character of the dwelling.

Zoning and city-planning regulations, while related to the question of public health, also involve considerations of convenience, comfort, esthetics, and property values. Indeed, an important purpose of zoning laws is to prevent the depreciation of certain property by the erection of other types of construction. Such regulations determine the type of dwelling that may be erected on a given location or in a given area, as well as the proportion of the plot that may be occupied by the building, the distance from the lot lines, and other details. They are of much later origin than building codes and have received increasing attention in recent years. In the United States at the close of 1930 there were 981 municipalities, having a total population of over 46,000,000, with zoning regulations and 786 with official city-planning commissions; in thirty-eight others there were unofficial commissions.[6]

Building codes represent a very desirable and necessary effort on the part of government to protect the public, and have been of extreme value to the home owner and to the tenant. Nevertheless they contain many defects, and in the aggregate have compelled a needlessly heavy addition to the cost of construction; a great many have been framed on unscientific lines. Almost inevitably code provisions become obsolete as materials and methods change or improve and communities grow.

" The building codes of the country have not been developed upon scientific data, but rather on compromises; they are not uniform in principle and in many instances involve an additional cost of construction without assuring more useful or more durable building." [7]

Ernest P. Goodrich has said that building codes are " founded on custom rather than reason." [8]

6 USDC, " Commerce Year Book," 1931, Vol. I, pp. 340–341.

7 United States Senate, " Report of the Committee on Reconstruction and Production" (Quoted in " Report of the Building Code Committee, July, 1922 " [GPO, Washington, 1923], p. 1).

8 New York Times, January 19, 1930.

A general criticism of many codes is that they tend toward detailed specifications and are as a result unnecessarily complicated. According to Albert Kahn there are 1500 codes in the United States, each containing from one to four hundred pages of closely printed matter.[9] Many architects contend that the proper function of the building code is simply to lay down broad, general principles of sound construction.

" Building laws to serve their purpose best should deal only with fundamental requirements insuring safety to life and health. It is not the province of a code to prescribe the kind of plaster to be used or the number of nails required to hold down slates." [10]

Because of such concentration on detail codes have become obsolete through changes in methods of construction. According to a survey made in 1931, there were eighty municipalities with codes twenty or more years old, 126 with codes fifteen to twenty years old, and 162 with codes from ten to fifteen years old.

A frequent complaint against building codes is that they call for unnecessary strength of materials or needlessly expensive methods of construction. For example, until very recently it was a common provision that floors in dwellings should (with a proper " factor of safety ") be capable of sustaining a load of 100 pounds per square foot, whereas the Building Code Committee of the United States Department of Commerce has held that an allowance of 40 pounds is ample in ordinary construction, and that one of 30 pounds is sufficient in floors of monolithic construction or of solid or ribbed slabs.[11] Ernest Flagg has contended that the net effect of various floor-load provisions in the codes of New York City was " a requirement of 480 pounds to stand a probable load of 10 pounds." [12]

9 New York Times, April 16, 1933.

10 Ibid.

11 USDC, " Report of Building Code Committee, Recommended Minimum Requirements for Small Dwelling Construction " (GPO, Washington, 1923), p. 24.

12 " Minority Report to the Mayor's Committee on Plan and Survey " (New York, 1928).

—— CHART 59 ——

COMPARISON OF BUILDING-CODE REQUIREMENTS FOR MINIMUM THICKNESS OF BEARING WALLS, IN SELECTED CITIES OF THE UNITED STATES : 1926

Charted from Material prepared by Professor E. Mirabelli

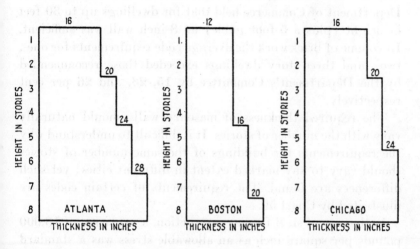

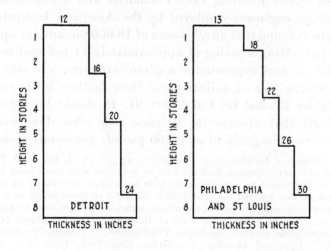

Again, in the case of brick walls an investigation by the United States Bureau of Standards, covering 134 building codes, showed that a thickness of more than 8 inches was required in 37 cities for one-story buildings, in 79 cities for two-story buildings, and in 125 cities for buildings of three stories, whereas the Building Code Committee of the United States Department of Commerce held that for dwellings up to 30 feet in height (plus a 5-foot gable) an 8-inch wall was sufficient. In volume of brick work the average code requirements for one-, two-, and three-story dwellings exceeded those recommended by the Department's Committee by 15, 23, and 26 per cent respectively.[13]

The required thickness of masonry walls should naturally vary with the number of stories. It is difficult to understand why the requirements for buildings of the same number of stories should vary to any marked extent in different cities; yet such differences are found. The requirements of certain codes are illustrated by Chart 59.

In the case of steel-frame construction, a provision of 16,000 pounds per square inch as an allowable stress was a standard feature of building codes for nearly thirty years. Both the United States Building Code Committee and a committee of consulting engineers employed by the American Institute of Architects found that an allowance of 18,000 pounds per square inch, permitting a saving of approximately 11 per cent in the amount of steel required for a given structure, was safe and proper. The lack of uniformity in these matters is illustrated by Tables 67 and 68 and Chart 61. It should be noted in Table 67 that whereas the Chicago code allowed a bearing value across the grain of only 150 pounds per square inch for

13 " Report of Building Code Committee," pp. 12–13, 32, and 37. A Philadelphia architect estimated that the cost of a 12-inch wall for a brick house 20 by 30 feet would be approximately $600 more than the cost of an 8-inch wall. He further pointed out that with a thinner wall there would be a substantial gain in interior floor space almost sufficient on each floor to provide space for a small bathroom or two or three large closets (Boyd, D. K., " Standardization of Parts in House Construction," " Housing Problems in America " [National Housing Association, New York, 1920], Vol. VIII, p. 84).

—— CHART 60 ——

COMPARISON OF COEFFICIENTS OF BENDING MOMENTS AT VARIOUS POINTS IN MULTI-SPAN CONCRETE STRUCTURES IN VARIOUS CITIES OF THE UNITED STATES: 1928

Charted from Material prepared by Professor E. Mirabelli

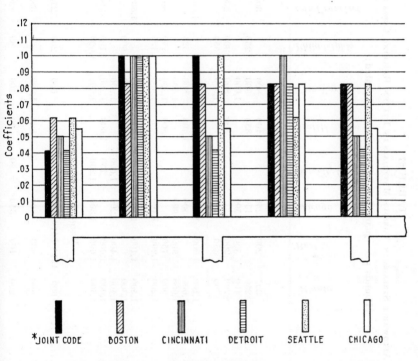

*JOINT CODE   BOSTON   CINCINNATI   DETROIT   SEATTLE   CHICAGO

*1928 JOINT STANDARD BUILDING CODE OF THE AMERICAN CONCRETE INSTITUTE

hemlock lumber, the New York code allowed 800 pounds. It is evident that either the former code does not provide a sufficient factor of safety, or the latter adds unnecessarily to the amount of material required and consequently to the cost of the building.

For Douglas fir, bearing value across the grain was 800 pounds per square inch in New York and 200 pounds in Boston.

TABLE 67

MAXIMUM ALLOWABLE STRESSES IN VARIOUS MATERIALS IN ELEVEN BUILDING CODES IN 1926 [a]

(Pounds per square inch unless otherwise stated)

	Atlanta	Boston	Chicago	Detroit	Seattle	New York	Philadelphia	San Francisco	St. Louis	Cincinnati	National Board of Fire Underwriters
Timber											
Bearing (across grain)											
Douglas fir	325	200	250		400	800		300	250		325
Hemlock	250		150		350	800	250		150	500	250
Oak	400	500	500			1,000			500	500	400
Spruce	200	200			300	800	300	200		400	200
Longleaf yellow pine	350	350	250			1,000	550		250	350	350
Bearing (with grain)											
Douglas fir	1,100	1,000	1,100		1,600	1,200		1,600	1,100	500	1,100
Hemlock	1,000		500		1,400	800	525		500	900	1,000
Oak	1,000	900	900			1,400			1,000	800	1,000
Spruce	900	750			800	1,200	750	800		1,000	900
Longleaf yellow pine	1,200	1,200	1,100			1,600	1,125		1,100	1,200	1,200
Bending (extreme fiber)											
Douglas fir	1,500	1,100	1,300		1,600	1,200	900	1,600	1,800	600	1,500
Hemlock	1,300	1,400	600		1,400	800			600	600	1,300
Oak	1,400	1,000	1,200	1,000		1,200			1,800	1,000	1,400
Spruce	1,000	1,000		750	1,000	1,200	1,100	700		800	1,000
Longleaf yellow pine	1,600	1,600	1,300	1,250		1,600	1,600		1,800	1,200	1,600
Masonry (compression)											
Concrete:											
Portland cement, 1:6	600	451 [b]	347 [c]	400 [d]	500	500	208	278	350	208	500
Granite:											
Portland cement mortar	600	833	600		800	1,000		389	600	600	600
Terra-cotta blocks:											
Cells vertical	200	100	350 [e]	90	90	100	80	150 [e]	80		120

Steel

Compression:											
Short length	16,000	18,000	14,000	16,000	16,250	16,000	16,000	18,000	14,000	18,000	16,000
Shearing:											
Shop rivets	10,000	13,500	12,000	10,000	11,000	12,000	12,000	13,500	12,000	13,500	10,000

Cast iron

Bending:											
Compression	16,000	10,000	10,000	—	16,000	16,000	10,000	16,000	10,000	16,000	

Steel columns †

Fibre stress, L/r = 80	10,400	13,200	13,280g	10,400	11,700	—	10,400	13,279	11,000	10,400	10,400

Reinforced concrete

Bending:											
Compression	750	715	700	650	750	650	650	715	800	700	650

(*a*) Taken from an analysis of building codes of various cities especially prepared for the authors by Professor Eugene Mirabelli of the Massachusetts Institute of Technology.

(*b*) For piers of height not more than six times their least dimension and walls of height not more than nine times their least dimension.

(*c*) For brick piers of height from six to twelve times their least dimension and for brick and concrete walls of height from nine to twenty times their least dimension.

(*d*) Machine-mixed.

(*e*) On net area.

(*f*) There are five principal formulae for determining these allowances.

$$P/A = 16,000 - 70L/r \quad \begin{cases} \text{Atlanta, Chicago,} \\ \text{Seattle, St. Louis,} \\ \text{National Board of} \\ \text{Fire Underwriters} \end{cases}$$

$$P/A = \frac{18,000}{1 + \dfrac{L^2}{18,000r^2}} \quad \begin{cases} \text{Boston, Detroit,} \\ \text{Cincinnati,} \\ \text{American Institute of} \\ \text{Steel Construction} \end{cases}$$

$$P/A = 16,000 - 80E \quad \begin{cases} E \text{ is excess} \\ \text{of L/r} \\ \text{over 50} \end{cases}$$

$$P/A = \frac{16,250}{1 + \dfrac{L^2}{11,000r^2}} \quad \text{Philadelphia}$$

$$P/A = 15,000 - 50L/r \quad \text{San Francisco} \quad \begin{array}{l} \text{American Society of} \\ \text{Civil Engineers} \end{array}$$

(*g*) For framed steel structures only.

TABLE 68

Selected Minimum Requirements for Live Loads for Floors and for Thickness of Piers and Walls in Twelve Building Codes in 1926 [a]

	Atlanta	Boston	Chicago	Detroit	Seattle	New York *	Philadelphia	San Francisco	St. Louis †	Cincinnati	National Board of Fire Underwriters *	U. S. Dept. of Commerce
Live loads for floors (pounds per square foot)												
Dwellings	60	50	40	50	40[b]	40	40	40	50	40	40[c]	40[d]
Apartments	60	50	40	80[e] 50[f]	40[b]	40	40	40	50	40	40[c]	40
Thickness requirements, masonry $\left(\text{maximum ratio }\dfrac{\text{height}}{\text{least dimension}}\right)$ (in inches)												
Brick piers	8	12	12[g]	10		10		10		10	10	
Concrete walls	15[k]	12[h]	18[i]		20	20[h]			12[g]		15[h]	
Foundations, wood frame dwelling — *Same (in inches)*												
Concrete	12[j]	12			10[k]			—[l]		8	12[j]	
Brick	12[j]	12			12[k]		13	—[l]		12	12[j]	

* For year 1922. † For reinforced concrete structures.

(a) Taken from an analysis of building codes of various cities especially prepared for the authors by Professor Eugene Mirabelli of the Massachusetts Institute of Technology. (b) For rooms exceeding 500 square feet floor area: 75. (c) Ground and lower floors: Atlanta National Board: clubs 90, dwellings 60, tenements 60, garages 150, hospitals 90, hotels 90, schools 90, stores 120. (d) For monolithic, solid, or ribbed floors: 30. (e) First floor and all public portions. (f) Other floors. (g) When H/D exceeds 6, the unit stresses are to be reduced according to the formula P = C(1.25−H/20D). (h) Unless properly braced by pier, cross wall, or buttress. (i) When height exceeds 30 feet, use 16 inches for upper 15 feet and increase 4 inches in thickness for each additional 15 feet below. (j) 8 inches from grade to sill. (k) For buildings more than 30 feet or two stories high. (l) One- and two-story dwellings: 8 inches when not more than 4 feet high. Three-story buildings: 13 inches. 13 inches when more than 4 feet high. Over three stories: 17 inches.

If used as retaining wall: {13 inches: not more than 8 feet to bottom of first floor. / 17 inches: not more than 10 feet to bottom of first floor.

For spruce it was 800 pounds in New York and 200 pounds in Atlanta, Boston, and San Francisco, as well as under the National Board of Fire Underwriters code. Numerous other marked variations in allowable stresses for timber might be cited.

In the case of plain concrete work the allowable compressive stress in the codes of Philadelphia and Cincinnati was 208 pounds per square inch, while in the Atlanta code it was 600 pounds. For granite set in Portland cement the San Francisco code gave 389 pounds, the New York one 1000 pounds.

It is natural that there should be more or less diversity in code provisions (and this would appear even greater were more cities considered),[14] since the materials covered by these detailed codes often vary widely in strength and other qualities between different times and localities. But inconsistencies are found in cases where accurate determination is possible. For example, the bending-moment factors for concrete slabs and beams continuous over a number of supports are susceptible of absolute mathematical determination in accordance with well-known principles for any given conditions of relative rigidity; none the less, investigation in five cities reveals wide diversity for identical conditions. The code factors for bending moment, expressed as a fraction of load times the square of the span, were as follows in the codes of the cities specified:

	Exterior support	1st center span	1st interior support	2nd center span
Boston	1/16	1/12	1/12	1/12
Cincinnati	1/20	1/10	1/18	1/12
Detroit	1/24	1/10	1/24	1/12
Seattle	1/16	1/10	1/10	1/16
Chicago	1/18	1/10	1/18	1/12 [a]

(a) Subject to further restriction.

14 The variations are not all as ridiculous as they seem. For example, the stresses allowed for hemlock are consistently higher in Seattle than elsewhere. This may mean merely that the hemlock obtainable in Seattle is on the average of a much better grade than that, say, in Chicago, which allows only low stresses for it. Similarly, allowable concrete stresses may be low because the aggregates obtainable in the locality in question are inferior. None the less, these variations are a great hindrance.

The decimal equivalents of these factors are shown graphically in Chart 60.

With respect to the quality of materials, one code requires that a given mix of mortar shall have a strength not less than 70 per cent of a similar mix with standard materials. While another demands a strength greater than that of the standard mix. Again, some codes contain wind-pressure requirements sufficient to provide against a velocity of 90 miles an hour, while others provide against a velocity of only 50 miles; the latter requirement is generally regarded as sufficient.[15]

Such lack of uniformity obviously involves great waste. It imposes a serious obstacle to the development of sound standardization and simplified practice, and precludes numerous economies in virtually all elements of shelter. We may fairly ask where the railroads would be if in every city and town — or state — a different code of structural or operating conditions had to be complied with.

The wide variation in codes is not always, however, as ridiculous as it appears. What *is* ridiculous is to lay down arbitrary rules which so frequently defeat their own purposes. It is ridiculous to assign stresses to steel without regard to the type of steel, or to hemlock without regard to the quality of the wood. In practice this encourages the use of the poorest material. It is positively puerile to demand that the concrete foundation wall for a frame house shall always be 12 inches thick, whether for a one-story cottage on high, dry land or for a stone mansion set in marshy ground. It is unscientific to make no distinction between 12 inches of high-strength, finely ground cement and carefully graded aggregate, designed with a proper water ratio, and 12 inches of poor cement and cinders poured in wet. What really concerns the code is that with due regard to factors of safety the wall shall not fall down, the timber crack, or the steel bend unduly or break.

To adopt the practice of fire underwriters in this connection would be advantageous. They are continually encountering new

15 This depends on normal climatic conditions in the particular locality.

—— CHART 61 ——

COMPARISON OF MAXIMUM AND MINIMUM REQUIREMENTS
OF BUILDING CODES FOR A NUMBER OF IMPORTANT STRUCTURAL CONDITIONS
IN VARIOUS CITIES OF THE UNITED STATES: 1926

Charted from Material Prepared by Professor E. Mirabelli

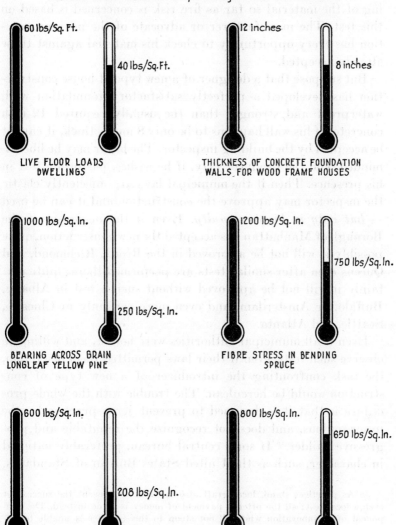

60 lbs/Sq. Ft.

40 lbs/Sq. Ft.

LIVE FLOOR LOADS
DWELLINGS

12 inches

8 inches

THICKNESS OF CONCRETE FOUNDATION
WALLS FOR WOOD FRAME HOUSES

1000 lbs/Sq. In.

250 lbs/Sq. In.

BEARING ACROSS GRAIN
LONGLEAF YELLOW PINE

1200 lbs/Sq. In.

750 lbs/Sq. In.

FIBRE STRESS IN BENDING
SPRUCE

600 lbs/Sq. In.

208 lbs/Sq. In.

COMPRESSION IN PLAIN CONCRETE

800 lbs/Sq. In.

650 lbs/Sq. In.

COMPRESSION STRESS IN BENDING
REINFORCED CONCRETE

types of walls and the question is under what conditions these shall be regarded as firesafe. The procedure is simple: through a national board of testing or a university of high standing a test is made in accordance with definite principles and the rating of the material so far as fire risk is concerned is based on this test. The manufacturer or advocate of the new construction has every opportunity to check his material against those already accepted.

But suppose that a designer of a new type of house construction has developed a perfectly satisfactory foundation wall, waterproof and stronger than the usually required 12-inch concrete. If his wall happens to be only 8 inches thick, it cannot be accepted by the building inspector. The latter may be liberal-minded, and the producer may, if he wishes, perform a test in his presence. Then if the municipal laws are sufficiently elastic the inspector may approve the construction and it can be used — *but only in his community.* Even if the inspector of the Borough of Manhattan has accepted the new construction, quite possibly it will not be approved in the Bronx, Richmond, and Queens even after similar tests are performed there; quite certainly it will not be approved without such a test in Albany, Buffalo, or Amsterdam, and even more certainly in Chicago, Seattle, and Atlanta.

Even if all municipal authorities were honest, and willing to observe such tests, even if their laws permitted them discretion, the task confronting the introducer of a new type of construction would be herculean. The trouble with the whole procedure is that it is designed to prevent jerry-practice by the unscrupulous, and does not recognize the reputable and progressive builder.[16] If some central bureau, preferably national in character, such as the United States Bureau of Standards,

[16] As practices stand, local graft also operates to prevent the success of even a local test; all too often a payment of money is made instead. The proponent of an innovation who will not stoop to this practice is unable to advance his art, while the unscrupulous builder "gets by" with practices not countenanced by any code and not to be countenanced by any standard of public safety or welfare.

could make the test once and for all, and if the codes of the cities provided that the results of such a test should be binding, rapid progress might be made. Even if no further federal control were desired, state boards would materially improve the situation. It might be possible for a manufacturer to conduct forty-eight conclusive tests; the thought of conducting ten thousand or more is appalling.

Similar criticism has been directed against plumbing codes; a subcommittee of the Plumbing Code Committee of the United States Department of Commerce described the situation in this country as " chaotic." Besides pointing out inconsistencies, the Committee emphasized the inconvenience and red tape incidental to the administration of such codes; it observed, for example, that the owner or contractor frequently has to obtain permits from many different city authorities — street department, city engineer, water department, health department — on a comparatively small job. Many plumbing codes forbid the use of 3-inch soil pipe in the partition formed by the 4-inch stud common in this country; yet the United States Department of Commerce holds that a 3-inch pipe is fully as sanitary as a 4-inch one.[17]

It is unnecessary to multiply illustrations. As an indication of how such code provisions have added to construction costs, the following statements may be cited: " It is the opinion of competent authorities that as much as 20 per cent of the cost of building would be saved in some cities by the adoption of codes based on accurate knowledge." [18]

" The building code is an important factor in the cost of building construction and it has a definite influence upon the volume of building construction which affects the prosperity and welfare of the community. The code can and does invite or repel capital investment in building construction. It is one of the most important

---

[17] " Report of Subcommittee on Plumbing of the Building Code Committee, Recommended Minimum Requirements for Plumbing " (GPO, Washington, 1929), p. 58.
[18] Haber, William, " Industrial Relations in the Building Industry," p. 83.

THE EVOLVING HOUSE

items of community or state legislation in its effect on social and economic welfare." [19]

Similar complaints in Great Britain are made concerning the effect of building codes on the building industry. The London Builder recently pointed out that since the building laws of many communities were drawn up there had been changes not only in the methods of construction but also in the habits and requirements of the population. In this connection it said:

"It is an undeniable fact that by-laws and building regulations have not kept pace with this change, and today form serious and increasing obstacles to cheaper building, not only in our cities and large towns but throughout the United Kingdom." [20]

It suggested the adoption of a national code for three different types of localities, viz., major cities and towns, smaller cities and towns, and villages and rural districts. The use of new materials and methods in addition to the adoption of such a code, it held, would give a real impetus to building throughout the country.

The British Building Industry Council of Review in 1930 maintained that the Building Acts and Regulations were responsible for a large element of waste and for avoidable additions to building costs.[21] It pointed out that owing to a rigid system of administration of the codes there was frequent delay, involving waste of time and effort, in securing approval of schemes submitted to Local Authorities. As in the United States, the Council asserted that revision of regulations had not kept pace with changes in building practice and progress in the manufacture of materials, with the result that codes often required excessive strength and weight of materials.

[19] Burton, Frank, "The Building Code: A Symposium" (American Institute of Steel Construction, Inc., New York), pp. 12–13.

[20] The Builder (London), February 17, 1933, p. 273.

[21] It is impossible in London to erect a shed for a perambulator without submitting a plan to the Local Authority and paying for a license which has to be renewed every three years (Townroe, B. S., Special Report to the authors).

" The rigidity of the regulations frequently compels the production of a building in which the material used will long outlast the period within which the building itself becomes obsolescent and needs replacement to adapt it to changed conditions. More appropriate and less costly material could often be used without detriment to any interest." [22]

Lack of uniformity among the codes of different communities was cited as an obstacle to standardization. In summarizing its findings the Council expressed its conviction that " unless Building Acts and regulations are drastically adapted to modern needs and to technical progress which is transforming building methods, any action taken by the industry itself must fail to yield its full potential benefits." [23]

To bring about much needed improvements in government regulation a new style of procedure should be followed. Masses of technical details, conflicting and endless, are not what laws or lawmakers need; they merely cumber the ground and obstruct social and industrial progress. Sound general principles, scientifically determined and expertly administered, are available in this age of engineering and should be brought into play.

In recent years considerable progress toward the revision and standardization of code requirements has been made through the various organizations in the building industry and the Building Code Committee of the United States Department of Commerce, working in cooperation with city and state governments. There is no sound reason for the bewildering multiplicity of city and town building codes and sanitary regulations within each of our forty-eight states; a vast amount of such legislative action, ill-considered and wasteful to a degree, might be eliminated if each state would take to itself the sole power of legislation on all such matters. Yet the large number of states involved makes ultimate success hopeless unless each state assumes full authority. A small fraction of the effort thus wasted would concentrate the highest engineering talent in this country on defining the needed uniform codes. As in Great Britain

[22] Townroe, B. S., Special Report to the authors.   [23] *Ibid.*

such codes should differentiate between the requirements for major cities, towns, and country.

Sound state laws governing occupancy would reduce slum conditions; practical laws on hygienic matters would safeguard and improve public health, as they do already in other fields. The right road to progress is through state control of essential conditions and the wider adoption of scientific principles.

Zoning laws founded upon the principles defined by the state building code should remain under municipal sovereignty, for obviously each city or town should control its own growth. Local administration should be entrusted with the proper correlation of social, economic, and political elements, and with every question of beauty and taste.

The building industry and the home-owner suffer from the multiplicity of minor and conflicting limitations incident to individual city codes. Piled high in forty-eight different state codes, they impede all change. Any effort toward improvement of the structure is met by endless and excessive requirements. The maze of code specifications seriously hampers earnest effort toward better practice. *The standardization of structure to fit such a mass of varied requirements would mean standardization based on the maximum for every item found anywhere in any of the codes.* That would threaten defeat from the start. Fortunately this state of things is constantly becoming more apparent; greater and greater effort to improve and standardize codes is being made.

If the building industry could be modernized through simpler, standardized structures, and superior financial and technical organization consisting of fewer and more responsible contractors, then the laws and their administration could be readily simplified; legislation also would react more readily to improved building standards and higher social and civic requirements. Improvements filter but slowly into the minds and acts of legislators through the present network of fifty or more crafts and a multitude of poorly harmonized industries.

If building structure were standardized, regulations could be made simpler and more definite, and more effective in safeguarding the public interest on the one hand and fostering sound structural practice on the other. The present-day unstandardized structure varies so widely that the laws to regulate it are about as helpful to the public welfare, and to economy and sound development, as a thick fog is to traffic.

CHAPTER IX
The Architect and Housing

ARCHITECTURE as a profession grew from the development of group life and the demands of priestly and civil rulers. Power, ambition, civic and religious ceremony, and administration required suitable housing in relatively large buildings. The need for the master builder thus arose. Only in recent times has the dignified title " architect " been allowed to the master builder.

In seeking to define the functions of architecture and the architect, we may again refer to the Greek derivation. " Architect " comes directly from ἀρχιτέκτων, " chief builder." Not only in the Greek civilization was the architect the chief builder, but throughout all early civilizations of which we have record the functions of the two have been interchangeable.

Architecture as a profession had its inception among the religious orders of early times, and has come down through the Gothic period of the Middle Ages. Many artists of the Italian Renaissance were both architects and painters. The École des Beaux-Arts of Paris was probably the first educational institution specializing in the teaching of architecture as it is known today.

With the development of modern civilization, architecture seems to have shifted more and more away from structural engineering [1] to the more specialized field of esthetic design — to

[1] The original purpose of the École des Beaux-Arts was to give architectural students a thorough grounding in the principles of construction. This aim has become more and more confused with the passing years, and today the organic nature of good architecture is if anything less stressed in French educa-

the expression in the physical structure of the social and spiritual temper of the times.

There is little evidence of architectural interest in homes other than palaces or monasteries until the time of Inigo Jones and Sir Christopher Wren, in the reign of Charles II of England. Toward the close of the Elizabethan period a book on domestic architecture was published in England. Perhaps it was this book, or the work of Wren and Jones and their successors, that transferred the interest of the architect from structure to the stylistic extravagances which have persisted to the present day. This illogical tendency in the domestic architecture of Europe and America has estranged housing design from true esthetics.

The popular conception of architecture has naturally followed that of the architect himself; the profession has come to be associated with matters of style — the type of roof, the shape and arrangement of the windows — and even with those of ornamentation. Architecture should signify the art of building in all its phases — sound construction, practice of applied mechanics, selection and proper utilization of materials and specifications, as well as attaining esthetic effects. It thus includes engineering problems, although their solution belongs properly to the engineer.

In its broader sense, the term architecture implies the coordination of community needs as related to shelter in such a way as not only to promote sound construction, convenience, and comfort but at the same time to express the esthetic aspirations of the times. It thus represents an ideal rather than an accomplishment, at least so far as dwelling-house construction is concerned. In the modern skyscraper, as typified in the lofty

---

tion than in our own. In Germany, on the other hand, as might be expected, the architect has to be something of an engineer, and the training in construction is very thorough. Many German architects have worked in the building trades in preparation for their profession. In the schools of America an attempt is being made to teach future architects the principles of engineering, but the courses given are too brief and insufficiently thorough; the basic requirements of mechanics and mathematics are slighted; and finally about all the young student is expected to do is to obtain a passing grade.

Empire State Building in New York City, the coordination of all factors — design, engineering, materials, form — has been brought to such perfection that structures of this sort are the outstanding contribution of this country to architecture.

The great modern office-building constitutes a new motif in architectural design. Barring the results of the Industrial Revolution, revealed chiefly in details, no such motif had appeared since the medieval cathedral. It is being developed with the utmost skill by the leading architects of our time. It seems to dominate not only architecture but the architect as well. Attracted by the unit mass of the office-building, he has overlooked the small home — its dominantly social motif and its bewildering conglomeration.

A fundamental reason for this is a failure to coordinate the various elements that in a true sense are included under architecture. In many other types of construction, such as the suspension bridge, the dam, or even the automobile, scientific research into methods, materials, and engineering and other problems has determined the soundness of some and the weakness of others; conflicting factors have been harmonized to a high degree. One has only to contrast the assembling of an automobile with the wasteful tearing out of brick work and carpentry to make room for plumbing and other equipment to realize how far dwelling-house construction falls short of effective coordination. Imagine an assembly platform in an automobile factory where the engine block had to be bored on the assembly line in order to attach the carburetor, or a thread had to be cut on a steering post to fit another specially cut thread.[2]

<hr/>

[2] Alfred C. Bossom, a British architect, writes:

" We shall not get speedy and economical building in Great Britain until all who are concerned in a given piece of work, from the owner and architect to the plumber's mate, have acquired the habit of thinking everything out together, before a single brick has been bought, or a single spade stuck in the ground. When this is done every constructional job, from the building of a cottage to the erection of a Thames House, goes forward on a clockwork time-table, smoothly, expeditiously, step by step, with no hanging about, no hide-and-seek games between the men and their materials, no waste and no waiting. That, I submit, is the only right, efficient and economical method of building." " Wasting £30,000,000 a Year " (The National Review, September, 1931, pp. 330–337).

"It is true that much has been done in experimenting with different materials: brick, cement, wood, steel, etc. It is true also that architects have been studying problems of planning small houses for many years. The need is not so much for new materials as for scientific study of all the elements in planning and construction." [3]

That the status of dwelling-house architecture in the United States is unsatisfactory is conceded. The Committee on Design of the President's Conference expressed the opinion that "the design of the average small American dwelling is seriously defective." [4] A well-known architect has asserted that 90 per cent of the buildings erected in the United States in 1930 "belong to that bad building which makes cities so intolerably ugly." [5]

The defects of domestic architecture are due not so much to lack of ability or imagination on the part of the architect as to the fact that his energies have mostly been devoted to larger structures. In these he beholds a brighter prospect of profit and, he thinks, wider opportunity for the exercise of his talent. Some reasons for the architect's lack of interest in houses are the average home-owner's willingness to purchase a house already built; his satisfaction with a stock building plan that roughly duplicates his neighbor's dwelling; and his desire to avoid the expense of an architect. There can be little doubt that architects are available to the home-builder and ready to supply his needs; the fact remains that a large number of leading architects have deliberately ignored the field of residences in order to concentrate on larger undertakings.

That the dwelling-house, serving a basic and indispensable need of mankind, is worthy of the best effort of the architect should be self-evident. He can hardly be blamed for devoting himself to those branches of construction which offer the largest reward, but the design and construction of dwelling-houses is a field which should have received more of his attention. In this

[3] Whitten and Adams, "Neighborhoods of Small Homes," p. 107.

[4] The President's Conference on Home Building and Home Ownership, Vol. V, p. 1.

[5] Cheney, Charles, "Architectural Control" (The American Architect, April, 1931, p. 23).

connection we cite the following statement with reference to dwelling-house construction in Great Britain:

" In considering the present position of house building as a craft or group of crafts with a view to reporting upon economy in construction, we think it well to recall how that position has been reached; for no country has a finer tradition in reference to the building of the small house than our own. Yet cottage building during the last century came to be regarded as the easy job of the building trade requiring neither skill in design nor science in erection. . . . While science and skill were devoted in ever-increasing measure to the development of industrial processes, no such attention was paid to house building. In view, however, of the multiplicity of the requirements of human life to be provided for, and the diversity of materials, processes, and skilled labours which have to be assembled and combined, each in its due order and under the proper conditions which alone ensure success, the cottage must be regarded as one of the most complicated and difficult of productions. In the absence of traditional skill and guidance, which rapidly changing conditions have largely destroyed, such a product needs scientific study of all its parts and thorough organization of its erection, if a result at once efficient and economical is to be secured." [6]

The architect's preference for the large-building field is a perfectly natural one. The library, the station, the skyscraper, the school, even the warehouse, offer a better opportunity than does the small house for the effective use of large masses and detail. Moreover, the commercial reward is alluring, equivalent perhaps to that of a thousand homes. More important still may be the intangible reward, the memorial to be passed down to posterity. The great public building may stand for generations to record the achievement of its architect; the individual house or a group development is likely to escape the attention of the many and be forgotten in a generation.

[6] " Report of the (British) Committee appointed to Consider Questions of Building Construction in Connection with the Provision of Dwellings for the Working Classes in England and Wales, and Scotland " (His Majesty's Stationery Office, London, 1918), pp. 48–49.

This may partly explain why American architects are so far behind their European colleagues in the field of domestic design. Furthermore, we are inclined to regard the single-family de-

TABLE 69

DISTRIBUTION OF PRINCIPAL ARCHITECTURAL ESTABLISHMENTS IN THE UNITED STATES, BY STATES, 1932 [a]

Alabama	38	Montana	16
Arizona	21	Nebraska	45
Arkansas	25	Nevada	3
California	541	New Hampshire	20
Colorado	48	New Jersey	245
Connecticut	123	New Mexico	13
Delaware	12	New York	1,277
District of Columbia	101	North Carolina	59
Florida	129	North Dakota	13
Georgia	59	Ohio	304
Idaho	27	Oklahoma	81
Illinois	528	Oregon	54
Indiana	105	Pennsylvania	527
Iowa	66	Rhode Island	41
Kansas	56	South Carolina	32
Kentucky	54	South Dakota	12
Louisiana	50	Tennessee	70
Maine	20	Texas	227
Maryland	102	Utah	27
Massachusetts	441	Vermont	3
Michigan	184	Virginia	75
Minnesota	117	Washington	134
Mississippi	10	West Virginia	51
Missouri	178	Wisconsin	135
		Wyoming	9
		Total	6,508

(a) Furnished by C. Stanley Taylor, Merchandising Consultant, The American Architect.

tached dwelling-house as the ideal, while Europeans think more readily in terms of group life and group housing. Their office, commercial, and industrial buildings are very different from ours, smaller perhaps and much more permanent. Indeed, permanence for buildings and for whole sections of cities is a definite condition of European life, and city planning is no novelty there. *Siedlungen* such as the Siedlung Britz in Berlin have all the chief features of other public buildings, and their size and permanence, and therefore might well attract any architect.

But enough of generalization. Is it a fact that the architect at least in the United States is insufficiently concerned with the possibilities in domestic architecture?

According to one leading authority there are in the United States in normal times approximately 12,000 architects, yet fully 80 per cent of the architectural work of the country is handled by 6500 offices. The establishments in this so-called " primary list " are shown by states in Table 69. Of them, about 4000 were until recently chiefly concerned with residential construction; although one-half the remainder did some residential work, their chief activities were in other fields; the rest did no residential work whatever. The great curtailment in building activity in the past few years has, of course, so changed conditions that in 1932 nearly all architects were willing to undertake any work in the residential field.

While, as just stated, some 4000 architects are engaged in residential work, most of them conduct what may be termed a " one-man shop." It is a safe estimate that on the average individual members of this group do not design more than one house per month. On this basis they design only about 50,000 houses per year, as against a normal demand for about 400,000.

According to some estimates, fully 80 per cent of the dwelling-houses of the United States were erected without the direct assistance of an architect.[7] Such estimates presumably refer

[7] A sample survey made by the G. M. Basford Company of New York and Pittsburgh covering the years 1925–29 indicates that only 12.9 per cent of all work was supervised by an architect. The results of this study cannot be taken as conclusive, but are suggestive. ("Facts and Figures of the Building Field " [American Builder and Building Age, Chicago], p. 13.)

Of 187 replies to a questionnaire sent to members of the Railroad Cooperative Building and Loan Association of New York in 1931, 110, or 58 per cent, replied that an architect was employed, but as nearly 70 per cent of those replying purchased houses already built, this percentage has little significance. The homes owned by members were in the vicinity of New York, where the

chiefly to single-family and two-family dwellings, since a large proportion of multi-family dwellings were erected under such direction. Yet, as shown in Chapter V, dwelling-house construction represents well over 50 per cent of all building in the United States, and the single-family house represents at least two-thirds of all residential building.

Chart 62 attempts to show the extent to which architects of the United States participate in the design and construction of housing, both rural and urban, and indicates that their connection has been primarily with the urban apartment-house — which, it may be remarked, partakes of the character of the large building.

The house designing of American architects as a whole has received the following criticisms:

Too much concerned with style and too little with plan.

Too much impressed with tradition and charm.

Too little interested in new developments of construction and too conservative in their use.

(1) So far as style is concerned, the fundamentals of sound architecture are generally conceded to be utility, stability, and beauty, in that order of importance. These apply not only to the structure as a whole but to every detail of design.

(2) A criticism made with special frequency is that the architect, ignoring the changes that have occurred in materials and in purpose, has attempted to apply the traditions of Greece or Rome in an age when the steam railroad, the automobile, the elevator, not to mention steel and concrete construction, have revolutionized social conditions.

" Their [the architects'] great weakness lies generally in their failure to offer inspiration in the development of new elements with which structures of this machine age may be constructed. In other words, they are modern minded in regard to design but not as to methods or materials.

---

employment of architectural services would doubtless be very much above the average.

" We still use brick and stone in the manner long ago discovered and used by the ancients." [8]

" Too often architects are hidebound when it comes to anything new. They cling to old methods and materials like a drowning man to a straw. Few will take the time or trouble to thoroughly examine or investigate the merit claims of new products. The tendency is to discourage progress and development along that line when, for the best interests of the building industry, every architect should be keenly alert to welcome and to use the new innovations of genuine merit which are designed to reduce costs and increase construction values." [9]

(3) In the recent past the architect has failed to see his opportunity for public service in the design of the home. He has been lured away not only by the big unit but by a false notion of the function of domestic architecture. The charming lines and texture of the English cottage and the Colonial home have been his models. He has overlooked the fact that those forms and textures reflect the materials and social life of former times. The basic needs of the modern home have been matters of secondary consequence. Until quite recently, at any rate, he has shown no interest in expressing the current industrial and engineering technique. Domestic architecture, like the building industry, has been maladjusted to these times. The architect has been dealing with an ancient organization and an ancient product, but even so he might more adequately express the social economy and viewpoint of the present day; [10] instead he has expressed the spirit of the American colony, the reign of Eliza-

[8] Sleeper, Harold R., " We Need New Materials " (The American Architect, March, 1930, pp. 44–45).
[9] Editorial in The Michigan Architect and Engineer, October, 1930, pp. 144–145.
[10] Instead of building dream worlds. One has to live today in today and not in the Elizabethan Period. As Mr. Filene has so cleverly expressed it, the chicken just having broken from the shell and scratching the hard dirt might wish he were back in the shell. But he cannot get back there. A return to guild life or Colonial simplicity is quite impossible and domestic life should be in keeping with the demands of today and not merely an escape and refuge from them.

—— CHART 62 ——

PERCENTAGES OF VARIOUS TYPES OF DWELLINGS RECEIVING
ARCHITECTURAL SERVICE IN THE UNITED STATES(APPROXIMATE)

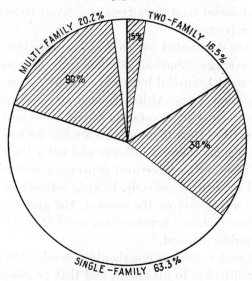

URBAN

MULTI-FAMILY 20.2%

TWO-FAMILY 16.5%

15%

80%

30%

SINGLE-FAMILY 63.3%

RURAL

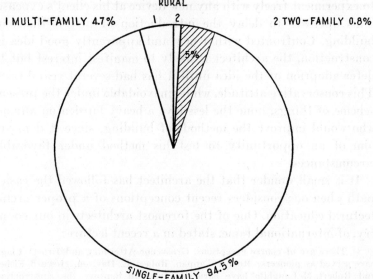

1 MULTI-FAMILY 4.7%   1   2   2 TWO-FAMILY 0.8%

5%

SINGLE-FAMILY 94.5%

///// WITH ARCHITECTURAL SERVICE   ☐ WITHOUT ARCHITECTURAL SERVICE

beth, and the Spanish Mission. There is, indeed, something to be said in favor of using the Colonial style in modern times, and English and Spanish Mission, too. They reflect some of the finest and best social traditions from which our present standards have largely come.

Tradition has dominated not only appearance but structure as well. Our average suburban developments have been drab, and even our most beautiful homes are chiefly clever modifications of traditional types. Although such architecture as these represent has real worth, it certainly cannot be termed creative.

The architect has thus thrown his influence definitely on the conservative side, becoming a follower and not a leader. Insistent upon old forms of architectural expression, and traditional materials and structural methods, lacking interest in architectural features expressive of the present, the architect has ignored new ideas in house construction until they were forced upon him by public demand.[11]

Along with such criticisms one should remember that the first duty of an architect is to his client, and that he cannot afford to experiment freely with any new device at his client's expense. This operates to delay the introduction of new methods of building. Confronted with a new and apparently good idea in construction, the architect is likely to manifest interest but to defer adoption of the idea until it has had several years' trial. This conservative attitude, while unavoidable under the present scheme of things, none the less lays a heavy burden on anyone who would improve the methods of building, since it deprives him of an opportunity to test his method under favorable circumstances.

It is small wonder that the architect has followed the easier path when one considers recent conceptions of a proper architectural education. One of the foremost architects in our country, of international fame, stated in a recent lecture:

11 There are of course exceptions. Grosvenor Atterbury and Ernest Flagg have served as pioneers; Robert Tappan, Robert L. Davison, Howard Fisher and Robert McLaughlin have earnestly tried to improve the construction of houses. This matter is discussed more fully in Vol. III.

" ' Architecture ' as taught in our schools isn't architecture — it is just plain imitation of something that has been and which might have been all right when it was called into being. But copying is not creative work. Real creative work in architecture is building to express the spiritual needs and physical necessities of one's own time. If the Greeks who devised the Greek architecture of 500 B.C. were alive today they would not create such buildings as they created at that time. For they were not imitators. They would create an architecture that would express today. And that is what we must do." [12]

While this statement does not recognize the more rational methods recently adopted by most of our architectural schools, it does clearly set forth the function of true architecture. That function should appear both in teaching and in practice — whether in design of the great office-building or of the small home.

In teaching there has been a tendency to place major emphasis upon the bigger projects. It is related that a professor of architecture in a large American university once urged his pupils not to be content to become " mere house architects " but to reach out for larger things. Of fifty-two collegiate institutions offering professional courses in architecture, none appears to give first place to domestic architecture; among schools not integrally connected with collegiate institutions, apparently only one specializes in such architecture.

Moreover, a considerable proportion of architectural institutions do not give specific courses in domestic architecture, and in only a very few is such a course required. The following summary shows the status of domestic architecture in a number of institutions:

39 have no course specializing in domestic architecture.

5 have an optional one-year course, usually in the third year.

3 have a course given in connection with home economics.

12 Wright, Frank Lloyd, in an address under the auspices of the Cambridge School of Architecture and Landscape Architecture, Cambridge, Massachusetts, November 18, 1932.

2 require such a course, in the third or fourth year.

1 has a separate course leading to a degree.

It should be emphasized that this absence of special courses in domestic architecture is not due to indifference or oversight, but is a matter of policy. It seems to be an accepted principle that a high degree of specialization is undesirable except in graduate work, and that an architectural course should deal with the subject in a broad way, with emphasis on fundamental principles; if a student is well grounded in these he should be able, it is contended, to devote himself to any special line of work that appeals to him. It is, moreover, asserted that some of the best work in domestic architecture has been done by architects whose training was of this kind. Be that as it may, the startling fact remains that the curricula of our architectural schools pay but little direct attention to the home, although it comprises three-fifths of all the building construction in this country.

While the general principles of form and composition and color apply to all sorts of esthetic design, of buildings, textiles, ceramics or automobiles, specific features introduce differences of practice. The oval form, for instance, is a beautiful one, and is often advocated as nearest the perfect in composition of a plan; satisfactory for a skating rink or an arena, it evidently fails to meet the requirements of a railroad station or a house. In the case of a railroad station practical considerations dictate form. In the case of a house the buyer or client is usually unable to formulate definite demands. His notions of the life that he and his family will live in the house that is to be are vague aspirations where they are not bad guesses. The basic principles of design fail to meet this human situation. The architect must have deep experience and profound sympathy with the needs of contemporary domestic life, and that cannot come from placidly contemplating the architecture of the past, however beautiful and true to life that may once have been.

There is a tendency to subject the practice of architecture to state regulation, but this has developed only in the last few years. Indeed, one-third of the states are still without registration laws.[13]

The architectural profession is not unaware of the difficulties confronting it. Some of its leaders have urged that the architect must assume leadership and direction of the entire building industry if its present disorganized condition is to be improved. This applies not only to matters of design but to the selection and purchase of materials, financing, and all other major factors. As shown elsewhere, one difficulty lies in the attempts of competing interests, chiefly producers of building materials, to promote the acceptance of houses which will provide the largest market for their particular product. In the absence of some central authority such competition may make matters worse instead of better. It is contended that if the architectural profession would assume this authority it could compel the coordination which is as yet sadly lacking. On the other hand, it is urged with equal force that before the architect can be entrusted with such influence he must prove himself receptive to modern tendencies, such as original ideas in design adapted to an industrial age, the use of new materials in place of traditional brick and lumber, the standardization of parts, and mass production. At the moment it seems a fair question whether the controlling influence may not rest with the pioneers in new methods of production, to whom the architect will be a servant rather than a master.

Some noted architects are in fact now employed by industry.

[13] As follows:

Arkansas	Missouri
Connecticut	Nebraska
Delaware	Nevada
Kansas	New Hampshire
Maine	Rhode Island
Maryland	Texas
Massachusetts	Vermont
	Wyoming

In several of these states the adoption of registration acts was under consideration during 1933.

A list of the states having statutory requirements, with the name of the administering board, may be found in the Appendix, p. 577.

One well-known firm has specialized in buildings for a prominent utility company and has produced some beautiful designs;
another has done remarkable work for a merchandising firm.
These architects maintain the appearance of purely professional consultants and are free to engage in other work. Both
the industries and the architects might be better off if the architects were highly remunerated executives of the concerns, in
charge of all the building projects. A similar development may
take place in housing unless the architect looks to his last. He
has the opportunity to be the leader; if he wastes it he must
expect that the producing unit will employ his services rather
than he theirs.

But as things are nowadays, the owner cannot afford as much
of a house as he needs and wants; the one he gets is poorly
adapted to his family life. The building of the house is a clumsy,
antiquated, laborious process, and the esthetic result, usually
negative, is marred by pretentious and false decoration. What
with the conservatism or false motives of domestic architecture,
the building industry's diverse and unresponsive organization, and the innumerable uncoordinated and slowly changing building codes, it is not strange that house structure is still
undeveloped.

The great cathedral or office-building or state capitol forces
a standardization of materials and methods for itself alone. The
relative smallness of each house and the obvious restrictions of
individual needs handicap such standardization. Nevertheless,
the architect of individual homes should serve the homes of the
many through communal features of design; this would bring
to the masses the economic advantage of standardization which
the great building enforces by its very size. Only thus can the
small home command the architectural service it deserves.

During the past decade in Germany and some other countries
domestic architecture has broken away from tradition, especially in community housing. This school of architectural
thought places first emphasis upon utility, or — to employ a
more widely used term — function. The resulting designs are

simple and direct, compact and economical, with chiefly rectangular motifs informing the mass. The general effect of such
developments is harmony and balance, in sharp contrast to the
miscellaneous individuality so characteristic of most American
communities. While some criticize the result as repellent monotony, the more common opinion is distinctly favorable, even from
the esthetic viewpoint. One prominent authority has said in this
connection:

" Under the cloak of individuality, personality, free expression,
the partisans of the free-standing house have accepted the utmost
refinements of monotony and unintelligent standardization. . . .
That is the paradox of modern architecture: we can achieve individuality only on a communal scale; and when we attempt to
achieve individuality in isolated units, the result is a hideous
monotony, uneconomic in practice and depressing in effect." [14]

These German developments, while most conspicuous in
apartment-houses, are also apparent in single dwellings. Other
features of the new housing are improved orientation in order
to utilize the sunlight more fully and more appropriately, making it available to every family, and improved surroundings
such as garden spaces, playgrounds, and the relation to public
ways. Similar ideas have been used to some extent in England
and France. They are also clearly reflected in the most recent
work of many American architects, especially in group developments and in connection with organizations interested in the
standardization of building materials, factory methods, and
mass production. The new architecture is better adapted for
mass production and the use of modern materials.

Together with these new developments in design, greatly increased importance is attached to community planning. This
has been a conspicuous feature of post-War housing in England, but has also been characteristic of building in Germany.
Several leading American architects have strongly urged the
importance of community planning, and some of them have

[14] Mumford, Lewis, " Mass-Production and the Modern House " (The
Architectural Record, February, 1930, pp. 113–114).

taken the position that the detached single house until now so typical of American suburban architecture must to an increasing extent give way to group housing. The Committee on Design of the President's Conference has strongly urged the necessity of group design,[15] holding that the lack of this was the " chief cause of the failure in the design of the current product of small dwellings in the United States." [16] It has insisted that the neighborhood is " the true unit of design " [16] from every point of view — architectural, financial, social, and civic — as well as from the standpoint of layout of public utilities and other factors.

It would be difficult to give full credit to every architect either here or abroad who has shown appreciation of the modern trend but a few may be mentioned. On the side of community planning for homes the Americans Henry Wright, Robert Kohn, and Clarence Stein have given much of their time and effort to this problem. From the point of view of the single-family house, the early work of Atterbury and Flagg is being carried on along different lines by younger men; Frank Lloyd Wright, another of the older architects, was a pioneer in this field. More recently the work of Neutra, Howe, and McLaughlin may be mentioned. Mr. Howe, a Beaux-Arts graduate, has over many years produced some of the most exquisite examples of traditional house design in this country; he has made a real success of design of the individual domestic unit. Lately his firm has been laboring with the problem of reconciling modern housing to the requirements of modern life. In Europe nearly every architect of importance is interested in community housing, and many have tried to re-design the single house for the living of today. Le Corbusier of France, Dudok and Mies Van der Rohe of Holland, Gropius of Germany, and the group in the Bauhaus Dessau [17] may be mentioned as of prime importance.

In the work and writings of the most progressive architects

[15] The President's Conference on Home Building and Home Ownership, Vol. V, pp. 1–9.

[16] *Ibid.*, p. 2.

[17] Closed by act of the Nazi government.

of our day we find ample testimony to the need of modernizing building structure; they find therein not only the prospect of lower cost and greater efficiency of the home but an ample chance to reflect the spirit of the age. Standardization resulting from large housing units is already evident both in this country and in Europe. Here we see it in the city apartment building; in Europe we see it in recent developments in the outskirts of Stockholm, Amsterdam, the *Siedlungen* of Frankfurt and Vienna, and some of the garden-cities and public-utility developments of Great Britain. Domestic architecture should be socialized for the benefit of the many and not specialized for the pride of the few.

In 1929 the American Institute of Architects awarded their highest " craftsmanship medal " to Cheney Brothers for " distinguished achievement in textile design and fabric." For the first time they recognized the great possibilities in artistic expression when the composite artist uses the technique of mass production. In " The City of Tomorrow " Le Corbusier predicts that purposeful civic grandeur and beauty never before equaled will result from such coordination. The modest home of the future will come from similar methods of design and similar tools, in infinite variety and at reduced cost. It will better satisfy the changing wants of community life, and increased variety and charm will mark its architecture.

CHAPTER X

Financing of the Home

NOT only does the average purchaser of a home resort to the use of credit, but in most cases his borrowing represents the major part of the initial cost. As already pointed out, the purchase of a home is usually the largest single investment ever made by the average family in wage-earning or other low-income groups. Moreover, except for the purchase of an automobile, it often is the only major capital outlay connected with the family budget. Food is bought as needed from time to time, sometimes from day to day, as are most incidentals. Fuel and clothing are purchased at intervals, yet as a rule involve no large outlay at any one time. But a home for the average family cannot be financed out of current income or even out of accumulated savings. While in many instances the resultant indebtedness is liquidated, at least in part, a high percentage of our homes are continually encumbered by debt. In 1920, according to the Census, 38 per cent of all owned homes were mortgaged. The ratio had been steadily rising for many years,[1] and is almost certainly higher at the present time than it was in 1920. Similar information for rented homes is not available, but as a large part of multi-family homes, nearly all of which are rented, are financed in part by borrowed funds, it is fairly certain that the proportion of rented homes subject to mortgage is substantially higher than that of owned homes.

While comprehensive statistics are lacking, individual surveys indicate that in many instances the purchaser of a home is unable to provide more than 20 to 30 per cent of the purchase

[1] It was 28 per cent in 1890.

price out of his own resources. This means not only that the home is burdened with a first mortgage, but that in a large proportion of cases it carries at the outset a second mortgage as well.[2] A special study made for the purposes of this book, covering 918 single-family homes, showed that in 95.7 per cent of these the purchase was financed in part by borrowing of some sort; only 4.3 per cent, in other words, were paid for in full at the time of purchase.[3] A part of this borrowing was through notes. Of the 918 homes, 712, or 77.6 per cent, were financed in part by first mortgage; there were second mortgages on 359. First-mortgage borrowing approximated 53.5 per cent of the average value of the home, and second mortgages, where used, 27.5 per cent. Where homes carried both a first and a second mortgage the indebtedness was approximately 80 per cent of the purchase price or value.

A sample study of 789 owned homes in Buffalo by a committee of the President's Conference showed that there was a first mortgage in 779 cases and a second mortgage in 444.[4] In 619 homes the first mortgage represented 52.1 per cent of the total cost and the second mortgage 24.8 per cent, the down payment by the purchaser constituting the remainder.[5] These averages appear to include some homes on which there was no second mortgage.

[2] " Usually when a home has been purchased, the prospective buyer has not the necessary funds to pay for it. There is generally a first mortgage on the property and usually a second " (The President's Conference on Home Building and Home Ownership, Vol. II, p. 6).

[3] At the request of the author, Professor D. S. Tucker, of the Department of Economics and Statistics at the Massachusetts Institute of Technology, undertook in 1928 a study of home financing; the questionnaire method was used. While the results were most interesting, the study was not sufficiently broad in scope to warrant positive conclusions. Some of the salient data collected in the course of this study are given in the Appendix, p. 581. In this chapter there will be frequent occasion to refer to this report, which will hereafter be identified as " Tucker, D. S., Special Report."

[4] The number of mortgaged homes may have been slightly higher, since in a few cases no information was obtained. Moreover, the Committee noted that second mortgages may have been paid off on some of the homes prior to the time its survey was made.

[5] The President's Conference on Home Building and Home Ownership, Vol. IV, pp. 86 and 103.

In a questionnaire conducted by the Railroad Cooperative Building and Loan Association of New York in 1931, 522, or 85 per cent, of the 613 persons who replied to the question whether there was a mortgage on the home answered in the affirmative.[6] A high proportion would, of course, be expected in the case of building-and-loan association homes.

In the face of this general dependence upon credit, there is widespread complaint that the facilities for furnishing it are inadequate and badly organized and that financing costs are burdensome; this is especially true of junior financing.[7] Herbert Hoover, in an address before the Conference on Home Building and Home Ownership in September, 1930, said:

" The finance of home building, especially for second mortgages, is the most backward segment of our whole credit system. It is easier to borrow 85 per cent on an automobile and repay it on the installment plan than to buy a home on that basis — and generally the house requires a higher interest rate.

" The whole process of purchase and finance involves a ceremony like a treaty between governments, and yet the home is certainly as good collateral as an automobile. . . ."[8]

The tenant is almost as much concerned as the home-owner with the cost of financing. As shown in Chapter III, interest (hidden in " net return " in Table 23 and used interchangeably with it) is the most important single factor in an economic rental, amounting almost to the sum of all the other factors. In other words, whether the individual owns his home or rents it, he is paying for interest and other financing costs, although in the case of a tenant this payment may not be so apparent.

It is unnecessary to emphasize further the importance of financing costs; they are recognized as constituting a great and perhaps the greatest burden on the prospective home-owner. The principal sources of credit and the instruments and methods of financing will now be described.

[6] " Financing Home Ownership " (1931), p. 6.

[7] This term, while often applied to second-mortgage financing, covers all forms of borrowing subsidiary to the first mortgage.

[8] New York Times, September 25, 1930.

PRINCIPAL LENDING AGENCIES

The chief lending agencies for home financing in the United States are these:

Building and loan associations [9]   Land banks
Insurance companies   Mortgage companies
Savings banks   Philanthropic institutions
National banks   Industrial employers
Trust companies   Builders
                    Private lenders

Savings banks, insurance companies, national banks, trust companies, and land banks as a rule lend only on first mortgage. This is also true in the case of the great majority of building and loan associations. In Pennsylvania, however, and in a few localities in other states, such organizations, as noted later, have loaned extensively on second mortgages. Mortgage companies may lend on either first or second mortgage, but some second-mortgage companies deal exclusively with the latter type of loan. The other agencies noted above lend on either first or second mortgage.

Many years ago the private lender [10] was the principal source of funds for the acquisition of homes; but banking institutions, life-insurance companies, mortgage companies, and especially building and loan associations have steadily increased their operations in home financing, until today they handle the major share so far as first mortgages are concerned.

Study of the total loans of several of the agencies in 1913 and 1931 (Table 70 and Chart 63), aside from showing a great expansion in the total of real-estate loans, brings out clearly the relative gain made by building and loan associations, in-

[9] The names of such organizations differ in different sections of the country.

[10] The private lender is still an important and perhaps the principal source of second-mortgage funds. A study covering 444 homes in Buffalo in 1930 showed that 91 per cent of second mortgages were held by private individuals (The President's Conference on Home Building and Home Ownership, Vol. IV, p. 86). The special study made for this book indicated that well over 80 per cent of second mortgages were held by the sellers of the properties (Tucker, D. S., Special Report).

surance companies, and national banks; on the other hand, it shows that the proportion of such financing handled by savings banks and state banks declined sharply.[11]

There is no authoritative compilation of the total loans on homes exclusively. A special study by the United States Census in 1920 [12] reported the total amount of mortgages on 1,892,537

TABLE 70

TOTAL REAL-ESTATE LOANS OF CERTAIN AGENCIES IN THE UNITED STATES ON JUNE 30, 1913, AND JUNE 30, 1931

	1913 [a]	Per cent	1931 [b]	Per cent
Building and loan associations .	$1,023,800,000	16.9	$7,760,100,000 [f]	31.0
Insurance companies	1,485,100,000 [e]	24.5	7,650,000,000 [f]	30.3
Savings banks .	2,303,700,000	38.0	5,820,000,000	23.3
State (commercial) banks ..	555,600,000	9.2	1,357,200,000	5.4
National banks .	76,800,000 [c]	1.3	1,280,600,000	5.1
Loan and trust companies ...	576,300,000	9.5	1,232,900,000	4.9
Private banks .	35,200,000	.6	4,700,000	— [d]
	$6,056,500,000	100.0	$25,105,500,000	100.0

(a) "Economics of the Construction Industry," p. 216. Estimated total *loans* of building and loan associations in this year have been used instead of *assets*, as in the original compilation. This change resulted in a slight revision of the percentages.

(b) The figures for 1931, for banking institutions, were taken from the "Report of the Comptroller of the Currency, 1931." Those for insurance companies are from The Insurance Year Book, 1932 (The Spectator Company, New York, 1932), p. A-134. Those for building and loan associations were furnished by H. F. Cellarius, Secretary-Treasurer of the United States League of Building and Loan Associations.

(c) As noted in the text, national banks at this time were, broadly speaking, forbidden to make loans on real estate. The total here given for 1913 may include banking quarters owned.

(d) Negligible.

(e) Figures are as of January 1.

(f) Figures are as of December 31, 1931.

[11] These figures cover only the operations of the institutions named, and include all classes of real-estate loans and not merely loans on homes.

[12] "Mortgages on Homes in the United States, 1920" (GPO, Washington, 1923), p. 43.

owned mortgaged homes not on farms at a little over $4,000,-
000,000 and estimated the total for 2,855,577 such homes at
$6,000,000,000. This was equivalent to an average of $850 for
all owned homes not on farms, mortgaged and unmortgaged.
Using this figure as a basis for estimating total borrowing on
all non-farm homes (whether owned, rented, mortgaged, or non-
mortgaged) and allowing a considerably lower average amount
of debt for farm dwellings as distinct from farms, we reach a
conservative estimate of $16,000,000,000 as the total indebted-
ness on all homes in the United States in 1920; by 1930 the
total was at least $20,000,000,000.

—— CHART 63 ——

PERCENTAGE DISTRIBUTION OF TOTAL REAL-ESTATE LOANS
OF CERTAIN LENDING AGENCIES IN THE UNITED STATES ON
JUNE 30, 1913 AND JUNE 30, 1931

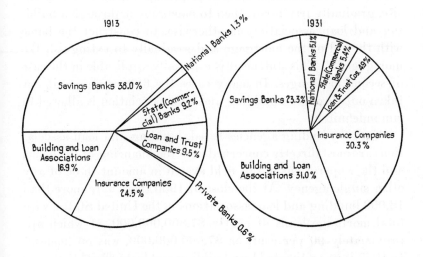

Notes:- For sources of data see footnote to Table 70 on page 350
    Percentages for Insurance Companies and for Building
    and Loan Associations are as of January 1, 1913 and Dec-
    ember 31, 1931.
    Percentage of Private Bank Loans for 1931 is so small as
    to be negligible.

If the estimate of $90,000,000,000 as the value of homes in the United States on January 1, 1930, given in Chapter II be accepted, a total mortgage debt of $20,000,000,000 would represent over one-fifth of the total value. Since a large percentage of owned homes are unencumbered,[13] the ratio of debt to value in the case of mortgaged homes alone would be much higher. In 1920, according to the special study by the United States Census, the mortgaged debt on owned mortgaged homes amounted to 42.6 per cent of their value; it is doubtless higher today. It would not be far from the mark to say that mortgage indebtedness on *owned mortgaged* homes in 1930 represented nearly 50 per cent of their normal value.[14]

No conflict is apparent between the proportions here given and the statement at the beginning of this chapter that the acquisition of a home involves borrowing in a great majority of cases. The Census in its report on mortgages on homes in 1920 said: " The American method of acquiring a home is to buy the site, gradually pay for it, then to mortgage it through a building and loan association or otherwise, to construct the home with the aid of the mortgage and gradually to extinguish the mortgage." [15] This statement is especially applicable in the case of second mortgages. In many cases the first mortgage if not taken out through a building and loan association is allowed to run indefinitely.

Of all the lending agencies listed, building and loan associations are most directly concerned with the financing of the home, and their operations in this field exceed in amount those of any other single agency. At the close of 1930 there were more than 13,000 building and loan associations in the United States, with total mortgage loans of nearly $7,800,000,000, of which approximately 90 per cent, or $7,000,000,000, was on homes.[16] In 1927 it was estimated by a building and loan official that over

[13] As shown later in this chapter (p. 392 f.).

[14] It frequently exceeded the actual market values prevailing in 1932 and 1933.

[15] "Mortgages on Homes in the United States, 1920," p. 12.

[16] During the years 1931–32, there was an appreciable decrease both in the number and in the total assets of these organizations, largely due to the abnormal economic conditions then prevailing.

40 per cent of the mortgages on homes in the United States were held by building and loan associations.[17]

According to H. F. Cellarius, Secretary-Treasurer of the United States Building and Loan League, fully 8,000,000 homes in the United States have been financed through these organizations during the past hundred years; about 6,000,000 of these have been financed since 1901 and more than 4,000,-000 since 1920.[18] These figures do not indicate the number of *new* homes financed through these organizations, since such loans are often made to finance the purchase of an existing home. There seems to be no basis for estimating the number of new homes so financed.

Building and loan associations are essentially cooperative — in Massachusetts, indeed, they are called cooperative banks. Members subscribe for shares on which they are required to pay in a sum each month as dues. Interest is credited on such payments, which are in the nature of bank deposits, although except in the case of full-paid subscriptions [19] they are technically instalments toward the payment of a certain number of shares in the association, which do not become full-paid until the requisite number of monthly instalments has been completed. Penalties are imposed for failure to make monthly payments on the due date. When a member has completed the payments on his shares, he is entitled to receive their face value from the association. In Massachusetts and numerous other states the face value is $200 per share.

A member need not contemplate the purchase of a home, but may simply use these associations virtually as banks of deposit, the rate of interest being in most instances higher than that paid by savings banks.

In the financing of homes through building and loan associa-

17 McAllister, W. W., "Do Building and Loan Associations Compete with Other Financial Institutions?" In Annals of Real Estate Practice, Vol. V, "Real Estate Finance" (National Association of Real Estate Boards, Chicago, 1927), p. 365.

18 In 1928 the yearly total reached a peak of 615,000 as against an average of about 225,000 in the years 1920–22.

19 Some building and loan associations issue full-paid shares, to attract additional funds from investors who do not wish to borrow.

tions there is a variety of practice. A common arrangement is for the borrower to subscribe to a number of shares sufficient, at the par or full-paid value, to cover the face of the loan. Thus, on a $4000 loan he would take out, say, 20 shares of a face value of $200 each, on each of which he ordinarily would pay $1 per month as dues, chiefly to amortize the loan, and $1 per month as interest, where the normal rate of interest is 6 per cent. Under this arrangement his shares would become full-paid, or " matured," in something less than twelve years. This systematic amortization of the loan, at a fairly rapid rate, is one of the distinguishing characteristics of building and loan associations.

There are various minor charges for examination, appraisal, and other services. Where the borrower is building a new house, instead of purchasing one already built, the building and loan association ordinarily makes anywhere from five to seven inspections of the property as construction progresses to see that the work is of the required standard, a small charge being made for each of these inspections.

Mention may here be made of the " building societies " of Great Britain, which are the counterpart of American building and loan associations. These organizations, which have been in existence for more than a century, had a phenomenal development immediately following the World War. Their membership has almost tripled since 1900, and the amount loaned annually on mortgage rose from an average of about £9,000,000 in the ten years preceding the World War to more than £90,000,000 in 1931, when their total outstanding mortgages were more than £360,000,000.[20] The chairman of the National Association of Building Societies of Great Britain has been quoted as saying that 2,500,000 homes have been acquired through the assistance of these agencies since they began operations. This figure is of course considerably in excess of the number of homes now standing which have been so financed; however, the same authority stated that during the five-year period 1925–29 the operations

[20] Bellman, Sir Harold, " Building Societies — Some Economic Aspects " (Economic Journal, London, March, 1933, pp. 30 and 12).

of British building societies exceeded their total activities during the previous seventy-five years.

The total real-estate loans of insurance companies in 1931 were almost as large as those of building and loan associations. Many of these insurance loans are on business property, and it is likely that the proportion of the total real-estate loans of life-insurance companies placed on homes is a good deal less than in the case of building and loan associations. Nevertheless, insurance companies have cultivated the home-loan market extensively in recent years, both with respect to single-family dwellings and apartment-houses. Complete statistics are not available. A study by the National Association of Real Estate Boards in 1929, covering seventy-four leading companies, gave these figures: [21]

69 loaned on single-family dwellings
62 loaned on duplex dwellings
58 loaned on two-apartment buildings
51 loaned on apartments and stores combined
46 loaned on large apartment-houses

The mortgage on a single-family dwelling is therefore a popular form of investment with large insurance companies. Of $194,467,000 of real-estate loans authorized by the Metropolitan Life Insurance Company in 1930, approximately $121,-500,000, or 62½ per cent, was loaned on dwellings and apartments.[22] Of real-estate loans authorized by the Prudential Life Insurance Company in the first half of 1930, aggregating $84,-912,000, approximately $54,000,000, or 63½ per cent, was on small dwellings and apartments.[23]

The typical insurance company loan covers 50 per cent of the combined value of land and building and frequently runs from ten to fifteen years, although the average period is shorter. Such loans usually provide for amortization in the form of semiannual or monthly instalments. In some cases the loan provides

[21] Philadelphia Public Ledger, April 7, 1929.
[22] Data furnished by W. S. Norton, Comptroller, Metropolitan Life Insurance Company. This represented loans on 16,382 dwellings and 515 apartments.
[23] New York Times, July 6, 1930.

that the borrower may repay the loan before maturity; sometimes the borrower is also required to take out a life-insurance policy equal to the amount of the loan.

Savings banks are peculiarly suited to home financing. Deposits in such institutions are not checking accounts, and while in the absence of special conditions, when these banks may insist upon thirty, sixty, or ninety days' notice before paying out deposits, withdrawals may be made at any time, they are made far less frequently than in the case of ordinary commercial banks. Accounts often lie undisturbed, accumulating at compound interest, over a long period of years. This condition obviously favors the investment of funds in long-term real-estate mortgages. In addition, the mutual savings bank [24] extends special consideration to home-owners. In the East, a considerable proportion of the mortgages of savings banks are on homes. In some states the maximum proportion of total funds which can be loaned by savings banks on mortgage is fixed by law. In Massachusetts, for example, real-estate loans cannot exceed 70 per cent of the total assets, whereas building and loan associations are not restricted in this way. In many states, moreover, the law sets a maximum ratio of loan to the value of the property.

The home-financing methods of savings banks are differentiated from those of building and loan associations in that the former do not issue shares on which instalment payments must be made. Instead, the borrower secures a loan about as he would from a commercial bank or private lender. Furthermore, savings banks as a rule have not insisted on amortization; a mortgage may be payable at the end of a stated period of years or

[24] While a large number of savings banks in the United States are joint-stock organizations, the total resources of these are only a small fraction of those of the mutual savings banks. On June 30, 1930, the total resources of the two classes compared as follows:

714 stock savings banks	$ 1,521,109,000
606 mutual savings banks	10,295,308,000
Total	$11,816,417,000

(United States Treasury Department, " Report of the Comptroller of the Currency, 1930," GPO, Washington, 1931), pp. 103–105.

may nominally fall due at the end of one or more years, and then run on indefinitely subject to call.[25] Where the security is ample, this policy has the advantage of avoiding the trouble of reinvesting funds. The abnormal conditions in real estate since 1929 have led to considerable change in policy, and there is a distinct tendency among savings banks in some sections to insist upon the amortization principle. While this tendency has as yet been less marked in the case of loans on homes than in the case of those on business property, there is a growing sentiment among savings bank officials that no loan should be considered permanent but should contain provision for its ultimate retirement.

The practice of savings banks with respect to loans on homes further differs from that of building and loan associations in that whereas the latter lend extensively on construction loans (i.e., loans for the erection of new houses or other buildings), savings banks as a rule prefer to lend only on the completed home.

Since the first consideration of national banks must be to keep a large proportion of their funds liquid so that they can at all times meet the demands of depositors, it is impracticable for them to lend extensively on real estate. Indeed, prior to the creation of the Federal Reserve System national banks were virtually prohibited from making loans on real-estate mortgages. The Federal Reserve Act permitted such loans under various restrictions, and gradually a small portion of the funds of national banks was invested in real-estate loans. The McFadden Act of 1927 materially increased the latitude of national banks in this respect, particularly in that it permitted them to make loans on real estate running for five years, whereas previously the limit had been one year. This change was immediately followed by a marked increase in the loans by national banks on real estate. Thus, on June 30, 1926, the total of such loans

---

[25] John W. Sandstedt, Executive Secretary of the National Association of Mutual Savings Banks, states: " In the State of New York the duration of the average loan is three years and in practically all cases it is renewed automatically for an indefinite period."

other than loans on farm lands was only $473,400,000, representing 3½ per cent of the total loans and discounts of national banks; on June 30, 1931, the total was $1,280,600,000, or 9.72 per cent.

There is no way of determining what proportion of real-estate loans by national banks is made on homes. We know, however, that many national banks in the eastern part of the country, especially the smaller institutions, have in recent years substantially increased the amount of funds which they have loaned on homes.

Trust companies have somewhat greater latitude than national banks, but their total loans on real estate are much less than those of savings banks or of building and loan associations.

The aggregate mortgages of the twelve Federal Land Banks on June 30, 1930, were $1,682,000,000; in addition, joint-stock land banks had outstanding on that date loans of $900,000,-000. In the case of land banks it is difficult to segregate the amount of funds loaned on homes from the amount loaned on land.

There are numerous first-mortgage companies in the United States, including title, guaranty, and trust companies, and private institutions. Some of them issue their own mortgage bonds against the individual mortgages which they hold.

After the World War, a fairly large number of second-mortgage companies, frequently operating over a large section of the country, were organized, but the excessive shrinkage in real estate values since 1929 has forced many of these out of existence. A number of large first-mortgage companies, moreover, became financially embarrassed.[26]

Evidently the number of agencies available to the would-be borrower are many and diverse. It requires technical knowledge far in excess of that of the average citizen to know what agencies are available in a given instance, and of these which ones are best for him to utilize. Coordination and simplification of the agencies of credit is undoubtedly needed.

[26] Some estimates place the amount of real-estate mortgages and real-estate mortgage bonds which were in default in 1930 as high as $5,000,000,000.

INSTRUMENTS USED IN HOME FINANCING

The principal instruments used in home financing are:

(1) The first mortgage.

(2) The trust deed.

(3) The second mortgage.

(4) The third mortgage (chiefly used by speculative builders).

(5) The land contract.

(6) The ground rent (infrequent and local).

The commonest of these is the mortgage, and it is used in all sections of the country except in those few where it has been almost entirely supplanted by the trust deed.

(1) The first mortgage, as the name indicates, is a prior lien on the property. If interest, or the principal, is not paid when due, the holder can foreclose and, subject to stipulated procedure, sell the property, in which case all obligations under the first mortgage must be met before the holders of any subordinate liens receive anything. However, in many states the mortgagor is allowed a certain length of time to redeem the property after foreclosure proceedings are commenced before title finally passes. In some states this period is from six months to one year, but in a few it is longer. On the other hand, in many states there is no " equity of redemption," as this right to redeem is technically called.[27]

(2) The principal difference between the trust deed and the mortgage is that, in the event of default, possession of the property can often be secured with less delay under the former than through foreclosure under the latter, since under the trust deed the borrower has no right or equity of redemption. In some cases possession can be secured in a few months.

(3) Second mortgages are so called because, as explained above, they rank below the first mortgage or other prior liens.

---

[27] This provision, while intended to protect a borrower from being victimized, has often been criticized as unduly limiting the rights of the lender and as tending to increase financing costs. Where the redemption period is unusually long it practically deprives the lender of the opportunity to protect his investment.

They are extensively employed in home financing, and as a rule run from one to three or five years.

(4) The third mortgage ranks below the second as a lien on the property; its use by home owners is infrequent. For the most part this class of mortgage imposes an intolerable burden upon the home purchaser.

(5) The land contract is used principally in the north central and a few western states. It is in effect a substitute for a deed and purchase-money mortgage (i.e., a mortgage taken by the seller of the property as part payment), although it may be used concurrently with a first mortgage and thus serve as a junior mortgage. The seller does not transfer title at the time of purchase, but delays giving deed until a substantial portion of the purchase price, usually about 50 per cent, has been paid. Annual payments under a land contract are likely to be larger than under a mortgage.

The land contract is seldom used in the Atlantic states or in the South. In the Middle West it is estimated that 65 per cent of all sales of dwellings and 85 per cent of all sales of vacant lots are made by this method.[28] While the land contract has certain advantages, it has some objectionable features. On this point the Committee on Finance of the President's Conference reported:

" The land contract succeeds in avoiding some of the disadvantages of the first and second mortgage method because it simplifies the system of payments on the part of the owner. Under it, the

[28] American Real Estate Institute of the National Association of Real Estate Boards, " Financing the Home Buyer " (Chicago, 1924), p. 15.

In a special questionnaire study (Tucker, D. S., Special Report), covering 918 instances of home financing, the proportions financed by the land contract method in various states were as follows:

	Per cent		Per cent
Michigan	87	Indiana	75
Iowa	82	Illinois	37
Minnesota	48	Kansas	43
Utah	72	Washington	50
Montana	28	Idaho	46
Colorado	27	Ohio	24
Pennsylvania	5		

seller retains the title until the purchaser has an equity sufficiently large to enable him to obtain a first mortgage for the remainder. This method works satisfactorily so long as the seller is thoroughly honest and financially responsible. However, it cannot be recommended for universal adoption, partly because of the possibility that the seller may become involved financially and not be able to carry through his covenant to deed over the property under the agreed conditions at the time stated, and partly because the seller in effect acts as a trustee usually without the supervision and opportunity for examination of accounts by the buyer and by public officials that has been found by experience to be advisable for trustees. Possibly a system of trusteeship can be worked out that would obviate all or most of these dangers." [29]

(6) From one angle, a ground rent is the capitalized rental value of a given piece of real estate. For example, a person who owns a piece of land or a home and needs funds can, instead of borrowing a given amount on a first mortgage, raise the same sum by means of a ground rent, on which loan he pays the same rate of interest as he would pay on the mortgage. In Baltimore, where the ground-rent system is at present most extensively used, he may pay off the amount of the ground rent after a given number of years or continue the arrangement indefinitely at his option; such a ground rent is thus a form of mortgage which permits the lease-holder to continue it as long as he wishes. In some other states the ground rent runs for a fixed but long term of years — usually 99 or 100, the theory being that so long a period enables a person to erect a building on the property and secure the full return of his capital before the arrangement expires.[30]

The chief advantage of the ground-rent system to the prospective home-owner is that he merely pays a sum annually for the use of the land over a long term of years and can thus devote all of his available funds to the construction or purchase of

[29] The President's Conference on Home Building and Home Ownership, Vol. II, p. 29.

[30] On expiration of the rental term, ownership of the building would pass to the owner of the land.

the house. Where a ground rent is sold on a completed home it simply represents a medium for raising funds very much as a mortgage does, with the exception, already noted, as to the maturity date.

Like the agencies, the instruments of home credit are diverse and complicated. Laws differ widely, and the harassed borrower flounders in the dark. Here, too, coordination and simplification are needed.

PRINCIPAL METHODS OF HOME FINANCING

Borrowers, and the principal methods of borrowing, may be grouped as follows:

Group	*Usual method of financing*
1. Those able to pay 50 per cent or more of the purchase price in cash.	First mortgage (or trust deed) only.
2. Those who pay 25 to 50 per cent in cash.	(*a*) In some cases, first mortgage only, especially where building and loan associations are used.
	(*b*) First mortgage for about 50 per cent of purchase price; second mortgage for balance over owner's equity.
	(*c*) Land contract, sometimes with a first mortgage.
3. Those paying 25 per cent or less in cash.	(*a*) First, second, and sometimes third mortgages, and unsecured notes.
	(*b*) Land contract, frequently subsidiary to a first mortgage.
	(*c*) Special instalment arrangements made with builder or seller.

In normal times no serious problem confronts borrowers in Group 1, nor those in Group 2-*a*, who require only a first mortgage to supplement their own resources.

" On the whole, there is really no difficult problem connected with financing the purchaser who is able to pay as much as forty per cent of the purchase price. There is in ordinary times plenty of money for investment in first mortgages, and the costs are reasonable." [31]

The chief difficulty in home financing is found in connection with second-mortgage borrowing. Herbert Hoover, in addressing the Conference on Home Building and Home Ownership in December, 1931, said on this point:

" We have in normal times, through the savings banks, insurance companies, the building and loan associations, and others, provided abundant and mobile finance for 50 per cent of the cost of a home through the first mortgage. But the definite problem is not presented by those who can find 50 per cent of the cost of a home. Our chief problem in finances relates to those who have an earnest desire for a home, who have a job and therefore possess sound character credit, but whose initial resources run to only 20 or 25 per cent. These people would willingly work and apply all their rent and all their savings to gain for themselves this independence and security and social well-being. Such people are a good risk. They are the very basis of stability to the Nation. . . . To find a way to meet their need is one of the problems that you have to consider; that is, how we can make a home available for installment purchase on terms that dignify the name credit and not upon terms and risks comparable to the credit extended by a pawnbroker." [32]

COST OF FIRST-MORTGAGE FUNDS

The rate on first-mortgage money depends on the section of the country, the size of the mortgage as related to the value of the home, the lending agency through which the loan is made, and many other conditions. But, broadly speaking, the rate paid for first-mortgage credit does not involve a serious burden.

In the case of loans made through savings banks, life-insurance companies, national banks, and trust companies, the rate in the eastern part of the United States in normal times is around 6 per cent, with a range from 5 to 7 per cent. In sections

[31] American Real Estate Institute of the National Association of Real Estate Boards, " Financing the Home Buyer," p. 11.
[32] New York Times, December 3, 1931.

where general interest rates are relatively high, the rate on first-mortgage funds is correspondingly affected. The Committee on Finance of the President's Conference reported that the rate of interest on first mortgages " ranges ordinarily from 5 to 7 per cent, with 6 per cent as the prevailing standard, but extends in certain areas up to 8 or 9 per cent." [33]

In arranging for a mortgage on a home, there are certain fees for examination of the property, title search, recording of deed, and other services. For example, there may be a fee of about $5 for appraising the property, one of $15 to $50 for examining the title, and one of $5 to $15 for recording the deed. As a general rule, these various service charges amount to from 1 to 2 per cent of the face of the first-mortgage loan; if this runs for a considerable period of years, these incidental charges add only a fraction of 1 per cent to the annual cost of the loan. In some cases there is also a commission to cover brokerage service for securing first-mortgage funds, but in normal times this is small, about 2 per cent, and adds comparatively little to the interest cost when prorated over the life of a long-term loan. In many cases this commission goes to the broker and not to the lending agency.[34]

Where the first mortgage is obtained through a building and loan association the rate may be somewhat higher, first because these organizations ordinarily lend a larger proportion of the value of the home than do most other lending agencies, and second because of fees and other considerations already mentioned.

In some states, building and loan associations are permitted to lend as much as 80 per cent of the value of the home on first mortgage. One reason for this is the fairly rapid rate of amortization of such loans, already referred to; but so high a ratio is uncommon. According to one writer, the average loan permitted by law in twenty-three states where there is legislation governing building and loan associations is a little over 62 per

[33] The President's Conference on Home Building and Home Ownership, Vol. II, p. 16.
[34] See also p. 370.

cent of the value of the home; the average percentage of value for loans actually made is only a little over 58 per cent.[35]

Broadly speaking, the actual cost of first-mortgage money obtained through building and loan associations ranges from 6 to 7 per cent in the eastern section of the country and from 8

—— CHART 64 ——

PERCENTAGE DISTRIBUTION AND AMOUNT OF MORTGAGE DEBT OF OWNED MORTGAGED HOMES, BY RATES OF INTEREST, IN THE UNITED STATES: 1920

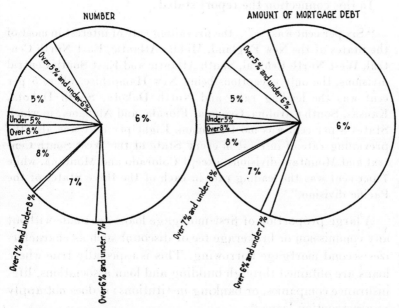

to 10 per cent in the southern and western sections; the rate is seldom less than 6 per cent anywhere. Table 71 shows the annual cost of first-mortgage money when borrowed from building and loan associations, including premiums, fees and other considerations, as well as the nominal rates.[36]

[35] Rogers, Tyler Stewart, "Trends in Home Financing" (Architectural Forum, March, 1931, Part 2, pp. 371–376).

[36] Data collected for the President's Conference gave the following aver-

According to a report by the United States Census in 1920, a 6-per-cent rate applied to 58½ per cent of all mortgaged homes reporting and to 61 per cent of the total mortgage indebtedness. This rate included any borrowing on junior liens on which the rate presumably was higher and represented all outstanding mortgages many of which may have been running for years. The Census figure, however, did not include discounts, bonuses, commissions, or other similar charges. The distribution of total mortgage indebtedness by different rates of interest as well as by numbers of mortgages shown by this Census study is indicated in Chart 64.

In this connection the report stated:

" Six per cent was . . . the prevailing rate of interest in most of the States of the New England, Middle Atlantic, East North Central, West North Central, South Atlantic and East South Central divisions, the only exceptions being New Hampshire, where 5 per cent was the leading rate, and North Dakota, South Dakota, Kansas, South Carolina, Georgia, Florida, and Alabama, in which States 8 per cent was most common. Eight per cent was also the prevailing rate of interest in every State of the West South Central and Mountain divisions, except Colorado and Montana, while 7 per cent was the leading rate in each of the three States of the Pacific division." [37]

A large proportion of first-mortgage loans are made without any commission or brokerage fee or discount such as characterizes second-mortgage borrowing. This is especially true where loans are obtained through building and loan associations, life-insurance companies, or banking institutions; it does not apply to construction loans. [38]

----

age interest rates for 1242 building and loan associations replying to a questionnaire; in 1924, 6.98 per cent; in 1928, 6.91 per cent; in 1930, 6.88 per cent. The maximum ratio of loan to value of the property was 69.8 per cent. The average ratio in 1924 was 64.15 per cent; by the latter part of 1932 it was 57.36 per cent for current loans. (The President's Conference on Home Building and Home Ownership, Vol. II, p. 67.)

[37] " Mortgages on Homes in the United States, 1920," p. 124.

[38] See p. 372 f.

TABLE 71

COST OF LOANS OBTAINED THROUGH BUILDING AND LOAN ASSOCIATIONS
IN THE UNITED STATES IN 1924 [a]

Section	Ostensible interest rate, model average	Actual interest rate
New England	6	6.14
Middle Atlantic	6	6.91
South Atlantic	6	7.30
East north central	6	6.48
West north central	8	8.47
South central	10	9.32
Rocky Mountain	10	10.23
Pacific	8	8.94
Lowest (New Hampshire)	5	
(Delaware)		5.14
Highest (13 states)	10	
(Oregon)		13.30 [b]

(a) Clark, H. F., and Chase, F. A., " Elements of the Modern Building and Loan Associations " (The Macmillan Company, New York, 1927), pp. 509–510.

(b) Other high actual averages were Montana 13.23, Arizona 11.21, New Mexico 11.63, Alabama 11.57.

In abnormal times it is frequently necessary to pay a substantial commission or premium for first-mortgage funds. In the latter part of 1929, according to one agency, very high premiums or bonuses were demanded.[39] Such premiums are equivalent to discounts from the face of the loan, and are distinct from brokerage commissions.

COST OF SECOND-MORTGAGE FUNDS

Quite different conditions obtain in second-mortgage borrowing; here the nominal rates are often much higher than those for first-mortgage loans. A common practice in the United States, however, especially among second-mortgage companies, is to make the nominal rate about the same as the rate for first mortgages but to impose certain discounts from the face of the loan

[39] "Standard Trade and Securities Service," October 16, 1929 (Standard Statistics Company, Inc., New York), General Section, pp. 1–2.

which make the actual cost of funds much higher than the nominal rate. For example, if a mortgage for $3000 at an interest rate of 6 per cent per year is subject to a discount of 15 per cent, this means that the borrower receives only $2550. This results in a true interest rate, on the funds actually obtained, much above the stated rate. Frequently such mortgages are amortized by monthly instalments, and this practice in connection with the discount tends to increase the true interest rate.

As a general rule, interest is figured on the amount of the unpaid balance. If in the case assumed the mortgage ran for 30 months the borrower would pay, in addition to interest, the sum of $100 monthly on account of the principal, and this payment would be credited against the face of the loan. Interest for the second month would be figured on $2900, for the third month on $2800, etc.[40]

The effect of the discount on the cost of second-mortgage funds is well illustrated by the following extract from a Department of Commerce publication:

" Under the usual regularly amortized loan the real discount rate is approximately double the advertised rate. But, expressed entirely as an interest charge, the rate paid by the borrower is even higher than the total of the combined nominal interest rate and the actual discount rate, because ' discount ' differs from ' interest ' in that it is paid at the beginning of the loan term and not during the term or at the end of it. Thus, on a typical monthly payment three-year second-mortgage loan bearing 7 per cent nominal interest and a 15 per cent discount (5 per cent annually, so called) the rate paid by the borrower is approximately 18 per cent a year." [41]

In a large number of cases such discounts are employed to safeguard lenders from penalties imposed by usury laws. In many states there is a statutory maximum rate of interest; if

[40] In some cases interest is figured on the face of the mortgage throughout. This results in practically doubling the cost of funds and is usually considered as sharp practice.

[41] Gries, John M., and Curran, Thomas M., " Present Home Financing Methods " (GPO, Washington, 1928), p. 10.

the lender demands or accepts a rate in excess of the statutory limit he is liable to punishment. But the purchaser of a second mortgage is free to sell it at whatever discount he chooses to accept. A common practice in some states is to set up a third party as a " straw " man who takes the mortgage note in the first place and endorses it over to the mortgage dealer, who sells it at a discount, the net proceeds being turned over to the borrower. The practice varies in different states, largely with the character of state legislation on usury. In some states the borrower can deal directly with the lending agency, in which case he receives the net proceeds of the loan directly from the lender; this is a common procedure in the case of second-mortgage companies. The standard schedule of discounts used by a large second-mortgage company (applicable in April, 1929) was as follows: [42]

No. of years	Per cent
1	8 to 10
2	12
3	15
4	18
5	20

The discount is deducted at the time the loan is made. That is, on a $3000 loan running for one year the borrower would receive $2760 or $2700; on a five-year loan he would receive only $2400; in either case he would have to repay $3000. The discount is in addition to the stipulated rate of interest, which, as just stated, is computed on the amount of the unpaid balance. In 1927 the following general situation was reported:

" So far as data can be obtained it seems to be well established now among the reputable junior mortgage companies that a commission or discount of ten per cent for one year, fifteen per cent for two years, twenty per cent for three years, in addition to the interest rate, represents current practice." [43]

[42] United States Bond and Mortgage Company of New York. The 1929 rates are more representative than those prevailing since that year. Since 1930 second-mortgage money has been almost unobtainable.

[43] Trott, C. V., " Junior Liens on Income Property." In Annals of Real

In addition to such discounts, the borrower frequently has to pay a commission of 2 per cent, 3 per cent, or more on the face of the loan for the mortgage broker's services in placing the loan. In the case of a three-year loan, this would add roughly from two-thirds of 1 per cent to 1 per cent or more to the nominal interest rate. A further addition would have to be made to cover recording fees and certain other charges, as in the case of first-mortgage borrowing.

As a result of such discounts, commissions, and service charges, the real cost of money often is nearly three times the stated rate. For example, on a three-year loan at 7 per cent with a discount of 15 per cent, the true rate of interest including miscellaneous charges is frequently 20 per cent or more.

While, as in the case of first-mortgage loans, second-mortgage rates vary in different sections, they depend more upon the necessity of the borrower and upon general credit conditions than upon geographical considerations. In New York City in 1925 it was reported by a legislative committee that 10 per cent was a conservative rate for second-mortgage funds and 15 per cent not far from the average rate.[44] These figures, moreover, did not include various brokerage and other fees, which in many cases would bring the total annual cost almost to 20 per cent.

In Chicago, a study of financing costs made by the Institute for Research in Land and Public Utility Economics in 1925 indicated for second mortgages on a small group of homes a total cost of 12.9 per cent to 18.1 per cent.[45]

In California the law forbids a corporation to make a charge for mortgage financing that will yield more than 12 per cent on the capital invested; this has resulted in a usual charge of 12 per cent. In the case of one large company the interest rate

---

Estate Practice, Vol. V, " Real Estate Finance " (National Association of Real Estate Boards, Chicago, 1927), p. 343.

[44] State of New York, "Report of the Commission of Housing and Regional Planning, March 6, 1925," Legislative Document, 1925, No. 91 (J. B. Lyons Co., Albany, 1925), pp. 36–37.

[45] Bodfish, H. M., and Bayless, A. C., " Costs and Encumbrance Ratios in a Highly Developed Real Estate Market " (The Journal of Land and Public Utility Economics, May, 1928, p. 136).

proper is 7 per cent, but a discount is charged which makes the actual rate 12 per cent.

Instead of deducting a discount from the proceeds of the loan, some second-mortgage companies add a bonus to the face of the loan. In other instances, notably in the South, it is more or less common to require a borrower to sign notes for a bonus and for total interest in addition to a note for the face of the mortgage. For instance, on a $1000 loan the borrower would be required to sign the following notes:

For the loan	$1,000
For bonus	150
For three years' interest at 6 per cent	180
Total	$1,330

The total amount would be repayable in thirty-six monthly payments. The cost of the money actually available to the borrower would be about 22 per cent per year.

The special questionnaire study made for this book showed that for second mortgages on about 300 homes the average nominal interest rate was only a little over 6 per cent, but that discounts and other items brought the true rate above 11 per cent.[46]

In 1924 it was estimated that the average cost to the borrower on second mortgages for the country as a whole was " well over 10 per cent per annum "[47] — a decidedly conservative estimate. The Committee on Finance of the President's Conference found that " the total initial charges for obtaining a second-mortgage loan for one to three years may range from 15 to 25 per cent," and sometimes in addition to annual interest.[48]

[46] Tucker, D. S., Special Report.

[47] American Real Estate Institute of the National Association of Real Estate Boards, " Financing the Home Buyer," p. 14.

A survey by the National Association of Real Estate Boards in the latter part of 1924, covering about 150 cities, indicated interest costs on second mortgages of about 8 to 10 per cent in about 100 cities, 12 to 15 per cent in twenty cities and 15 per cent or more in about thirty others; the cost seldom was less than 8 per cent. Broadly similar costs were indicated by a survey made by the same agency in 1927.

[48] The President's Conference on Home Building and Home Ownership, Vol. II, p. 17.

A survey by the Division of Building and Housing of the Department of Commerce about 1920 showed that discount rates on second mortgages in various cities ranged from 2 to 50 per cent.[49] The higher rate, if the loan ran for only a year, would mean that the borrower paid over 100 per cent per year for his second-mortgage credit. Such a discount would ordinarily be prohibitive, but is sometimes paid for small loans.[50]

It may, therefore, be considered as established that the total cost of second-mortgage funds, including all incidental charges, in the United States is frequently from 10 to 15 per cent and that in a great many cases the rates are still higher. A particularly onerous feature is that in many instances second mortgages have to be renewed and that the heavy incidental costs are repeated.

Mention has been made of construction loans. Many loans made by building and loan associations are of this type, but except for a few inspection charges they are equivalent to a loan on a home already completed, and the cost is as already described.

In some other cases construction loans are merely temporary financing intended to cover the erection of a building. In addition the owner must arrange for permanent financing, which may involve both first- and second-mortgage borrowing. Such loans sometimes involve exceptionally heavy expense.

The following extract from a report of the Massachusetts Special Commission on the Necessaries of Life, while omitting some incidental charges in each case, compares the financing of a construction loan through a building and loan association [51] with temporary financing and refinancing through private lenders.

[49] "Mortgages on Homes in the United States, 1920," p. 50.

[50] In the latter part of 1929, discounts of 40 per cent on second mortgages were commonly demanded, and the supply of funds even at that rate was very limited.

[51] In Massachusetts, as already stated, these organizations are called "co-operative banks."

Co-operative Bank [a]		Temporary Construction Loan Replaced by Permanent Mortgages	
Total loan (80 per cent) $8,000			
Cost of application	$5	Commission (2 per cent) to broker for construction loan	$160
Estimated attorney's fee for examination of title	$30 to 35	Interest charge on loan at 1 per cent per month (four	
Interest for four months at 6 per cent per annum	160	months)	320
Total	$200	Bonus or commission to lender from	$50 to 150
		Estimated attorney's fees for examination of title and drawing agreements	75
		Commission (2 per cent) to broker for procuring first mortgage, $6,000, three years at 6 per cent	120
		Attorney's fee for bank loan	50
		Bonus on second mortgage, $2,000 for three years at 6 per cent from	$240 to 360
		Commission (3 per cent) to broker procuring second mortgage	60
		Attorney's fee for second mortgage	50
		Total	$1,345

(*a*) Under a co-operative bank mortgage loan of $8,000, the borrower is compelled to reduce the principal of the mortgage at the rate of $40 per month.

The report stated that " these examples may be regarded as approximately the two extremes in the cost of financing residential construction." [52]

The higher rates charged for second-mortgage than for first-mortgage funds are largely explained by the greater risk involved. Some housing students have contended that these risks are greatly exaggerated; the prevailing opinion in real estate circles, however, is this:

" In the mortgage loaning field it is not now contended with any degree of seriousness that a junior lien is not subject to many more risks and hazards than a senior lien. It is also admitted generally that because of such increase of risks and hazards a

[52] Massachusetts Special Commission on the Necessaries of Life. House Document, 1929, No. 200, p. 42.

junior mortgagee is entitled to require as compensation for making such loans, service charges, commissions, discounts, interest or other charges, commensurate with the risks and hazards assumed." [53]

The rapid increase in the number of foreclosures in recent years gives much support to the conservative viewpoint.[54] More specific evidence of the risks involved in second mortgages is afforded by a sharp increase in failures of building and loan associations in Pennsylvania, where, as already stated, the practice of lending on second mortgage by such organizations has been fairly general. Following are the figures for recent years as reported by the United States Building and Loan League.[55]

Year	Total number building-and-loan failures in the United States	Total number in Pennsylvania	Number in Pennsylvania attributed to second-mortgage loans
1927	21	10 [56]	10 [56]
1928	23	15 [57]	15 [57]
1929	159	151	— [58]
1930	190	153	— [58]

Where second mortgages are taken by private lenders, as for instance by former owners of a property as a part of the pur-

[53] Trott, C. V., "Junior Liens on Income Property." In Annals of Real Estate Practice, Vol. V, pp. 342–343.

[54] See p. 395.

[55] In spite of the increase in the number of failures in 1929 and 1930, the ratio of estimated losses to total resources of all associations was only 0.0266 in 1929 and 0.2795 in 1930. In 1920 the ratio was only 0.00002 (United States Building and Loan League, "Building and Loan Annals," 1931, pp. 922–923). Over one-half the estimated loss in 1930 was due to a single failure in California. These figures, however, lose much of their significance in view of the fact that during the recent period of stress a great number of building and loan associations, taking advantage of their legal privilege, suspended the right of withdrawal by depositors.

[56] "1928 Year Book with Proceedings of the Thirty-Sixth Annual Meeting of the United States League of Local Building and Loan Associations" (American Building Association News Publishing Company, Cincinnati and Chicago, 1928), p. 90.

[57] "1929 Year Book," p. 60.

[58] Not given, but second-mortgage loans were an important factor.

chase price, the rates may be considerably lower than those just given. Moreover, second-mortgage loans are often taken by relatives or friends without discounts or commissions; a considerable amount of money is thus loaned on second mortgage, the true interest rate on which is comparatively low.

Builders frequently take a second mortgage as part of their price, disposing of it for cash on the best terms they can get. In such cases the nominal rate of interest may be low, say 6 per cent; this may also be the true rate. If, however, as often happens, the seller's price has been inflated in anticipation of selling the second mortgage at a heavy discount, the real rate of interest will be much higher. For instance, if a seller who would be satisfied with a cash payment of $2000 demands a $3000 second mortgage running, say, three years at 6 per cent, the borrower is in effect paying a $33\frac{1}{3}$ per cent discount, equivalent to over 11 per cent per year when prorated over a three-year period. His real interest cost on a basis of $2000 is approximately 25 per cent.[59] In Pennsylvania, as already noted, it is a common practice for building and loan associations to lend on second mortgages. In this case the actual cost of funds is decidedly less than the figures just given, but more than the cost of first-mortgage money.

Unusually low second-mortgage costs have at times been secured under the plans of limited-dividend housing companies, some of which have taken second mortgages at 6 per cent interest with no commissions, discounts, or fees. The difficulties encountered by some of these organizations during the recent years of depression do not warrant the hope that permanently lower second-mortgage costs can be obtained in this way.

The use of third mortgages by home owners, as previously stated, is infrequent. A study of conditions in one section of Chicago by the Institute for Research in Land Economics and Public Utilities in 1925 revealed but one third mortgage on all

[59] If the mortgage is amortized, the rate would be still higher, depending on the rate of amortization.

of the 325 properties examined.[60] Our own questionnaire study, covering 918 single-family houses, developed only fifteen third mortgages as against 359 second mortgages and 712 first mortgages.[61] The Buffalo study by the President's Conference, referred to on p. 347, revealed only nine third mortgages among 789 homes covered by the survey.[62]

Barring very short-time financing, third mortgages are too speculative to be satisfactory either to the average owner or lender, and necessarily involve high rates. They are extensively employed by speculative builders, particularly in connection with apartment-house properties, but are the source of frequent losses.

It has long been an accepted rule in conservative real-estate circles that, except in the case of financing through building and loan associations or other amortized loans, first mortgages should not exceed 50 per cent of the value of the home and that first and second mortgages combined should not run over 75 per cent. It is true that in many other cases lenders advance 60 per cent on first mortgage, but the loan is usually based on the lender's valuation of the property, which is likely to be conservative.[63]

EFFECT OF SECOND-MORTGAGE CHARGES ON TOTAL FINANCING COST

Despite the high charges for second-mortgage money, this class of mortgages represents on the whole a minor proportion of the cost of the home. As already shown, they seldom cover more than 25 per cent of the total cost; the average ratio for homes carrying such mortgages may be nearer 20 per cent; in many cases they are liquidated in the course of a few years.

Taking the higher ratio and assuming 6½ per cent as the

---

60 Bodfish and Bayless, "Costs and Encumbrance Ratios in a Highly Developed Real Estate Market," p. 126.

61 Tucker, D. S., Special Report.

62 The President's Conference on Home Building and Home Ownership, Vol. IV, p. 88.

63 See the Appendix, p. 583.

cost of first-mortgage money, including all incidental charges, and reckoning interest on the owner's equity at 6 per cent and the cost of second-mortgage money at 15 per cent, the total yearly financing cost would be approximately 8½ per cent, as follows:

		Per cent
First mortgage	50% of total cost @ 6½%	3.25
Second mortgage	25% of total cost @ 15%	3.75
Owner's equity	25% of total cost @ 6%	1.50
	Total	8.50

If second-mortgage money is obtained at 12 per cent, the average total cost — assuming no change in the other items — would be about 7¾ per cent. If, on the other hand, second-mortgage costs are 20 per cent, the total cost would be nearly 10 per cent.[64]

Since in the most densely populated sections first-mortgage funds are ordinarily obtainable at a total cost of about 6½ per cent, a total carrying cost of 8 to 8½ per cent, *including* second-mortgage borrowing, is fairly representative for a large part of the country in normal times. This is a matter upon which broad, accurate, consolidated information is lacking.

While the second mortgage, as stated, represents a minor proportion of home cost, our analysis shows that costs of junior financing may be the largest single item in the total cost of financing. A highly important consideration is that in cases where junior financing must be renewed, these charges are repeated, while in times of credit strain it may be difficult to renew on any basis. The Committee on Finance of the President's Conference, in emphasizing the " obvious burden " involved in a repetition of second-mortgage costs, urged that, if a resort to junior financing is unavoidable, the second mortgage should be of sufficient duration to enable the borrower " to pay off this

[64] In those sections of the country where first-mortgage charges run as high as 8 per cent of the total cost — assuming second-mortgage charges at 15 per cent and owner's equity at 8 per cent — it would be 9¾ per cent, and a 20 per cent cost for second-mortgage money in such sections would bring the total carrying cost well above 10 per cent.

indebtedness before expiration and thereby eliminate the need of a renewal." [65]

If the discount on a second mortgage, with commissions, fees, and other charges, amounts to 20 per cent of the mortgage, then on the assumption that that mortgage represents 25 per cent of the cost of the home, 5 per cent of the total cost is absorbed by such initial financing charges. In many cases the percentage is higher, while in some types of highly speculative building, where discounts are larger and commissions are paid for first-mortgage funds as well, the proportion may exceed 10 per cent or even 20 per cent.

In the economic rental of 14 per cent described in Chapter III, interest was taken at 6 per cent. If the total interest cost be 8½ per cent, this means an increase of nearly 18 per cent in the total economic rental. Expressed in absolute terms, an increase of 2½ per cent in total interest cost on a $5000 home means an increase of $125 in the annual rent, or of over $10 in the monthly rent. The substitution of an 8½ per cent interest cost for a 6 per cent rate in the economic rental of 14 per cent, given in Chapter III, would mean that almost 50 per cent of the rental was for interest. Conversely, a reduction of 20 per cent in the interest costs in this case would mean a reduction of nearly 10 per cent in total rental.

Broadly speaking, a reduction of 1 per cent in interest charges can effect almost as large a saving in rent as a reduction of 10 per cent in direct construction costs. For example, if the building represents 65 per cent of the cost of a $10,000 home, a 10 per cent reduction in construction costs means a direct saving of $650; on an assumed rental ratio of 14 per cent this would mean a saving of $91 per year.[66] A reduction of 1 per cent in interest on the total cost (including the owner's equity) would be $100. If computed on borrowed funds only, such a

[65] The President's Conference on Home Building and Home Ownership, Vol. II, p. 10.

[66] The total saving in rent through a 10 per cent reduction in direct construction cost would be somewhat greater than here shown, since there would be an attendant reduction in financing and other costs.

reduction, where indebtedness was 75 per cent of the value, would mean a saving of $75.

COMPARISON WITH AUTOMOBILE FINANCING

Compared with the financing of the purchase of automobiles on the instalment plan, home financing is at a disadvantage. The former is far simpler and the buyer has to deal only with the seller, but the cost is on the whole higher than that of home financing. The usual method of automobile financing is to split the unpaid balance into twelve equal parts, the purchaser giving twelve separate notes maturing in a monthly series. On cars costing $1000 and over, the aggregate value of the face of these notes is often 10 to 12 per cent more than the amount of the unpaid balance.[67] In many cases the true interest rate ranges from 10 to 13 per cent, exclusive of an allowance for fire and theft insurance. Formerly financing costs in the case of automobile purchases were much higher than those given here.

THE FEDERAL HOME LOAN BANK SYSTEM

Owing to the difficulties involved in home financing, many efforts have been made in the United States to secure legislation which would alleviate the burden of the home-owner. In a few cases, direct state assistance has been attempted; discussion of this matter is reserved for Chapter XI. The recent years of depression, with the accompanying rapid rise of foreclosures, gave a strong impetus to the movement for legislation, and in July, 1932, the Federal Home Loan Bank Act was passed by Con-

[67] For example, in the case of one company these charges were as follows for a medium-priced *new* car for a twelve-month repayment period; payment made in twelve equal instalments.

Unpaid balance	Total amount of notes	Amount of each note
$300	$339.72	$28.31
500	558.24	46.52
800	885.96	73.83
1,000	1,104.48	92.04
1,200	1,323.00	110.25
1,500	1,650.72	137.56

"National Retail Financing Rates" (Commercial Credit Company, Baltimore, 1928), pp. 4–5.

gress. This act, while designed in part to relieve the existing strain on building and loan associations and various other lending agencies engaged in home financing by providing for a system for rediscounting mortgages held by them, was also intended permanently to strengthen such institutions and thus to give encouragement to home-ownership.

By advancing funds to the existing agencies it was hoped to reduce the necessity for insisting upon foreclosures and at the same time create a supply of fresh capital for the building or purchase of homes. President Hoover on signing the bill said: " The purpose of the system is both to meet the present emergency and to build up home ownership on more favorable terms than exist today." [68]

The act provided for not less than eight and not more than twelve districts,[69] in each of which there was to be a Federal Home Loan bank. While in many respects the system is modeled upon the Federal Reserve banking system, the Home Loan banks are independent of the Federal Reserve banks. They are prohibited from transacting any banking or other business not expressly authorized by the act. The districts in which they operate are not identical with the Federal Reserve districts.

Home Loan banks deal only with member organizations, such as building and loan associations, savings banks and insurance companies. The minimum capital of each bank is fixed at $5,000,000, and is to be provided in part by subscriptions of member organizations and in part by the Government. On December 31, 1933, the total capitalization of all Federal Home Loan banks was $145,400,000, of which $124,700,000 was subscribed by the United States Treasury. The act contemplates that the subscriptions made by the Treasury will eventually be repaid out of funds paid in by member institutions as the sys-

68 Financial Chronicle, July 30, 1932, p. 723.

69 Twelve districts are provided with Federal Home Loan banks in the following cities: Boston (originally Cambridge), Mass.; Newark, N. J.; Pittsburgh, Pa.; Winston-Salem, No. Carolina; Cincinnati, O.; Indianapolis, Ind.; Evanston, Ill.; Des Moines, Iowa; Little Rock, Ark.; Topeka, Kan.; Portland, Oregon; Los Angeles, Cal.

tem expands, so that the Government will retire from participation in the operation of the system. On the funds subscribed by the Government the Home Loan banks are to pay 2 per cent dividends and may pay more, but not in excess of the rate paid on stock subscribed for by other interests.

The principal business of Home Loan banks is the lending of funds to member organizations on mortgages or certain other collateral deposited by them as security. Up to December 31, 1933, lines of credit of approximately $211,491,000 had been established, with about $88,441,000 in loans actually consummated. Some time elapsed before the system got fairly under way. One reason was that in many states new legislation had to be enacted in order to enable existing home-financing agencies to take advantage of the new system.

Advances by Home Loan banks are to be made only on first-mortgage or similar first liens upon dwellings housing not more than three families. Advances are not to be made where the mortgage has more than fifteen years to run to maturity, where the real estate covered by it has a value of more than $20,000, or where the mortgage has been past due more than six months. It will be seen, therefore, that the system is intended chiefly to assist the individual home-owner and not the builder of large apartment-houses.

Where the mortgage presented as security for a loan is of the amortizing type, originally running eight years or longer, advances by the Home Loan banks are limited to 60 per cent of the unpaid balance of the mortgage, and are in no case to exceed 40 per cent of the value of the property securing the mortgage. On other mortgages advances are not to exceed 50 per cent of the unpaid balance of the mortgage, and in no case are they to exceed 30 per cent of the value of the property.

Home Loan banks may borrow money, and may issue bonds and debentures secured by the mortgages or other eligible obligations of borrowing institutions. All securities so issued are exempt from all taxes — federal, state, and local — except surtaxes and estate, inheritance, and gift taxes. The earnings of the banks are derived from the difference between the rates which are charged borrowers and the rates which they pay on funds borrowed or on the securities issued by them.

The act had the active support of very influential interests, including the National Association of Real Estate Boards and the United States League of Building and Loan Associations, but was strongly opposed by numerous agencies. One objection was that it might tend to overstimulate building and thus lead to eventual depreciation of real-estate mortgages. In some sections of the country the act, while not actively opposed, was held to be unnecessary in view of the existing facilities for home financing.

The Home Loan Bank bill as originally drawn provided that in certain cases loans might be made directly to individual home owners. By a new act of Congress passed in 1933 this provision of the Home Loan Bank Act was eliminated and a new agency, the Home Owners' Loan Corporation, was created. While this corporation is under the supervision of the Federal Home Loan Board, it is otherwise entirely independent of the Home Loan banking system. By the end of 1933 it was in active operation.

The primary function of the Home Owners' Loan Corporation is to aid home-owners who are in difficulty over mortgage loans. The act creating the corporation provides that it may issue bonds, interest on which — but not the principal — is guaranteed by the United States Government. Where a mortgage is in arrears, the corporation may under stated conditions offer to the agency holding the mortgage its own bonds up to 80 per cent of the appraised value of the property. The original mortgage is turned over by the private loan corporation to the Home Owners' Loan Corporation, which in turn takes a new mortgage from the individual home-owner. These new mortgages are to run for 15 years at a low rate of interest with a provision for amortization, which may, however, be waived by the Home Owners' Loan Corporation. Recent agitation indicates a tendency to have the government guarantee principal as well as interest.

While it is not intended that the Home Owners' Loan Corporation shall be used to finance properties which are hopelessly in arrears or undervalued as compared with the mortgage debt, the corporation may aid a home-owner whose home for the time being is worth less than the face of the mortgage.

EXTENT OF HOME OWNERSHIP

The high costs of financing are frequently cited as a serious obstacle to home-ownership. It cannot be denied that these costs often impose a serious burden. The proportion of owned homes in the United States has remained nearly stationary during the last forty years. From 1890 to 1920, in fact, the proportion of owned homes declined slightly, but this was due to a decrease in the proportion of farm homes owned and it is reasonably certain that conditions in agriculture had more to do with this than did the question of home-financing costs. For non-farm homes, the percentage owned increased from 36.9 per cent in 1890 to 45.9 per cent in 1930; in the decade 1920–30 the increase in this group was more than sufficient to offset a further decrease in the proportion of farm homes owned so that for all homes the proportion rose to 47.7 per cent against 45.6 per cent in 1920. As compared with 1890, however, there was practically no change. Chart 65 shows percentages by Census periods.

The increase in the proportion of owned homes from 1920 to 1930 occurred during a period of high building costs, but for a considerable part of this period workers were well employed at relatively high wages or salaries. A specific factor contributing to the increase was the great shortage of housing immediately after the World War, and the difficulty of securing satisfactory homes for rent even at the unusually high rentals prevailing during most of the post-War period.

The proportion of owned homes, excluding farm homes, is highest in the North Central states and the West, and is lowest in the South and the Atlantic, Middle Atlantic, and New England states. A low ratio in some Southern states is due largely to a high negro tenant population.

— CHART 65 —

PERCENTAGES OF OWNED AND RENTED HOMES
IN THE UNITED STATES: 1890-1930

Charted from Census Data

		Owned	Rented
All Homes	1890	47.8%	52.2%
	1900	46.7%	53.3%
	1910	45.9%	54.1%
	1920	45.6%	54.4%
	1930	47.8%	52.2%

		Owned	Rented
Homes not on Farms	1890	36.9%	63.1%
	1900	36.5%	63.5%
	1910	38.4%	61.6%
	1920	40.9%	59.1%
	1930	45.9%	54.1%

		Owned	Rented
Homes on Farms	1890	65.9%	34.1%
	1900	64.5%	35.5%
	1910	63.0%	37.0%
	1920	58.2%	41.8%
	1930	54.1%	45.9%

The ratios of owned homes in 1920 and 1930, by states, are furnished in Table 72. Chart 66 shows graphically those states reporting an increase and those reporting a decrease in the proportion of owned homes for the decade 1920–30. Chart 67 com-

— CHART 66 —

PERCENTAGE CHANGES IN HOME OWNERSHIP IN THE STATES OF THE UNITED STATES: 1920–1930

Charted from data of the United States Census

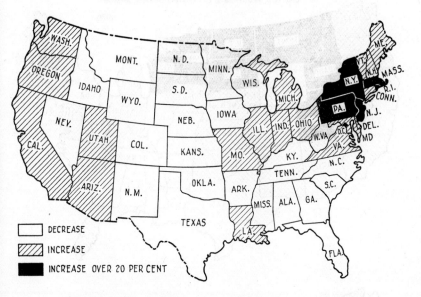

DECREASE

INCREASE

INCREASE OVER 20 PER CENT

STATES SHOWING AN INCREASE		STATES SHOWING A DECREASE	
STATE	PER CENT	STATE	PER CENT
RHODE ISLAND	32.5	KENTUCKY	0.4
DISTRICT OF COLUMBIA	27.4	GEORGIA	0.6
NEW JERSEY	26.1	WISCONSIN	0.8
MASSACHUSETTS	25.0	NEVADA	1.1
NEW YORK	20.9	FLORIDA	1.2
PENNSYLVANIA	20.4	KANSAS	1.6
CONNECTICUT	18.4	COLORADO	1.7
DELAWARE	16.4	WEST VIRGINIA	1.9
MARYLAND	10.6	ALABAMA	2.3
NEW HAMPSHIRE	10.4	TEXAS	2.6
WASHINGTON	8.6	MINNESOTA	3.0
OREGON	7.8	TENNESSEE	3.1
ILLINOIS	6.2	NEW MEXICO	3.4
CALIFORNIA	5.5	SOUTH CAROLINA	4.0
OHIO	5.4	MISSISSIPPI	4.4
ARIZONA	4.7	NEBRASKA	5.4
INDIANA	4.4	IOWA	6.0
VERMONT	3.8	NORTH CAROLINA	6.1
LOUISIANA	3.8	IDAHO	6.4
MAINE	3.5	WYOMING	6.9
VIRGINIA	2.4	OKLAHOMA	9.2
UTAH	1.5	MONTANA	9.9
MISSOURI	0.8	NORTH DAKOTA	10.3
MICHIGAN	0.2	ARKANSAS	11.1
		SOUTH DAKOTA	13.7

— CHART 67 —

PERCENTAGES OF OWNED HOMES IN THE STATES
OF THE UNITED STATES: 1920 AND 1930

Charted from data of United States Census

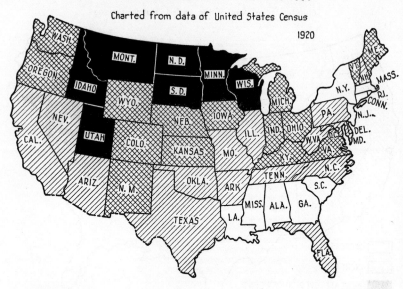

1920

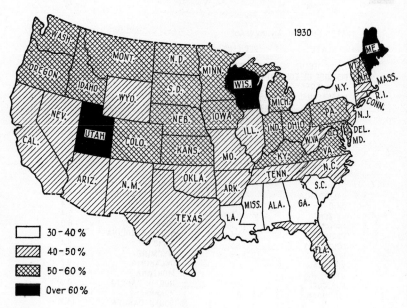

1930

30 – 40 %
40 – 50 %
50 – 60 %
Over 60 %

—— CHART 68 ——

PERCENTAGES OF OWNED HOMES IN SELECTED CITIES OF 100,000 OR MORE POPULATION, IN THE UNITED STATES: 1930

Charted from data in the 1930 Report of Bureau of the Census

	0	10	20	30	40	50	60	70	80	90	100

TACOMA, WASH.
GRAND RAPIDS
PORTLAND, OREGON
OMAHA
AKRON
PHILADELPHIA
DES MOINES
BALTIMORE
SEATTLE
ST. PAUL
TOLEDO
PEORIA
SALT LAKE CITY
WICHITA
MINNEAPOLIS
DENVER
SYRACUSE
SAN ANTONIO
BUFFALO
MILWAUKEE
INDIANAPOLIS
DETROIT
LOUISVILLE
PITTSBURGH
KANSAS CITY, MO.
HOUSTON
WASHINGTON, D.C
MEMPHIS
CINCINNATI
LOS ANGELES
CLEVELAND
BIRMINGHAM
JACKSONVILLE
RICHMOND
MIAMI
SAN FRANCISCO
PROVIDENCE
ST. LOUIS
CHICAGO
ATLANTA
NEW ORLEANS
BOSTON
NEWARK
NEW YORK

pares the percentages of owned homes by states in 1920 and 1930, as reported by the Census.

The percentage of owned homes in selected cities having a population of 100,000 or more in 1930 is given in Chart 68. While several of the largest cities show a low ratio of owned homes, this is not invariably the case; the rate of growth is quite as important as the size of the city. The Census in its special 1920 report on mortgages on homes noted that in rapidly growing cities the inconvenience and difficulty of renting suitable homes has been a great stimulus to home-ownership. However, many other considerations are involved. The most striking fact brought out by Chart 68 is the relatively high ratio of owned homes in many large urban communities.

The ratio of home-ownership among wage-earners is considerably less than that just given for the country as a whole; no comprehensive recent figures are available. An investigation by the United States Commissioner of Labor in 1901, covering 25,440 wage-earners' homes, showed the following: [70]

	Number	Per cent
Homes owned	4,825	18.97
Homes rented	20,615	81.03
	25,440	100.00

The percentages by major geographical sections were as follows: [71]

	Percentage of Wage-Earning Families in 1901 Occupying —	
	Owned homes	Rented homes
North Atlantic states	13.34	86.66
South Atlantic states	19.56	80.44
North central states	27.56	72.44
South central states	20.80	79.20
Western states	30.97	69.03

In Canada the percentage of home-ownership is much higher than in the United States. The Census of 1921 showed that 62

[70] USDL, "18th Annual Report of the Commissioner of Labor," p. 52.
[71] Ibid.

per cent of Canadian homes were owned and 38 per cent rented, as follows: [72]

	Per Cent		
	Owning	Renting	Total
Rural families	78.50	21.50	100
Urban families	46.06	53.94	100
Total families	61.91	38.09	100

No official statistics on the subject of home-ownership are kept in Great Britain. Prior to the World War the proportion of owned homes, especially for low-income groups, was small. Some British housing authorities believe there has been a relative increase in home-ownership since the War. One writer has stated that "there is not the slightest doubt that the trend in Great Britain since the war has been strongly towards home ownership, and the possession of a single-family house." [73]

However, the great majority of homes in Great Britain are still rented.[74] On an arbitrary basis it may be estimated that of 9,250,000 dwellings in England and Wales at the end of 1930, 25 per cent were owned by their occupants and 75 per cent were rented.[75]

In France the proportion of owned homes is relatively high, one estimate placing it at 80 per cent.[76] Data for other European countries are not available, but in many the proportion is low. In fifty-three Swedish towns and communes between 1912 and 1926 the proportion of owned homes rose from 11 to 17

[72] "Sixth Census of Canada, 1921, Vol. III — Population" (F. A. Acland, Ottawa, 1927), p. 54.

[73] Dalzell, A. G., "Current Trends in House Building" (Journal of the Town Planning Institute of Canada, April, 1930), p. 30.

[74] The Inter-Departmental Committee on the Rent Restrictions Acts said: "Considering the problem of the country as a whole, we have no doubt that it remains true to say that the great majority of the working classes are not in a position (even if they wished) to buy their houses" (Report, July, 1931, p. 21).

[75] Sir Harold Bellman in the March, 1933, Economic Journal (p. 36) notes that a ratio of 20 per cent for owned homes has found general acceptance, a proportion which he states may be "unduly conservative."

[76] Tugwell, R. G., Munro, Thomas, and Stryker, R. E., "American Economic Life" (Harcourt, Brace and Company, New York, 1925), p. 377.

TABLE 72

PERCENTAGES OF OWNED HOMES IN THE UNITED STATES, 1920 AND
1930, BY STATES [a]

| | Per Cent Owned | |
States showing an increase	1920	1930
Maine	59.6	61.7
New Hampshire	49.8	55.0
Vermont	57.5	59.7
Massachusetts	34.8	43.5
Rhode Island	31.1	41.2
Connecticut	37.6	44.5
New York	30.7	37.1
New Jersey	38.3	48.3
Pennsylvania	45.2	54.4
Ohio	51.6	54.4
Indiana	54.8	57.2
Illinois	43.8	46.5
Michigan	58.9	59.0
Missouri	49.5	49.9
Delaware	44.7	52.0
Maryland	49.9	55.2
District of Columbia	30.3	38.6
Virginia	51.1	52.3
Louisiana	33.7	35.0
Arizona	42.8	44.8
Utah	60.0	60.9
Washington	54.7	59.4
Oregon	54.8	59.1
California	43.7	46.1

(a) Census data. In computing the percentages the homes reported as of
unknown proprietorship and encumbrance have been distributed in the same
proportion as those where this was known.

TABLE 72 (*continued*)

PERCENTAGES OF OWNED HOMES IN THE UNITED STATES, 1920 AND 1930, BY STATES

	Per Cent Owned	
States showing a decrease	*1920*	*1930*
Wisconsin	63.6	63.1
Minnesota	60.7	58.9
Iowa	58.1	54.6
North Dakota	65.3	58.6
South Dakota	61.5	53.1
Nebraska	57.4	54.3
Kansas	56.9	56.0
West Virginia	46.8	45.9
North Carolina	47.4	44.5
South Carolina	32.2	30.9
Georgia	30.9	30.7
Florida	42.5	42.0
Kentucky	51.6	51.4
Tennessee	47.7	46.2
Alabama	35.0	34.2
Mississippi	34.0	32.5
Arkansas	45.1	40.1
Oklahoma	45.5	41.3
Texas	42.8	41.7
Montana	60.5	54.5
Idaho	60.9	57.0
Wyoming	51.9	48.3
Colorado	51.6	50.7
New Mexico	59.4	57.4
Nevada	47.6	47.1

—— CHART 69 ——

DISTRIBUTION OF URBAN AND RURAL HOMES, BY TENURE AND MORTGAGE STATUS, IN THE UNITED STATES: 1930

URBAN		RURAL			
		NON-FARM		FARM	
OWNED	RENTED	OWNED	RENTED	OWNED	RENTED

50%   80%   35%   40%   45%   55%

MORTGAGED

FREE

PROPER RATIO OF FAMILY INCOME TO COST OF HOME

Estimates of the price which a purchaser should pay for a home range, as a rule, from one and one-half to three times a year's income; the most conservative estimates fall substantially below the ratio of two years' income. Thus, a family with an income of $1500 per year should not acquire a home costing as much as $3000.

A study by the United States Building and Loan League in 1930 indicated that for families with incomes of $1200 to $1800 yearly, the proper ratio was about 1.75, while for those with yearly incomes of $2100 to $4800 it was placed at 1.9. This suggests that the proper cost of a home for different income groups would be approximately as follows: [81]

Yearly income	Indicated proper cost of home
$1,200	$2,100
1,800	3,150
2,100	4,000
4,800	9,000

There is a disposition on the part of purchasers to buy homes which are beyond their means, and as a result many home-owners have become involved in serious, indeed unbearable, burdens. The danger is clearly indicated by the rapid rise in foreclosures in times of financial stress. The number of sheriff's writs issued in Philadelphia rose from 1056 in 1921 to 17,985 in 1931; in the latter year these writs covered 20,813 separate parcels of which 19,383, or 93 per cent, were houses.[82] In Cuyahoga County, Ohio, the number of parcels sold under foreclosure rose from 143 in 1920 to 2355 in 1929.[83] These rapid

[81] American Building Association News, February, 1931.

[82] Newman, Bernard J., "Housing in Philadelphia," 1931, p. 34.

[83] A classification of 10,335 parcels thus sold in the ten-year period 1920–29 is given below:

	Number	Per cent of total
Single-family dwellings	5,590	54.1
Two-family dwellings	1,841	17.8
Apartment-houses	631	6.1
Stores and suites	577	5.6
Store buildings	53	0.5
Lots	1,300	12.6
Acreage	136	1.3
Commercial properties	207	2.0
	10,335	100.0

Ball, A. I., "The Truth About Foreclosures" (National Real Estate Journal, Dec. 22, 1930, p. 27).

increases are largely explained by the change in financial conditions which began in the latter part of 1929, but an increase had been evident some years earlier.

The great increase in the number of foreclosure sales does not complete the picture of the hazards of home-ownership, since great numbers of mortgages were in 1932 being carried by banks although the ratio of loan to value of the property was in excess of the legal limit. Indeed, appraisal values in 1932 frequently were less than the amount of the first mortgage. In many cases banks continued to carry mortgages and pay taxes rather than exercise the right to foreclose, feeling that it was better policy to rely upon the borrower to make good than to attempt to sell the property under the conditions prevailing in the real-estate market.

In connection with foreclosures, it may be of interest to point out the causes, in the order of importance, as indicated by replies of several hundred first-mortgage lenders.

A. *Personal causes*
  1. Borrower was unable to pay because of unemployment.
  2. Financial circumstances of borrower did not warrant purchase of a home.
  3. Borrower was unable to pay because of special assessments and increases in taxation.
  4. Borrower had contracted for too many other instalment purchases.
  5. Borrower had sustained business or stock-market losses.
  6. Borrower was a speculative builder or a holder who failed to find a purchaser.
  7. Domestic troubles of borrower.
  8. Borrower was dishonest.

B. *Contributing causes*
  1. General decline in home property values.
  2. Loan was too large a percentage of value.
  3. Intrusion in neighborhood of incompatible elements, or other change in the character of the neighborhood.
  4. Home out of keeping with neighborhood.

5. Poor construction of building.
6. Loan was made on property in a subdivision not yet developed.
7. Zoning law was inadequate.

" More than 85 per cent of the lenders found that the personal causes of default had more to do with the present situation than the contributing difficulties." [84]

This matter has in recent years received increasing attention from conservative lending agencies, some of which have urged real-estate operators to refrain from inducing a purchaser to attempt to acquire a home if this would involve an undue financial burden. It is pointed out that, aside from the distress caused in individual cases, the loss of homes through foreclosure tends to discourage home-ownership.

As a partial means of avoiding foreclosure, conservative interests advocate that the purchaser acquire sufficient resources to permit him to have a substantial equity in his home before attempting to purchase. Such interests are in general agreement that this equity should be at least 20 per cent and preferably 25 per cent of the total cost.

As opposed to this suggestion, some writers on housing hold that the purchaser should be able to finance a still larger proportion of the total cost, say 85 or 90 per cent, through borrowed funds. This suggestion has been condemned by many real-estate interests. In particular, the proposal that a larger proportion of the total cost of a home should be obtainable on first mortgage has been assailed on the ground that this is merely concealing the second-mortgage risk under the name of a first mortgage.

ARGUMENTS PRO AND CON HOME-OWNERSHIP

Among advantages of home-ownership, as contrasted with renting, are these:

1. The home-owner at the end of a period of years has an

[84] The President's Conference on Home Building and Home Ownership, Vol. II, pp. 17–18.

investment of substantial value, where the renter has nothing "but a bundle of rent receipts."

2. Home-ownership stimulates thrift.

3. Home-ownership assures a permanent residence, thus eliminating any anxiety over fluctuations in rent.

4. Home-ownership, partly because of the pride in possession, increases the social standing of the family in the community; it also improves the credit standing of the family.

On the other hand, it is frequently argued that renting is more advantageous since it involves no danger of shrinkage of capital; that the renter is free to move and take advantage of better opportunities in business; that it is less expensive; and that the excess outlay required for home-ownership, if wisely invested, would yield a better financial return than ownership in a home.

A study of approximately 2000 families in Chicago disclosed the following as the most frequently cited reasons against home-ownership: [85]

1. Renting is cheaper than owning.

2. Financing costs of owning too high.

3. Tax burden on owners too heavy.

4. Investment in house too fixed.

5. Renting increases freedom.

6. Instalment payments on house are dangerous.

7. Owned house a poor investment.

8. Costs incidental to purchase of house too high.

9. Land value too high.

10. Renting increases bargaining power (i.e., in regard to better position).

Whether or not renting is preferable to owning, large numbers of families are virtually precluded from owning a home. A vice president of the United States Building and Loan League stated in 1930 that of approximately 18,000,000 fami-

---

[85] Woodbury, Coleman, "Apartment House Increases and Home Ownership" (Journal of Land and Public Utility Economics, August, 1931, pp. 322–323).

lies living in rented quarters probably **8,000,000** were prevented from becoming home-owners because of the character of their employment.[86]

Many other families in low-income groups are prevented from owning homes at any time by shortage of funds. Even if the financial difficulty could be overcome, many of these families would still be too irresponsible to own and maintain a home.

Some prominent housing authorities believe that many families in low-income groups should not attempt home-ownership.

Lawrence Veiller, secretary of the National Housing Association, in 1916 held that for the $15-a-week man home-owning was not a possibility. Again, in 1930, in commenting on certain ratios of income to home cost worked out by the United States Bureau of Labor Statistics he said, " What the Department does not say — and what it might have said — is that these figures indicate clearly that there are some families who should not attempt to become home owners." [87]

A similar view was expressed in replies to a questionnaire sent out by the United States Building and Loan League in 1930, three of which held that home-ownership was " impossible " at that time for a family with an income of only $100 a month, while two others stated that a family with such an income " should not try " to purchase a home.

A leading American architect and housing authority has said:

" Ownership is unquestionably desirable in certain cases, but it does not appear to have sufficient cost advantages to offset the difficulties and restrictions which cannot be ignored. Community building along modern efficient lines is more likely to go forward if a satisfactory rental basis can be provided." [88]

Most sociologists and others who have discussed the subject strongly urge home-ownership to develop citizenship. As a tax-

[86] Myers, R. Holtby, " Stimulating Home Ownership " (Building and Loan Annals, 1930, p. 73).

[87] Housing, March, 1930, p. 7.

[88] Wright, Henry, " The Costs of Housing " (Architectural Forum, March, 1932, Part 2, p. 303.).

payer, the home-owner naturally is much more interested and influential in public affairs; in some particulars his social status is better. He feels more responsibility for sound economic and educational public policies; his home is an asset which may be passed down to his children. But for large numbers the ownership of a home is not practicable and for many others it is undesirable. Financing for the home by its hypothecation, however, should by no means be limited to the owner who occupies. It should be equally available to the owner who rents. Landlordism is one of the largest of businesses in every modern state. Low-cost and efficient financing strengthens its economic status and thereby helps both owner and tenant.

A very significant fact disclosed by this chapter is the large part of the home cost that is financed on its credit. Excessive dependence upon credit is always fraught with danger, whether in the grocery business, security speculation, or real-estate investment. The individual who attempts to operate with 85 per cent of borrowed capital in any undertaking invites disaster from the start. The purchase of a home, where there is a mortgage, is comparable to a margin transaction in securities; unless the purchaser's equity is sufficiently large to provide against all reasonable contingencies, there is always danger of foreclosure. Those who would make it possible for the purchaser still further to increase the proportion of borrowed funds may really be doing him an injury. A particular danger arises from the fact that in a period of rapidly declining real-estate values it is often almost impossible to find a purchaser at any price, or at least at a price anywhere near the value under normal conditions. Desirable as home-ownership may be in principle, it is not advisable for families who cannot afford a substantial part of the cost at the outset. The ratio of 20 to 25 per cent favored by various real-estate interests, as previously noted, would appear to be a minimum from the standpoint of safety. One of the most tragic consequences of the recent economic depression has been the loss of homes by tens of thousands of families after years of effort to reduce the amount of the mortgage debt. While in view of the abnormal shrinkage in values in recent years much of this distress probably could not have been averted, great numbers of families could have saved their homes had their initial equity been larger.

Burdensome as second-mortgage costs have been shown to be, under present conditions in the building industry they are in large measure justified by the risk involved. Under new methods of construction and financing, it should be possible to effect a degree of standardization which would permit a significant reduction in financing costs. But as long as houses continue to be built by a multitude of small, inefficient operators, in the present haphazard fashion, no real approach to standardization is possible.

In a large proportion of cases second mortgages are paid off in a comparatively short time. This is true also of first mortgages taken out through a building and loan association. But in a great number of cases the first mortgage is allowed to run indefinitely until because of individual reverses, illness, or change in business conditions it becomes a serious burden. The growing tendency among lending institutions other than building and loan associations to insist upon amortization of the principal is strongly to be commended, as much in the interest of the home-owner as from the standpoint of the lender.

To sum up this discussion of a highly complex and very important subject, let us recall that the agencies available for financing the home are bewildering in their number and variety and charges; that the legal restrictions imposed on the various types of credit instruments are complex and hard to understand; that the rates charged, while not too high from the point of view of the lender and the security and the difficulties of the individual transaction, are certainly too high from the point of view of the borrower and need a reduction which will not impair the creditor's position; that somebody has to pay the financing charges on property whether the occupant owns or leases it, and that therefore the question is of importance to owner and tenant alike.[89]

Solution of the home-financing problem lies in coordination of the agencies for lending and of the instruments by which they spread the credit risk, so that the individual transaction may become of less importance in the determination of the rate of interest; better liquidity and salability of credit; and reduction of the charges for inspection.

Although in a given state the general character of the mortgage obligation and the laws governing property titles are similar if not identical for all agencies, the individual has a bewildering array of financing agencies to choose between if he wants to borrow on his home. Except in the case of the building and loan associations, there is little coordination between the lending and building agencies, except through the individual owner. He is the coordinator, even though he knows little of building and of mortgaging, and has slight chance to learn except through the hard teacher, experience.

Beyond these primary agencies there are consolidated mortgaging agencies, including some of the insurance companies, which have made a substantial beginning in averaging and developing home credit through consolidation or refunding. An increasing percentage of the individual mortgages effected by primary agencies are thus combined into a form of credit more widely available to the general investor. This benefits the home-owner by making his house a more liquid asset whenever he may want to sell or borrow. The recently established Federal Home Bank system will undoubtedly prove a great boon in this particular; furthermore, it will help to standardize the mortgage instrument and simplify home-financing practice throughout the land. It will improve the credit of the home-owner and help to guarantee to him the means by which such credit may be utilized.

---

[89] The tenant, of course, pays the financing cost on his rent. If it is too high, it hurts him directly. By the amount it is too high he is deprived of the kind of housing he ought to be able to command.

Cooperative financing is not only managed on a relatively large scale through the building and loan associations, but is a factor in such significant developments as the garment-workers' cooperative apartments in New York City. It appears also in foreign countries, as in the public utility societies of Great Britain and in many of the extensive post-War developments in Germany whose financing has been aided by government loans. There is much to be said in favor of home financing of this character, and its development in this country should continue.

But after this coordination is achieved there is still a need of a broader basis for lending. Most housing credits are too small, too individualistic, and too specialized to justify either minimum rates or expectation of a ready sale. But certainly if better credit facilities are to be accorded housing, a broader market must be provided both for sale and hypothecation.

As previously stated, home-ownership is desirable from a political and a social viewpoint. Doubt is expressed regarding direct cost advantage in ownership compared with tenantry. If the individual home were made more salable, the economic position of the occupying owner would be much improved. Extension of the Torrens title system and other aids to easy and safe land-title transfers, both private and public, would help, as would better standardization of house structure. The production of " certified houses " by builders and manufacturers would stimulate such standardization and foster better financing means at lower rates.

Consolidated home-mortgage bonds well secured and widely available for investment are a most important factor in bettering the liquidity of the individual home, as well as the home itself. To regulate, standardize, and control the home-credit and investment mechanism of a nation is clearly a proper and desirable function of the state. It is not only a factor of the highest importance in the financing of the house, but one of the best kinds of governmental regulation and of government aid.

If the market for home credit could be substantially broadened, investment therein might become one of the best kinds of unemployment insurance. If from a man's savings he could acquire credit equity in the home he occupies, he might bridge the periods of slack work and deficient income by borrowing on it. In the periods of steady work and steady income that inevitably follow, his home credit could be reestablished. In this way home-ownership might help to carry the burden of unemployment.

The extremely small units into which the primary home credits are divided, the widely scattered location of the physical properties pledged, and their infinite variety of form and condition make these rates what they are; indeed it is surprising that they are not higher. There are three ways in which the cost may be substantially reduced. First, standardization of mortgage and title laws and practices throughout the United States would materially simplify and unify our home-credit machinery; it would reduce the labor and cost, clarify the means, and broaden the field for refunding. Second, under the lead of the Home Loan Bank system the averaging of risks between individuals and territorial sections would further broaden the availability of home credit as an object for general public investment; by thus increasing its liquidity, individually lower mortgage rates would be justified and would result. Third, the development of simplified practice in the building industry, so well started by Herbert Hoover, and other improvements in standardization should make simpler, sounder, and less costly the appraisal of individual home value; it would reduce the relative cost of the house, and hence the amount of financing. Distinct progress is being made in all three directions. Another decade should see housing credit much further developed for the benefit of both owner and investor.

National consolidated home-loan bonds would make an investment form of the soundest character, whether with or without partial tax exemption. It may be assumed that they would find a market at rates comparable with other sound securities of national scope. Furthermore, the average rate on credit extended to the individual would approximate perhaps 1 per cent more than that applying to the corresponding consolidated securities. On this assumption, rates to the individual might well be a full one-sixth lower than today. We have already indicated how increased standardization and improved materials and methods of construction might reduce the cost of the house by a maximum of one-third. If only half that reduction were effected, the reduction in cost of financing would approach one-third; one-sixth less value to finance and one-sixth lower rate on his mortgage. If his house cost one-third less, his financing would be lower by four-ninths.

Thus by coordination of the agencies, standardization of mortgage laws, spreading of credit risk through consolidated home-loan bonds, the house as a basis for credit may be much improved, financing made easier and lower, the house more easily bought and sold. Home-ownership may thereby be extended.

But none of these results can be fully achieved without a more simplified basis of value on which to determine risk and rate. Such a basis does not involve standardizing the house itself but the elements of which it is composed — its structure, finish, and accessories. The character of these features should be certified, moreover, by producers of well-established reputation.

CHAPTER XI
Government Intervention in Housing

STRICTLY speaking, direct government intervention in the providing of permanent shelter for groups of citizens is a development of recent times. One might find some precedent for it in the British Corn and Poor Laws of recent centuries, the bread and circus institutions of Rome, and the forms of dole granted by declining Athens.

Elsewhere we have considered governmental restrictions on building incident to the growth of community or city life; these safeguard the welfare of the people and assist their sound economic growth. Such intervention should not be confused with state provision of housing itself. The provision of housing means financial aid, whether directly by subsidy or indirectly by rent restriction or tax exemption. To provide shelter in any form for one section of the community, government taxes others; the effect being to undermine its revenue resources — or just the opposite of intervention in matters of construction and planning. Where direct financial aid or concessions have been given in the past they have often foreshadowed the decline of civilizations, as was the case, for instance, with the doles provided by Athens and Imperial Rome.

These principles apply to every state. No statecraft nor other means can change or annul them. They are vital to every economic order. Today government housing schemes are a commonplace in Great Britain, Austria, and other countries. Whether or not socially justified by poverty or a condition of dependence, or by a temporary local emergency, some lowering of the economic status has always resulted.

What is the psychological result when government thus donates housing? Is it not similar to the effect upon the tenant of a southern cotton mill who is *ostensibly* given his housing free or at a rental below its cost? If he is thus deluded as to the second largest expense item of his budget, can he be expected to have the right attitude toward government and the social structure of which he is a unit? As a social policy in a capitalistic state, removal of the item of rent from the family budget seems quite unjustified.

In every country and every civilization, there are the very young and the very old, the sick, the crippled, and others who are economic dependents of the state; naturally they must be provided with shelter and other essentials at public expense — a load which the economic structure of every community must carry, and which must be provided for in the public economy and offset by constructive social and economic measures.

By the same token, there will always be temporary economic unbalance and distress in one section or another. In the war-devastated area of Europe sixteen years ago there were millions without homes; the need of governmental aid in building at least temporary shelter was obvious. Indeed, such was the devastation, such the deficiency of houses and the destruction of other wealth, that the most extensive assistance was required to rehabilitate social and economic life. It was given and for the most part well given.

Except for sporadic efforts, government aid during the past century appears to have developed first in Great Britain, about 1850; it was at the outset concerned with the improvement of lodging-houses, and was for a long time mainly confined to preventing the building of the poorest types of dwellings. Assistance for the working classes in general, as distinct from the " submerged tenth " of the population, was not seriously undertaken until near the close of the nineteenth century; the mere fact that up to 1914 only 2 to 5 per cent of all dwellings were constructed with public assistance indicates that the efforts of the authorities were chiefly confined to improving special or isolated conditions.

In Germany, where before the World War government aid and intervention was practiced on a much larger scale than in any other country, it was chiefly applied to the housing of government employees and did not touch the problem of housing for low-paid industrial workers in general. Government aid in France was more or less sporadic, a special feature being provision for large families. Numerous acts were passed providing for the loaning of funds or for other forms of assistance. But although large credits were available, the sums actually utilized during the decade prior to 1914 ranged only from 2,000,000 to 4,000,000 francs [1] per year. Clearly this represents a trifling contribution to the housing requirements of a population of more than 40,000,000. In Belgium 63,000 working-class houses, it is estimated, had been built or purchased prior to the World War with the assistance of loans from the General Savings and Pension Fund, under the Act of 1889. For a country of 8,000,000 population this was an appreciable number, yet it was only about 5 per cent of the total housing of the nation.

The following summary gives some of the more important cases of national legislation in European countries for government assistance to housing up to the outbreak of the World War.

NATIONAL LEGISLATION

Apparently the earliest instance of national [2] housing-aid legislation in Great Britain was the Shaftesbury Act of 1851 (Labouring Classes Lodging-Houses Act). This gave certain Local Authorities [3] the right to erect lodging-houses at the

[1] Roughly $400,000 to $800,000.

[2] The Liverpool Building Act of 1842 is sometimes cited as an instance of government aid but was, rather, a sanitary measure.

[3] Since there will be frequent occasion to refer to Local Authorities in this chapter, it should be understood that these are the local governing bodies —

public expense. During the next fifty years this act was followed by various other measures considerably extending the scope of public aid; chief among them were the following:

Act of 1866. Authorized Public Works Loans Commissioners to lend funds for housing of laboring classes.

Act of 1868. Provided for alteration or destruction of unsuitable dwellings.

Act of 1874. Authorized public authorities [4] to grant or lease land for erection of workmen's dwellings.

Act of 1875. Provided that public authorities might themselves erect houses.

Act of 1879. Provided for lending of public funds to companies and associations.

Act of 1890. Consolidated and greatly enlarged scope of previous legislation; sought to encourage Local Authorities, public utility associations, and private agencies to provide houses.

Act of 1899. Provided for small loans to individual workmen desiring to acquire their own homes.

Act of 1900. Considerably extended powers of Local Authorities.

Act of 1909. Laid down a general housing policy; made it *obligatory* upon Local Authorities to take action under certain conditions.

In France, the government made an appropriation of 10,-000,000 francs as early as 1852; part of this was to aid the construction of workingmen's dwellings. From 1894 to 1913 various acts were passed providing for the lending of public funds and for tax exemptions, as well as for minor subsidies for the housing of large families.[5]

The Belgian Act of 1889 is sometimes styled the pioneer

---

i.e., municipal governments, of which there are nearly 2000 in England and Wales. They correspond to Boards of Selectmen or City Councils in the United States, but frequently have wider and more specific powers and duties.

[4] i.e., the Local Authority (see p. 408, note 3).

[5] Families with more than three children under sixteen years of age.

housing law; it was a comprehensive statute. Its essential feature was the lending of public funds at low rates of interest.

A housing fund was established by the State of Prussia in 1895. This marked the beginning of an aggressive policy of housing aid in Germany, chiefly for public employees.

From 1900 to 1910 various other European countries enacted housing-aid legislation, notably Holland in 1901, Italy in 1903, Sweden and Norway about 1904, Hungary in 1907, and Austria in 1908. In the same decade similar legislation was enacted by New Zealand and by some of the Australian states.

In addition to assistance rendered by national governments in Europe, there were many instances of local public aid by municipalities, notably in Great Britain, Germany, and the Scandinavian countries. The available records do not permit a summary of these local activities.

PRE-WAR METHODS

Prior to the World War, the principal method of extending public aid to housing was the lending of public or semi-public moneys (such as insurance and pension funds), sometimes at less than the market rate of interest, for real-estate loans. Such loans were made on a large scale to public welfare building associations and local governing bodies, and in some countries to employers; in several countries they were extended to individual home-owners. The greatest assistance was that made through building associations, the dividends of which frequently were limited to 4 or 5 per cent; in some cases the surplus of such associations in case of liquidation was to be applied to some public purpose. Tax exemption was commonly employed in continental European countries. Direct construction, either by the state or by municipalities, was undertaken in relatively few instances.

Except for certain rent subsidies for poor cottagers in Ireland and certain small grants in the case of large families in France, almost no direct subsidies were made before the War.

RESULTS OF PRE-WAR LEGISLATION

Some idea of the results of this pre-War legislation, as indicated by the number of houses provided through government aid, is afforded by Table 73. Broadly speaking, prior to the World War the housing problem in Europe was one of quality rather than of quantity; public authorities were concerned with improving the standards of certain classes of housing rather than with providing a large number of new houses.[6] There was comparatively little complaint of a shortage of houses. At the outbreak of the War, however, there was increasing evidence that the supply of homes in some countries was inadequate. Undoubtedly large numbers of dwellings were of distinctly low standard — although writers who stress the unsatisfactory quality of pre-War housing have not always distinguished between slum areas and wage-earners' homes in general. With respect to dwellings of wage-earners in Great Britain, the following statement from a source strongly in sympathy with the policy of government aid indicates that some of these criticisms may have been overdrawn.

" As far as the houses built by private enterprise in the 40 years between 1875 and 1914 are concerned, the writer has no hesitancy in placing on record his conviction that the advocates of private enterprise can claim with justice that the houses built by their agency in the period under consideration constituted remarkably good value for the money." [7]

The War inevitably gave a great impetus to the policy of public aid to housing. The normal increase in housing was tem-

6 It is interesting to note that because of the large number of dwellings erected in Europe since the War, the housing problem has again become one of quality rather than one of quantity. " The salient feature of the housing problem some 10 years ago was its quantitative aspect. At the present time, however, although the quantitative aspect of the problem is still by no means negligible, it is nevertheless the qualitative aspect that mainly demands analysis." (Méquet, G., " Housing Problems and the Depression " [International Labour Review, February, 1933], p. 161).

7 Aldridge, Henry R., " The National Housing Manual " (National Housing and Town Planning Council, London, 1923), p. 119.

TABLE 73

GOVERNMENT AID TO HOUSING IN CERTAIN COUNTRIES — PRE-WAR
APPROXIMATE a

Country and date of first legislation	Form of aid	Amount of funds advanced	Number of dwellings built	Per cent of population housed or aided
Great Britain				
1851	Loans; construction	$50,000,000	100,000	2.0
Ireland				
Before 1906	Rent subsidies	———	20,000	—d
1906	Loans	———	50,000	—
France				
1852 b	Loans; subsidies	$1,930,000	very few	negligible
1894	Loans; tax exemptions; subsidies in a few cases	$15,000,000	49,000 c	0.5
Belgium				
1862–71 b	Minor tax exemptions			
1889	Loans	$22,000,000	62,125	4.0
Netherlands				
1851 b	Minor aid			
1901	Loans Subsidies in special cases	$14,750,000	16,000	1.0
Germany				
1895	Construction; loans (chiefly for government employees)	$225,000,000	200,000	2.5
Austria				
1892	Tax exemptions; loans	$20,000,000	25,000	negligible
Hungary				
1870 b	Tax exemptions			
1901	Subsidies in some cases	———	25,000	—
Italy				
1862–66 b	Some aid by a few cities	———	———	—
1903–08	Loans; tax exemptions and interest subsidies (to cover part of interest on loans)	———	40,000	less than 1.0

(a) In the absence of complete authoritative data these figures are in large part necessarily estimated.

(b) Indicates that legislation was limited in scope and in time; does not indicate beginning of a continuous policy.

(c) Includes 29,000 houses aided by tax exemption.

(d) These rent subsidies were partly concerned with land holdings, not merely with housing.

TABLE 73 (*continued*)

Country and date of first legislation	Form of aid	Amount of funds advanced	Number of dwellings built	Per cent of population housed or aided
Switzerland 1896	No federal legislation; tax exemptions by Canton of Geneva	——	negligible	negligible
Roumania 1910	Tax exemptions	——	negligible	negligible
Spain 1911	Tax exemptions and miscellaneous aid	——	negligible	negligible
Sweden 1904	Loans	$12,500,000	——	—
Norway 1894–1903	Small subsidies; loans (chiefly to farmers)	——	9,500	2.0
Denmark 1887	Loans for slum clearance	——	——	—
1898	Loans; tax exemptions and subsidies	$1,550,000	——	0.5
Australia 1876–1913	Loans and minor tax exemptions	$8,000,000 *e*	——	—
New Zealand 1896–1913	Loans	$12,500,000 *f*	——	—
Cuba 1910	Construction	$1,300,000	1,000 *g*	negligible
Chile 1906–07	Loans; tax exemptions and miscellaneous	——	negligible	negligible

(*e*) For four states up to 1912.
(*f*) Up to 1913.
(*g*) Up to 1914.

porarily halted, and in some countries virtually stopped, because the resources of labor and of funds were required for the prosecution of hostilities. As a result, the close of the struggle found a shortage of accommodations fairly general. At the same time the demand for homes was augmented by a marked increase in the number of marriages — a usual consequence of a great war — and by abnormal shifts in population resulting from concentration of workers in shipbuilding or munition-making centers, influx of war refugees, return of emigrants, and other causes. In France and some other countries the restoration of devastated areas presented a particularly urgent problem, which is nevertheless regarded as distinct from the question of government aid as a broad policy.[8] Necessity for suddenly providing for large numbers of war refugees created a special problem in Greece.

In general the extremely high cost of labor and building materials and, even more important, the shortage of capital created an acute crisis in housing which was regarded as beyond the ability of private credit and private enterprise to meet. Moreover, notably in Great Britain, there was a widespread sentiment that soldiers returning from the trenches should be provided with a better quality of housing than they had formerly known. " Homes fit for heroes to live in " became a national slogan. As we have seen, prior to the War public employees were sometimes assisted, as in Germany and other European countries and occasionally slum dwellers in Great Britain, but the quality of housing was the point of attack, while the quantity and cost presented no serious problem. Grossly deficient quality in the home was seen as a defect in the social structure, and the government took measures to correct it. The impetus given government building by the War is clearly shown in Chart 70, which gives the percentage of all dwellings built by the government for several European nations before the War and in 1932, when the forces engendered by the conflict had had time to take their full effect.

RESTRICTIVE RENT LEGISLATION

In all countries directly affected by the War the normal process of housing provision was greatly upset. Throughout large invaded areas not only houses were destroyed but other build-

---

[8] The rebuilding of devastated areas can hardly be styled government aid. It was a government obligation and treated as such. So, too, it was a government obligation to revamp the normal functioning of economic life by graded adjustments from the abnormal conditions resulting from drastic war measures. Building had to be started to replace basic shortages and to eliminate the need of rent restrictions.

ings and public services as well. As the War progressed, the increasing shortage of homes made rent-restricting measures necessary to equalize rentals and prevent profiteering. These restrictions have to a considerable degree persisted until the

—— CHART 70 ——

PERCENTAGE OF TOTAL NUMBER OF DWELLINGS RECIPIENTS OF
GOVERNMENT AID IN VARIOUS COUNTRIES : 1914 AND 1932

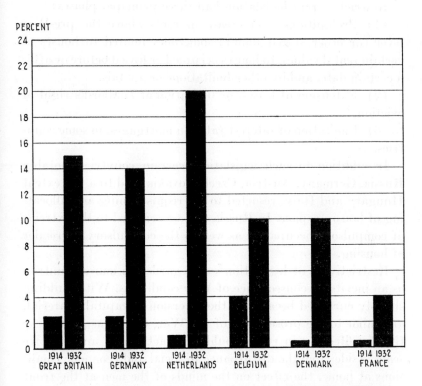

present, and may continue for some years more. The War destroyed the shelter of millions, prevented the normal increase over five entire years for other millions, and hindered the natural working of landlordism.

Thus in practically every European country during and after the War government aid was brought into house-building as a consequence of the artificial control of rents by legislation. This legislation may advantageously be reviewed at this point.

Unlike government aid to housing, restrictive rent legislation was distinctly a product of the War. The International Labour Office noted that it " originated in the moratorium policy adopted by most countries on the outbreak of the War," [9] and that previously the legal relation between landlord and tenant had attracted comparatively little attention.

Restrictive rent legislation had three principal phases:

(1) Prohibitions of increase in rents above the pre-War level (or other stated limit) ; sometimes limited to houses of certain rental values, to houses occupied or leased before or after a certain date, and by other limitations on rentals.

(2) Extension of leases, or limitation of landlord's right of eviction.[10]

(3) Limitation of interest rates on mortgages, in some countries.

In addition to such legislation, certain countries, notably Russia, Germany, Austria, Czechoslovakia, and to a less extent Hungary and Italy, resorted to the requisitioning and allocating of housing space. In Russia this was carried to the extreme of compulsory occupation as well as the compulsory surrender of housing.

Restrictive rent legislation was regarded in many countries as an inevitable consequence of War conditions. With building sharply curtailed because of the diversion of capital, material, and labor to the prosecution of the War, there was grave fear that profiteering in rents would be practiced on an extensive scale. Aside from the disturbance to social and economic conditions at home, the effect on the minds of the men at the front had to be considered. Thus in France " the principle adopted

[9] ILO, " European Housing Problems since the War," p. 17.
[10] Technically these limitations were upon the landlord's right to give notice to quit.

from the outset was that persons who were risking their lives or their property in the defense of the country should at once be freed from all anxiety about their own homes." [11]

When the first restrictive rent act in Great Britain was passed in December, 1915, it was approved, according to one writer, ". . . reluctantly, and with full knowledge that it was unwise to interfere with economic laws, but with an equally full knowledge that action had to be taken. . . ." [12] An important feature of the British act was the accompanying limitation of rates of interest on mortgages:

"The measure was passed just as much in the interest of the small property owner as in the interest of the tenant. . . . This is an aspect of the question which is only too often lost sight of and explains quite clearly the reason why the representatives of the property owners were in favor of the provisions of the new Act." [13]

In Germany, steps to control rents were taken immediately on the outbreak of the War. On August 7, 1914, an order was issued empowering the courts to allow a period of grace in meeting arrears in rent, and in December of that year rent conciliation offices were established. It was nearly two years later before rent control in comprehensive form was undertaken.

As the War progressed, other European countries initiated such legislation, as follows:

Finland		1915
Russia (Empire)	August	1915
Norway	December	1915
Sweden	May	1916
Denmark	June	1916
Hungary	November	1916
Italy	December	1916
Austria	January	1917
Netherlands	March	1917

[11] ILO, "European Housing Problems since the War," p. 115.

[12] Veiller, Lawrence, "How England Is Meeting the Housing Shortage" (Spottiswoode, Ballantyne and Co., Ltd., London, 1920), p. 52.

[13] "The National Housing Manual," p. 145.

Switzerland	June	1917
Russia (Soviet)	November	1917
Czechoslovakia	December	1918
Belgium	April	1919
Poland	June	1919

" By the end of the War nearly the whole of Europe was covered by some form of tenant protection. In some countries it applied only to specified classes of tenants; in others it covered all leases without exception." [14]

Restrictive rent legislation was enacted in various other countries, including Australia, New Zealand, India, several South American republics, and parts of the United States. With the exception of Australia and New Zealand, most of it was of local or limited character, and did not compare in importance with similar efforts in Europe.

In Great Britain it was estimated that the first rent act covered 88 per cent of all tenants in London and 97 per cent of those in other communities. In France certain classes of tenants paid no rent whatever during the War, and practically the whole population was protected against increases in rent so that the index number for rent remained at 100 during the War period.

Under a Belgian Act of August 14, 1920, *all* tenants fulfilling their obligations could, except on court intervention, extend their leases for approximately three years.

As the housing shortage became more acute, there was a general disposition to increase the severity of these restrictions. After the close of the War, however, rent legislation was amended in most countries with a view to bringing about a gradual restoration of normal competitive conditions. In various countries substantial increases in rent were authorized, usually being limited to a stated percentage over pre-War

[14] ILO, " European Housing Problems since the War," p. 18. A report of the Swiss Labour Office in 1924, in observing that four Cantons of that country had never regulated rents, added that they were "probably the only parts of Europe at the moment to which rent control has not penetrated " (" Industrial and Labour Information," April 20, 1925, p. 56).

rents. Restrictions on the landlord's right of eviction also were relaxed. In many countries buildings erected after the War or after some specified date were made exempt from the rent acts.

From 1922 to 1925 attempts were made in several countries to repeal restrictive rent legislation. These efforts at " decontrol " were successful in only a few countries, notably in Finland from 1922 to 1924, in Sweden in 1923, in Switzerland in part in 1922 and completely in 1926,[15] and in the Netherlands in 1927. In Italy the Fascist government attempted to put decontrol into effect in 1923; it actually did so in part in 1923, and for the country as a whole in 1926. In 1927 control was temporarily resumed; but it was definitely terminated in June, 1930. In many countries, however, as the date of decontrol drew near new laws continuing the restrictions were passed, although sometimes on a modified basis.

In Great Britain, where a departmental committee had recommended gradual decontrol commencing in 1923 and the abolition of " the last vestige of control " by the summer of 1925, restrictive legislation has been continued by successive acts and is still in force. It was estimated by the Inter-Departmental Committee on the Rent Restrictions Acts in July, 1931, that of 7,500,000 pre-War houses in England and Wales, about 6,250,000, or 83 per cent, were still subject to rent control. Repeated questions in Parliament as to when decontrol might be expected met with the reply that no definite date could be set. It may be noted that a memorandum in 1931 by the Chartered Surveyors' Institute of Great Britain, while strongly urging decontrol, limited its immediate application to houses of relatively high rentals and did not urge complete decontrol for all classes of dwellings earlier than Christmas, 1935.

In 1933 a bill was introduced in Parliament providing for the termination of rent control on June 24, 1938. As finally approved, however, in July, 1933, the act freed only certain classes of houses from control, and provided that for lower rental

---

[15] An attempt to reestablish control in modified form in 1928 was defeated.

(" Class C ") houses the question should again come up for consideration in 1938.

In France an act passed as early as 1918 was intended to prepare for a return to normal conditions, but was repeatedly amended; indeed the scope of control was increased. Again, it was intended to terminate rent control in 1926, but an act of June, 1929, extended this legislation for certain classes of dwellings until July 1, 1932, and for lower-class dwellings until July 1, 1939.

In Germany partial decontrol for certain classes of buildings and for communities of a certain size has been accomplished, but complete decontrol is considered impracticable until the housing shortage has been eliminated. It was intended to abolish rent control in 1936, but the Nazi government's intentions are not clear.

In Austria, where at the outset rent legislation was comparatively moderate, all idea of returning to an economic basis, at least in certain cities, has apparently been abandoned.

In Russia, payment of rent was abolished by the Soviet government, but was later restored. There were indications of a partial return to an economic basis, but this appears to have been a temporary modification of the regulations. Information is meager and conflicting.

In various other countries the date for decontrol was postponed from time to time. Complete decontrol [16] in Europe is at present found only in Sweden, Norway, Denmark, Finland, the Netherlands, Italy, and Switzerland.

RESULTS OF RESTRICTIVE RENT LEGISLATION

The first and most obvious result of restrictive rent legislation was that rents were kept far below the point that they would otherwise have reached. While this tended to make rentals uneconomic, it did greatly reduce the portion of the family budget required for rent. Table 74 illustrates this influence.

---

[16] Some countries which repealed their special restrictive rent acts enacted general legislation to prevent profiteering in rents.

Inevitably also this legislation tended to curtail new building operations. With building costs rapidly advancing because of rising prices of building materials and increasing wages, this seems hardly to call for proof.

TABLE 74

PERCENTAGE OF TOTAL BUDGET EXPENDED FOR RENT IN VARIOUS EUROPEAN COUNTRIES, 1918–1923 [a]

(July of each year unless otherwise indicated)

Country	Pre-War	1918	1919	1920	1921	1922	1923
Great Britain	16.0	—	—	7.4	10.95	13.55	13.07
France	12.0	—	5.04	3.52	4.3	6.4	7.2 [c]
Germany [b]	18.0	—	—	—	—	1.15	0.34
Austria [b]	14.6	—	—	—	—	0.12	0.66
Hungary [b d]	18.0	2.54	1.08	0.69	1.06	0.43	0.22
Italy	11.4	3.99	4.07	2.79	3.21	4.86	4.94
Poland [b]	18.1	—	—	—	1.13	2.23	3.44
Switzerland	10.4	—	—	—	7.03	9.88	9.9 [c]
Denmark	14.2	8.4	7.6	7.1	8.5	11.06	11.14 [c]
Sweden	11.9	6.1	5.6	5.7	5.8	10.2	11.2 [c]
Norway	15.7	6.83	7.02	7.6	8.4	10.3	11.4 [c]
Finland	11.8	—	—	4.3	5.4	7.9	10.3

(a) ILO, " European Housing Problems Since the War," p. 30.
(b) Comparisons largely invalidated because of depreciation of currencies.
(c) Figures refer to June.
(d) The figures for Hungary refer to December of each year except 1923 (July).

A well-qualified American observer has given as the consensus of opinion that this legislation was one of the chief factors in stopping the construction of new buildings by private enterprise after 1915.[17]

The British Departmental Committee on the Increase of Rent and Mortgage Interest (Restrictions) Act said:

" On the whole, we cannot but conclude that the Rent Restriction Acts, although their necessity in the past may not be challenged, have had an adverse effect on the provision of new houses. . . .

[17] Veiller, Lawrence, " How England Is Meeting the Housing Shortage," p. 53.

" We are strongly of the opinion that all restrictions should be removed at the earliest possible date. . . ." [18]

A recent report of the International Labour Office repeatedly refers to the effect of restrictive rent legislation in hampering building.

" The building difficulties experienced by nearly all European countries since the war can be traced principally to the difference between the rents which could be asked for new and for pre-war dwellings. . . .
" The effects of the three essential factors described above — high building costs, high rate of interest and restriction of the rent of old dwellings — have been more prolonged and lie at the root of post-war building difficulties in all countries." [19]

The report, however, took exception to the contention of some critics that restrictive rent legislation was the sole cause of the post-War difficulties encountered by the building industry. It cited the experience of several countries that after restrictive rent regulations were repealed commercial building steadily revived. This was notably the case in Finland, where the repeal of restrictive rent laws was almost immediately followed by a rapid recovery in building. In 1923–24 the number of houses built in that country was as large as before the War, and later it materially increased. Likewise in Sweden and in the Netherlands, which abolished rent control at a fairly early date, the report held that there was furnished " an example of the stimulus to building enterprise provided by a return to ordinary legal conditions as regards rent." [20]

A further result of restrictive rent legislation was neglect of the proper maintenance and repair of the protected dwellings; this was reported in several countries. For example, the London County Council stated:

[18] Ministry of Health (Great Britain), Final Report of the Departmental Committee on the Increase of Rent and Mortgage Interest (Restrictions) Act, 1920 (His Majesty's Stationery Office, London, 1923), p. 8.
[19] " Housing Policy in Europe," pp. 7–8.
[20] *Ibid.*, p. 17.

" At the present time a landlord is prevented from dealing with his property in such a way that much house property is standing in London today which, but for the operation of the Rent Restriction Acts, would have been swept away . . . the restriction from handling old house property from which the landlord now suffers is acting most detrimentally, and is throwing greater burdens on the local authorities in the matter of slum clearance and the oversight of such bad property. In the past, the principal agent for the removal of insanitary houses and the renewal of old and worn-out homes was the owner." [21]

Various British writers insisted that the rent acts had a tendency to delay the work of slum clearance.

The Norwegian Ministry of Social Affairs referred to the unsatisfactory state of repair of leased houses, which it attributed to housing legislation. In Austria neglect of repair and upkeep of houses by their owners was general, while in Russia the taking over of buildings by the Soviet government during the two and one-half years following the Bolshevist revolution resulted in " the partial or complete dilapidation of houses and dwellings, and, secondly, the complete cessation of the building industry which made it impossible to maintain, repair or reconstruct existing dwellings." [22]

Another result of restrictive rent legislation which led to much complaint was the extensive abuse of subletting; it was the cause of repeated complaints in Great Britain.[23] The evil reached excessive proportions in Hungary; in Budapest, out of a total of 208,189 dwellings, 97,308 were at one time sublet.

In numerous countries the tenant received from the sublet rooms more than he himself paid for the whole dwelling. One

[21] " Housing " (P. S. King and Son, Ltd., London, 1928), pp. 11–12.

[22] ILO, " European Housing Problems since the War," pp. 458–459.

[23] Captain B. S. Townroe, in a Special Report to the author, states: " There are thousands of cases, thoroughly authenticated, of landlords receiving today about 15s. for a three-story house. The tenant cannot be evicted, although he is subletting various rooms at as much as 10s. a room each, and is therefore profiteering to the extent of £2 or £3 weekly. In short, the effort of the state to interfere in the economic laws governing rents may have alleviated conditions under unprecedented circumstances, but has led to new and unforeseen evils."

critic pointed out that whereas the rent acts originally were intended to protect tenants against excessive increase in rent, or unreasonable notice to quit, " economic rents are being charged and secured, and by those who are least entitled to them, being neither the true owners of the property nor paying themselves an economic rent." [24]

General complaint was voiced throughout Europe that restrictive rent acts worked an unreasonable hardship upon the landlord or owner. One writer has said:

" The first Rent Restriction Act of 1915 was devised to protect tenants and check profiteering by landlords. Later the complete cessation of house building and the growing shortage made it necessary to continue restriction, but subsequent Acts were unfair to landlords because in spite of enormously increased prices they were not allowed to raise rents. It was not until 1920 when landlords were found to be suffering serious hardships that an increase of 30 per cent was permitted, and the full 40 per cent increase now in force was not permitted until July 2nd, 1921. The Act of 1923, on the other hand, inflicted hardships on tenants by enlarging the grounds on which the landlord could claim possession, and by gradually decontrolling some of the protected houses. The present position is therefore regulated by a complicated series of Rent Restrictions Acts (which worked adversely towards landlords and tenants in turn) resulting from a succession of compromises. The law of supply and demand having broken down, legislation attempted to mete out rough justice to both landlord and tenant in accordance with the varying tides of public opinion." [25]

A qualified observer has stated that the British Act of 1920 " was essentially a tenants' protection Act, passed to protect 6,000,000 working-class and 1,000,000 middle-class tenants at the expense of the owner who was often poorer than the tenant himself." [26]

[24] Chambers, Holroyd F., quoted in Housing, March, 1928, p. 22.
[25] Simon, E. D., " Housing: The Rents of Working Class Houses " (Contemporary Review, May, 1924, p. 553).
[26] Fremantle, Lt. Col. F. E., " The Housing of the Nation " (Philip Allan & Co., Ltd., London, 1927), p. 119.

A repeated complaint in Great Britain was that the restrictive rent acts prohibited large numbers of owners of single houses (which they had purchased for their own occupancy) from getting possession of them. A member of Parliament said in this connection: " It is purely a question of whether the person who owns the house, who has saved the money in order to buy it, has a better right to live in it than anyone else." [27]

The laws obviously operated to the disadvantage of investors in housing property. A member of Parliament in one of the debates on housing pointed out that dwelling-houses had been a popular form of investment among persons of limited means. He urged that it was an injustice to restrict the return on such property when no similar limit was placed upon the income from stocks and bonds.[28]

Among other baneful effects of these restrictive rent laws was a vast amount of petty litigation. " The lawyers were enriched, and the Courts overworked, while the population were, as far as possible, prevented from taking houses on any agreement." [29]

The general economic effects of restrictive rent legislation were summarized in the International Labour Review,[30] as follows: (1) to reduce the power of the wage-earner to pay an " economic " rent; (2) to remove the inducement to private capital to invest in building; (3) to lead to an absolute reduction in the quantity and quality of housing available.

The following extract from an official report covering the operation of rent control in Belgium epitomizes the experience of various other countries:

" The effect of the restrictive rent legislation on building operations was disastrous. Although new buildings were not affected by the law, the legislation discouraged builders. The maintenance of

[27] Peto, Sir B., " Parliamentary Debates," House of Commons, July 15, 1929, p. 181.

[28] Hurst, Gerald, " Parliamentary Debates," House of Commons, June 7, 1923, p. 2442.

[29] The Builder, London, November 5, 1926, p. 722.

[30] August, 1924, p. 294.

buildings suffered terribly as proprietors flatly refused to effect repairs, the cost of which very often exceeded a whole year's rent. Sub-letting increased in all cases where the contract did not forbid this practice, with the result that some tenants were making large profits when the proprietor received a comparatively small rent." [31]

POST-WAR AID TO HOUSING

Rent restriction, having made ownership unprofitable, also made building unprofitable. Accordingly, the close of the War found an acute shortage of housing in many European countries. The following estimate, compiled by the International Labour Office, gives an approximate idea of this shortage in several leading countries, exclusive of housing required to replace the destruction in the devastated areas. It was submitted as " an indication rather than an exact statement."

ESTIMATED SHORTAGE OF DWELLINGS IN CERTAIN EUROPEAN COUNTRIES AT THE CLOSE OF THE WORLD WAR [32]

Country	Estimated shortage of dwellings
Great Britain	500,000 — 1,000,000
Germany (deficiency for 1914–21)	1,400,000
France — Paris and suburbs	60,000
Belgium	90,000 — 240,000
Netherlands	100,000 — 164,000
Denmark, towns	12,100
Sweden, towns	19,100 [a]
Switzerland	20,000 — 35,000

a Number of rooms.

Confronted by this urgent need and the difficulties of meeting it through individual effort, shortly after the close of the War nearly all the leading countries of Europe undertook some form of encouragement to building. Indeed, in Great Britain and some other countries comprehensive plans for such assistance were taken up while the War was still in progress.

[31] Hunt, Leigh W., Assistant Commercial Attaché to the United States Department of Commerce, Brussels.
[32] International Labour Review, September, 1924, p. 459.

The methods of granting such assistance were numerous and varied. A list of the expedients most extensively used includes:

1. Loans of public or of semi-public (insurance, pensions, etc.) funds.
   a. Subscription to stock or bonds of building agencies.
2. Direct subsidies.
   a. Lump sum or annual grants.
   b. Waiver of demand for repayment of part of funds loaned.
   c. Waiver of interest, in whole or in part, or payment by public authorities of part of interest (and redemption charges).
   d. Loans at a lower rate of interest than that paid by the lending agency.
   e. Bonuses on construction or sale of dwellings.
   f. Provision of sites, free or at low prices.
3. Indirect subsidies.
   a. Exemption from taxes, or from certain fees.
   b. Guarantee of loans made by other agencies.
   c. Remission of import duties on building materials.
4. Direct construction (especially by municipalities).

In Great Britain the actual execution of government-aided schemes was left to the Local Authorities. In many cases they placed contracts with private builders, turning over to them the subsidies advanced by the national government, as well as their own contributions, if any. Sometimes the Local Authorities themselves conducted the work of construction, purchasing the materials and hiring workmen. In some countries the national governments dealt with public utility building societies; in others, they acted through special housing organizations.

A part of the original cost of the houses in Great Britain was provided through public loans by the local governments. A large number of such loans were made as a result of general campaigns very similar to the flotation of the Victory Loan in the United States. A national loan for the purpose was deemed inadvisable,[33] but a large part of the cost was obtained by the

[33] " The Government gave very careful consideration to these suggestions

Local Authorities by means of extensive loans from the Public Works Loan Board.

Since it was apparent that the rents which could be charged for the new houses, erected at the high costs then prevailing, would be much less than the economic rental necessary to maintain them and cover interest on the loans, this annual deficit was to be made good in part by local taxes levied by the Local Authorities, but chiefly by national subsidies paid from the British Exchequer to Local Authorities, building societies, or other agencies. In addition to such subsidies, loans were also employed; they were made by the national government to the Local Authorities and by both the national government and the Local Authorities to certain building agencies. In some cases Local Authorities in Great Britain guaranteed the repayment of loans made by building societies to persons desiring to build or purchase a house.[34]

In many continental European countries the condition of state finances precluded the raising of large special loans or extensive granting of subsidies by central governments; instead, public assistance often took the form of loans of state pension and similar funds, tax exemption, provision of building material or land at special prices, and various other expedients. In Germany, Austria, and Poland, and to a limited extent in Sweden, a special rent tax on houses already standing was employed; in Germany this was one of the chief sources of funds. From 1926 to 1932 the German rent tax produced more than $2,500,000,000, of which 46 per cent was used to finance new housing.[35] A large part of the funds so employed were loaned

---

for a National Loan, but it became quite clear that, having due regard to the stability of the finances of the nation, it would not do to float another vast National Loan, and the Chancellor of the Exchequer and other financial leaders made this plain to the public at an early date.

"Moreover, the financial authorities thought the responsibility for raising the money should not be taken by the State alone, but should be shared by the Local Authorities, and accepted by them as a public duty" (Veiller, Lawrence, "How England Is Meeting the Housing Shortage," p. 5).

34 For further details concerning Great Britain, see pp. 445–466.

35 Monthly Labor Review, September, 1932, p. 599.

on second mortgage, usually at from 2 to 3 per cent, thus off-setting to some extent the much higher rates paid for first-mortgage funds in the open market. This assistance was supplemented by extensive loans by municipalities. Subsidies were attempted by the German government shortly after the close of the War, but the condition of the federal finances apparently did not permit of their use on an extensive scale.

In France, a variety of expedients were used. Subsidies were resorted to on a limited scale; loans were extensively employed; tax exemption, which apparently was not used in Great Britain, was one of the commonest forms of assistance in France and in other countries of continental Europe. A description of all the methods employed is beyond the scope of this summary.

Table 75, rearranged from International Labour Office data, gives the number of new dwellings constructed in specified European countries from 1920 to 1929, inclusive, except that in some cases the figures are for the net increase; in several countries they cover only certain towns and cities.

It is impossible to give an accurate statement of the number of such new dwellings erected through public assistance. The International Labour Office reported that in most European countries they represented two-thirds of all new houses in years when the housing crisis was most acute, and that in many countries the proportion in such years exceeded 80 per cent.[36] Figures given elsewhere (p. 448) for Great Britain indicate that for the period 1919–33, 60 per cent of all new dwellings erected received public assistance.[37] In Prussia, from 1926 on, according to the International Labour Office, 85 per cent of all dwelling-house construction was so assisted and the proportion in the larger German towns in 1928–29 was slightly higher.[38]

In France, state loans from 1920 to 1927 amounted to 1,416,-000,000 francs, representing assistance to some 58,000 dwell-

[36] ILO, " Housing Policy in Europe," p. 38.
[37] In this connection, see Chart 71.
[38] ILO, " Housing Policy in Europe," pp. 353–354.

ings;[39] but this signifies only 7250 dwellings assisted yearly, a very small percentage of the annual requirements of that country.

TABLE 75

NUMBER OF NEW DWELLINGS CONSTRUCTED IN SPECIFIED EUROPEAN COUNTRIES, 1920–1929 [a]

Figures Covering Entire Country

Year	England and Wales	Nether- lands	Belgium [c]	Germany
1920	42,000 [b]	——	——	75,928
1921	115,000 [b]	40,364	9,039	108,596
1922	81,000 [b]	45,496	14,780	124,273
1923	86,210	43,132	20,718	100,401
1924	136,889	46,712	22,347	94,807
1925	173,426	47,190	24,000 [b]	164,437
1926	217,629	48,833	26,000 [b]	199,084
1927	238,914	50,246	25,000 [b]	284,444
1928	169,532	47,335	24,000 [b]	306,825
1929	202,060	47,347	——	315,703

Figures Covering only Portions of Country [d]

Year	Sweden	Denmark	Norway	Czecho- slovakia	Finland	Austria (Vienna)
1920	4,524	5,757	——	3,838	1,316	375
1921	6,365	7,735	2,636	7,227	1,526	245
1922	6,360	5,465	2,641	6,958	2,406	873
1923	9,461	7,446	2,922	10,317	3,082	1,210
1924	11,901	6,001	2,469	14,592	3,314	2,239
1925	13,042	7,454	2,227	10,699	3,991	2,400
1926	14,221	8,266	1,637	12,389	5,270	3,486
1927	15,095	8,515	1,391	19,222	7,323	2,691
1928	16,399	9,012	1,920	30,429	9,547	4,669
1929	16,000 [b]	9,451	2,847	23,560	——	7,038

(a) ILO, "Housing Policy in Europe," p. 18.
(b) Estimated figures.
(c) Figures are for houses, not dwellings.
(d) Figures for Sweden, Denmark, and Finland include all towns; those for Norway, twenty-six of the larger towns; those for Czechoslovakia, seventy-eight of the larger towns.

[39] ILO, "Housing Policy in Europe," p. 211. Owing to changes in the value of the franc, the equivalent amount in United States currency cannot be stated. It probably was less than $100,000,000. In 1928 the franc was stabilized, its par value on a gold basis in United States currency being 3.92¢.

In 1928 France inaugurated a much more extensive campaign in the passage of the Loucheur Act, under which it was
proposed to erect 200,000 " cheap " and 60,000 " moderate-
rent " dwellings by 1933.[40] This is the most ambitious housing-

—— CHART 71 ——

NUMBERS OF DWELLING HOUSES ERECTED WITH AND WITHOUT
STATE AID IN ENGLAND AND WALES: 1920-1932

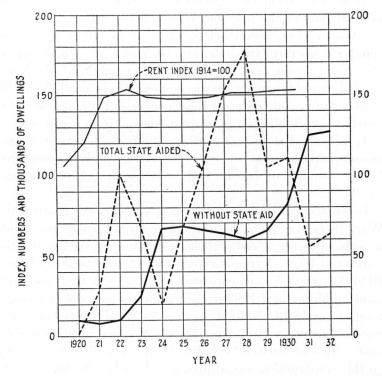

aid program thus far undertaken by France, always excepting
the restoration of the devastated areas. However, this contemplated total of 260,000 dwellings is only 2.5 per cent of the
total number in France. It is clear, therefore, that even includ-

[40] ILO, " Housing Policy in Europe," p. 217.

ing the Loucheur scheme the results of government aid to housing as measured by the volume of construction do not compare with those in Great Britain and Germany.

According to data submitted to the Financial Committee of the French Senate, on the basis of conditions at the end of 1929, the loss of interest suffered by the state under the Loucheur Act alone was to be 73,000,000 francs in 1930, and would rise year by year in the same proportion as the loans issued were increased, until in 1934 a figure of 240,000,000 would be reached. This figure will be repeated every year until 1969.[41]

It is clear, then, that government aid played a highly important part in the provision of new housing in Europe after the World War. Nevertheless, with the exception of certain countries, notably Great Britain, Germany, Sweden, Belgium, the Netherlands, and Denmark, the number of dwellings erected by public assistance was comparatively small. Table 76 shows approximate data for those countries where public-aided construction reached large proportions and for a few others.

It is true that in many other countries there was a vast amount of housing-aid legislation, but the results as measured by the number of houses built relative to population were small.

In Austria, where private building virtually ceased after the War, there was much legislation, but apparently the funds were lacking for a comprehensive building program for the country at large. A special report states that between 1923 and 1930 the city of Vienna constructed 38,300 dwellings in apartment buildings, and 4899 in houses for one or more families, a total of nearly 43,250 dwellings. As the total number of dwellings in Vienna in 1917 was 554,545, this represents a significant volume of construction. The total expenditure by the city on this construction was approximately $93,430,000.[42]

In Hungary, according to a report of the United States De-

41 ILO, " Housing Policy in Europe," p. 218.
42 Harris, Ernest L., American Consul General, Vienna. (Monthly Labor Review, May, 1931, pp. 6–9.)

partment of Commerce, the national government had expended $40,000,000 on housing alone since the close of the War.[43] This sum, however, would provide shelter for only a very small percentage of the population.

A mass of housing-aid legislation was enacted in Italy and a great number of organizations participated in the task of

TABLE 76

AMOUNT OF HOUSING PROVIDED IN CERTAIN EUROPEAN COUNTRIES UNDER GOVERNMENT AID — POST-WAR

(Approximate and incomplete)

Country	Period covered	Form of aid	Number of dwellings constructed with government aid	Proportion of total population housed
Great Britain				
England and Wales	1919–32	Subsidies and loans	1,200,000	12½%
Scotland	1919–32	Subsidies and loans	150,000	12%
Germany	1918–30	Loans, subsidies, federal guarantee of loans, rent tax, tax exemptions	1,800,000	12%
France	1919–33 a	Loans and subsidies	425,000	4%
		Tax exemptions	c	c
Belgium	1920–29	Loans, subsidies, bonuses, tax exemptions	135,000	8%
Netherlands	1918–30	Loans and subsidies	300,000	20%
Denmark	1916–27	Loans and subsidies	64,000	10%
Sweden	1917–29	Loans and subsidies	30,500 b	2½%
Czechoslovakia	1919–30	Loans, subsidies, tax exemptions	82,000	3%
Russia	1919–30	Direct construction (see text)	Large	No data

(a) See p. 431.

(b) Exclusive of assistance to rural families under a special fund created in 1904.

(c) The number of houses assisted by tax exemption in France cannot be stated.

building. The national government set up several central agencies; there were nearly 500 housing societies and in addition about 100 " autonomous " bodies, which combine the characteristics of private societies and public agencies. The largest of

[43] "Commerce Reports," May 25, 1931, p. 449.

the national agencies — the National Deposit and Loan Fund — had up to the close of 1928 granted credits of over 2,000,-000,000 lire, but this sum would not represent housing for any considerable part of the population. Again, up to the close of 1926 the autonomous bodies had provided or were erecting some 50,000 dwellings, comprising 172,000 rooms, at a total cost of 1,700,000,000 lire.[44] Apparently these figures had been increased by about 50 per cent up to 1930. Since the population of Italy in this period was in excess of 40,000,000, it again appears that the proportion provided with shelter as a result of government assistance is relatively small, even allowing for the fact that the figures here given are not a complete statement.

In Spain the volume of public-aided housing was insignificant. Under the basic law of 1911, only 2800 houses were erected during a period of thirteen years.

During the four-year period that assistance was granted in Finland, the total number of dwellings erected with aid from the state and from municipalities combined was 1172, providing housing for 6438 families.

As noted in Table 76 there has been a large volume of dwelling-house construction directly by the state in Soviet Russia, this being a part of the Five-Year Plan. No satisfactory information as to the number of dwellings or as to cost is available. According to one authority, the capital so invested rose from approximately 420,000,000 roubles in 1928 to 1,100,000,000 roubles in 1931.[45] About 80 per cent of all dwelling-house construction is conducted by the state, including committees of the local soviets. Private enterprise building is practically limited to small wooden one-family houses, built for the owner's occupancy exclusively and not for profit.

Public assistance to housing was also undertaken in India, Australia, New Zealand, and various South American coun-

[44] ILO, "Housing Policy in Europe," pp. 181–191.

[45] Wibaut, F. M., President, International Housing Association, Housing, October, 1931, p. 191. (Roughly $220,000,000 to $560,000,000, taking the rouble at par, but only a fraction of this sum at the current value.)

tries, but in most of these the actual volume of operations was small.[46]

In Canada the Dominion government after the World War advanced $23,500,000 to various provinces for the construction of dwellings, largely for ex-service men. The total number of houses so built was 6244 — less than one-third of 1 per cent of all dwellings in the Dominion.

It appears, therefore, that notwithstanding the large amount of legislation enacted and the efforts made by numerous countries, the record of public aid to housing, except in the case of a few nations, is a measure of things attempted rather than things actually achieved.

Yet while the quantity of state-aided housing outside of the countries listed in Table 76 has been unimpressive, there is general agreement that in nearly all European countries government assistance resulted in higher quality. Not only were such accessories as bathrooms much commoner, but the design, construction, and equipment of government-aided houses represented a distinct advance over pre-War accommodations. An American observer of Great Britain's elaborate housing campaign, who found much to criticize in the government's policy on grounds of expense and in various other particulars, declared that government-aided housing in that country represented a standard previously unknown.[47] A recent survey by the International Labour Office bears out this conclusion; in the case of Great Britain it found that " post-War legislation undoubtedly had a decisive effect in improving the standard of the dwellings built throughout the country." [48] There was, however, widespread complaint that government-aided dwellings in Great Britain were too small.

In France government aid " resulted in conditions of sanitation and to some extent of comfort also, greatly superior to those obtained in the old houses." Under the Loucheur Act

[46] See Table 73, p. 413.
[47] Veiller, Lawrence, " How England Is Meeting the Housing Shortage," p. 106.
[48] ILO, " Housing Policy in Europe," p. 96.

bathrooms and central heat were required. Regarding state-aided housing in Belgium, the International Labour Office found that the dwellings were of a distinctly better quality than the pre-War houses, while in Austria they were of a very much higher standard, and in Poland " greatly superior " to most working-class dwellings built before the War. Similar comments were made with respect to the government-aided housing of other European countries. In the case of several where specific information was not given, a recent report of the International Labour Office notes a distinctly higher standard of sanitary and hygienic conditions.

A further idea of the characteristic type of post-War housing in some European countries, for single-family and for two-family dwellings, may be obtained from Figs. 1 to 5. In connection with Fig. 1, for British housing, it should be noted that while the single-family dwelling is the predominating type, the *detached* single-family dwelling is the exception; instead, a number of houses, from two to twelve, are arranged in groups, rows, or clusters. Fig. 1 gives a typical layout used extensively by the London County Council. A further important feature of British subsidized housing is that these groups are arranged over a given area with special reference to street and park layout and to open spacing adjoining each dwelling. Aside from the greater amount of light and air and esthetic advantages thus secured, such planning has resulted in a material saving in the installation of sewers and other utilities. In this connection it may be noted that of all dwellings built by the London County Council from 1919 to 1925, 84 per cent were cottages. Of the remaining 16 per cent which were in flats,[49] one-third were in buildings of not over two stories. In ten other large towns 97 per cent of the new dwellings were cottages.[50]

[49] The cottage in Great Britain, as just stated, is not as a rule a detached structure. The flat corresponds more or less closely to the American tenement. The two-story flat is often the result of converting old four-story buildings into two dwellings, each having two stories.

[50] Unwin, Sir Raymond, in Report of the International Housing and Town Planning Congress (Vienna, 1926), Part III, p. 31.

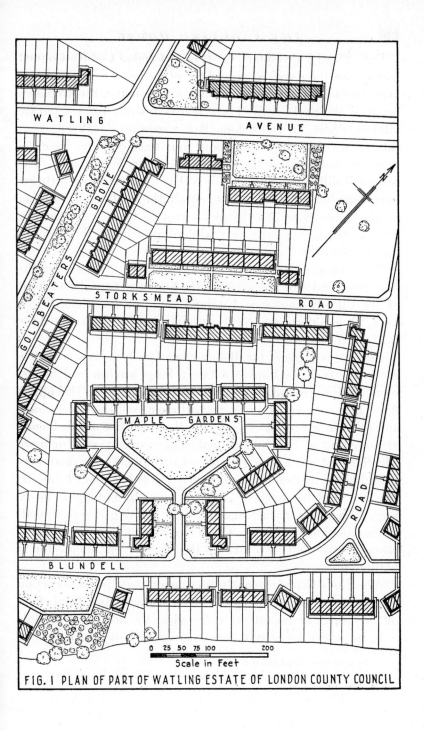

FIG. I PLAN OF PART OF WATLING ESTATE OF LONDON COUNTY COUNCIL

Figs. 2 and 3 give plans for typical London County Council houses, one for a five-room and the other for a four-room cottage. In each case the plan is for a double house, the fireplaces being in the party wall. These houses provide for a separate kitchen; where this is not done the law requires a scullery, separate from the living-room. Many four-room cottages have the same ground plan as the five-room cottage here shown. The principal difference in this case is that the four-room cottages have a smaller area and do not contain the small third bedroom on the upper floor. All the plans provide for a bathroom. In some sections, especially in coal-mining regions, the bathtub may be placed in the scullery.[51]

These houses rent for an average of 18s. per week for the four-room and 20s. per week for the five-room type. Since most of the subsidy houses in England rent for less than 10s. a week,[52] it would appear that the Council houses are designed for fairly well-paid workers.

Fig. 4 gives plans for Belgian two-family houses with five rooms for each dwelling — a fairly large kitchen and living-room on the ground floor and three bedrooms on the upper floor. It is compact; there is no bathroom, and the water-closet and coal-bin are in an extension at the rear. The old-fashioned arrangement of the chimney makes for economy and for more effective heating. Fig. 5 gives alternative plans for a small low-priced house in France of the type provided by the Chemin de Fer du Nord for some of its employees. It contains a fairly large living-room (which also serves as a dining-room), a small kitchen, and one bedroom. There is a water-closet but no bathroom in the first two plans; the third plan allows for a bathroom.[53]

Assertions have frequently been made that the construction of government-aided houses has had a distinctly beneficial effect on the health of tenants as reflected in the death rate. While

[51] The subsidy Act of 1924, however, provided that the bathtub must be in the bathroom.

[52] In both cases local taxes are included.

[53] The Viennese houses have been discussed in Chapter II, pp. 89–92.

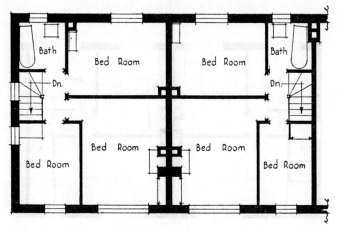

FIRST FLOOR PLAN

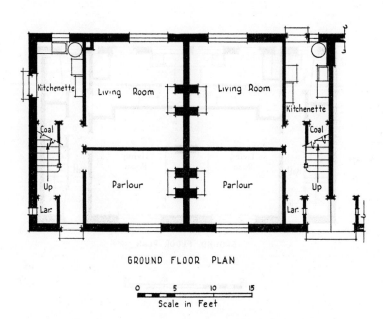

GROUND FLOOR PLAN

```
0        5        10        15
Scale in Feet
```

FIG. 2 TYPICAL FIVE-ROOM COTTAGE AS BUILT IN GREAT BRITAIN
UNDER SUBSIDY ACT

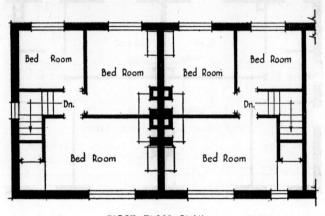

FIRST FLOOR PLAN

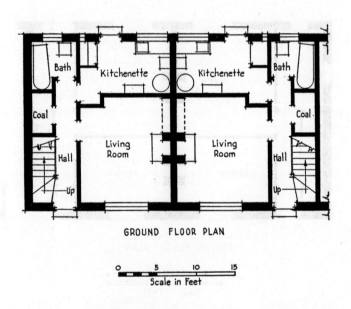

GROUND FLOOR PLAN

0   5   10   15
Scale in Feet

FIG.3 TYPICAL FOUR-ROOM COTTAGE AS BUILT IN GREAT BRITAIN
UNDER SUBSIDY ACT

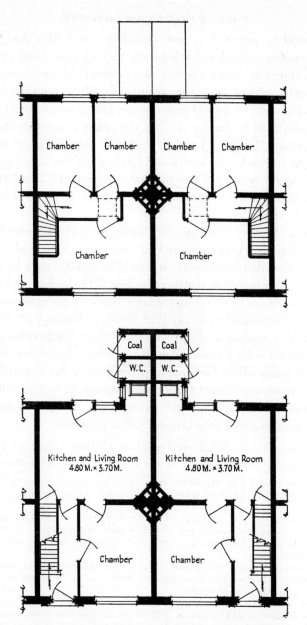

FIG. 4 TYPICAL BELGIAN HOUSE AS BUILT BY SOCIÉTÉ NATIONALE
DES HABITATIONS ET LOGEMENTS À BON MARCHÉ

this would be natural in new structures of better design and appurtenances, there is little in the way of statistical proof. A great number of other factors enter into that problem. Death rates had declined in many countries before government aid was undertaken on an extensive scale, and in some countries, at least, continued to decline during the years of most acute housing shortage.[54] The " crude " [55] death rate in England and Wales, as shown by the census of 1921, when the housing shortage was acute, was 13.3 per thousand against 14.7 in 1911 and 18.4 in 1901; the " standardized " rate fell from 19.2 in 1901 to 12.9 in 1921.[56]

It would be easy to fill pages showing high death rates among families living in one-room or two-room houses, or under otherwise overcrowded conditions; it would be equally easy to supply statistics showing that death rates are little higher under such conditions than in dwellings where there is no overcrowding. This is not intended to imply that housing does not affect death rates. Our purpose is simply to show that death rates cannot be compared with housing conditions alone, but must take account of many other factors; improper food, for example, may be much more significant than poor housing. It is generally conceded that vital statistics are exceedingly dangerous material from which to draw conclusions.[57] For example:

" Tuberculosis is often spoken of as a ' house disease.' It is, in fact, a family affair because it is caught by contact with an open

[54] In New York City the death rate fell in every year from 1916 to 1921 with the exception of 1918 when an unusually serious influenza epidemic occurred.

[55] The crude death rate is the number of persons of all ages dying per given unit of measure, usually per 1000, in a year. Standardized rates apply to groups more or less homogeneous either with respect to age, sex, race or other basis of segregation.

[56] Board of Trade, " Statistical Abstract for the United Kingdom, 1931 " (His Majesty's Stationery Office, London, 1933), p. 32. (Figures are average for three years about each census.)

[57] An illustration is furnished by an intensive survey by the Health Department of the City of Chicago, in 1917, of twenty-two blocks where the occurrence of tuberculosis was marked. It was brought out that no constant and definite relation between housing and health was proved, and further that it was difficult to establish any such relation by statistics. (Regional Survey of New York and Its Environs, Vol. VI, pp. 208–210.)

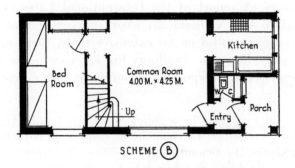

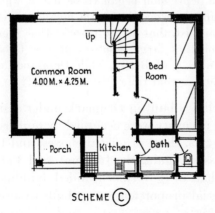

FIG. 5 ALTERNATIVE PLANS FOR A WORKING MAN'S HOUSE AS
SUGGESTED BY THE NORD RAILWAY IN FRANCE

case. One who lives in close contact with an active case of pulmonary consumption, without proper precaution, runs a great hazard of becoming infected and reinfected. . . . The house itself need not be blamed so much for the spread of tuberculosis as its occupants. Tuberculosis will spread from person to person in a palace as well as in a tenement or hut." [58]

CLASSES BENEFITED

One criticism of government-aided housing, frequently heard in the case of Great Britain but also applicable to some continental European countries, is that the houses go not to the poorest classes but to middle-class families or higher-paid wage-earners. A report of the International Labour Office [59] notes that in the Netherlands, where government assistance was for a time applied on an extensive scale, there was difficulty in providing new dwellings for low-income families. A similar experience is reported in Germany, where, one writer states,

" The results achieved by a policy of intervention by the public authorities were indeed remarkable, in respect of both technical achievement and the amount of new building. But when the effects of the economic depression began to be felt it was seen that the new dwellings built were mainly for the middle or well-to-do classes — so much so, indeed, that at the present time there is the paradoxical situation that large numbers of new flats are standing empty in the suburbs of Berlin, while thousands of families are still housed in huts or old railway carriages." [60]

Of 30,000 dwellings built in Denmark under assistance from a state fund, the majority were occupied by higher-paid workers, salaried employees, those of official classes, and to some extent the middle classes. Again, the International Labour Office report stated that of government-aided buildings erected in Poland a material proportion were " built to meet the require-

[58] The President's Conference on Home Building and Home Ownership, Vol. VIII, p. 6.
[59] ILO, " Housing Policy in Europe," p. 116.
[60] Méquet, G., " Housing Problems and the Depression," p. 174.

ments of persons with some means." [61] In Great Britain, as shown later, similar complaints were frequent.[62]

It may be noted, moreover, that there was some complaint in Great Britain that Local Authorities, which built a large proportion of the subsidy houses and had a financial stake in their success, tended to select desirable tenants and those likely to pay the modest rent demanded, thus excluding many of the poorest families. One writer who is distinctly friendly to government aid said in this connection:

" Even municipal authorities, when they come to let houses, tend, like any other landlord, to forget the slum problem and to let the houses to the most eligible tenant — that is to say, to the applicant who has most money and fewest children." [63]

In some instances, notably in Amsterdam, effort was made to exercise social control over tenants and at the same time to stimulate their desire for and appreciation of better quarters, by classifying tenants according to the care which they exercised in maintaining the premises and by shifting families from one grade of house to another on this basis.

GOVERNMENT AID IN GREAT BRITAIN

Since Great Britain affords the outstanding instance of government assistance to housing, and since it is the only country

---

[61] ILO, " Housing Policy in Europe," p. 338.

[62] Such complaints in Great Britain were made in the case of pre-War aid to housing.

" The housing policy of Liverpool has undergone several alterations. In 1869 the city put up a large building providing accommodation for over 600 people, but that was soon occupied by the better-paid workingmen, and those unhoused by the operations of the city council were not rehoused. In 1885 and in 1891 the city put up other buildings, which at the usual allowance of two persons to a room would provide for some 1,500 persons, but these like the earlier building were soon filled by the better-paid workers. In an effort to provide for the poorer classes up to 1896 the city sold the land it cleared to builders on condition that they put up houses for the working classes. The land was sold for much less than it cost the city, but the houses were still filled with the relatively better-off working classes." (USBLS, " Government Aid to Home Owning and Housing of Working People in Foreign Countries " [GPO, Washington, 1915], pp. 313–314.)

[63] Simon, E. D., " Slum Clearance " (The Nineteenth Century and After, March, 1930, p. 333).

for which complete data are most nearly obtainable, the British experience may be taken up in more detail. As already pointed out, the principal methods of extending aid were these:

1. Subsidies.
    a. By the state to Local Authorities, public utility societies, and private builders.
    b. By Local Authorities to public utility societies, private builders, and private individuals.
2. Loans by the National Government and by Local Authorities to public utility societies and private individuals.

The principal acts by which subsidy assistance was authorized were:

> Addison Subsidy Act of 1919
> Housing (Additional Powers) Act of 1919
> Chamberlain Act of 1923
> Wheatley Act of 1924
> Housing (Slum Clearance) Act of 1930

Chart 72 shows the volume of construction under several of these acts from 1919 to 1931.

Other acts under which state aid was granted in Great Britain were the following:

> Housing Act of 1925 [64] (largely for slum clearance)
> Housing (Rural Workers) Acts of 1926 and 1931
> Small Dwellings Acquisitions Act of 1899 (amended by certain of the above acts)

The great bulk of state-aided housing was erected under the first four of the acts mentioned above; in England and Wales during the period from the Armistice to March 31, 1933, over 1,110,000 subsidy houses were provided under them. During the same period over 940,000 houses were built without state assistance.[65]

For the whole of Great Britain, including houses built under

[64] This is termed the Permanent Housing Law.
[65] Ministry of Health (Great Britain), " Fourteenth Annual Report," year ended March 31, 1932 (His Majesty's Stationery Office, London, 1932), p. 95.

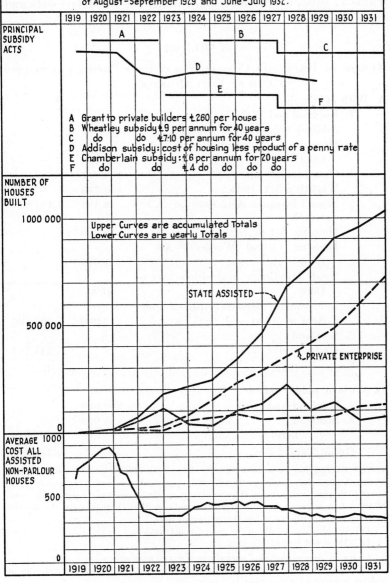

CHART 72

PRINCIPAL BRITISH HOUSING SUBSIDY ACTS, AND NUMBER
OF HOUSES BUILT IN ENGLAND AND WALES: 1919–1931

Based on Charts in "Garden Cities and Town Planning": Issues
of August–September 1929 and June–July 1932.

	1919	1920	1921	1922	1923	1924	1925	1926	1927	1928	1929	1930	1931

PRINCIPAL
SUBSIDY
ACTS

A   B   C   D   E   F

A   Grant to private builders £260 per house
B   Wheatley subsidy £9 per annum for 40 years
C   do   do   £7·10 per annum for 40 years
D   Addison subsidy: cost of housing less product of a penny rate
E   Chamberlain subsidy: £6 per annum for 20 years
F   do   do   £4 do   do   do   do

NUMBER OF
HOUSES
BUILT

1 000 000

Upper Curves are accumulated Totals
Lower Curves are yearly Totals

STATE ASSISTED

500 000

PRIVATE ENTERPRISE

0

AVERAGE 1000
COST ALL
ASSISTED
NON-PARLOUR
HOUSES

500

0

	1919	1920	1921	1922	1923	1924	1925	1926	1927	1928	1929	1930	1931

various legislation in addition to the four principal acts mentioned, the total number of assisted houses erected from the Armistice to March 31, 1933, may be placed at 1,350,000.[66] Table 77 gives the numbers built under the respective acts and those built by private enterprise, without assistance.[67]

TABLE 77

NUMBER OF DWELLINGS CONSTRUCTED IN GREAT BRITAIN FROM 1919 TO END OF FIRST QUARTER, 1933 [a]

A. With public aid
    1. England and Wales

Addison Subsidy Act, 1919	174,635	
Housing (Additional Powers) Act, 1919	39,186	
Chamberlain Act, 1923	438,047	
Wheatley Act, 1924	460,718	
Slum Clearance Act, 1930	8,491	1,121,077
Housing Act of 1925	45,000 [b]	
Housing (Rural Workers) Act of 1926	1,600 [b]	
Small Dwellings Acquisitions Act of 1899	50,000 [b]	
Rehousing of persons displaced under Acts of 1890 and 1925	12,000	108,600

    2. Scotland

Under various acts	145,784 [c]
Total	1,375,461 [b]

B. Without public aid

1. England and Wales	940,686	
2. Scotland	25,000 [b]	
Total		965,686
Grand Total [d]		2,341,147

(a) Except for estimated figures, data from Ministry of Health, "Fourteenth Annual Report," pp. 94 and 262.

(b) Figures comprising this total are partly estimated. Apparently some of these houses received aid under other acts, so that there is some duplication in these items with those for the principal acts.

(c) In addition, 22,315 were under construction.

(d) Does not include Ireland.

[66] Exact figures for this period are not yet available.

[67] Owing to a slight amount of duplication, as more than one act was involved, a precise total cannot be given.

Of houses built under the principal subsidy acts up to September 30, 1932, nearly one-third were erected by or under the direction of Local Authorities; virtually all of these were assisted. Of the remainder, erected by private enterprise, about one-third received state aid. Following is a summary for England and Wales:

	With state aid	Without state aid	Total
By Local Authorities	678,922	7,450	686,372
By private enterprise	417,465	789,799	1,207,264
	1,096,387	797,249	1,893,636

The total capital cost of all subsidy houses in England and Wales erected up to March 31, 1933, was approximately £651,-000,000. Of this total, approximately £400,000,000 represented the cost of the houses provided by the Local Authorities.[68] Practically the entire amount was borrowed by them either through the Public Works Loan Board, from the public through the sale of local government bonds, or on short-term obligations. In addition they borrowed large amounts under other housing acts.

Where the Local Authorities themselves built the houses, they retained the national subsidy as an offset to the loss incurred.[69] Where the houses were erected by private enterprise or by housing societies, subject to government aid, the usual procedure was to pay the national subsidy to the Local Authority for transmission to the actual builder. In some cases the national subsidy was paid direct to the building agency.

Houses built by the Local Authorities and all houses built under the Wheatley Act were to be rented. Most of those built under the Chamberlain Act were built for sale. In many cases the subsidy under this act was commuted from an annual grant to lump sum payments, amounting to about £75 to £100 per house for houses erected prior to September 30, 1927, and from

[68] Ministry of Health, " Fourteenth Annual Report," p. 105.

[69] This does not mean that the Local Authorities actually conducted the work of erection, although this was done in a small percentage of cases. The usual procedure was for the Local Authorities to let contracts at public bidding to commercial builders.

£50 to £80 for those erected since that date; the payments were usually made by the Local Authority to the builder, the former continuing to receive annual grants from the national treasury to offset these payments. Under the Housing (Additional Powers) Act of 1919, the subsidy was invariably paid in a lump sum.

BRITISH TAX BURDEN ON ACCOUNT OF HOUSING SUBSIDIES

Nearly all subsidy acts in Great Britain, as already stated, provided that the annual loss represented by the difference between an economic rental for the houses erected and the rental actually obtained should be borne by the national treasury and the various localities. Thus it fell on the tax payers and the " rates " payers.[70] Under the Addison Act, practically the entire loss fell on the national treasury.[71] The liability of the national government was in a sense unlimited or at least indeterminate, depending upon the cost of the houses. It frequently amounted to more than £50 per house per year, while the loss to the Local Authorities often was only £5 or £6 per house. This provision worked to the disadvantage of the national government, and under the Chamberlain and Wheatley Acts its liability was limited to a specific sum annually, this being subject to periodic revision. The Chamberlain Act provided for a national subsidy of £6 per house per year over a period of twenty years. In 1927 this was reduced to £4 per house, and in 1928 the subsidy was repealed so far as new construction was concerned, effective in October, 1929.

Under the Wheatley Act the subsidy originally was £9 per house per year in urban areas over a period of forty years.[72] It was voted in 1927 to reduce this to £7 10s. per year, and again in 1928 to £6, effective in October, 1929, but before that

[70] In Great Britain " taxes " are paid to the national government; " rates " are the local taxes. The tax to meet the local subsidy was in addition to the usual taxes levied on real estate.

[71] The only portion borne by the localities under this act was that represented by a tax of 1d. in the pound of " rateable valuation."

[72] In rural areas the subsidy was considerably higher.

date the labor government returned to power and rescinded the second reduction.

Any loss on buildings erected under the Chamberlain and Wheatley Acts which was not covered by the national subsidies fell upon the Local Authorities.[73]

Under the Slum Clearance Act of 1930 the national subsidy is £2 5s. per person displaced, or a little over £11 per house containing five persons. The local subsidy is about £3 15s. per house, making a total of £15 per house. Both subsidies run for forty years.

At one time it seemed probable that the aggregate loss to British tax payers and rate payers on account of housing subsidies might exceed £2,000,000,000. The loss under the Addison Act was originally estimated by one writer [74] at more than £1,000,000,000, while that under the Wheatley Act, which contemplated the erection of 2,500,000 houses, was officially estimated at £1,346,000,000, of which two-thirds was to fall on the national Exchequer and one-third on the Local Authorities. The Addison Act, was, however, repealed when the building program was only about one-third completed, and the number of houses erected under the Wheatley Act fell far below the scheduled output.[75] Early in 1933, moreover, Parliament voted to end the subsidy policy except in the case of slum clearance projects. This means a very sharp reduction in the ultimate cost of subsidies from early estimates; but the change in policy does not relieve the national or local governments from subsidy payments on account of houses actually completed or contracted for at the time the various subsidy acts were repealed.

If it could be assumed that the various factors involved — rents, taxes, interest, and subsidies — would remain unchanged until the various subsidy periods expired, it would be a com-

---

[73] For further data on this point see pp. 454–455.

[74] Veiller, Lawrence, "How England Is Meeting the Housing Shortage," p. 1.

[75] Thus against more than 1,000,000 houses contemplated under that Act by December 31, 1932, the number erected up to September 30 of that year was less than 440,000.

paratively simple matter to calculate the ultimate cost. As a matter of fact, all of these factors are subject to change; interest rates have already worked somewhat lower. What they will be in the years ahead cannot, of course, be forecast. The subsidy payments under the Chamberlain and Wheatley Acts are subject to periodic revision, and it seems probable that they will be reduced in the future if conditions permit. In the meantime, efforts are being made to increase the rents obtained for subsidy houses, not only by a general advance in rentals but by such an allocation of houses that persons unable to pay a relatively high rent will be housed in small houses or those of relatively low rental.[76]

As a result of these changes, there is reason to believe that the aggregate loss to British tax and rate payers will be far less than seemed probable a few years ago. Nevertheless the grand total is certain to reach an extremely high figure; an approximate idea of it may be gained from Chart 73.

The total amount actually disbursed by the national treasury on account of housing subsidies in England and Wales up to March 31, 1933, was approximately £123,000,000.[77] Payments on account of national subsidies to Scottish houses were

[76] Except in the case of the Addison Act, the loss to the national treasury will not be affected by changes in rents, interest, or taxes, since under the other acts the treasury's contribution is a fixed sum annually per house. Its loss will of course be affected by changes in the subsidy.

[77] The number of houses built under each principal subsidy act and the total payments from the national treasury for subsidies from 1919 to March 31, 1933, were as follows (England and Wales only):

	Number of houses	Total exchequer payments
Addison Act, 1919	174,635	£ 83,123,705 a
Housing (Additional Powers) Act, 1919	39,186	9,498,156
Chamberlain Act, 1923	438,047	15,103,856
Wheatley Act, 1924	460,718	15,498,341
Housing (Rural Workers) Acts of 1926 and 1931	5,787	21,899
Slum Clearance Act, 1930	8,491	55,230
	1,126,864	£123,301,187

(a) Includes expenditure on 12,419 houses under various acts, in addition to numbers here shown.

(Ministry of Health, " Fourteenth Annual Report," p. 262.)

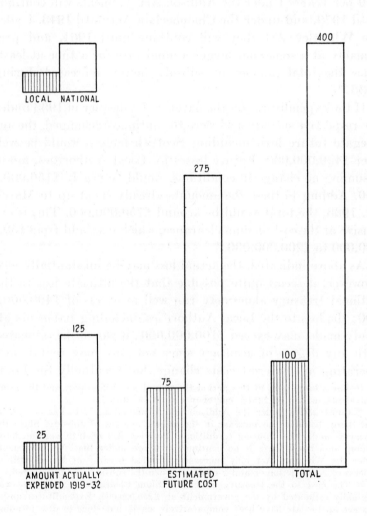

—— CHART 73 ——

COST TO TAX-PAYERS OF GREAT BRITAIN'S POST-WAR PROGRAM
OF GOVERNMENT AID TO HOUSING (ESTIMATED)

400

LOCAL NATIONAL

275

125

100

75

25

AMOUNT ACTUALLY   ESTIMATED   TOTAL
EXPENDED 1919-32   FUTURE COST

about £16,000,000, making a total of £139,000,000. In the fiscal year 1933, national subsidies, including those for Scottish houses, were running at the rate of over £15,000,000 yearly and were increasing. Those by Local Authorities were more than £3,500,000 in 1933, making a grand total of about £18,500,-000 per year.[78] Under the Addison Act payments will continue until 1979, and under the Chamberlain Act until 1943. Under the Wheatley Act they will continue until 1964, and presumably at a somewhat larger annual rate for a time at least, since the total number of subsidy houses increased during 1933.[79]

If the expenditures by the national Exchequer in 1933 under the respective subsidy acts were to continue unchanged, the aggregate future loss, including Scottish houses, would be well over £450,000,000. Future losses by Local Authorities, again assuming no change in conditions, would be nearly £150,000,-000. Adding to these the amounts already spent up to March 31, 1933, the total would be around £750,000,000. This is exclusive of the cost of slum clearance, which may add from £50,-000,000 to £200,000,000.[80]

As above indicated, the actual loss may be substantially less. However, it seems quite possible that the ultimate loss to the national treasury alone may run well in excess of £400,000,-000; the loss to the Local Authorities, including payments already made, may exceed £100,000,000; it cannot be estimated with any degree of accuracy since not only may rentals and operating and interest costs change, but eventually the Local

[78] For a large part of this period the pound was below par, and the exact equivalents in United States currency cannot be stated.

[79] Construction under the Addison and Chamberlain Acts has ceased, so that there should be no increase in the annual amount of subsidy. Since the payments under the Housing (Additional Powers) Act of 1919 were made on a lump sum basis, there is no continuing charge under that Act. Payments under the Wheatley Act may increase somewhat because of houses still in process of construction or under contract when the subsidy was terminated.

[80] The cost to the treasury under the Slum Clearance Act of 1930 was originally estimated by the government at £250,000,000. Expenditures under this act up to date have been comparatively small, but since in discontinuing subsidies under other acts it was proposed to continue slum clearance on an extensive scale, the ultimate cost will presumably be heavy.

Authorities will own large numbers of homes debt-free, the value of which can be set against losses incurred through subsidies.[81]

To sum up, it seems possible that Great Britain's post-War venture into government aid to housing, exclusive of slum clearance work, may involve a total loss of £500,000,000 on account of subsidies. There is a further loss, which cannot be determined, through some remission of interest or instalment repayments on loans, which were also extensively employed to aid housing. As in all cases involving future contingencies, this estimate is subject to a wide margin of error. A general return to an economic rent in Great Britain would, of course, cut the loss heavily. Even if rent control is abolished in 1938, this will

[81] Under the Chamberlain and Wheatley Acts, it is possible that the loss to the Local Authority may in some cases be practically *nil*, as shown in the following hypothetical case, taken from " Garden Cities and Town Planning " for August, 1930 (p. 196):

Cr.				Dr.
Exchequer subsidy, 40 years	£ 300	House and site		£ 400
Rate subsidy, 40 years [This is the special tax to provide the local subsidy]	150	Interest for 60 years (5 per cent)		865
Rent, 8s. 6d. weekly, 60 years	1,326	Repairs (£6 10 0 per house), 60 years		390
Tenants rate, 60 years [This is the ordinary local tax on real estate]	450	Cost of rate services		450
		Credit balance to general rate		121
	£2,226			£2,226

In this table the national or exchequer subsidy is figured at £7 10 0 yearly for forty years and the " rate " or local subsidy at one-half that amount. The weekly rent is the net rent exclusive of the ordinary local tax or " rate " paid by the tenant, the aggregate amount of which is shown as the last item in the first column, namely £450. Interest apparently is figured on the amount of money borrowed. The cost of the " rate " service is the cost to the Local Authorities of providing such services — gas, water, etc. The balance of £121 may be regarded as a credit against the special local subsidy rate of £150.

If the credit balance be realized, the net loss to the rate payers of the locality over the entire period would be only £29, viz., the difference between the credit balance of £121 and the local " rate " subsidy of £150. Indeed, it is possible that the Local Authority could make a profit (at the expense of the national treasury) if the houses have any substantial value when all debts incurred by the Local Authority for their erection are paid off. Such a profit to the Local Authorities is highly doubtful; instead, it appears that they, like the national Exchequer, will suffer a heavy loss. The Local Authority cannot make a profit under the Addison Act, since the national subsidy is not to exceed the actual loss to the locality. The national treasury loses under all acts.

not assure a return to an economic rent; moreover, the cost of many of these subsidy houses, especially those built under the Addison Act, was so high that an economic rental cannot be expected.

When the subsidy policy was inaugurated it was hoped that by 1927 rentals would have increased and maintenance costs would have fallen sufficiently to eliminate the need of further substantial payments. The fact that payments on account of the Addison houses alone, despite some reduction, are still running at the rate of over £6,800,000 per year shows that this expectation has failed of realization in no small degree.

EFFECT OF SUBSIDIES ON BUILDING COSTS

There has been a vast amount of discussion in Parliament and in the British press as to the effect of British housing subsidies on the cost of building. Many advocates of housing aid contend that subsidies *per se* have had only a negligible effect on costs. On the other hand, it is maintained with equal vigor that increases in the amount of subsidy have been a chief cause of increases in costs.

Table 78 gives figures of average cost, or average tender prices, of subsidized houses on various dates, together with principal changes in subsidy legislation. It will be seen that the passage of the Addison subsidy Act was accompanied by an extremely sharp rise in costs. The limitation placed on contract prices in February, 1921, was followed by a violent drop in these prices, with a still further decline later in the year after the Addison scheme was restricted to a total of 176,000 houses instead of 500,000 as originally contemplated. The passage of the Chamberlain Act in 1923 was followed by a moderate advance in prices, as was the passage of the Wheatley Act in 1924. After reductions in the Chamberlain and Wheatley subsidies in 1927 a drop in tender prices occurred, while the cancellation of the proposed further reduction in the Wheatley subsidy was succeeded by an increase.

On its face the table suggests a definite relationship between changes in the subsidy and changes in building costs. That this was the case was repeatedly asserted, and in turn denied, in Parliamentary debates on the housing question.

Mr. Neville Chamberlain, when Minister of Health, repeat-

TABLE 78

CHANGES IN AVERAGE TENDER PRICES OF NON-PARLOR SUBSIDY HOUSES IN ENGLAND AND WALES, 1919–27, WITH PRINCIPAL CHANGES IN SUBSIDY LEGISLATION [a]

Date	Average tender prices non-parlor houses	Comment
June, 1919	£643	
July, 1919	713	Addison Subsidy Act passed July 31, 1919.[b]
January, 1920	782	
October, 1920	888	
February, 1921	824	In February, 1921, Dr. Addison refused to consider tenders exceeding a certain figure.
March, 1921	700	Subsidy limited July, 1921, to a total of 176,000 houses (in England and Wales).
December, 1921	514	
August, 1922	370	
December, 1922	346	Chamberlain Act passed July, 1923.
March quarter, 1924	398	Wheatley Act passed July, 1924.
September quarter, 1924	424	
March quarter, 1925	438	
December quarter, 1925	444	
March quarter, 1927	425	Both Chamberlain and Wheatley subsidies reduced early in 1927.
March quarter, 1928	368	Chamberlain subsidy repealed in 1928.[c] Wheatley subsidy reduced in 1928.[c]
March quarter, 1929	339	Second reduction in Wheatley subsidy cancelled in summer of 1929.
March quarter, 1930	335	

(a) In this connection, see Charts 57 and 74.

(b) In nearly all cases changes in subsidies were preceded by discussion, so that the effect may have appeared before the changes were actually ordered.

(c) Effective October, 1929.

edly insisted in the House of Commons that increases in the rate of subsidy were the principal cause of increases in the cost of subsidy houses. That they were an important factor was asserted by the Earl of Onslow in the House of Lords, as follows:

" It is clear, I think, that whatever factors there might be in reducing or increasing the price of houses, one constant factor has existed all through . . . the price has regularly risen and fallen as the subsidy rose or fell. There has been that difference always. I contend that if you want cheap houses — houses that the poorest worker of the community can afford to pay for — the way to get them has been shown by a reduction of the subsidy." [82]

One member of the House of Commons said, " Whenever the subsidy was increased the price of houses rose." [83]

In 1933 the Minister of Health was reported as saying, " We know that subsidies have always had the effect of increasing costs. I do not explain it; I only know it is so." [84] On the other hand, the Parliamentary Secretary to the Ministry of Health in 1929 argued that the reduction in the cost of houses was largely a reflection of a decline in wholesale prices. In this connection she cited figures showing that the wholesale price index fell from 322 in 1920 to 197.7 in 1921 and to 159.9 somewhat later.[85]

An American writer, while holding that the major movement of building costs was not due to subsidies, said:

" The reduction in building costs since the peak at the close of 1920 has been world-wide and unconnected with Dr. Addison. But Great Britain's peak rose to an extra height because of the Government's policy, and it was that extra height which collapsed at the touch of an executive order." [86]

[82] Onslow, Earl of, " Parliamentary Debates," House of Lords, July 23, 1929, p. 209.

[83] Wood, Sir Kingsley, " Slum Clearance: A Reply " (Nineteenth Century and After, April, 1930, p. 481).

[84] Quoted by Harvey, Walter, Director and General Manager of the Burnley Building Society, " The New Housing Bill " (Statist, Building Societies Section, London, April 29, 1933, p. 8).

[85] Lawrence, A. S., " Parliamentary Debates," House of Commons, July 15, 1929, p. 128.

[86] Wood, E. E., " Housing Progress in Western Europe," p. 53.

A fair conclusion seems to be that while the course of building costs in a broad way reflected the course of wholesale prices and wages, intermediate fluctuations of considerable importance were directly caused or influenced by corresponding changes in subsidy legislation.

—— CHART 74 ——

COST PER CUBIC METRE OF STRUCTURE COMPLETE, OF A WORKING MAN'S HOUSE IN AMSTERDAM, HOLLAND, UNDER STATE-AIDED SCHEME AND UNDER PRIVATE ENTERPRISE: 1914-1924

Charted from Report of Chief Inspector of Housing, The Hague, for the League of Nations, furnished through courtesy of United States Department of Commerce.

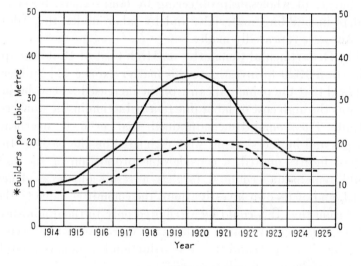

KEY
———— Cost under State aided scheme.
— — — Cost under Private enterprise.

✻ Guilder = 40 Cents.

In this connection, experience with the cost of subsidized building in the Netherlands shortly after the War is pertinent. As shown in Chart 74, building costs per cubic meter under state-aided schemes were for several years very much higher than the corresponding costs of houses built by private enterprise. Later on, the costs of subsidized houses began to approach those of privately built structures.

The feverish anxiety in England to secure houses under the Addison scheme at a time when the industry was not efficiently organized for the work had a direct tendency to increase costs. The following statement by the Chairman of the London County Council is suggestive:

" On the London County Council we were informed by the Housing Board that we were not to inquire too particularly into the cost; that we were to build houses at any cost. I said, ' At any cost?' and the answer was, 'Yes, . . . never mind the cost.' " [87]

Charges of wholesale profiteering by land owners, builders, dealers in building materials, and by labor under the Addison Act were repeatedly made.

The Departmental Committee on High Cost of Building appointed in 1920 to investigate this matter exonerated builders and held that the principal cause of the increased cost of building was the high cost of labor due to a reduction in the workers' output. The committee maintained that even if overhead charges and builders' profit were estimated on the basis of the highest figures quoted, a considerable proportion of the cost would remain unaccounted for; as a result of the evidence heard, and of its own investigations, the committee came to the conclusion that this could be attributed only to the diminished output of labor. " We are satisfied that there has in fact been a reduction in output, and that this reduction is common, though in varying degrees, to all trades." [88]

In connection with these charges of reduction in output, it may be noted that one housing authority presents comparisons of output for " straightforward " bricklaying based on rough estimates for certain large London County Council contracts

[87] Downham, Lord, " Parliamentary Debates," House of Lords, July 17, 1919, p. 705.

[88] Ministry of Health (Great Britain), " Report of the Departmental Committee on the High Cost of Building Working Class Dwellings " (His Majesty's Stationery Office, London, 1921), p. 23.

which indicated that as against an average output of 1000 bricks per man per day in 1914, only 200 bricks per day were laid in 1920.[89] In the meantime wages had advanced from 8s. 9d. to 18s. 8d., so that the indicated cost of laying 1000 bricks in 1920 was more than ten times that in 1914. After 1920 there was some improvement, the average number of bricks laid per day rising to 500 in 1922; but in 1924 it was only 469.

The assertion has repeatedly been made that housing subsidies in Great Britain did not provide homes for the poorest classes; the following statement is typical:

" The tragedy of Government Housing in the last ten years is that while 1,300,000 houses have been built by Local Authorities, Public Utility Societies, and private enterprise, at a total cost to the State estimated at 600 millions [£], yet the unskilled artisan with a large family is still miserably housed. That is the root of the problem. . . ." [90]

This opinion finds substantial corroboration in the reports of various governmental agencies. The British Ministry of Health held in 1931 that despite the construction of 1,250,000 new houses there was considerable evidence that there had been " discouragingly little improvement in the worst cases of overcrowding and unhealthy conditions." [91] The Inter-Departmental Committee for the Rent Restrictions Acts held in 1931 that of over 1,500,000 new houses erected since the War, only the 600,000 built by the Local Authorities could be considered as available to the lower-income classes of the population.

" It may be said that the supply of accommodation available for the poorer section of the population appears to have been increased by about 10 per cent. On the other hand, the supply of houses for the classes who can afford to buy has been increased

[89] Fremantle, Lt. Col. F. E., " The Housing of the Nation," p. 111.

[90] Townroe, B. S., Garden Cities and Town Planning, November, 1929, p. 258.

[91] Ministry of Health, " Twelfth Annual Report," year ending March 31, 1931, p. 99.

by about one million, which is an increase of about 50 per cent. . . ." [92]

" It is clear . . . from the evidence, that this large number of new houses has not had the effect of improving the conditions of the poorest workers to the extent which might have been anticipated. For this we think that there are two principal reasons; in the first place the increase in the number of houses, though large in itself, must be considered in relation to other relevant factors, such as the probable increase in the number of working class families; and, secondly the general moving or ' filtering up ' process, on which reliance was placed to improve the conditions of the poorest has, for reasons which we discuss later, not taken place to the extent which was hoped." [93]

There was more or less complaint that the subsidy legislation miscarried. In particular it was alleged that subsidies were sometimes granted for houses whose occupants owned motor-cars.[94] In one case a subsidy for a gamekeeper's cottage was reported.

In the debates in Parliament, criticism has frequently been made that housing subsidies tend to demoralize or pauperize the beneficiaries. Whatever the merit of this contention, it appears clearly established that many British tenants are not paying so high a rent as they could fairly afford to pay. A leading British statistician and economist, Arthur L. Bowley, after an elaborate study of the cost of living in several important industrial cities in England in 1924 held that there could be no doubt that this was true of a considerable proportion of wage-earning families. He found that the percentage of family income devoted to rent was much below the traditional ratio of one-sixth prevailing before the War. He reported that in Warrington his sample study disclosed forty-eight families,

[92] " Report of the Inter-Departmental Committee," p. 19.

[93] *Ibid.*, pp. 21–22.

[94] During the debate in the House of Commons on December 3, 1929, a member asked for the number of subsidized houses built in Glasgow during the past ten years and also for the number of those which were occupied by owners of motor-cars. The government was unable to answer the latter question (Train, " Parliamentary Debates," House of Commons, December 3, 1929, p. 2141).

and in Bolton fifty families, having weekly incomes of £8 (160 shillings) who were paying a rent of less than eight shillings. In this connection he remarked, " It is suggested that housing authorities are too timid to venture, and working-class families too unwilling to devote an adequate part of their income to house accommodation." [95] Studies of living conditions among groups of wage-earning families in certain British industrial centers by Mr. Bowley in 1913 and 1924 showed the following comparisons for the town of Warrington: [96]

	1913	1924
Average weekly family income	39s. 6d.	97s. 4d.
Average net rent	4s. 8d.	7s. 3d.
Ratio of rent to income	12%	7½%

This shows that against an increase of nearly 150 per cent in family income the increase in rent paid was about 55 per cent. A special point is that the proportion of the total budget expended for rent was generally lowest in the case of families with relatively high incomes. Mr. Bowley reported that in Warrington rent averaged 5 per cent or less of the income of families (one-sixth of all) whose income was over £7 weekly, whereas formerly it amounted to 10 per cent. Where the weekly family income was £3, the rent was in 1924 about 10 per cent; of the corresponding pre-War income of 30s. it was 14 per cent.[97]

Since restrictive rent legislation went into operation in Great Britain the real wages of British wage-earners have shown an appreciable increase. This is brought out by Chart 75. The curves for money wages and real wages are taken from the Ministry of Labour Gazette. The index for rent, compiled from data published in the Gazette, has been added for purposes of comparison.

That many British families were unwilling to pay as high a rent as they could afford was asserted by one writer, as follows:

[95] Bowley, A. L., and Hogg, M. H., " Has Poverty Diminished? " (P. S. King and Son, Ltd., London, 1925), p. 7.

[96] *Ibid.*, p. 91.

[97] *Ibid.*, p. 7.

"Alleged inability to pay economic rents is due largely or mainly to the *inordinate* proportion of the weekly expenditure of the household income set apart as a first charge to provide for items which are either unnecessary or are extravagantly excessive.

"The average weekly *excessive* expenditure of a considerable proportion of working class households in respect of drink, tobacco, amusements, betting, etc., far exceeds the weekly 'inclusive' [i.e., the rent plus local taxes] rent charged for the dwelling." [98]

That some British tenants are not paying as much rent as they can reasonably afford to pay is also clearly indicated by reports of the British Ministry of Health.

Representatives of labor raised the contention that housing subsidies and other so-called " social services " had a tendency to depress wages. A member of the House of Commons cited a report of the adjudicator of a committee of inquiry for the wool textile industry to the effect that in determining wages it was necessary to take account of the value of such indirect income received by the workers. He further asserted that widows' pensions were likewise taken into consideration in determining the rate of wages, adding, " I wish, as far as possible, to safeguard work people and to prevent employers of labor from using this or any other scheme as a means of subsidizing low wages." [99]

The most positive result of Great Britain's subsidy policy is that the supply of housing was substantially increased. Whereas the number of houses in England and Wales per 1000 population fell from 215 in 1911 to 212 in 1921, it was 244 in 1931.[100] This indicates an average of about 4.1 persons per house in 1931 as against 4.6 in 1911.[101] In Scotland the number of persons per house fell from 4.69 in 1911 to 4.21 in 1931. While a reduction in the average size of families may have been

[98] Shelton, A. W., " Housing of the People," p. 14.
[99] Davies, Rhys, " Parliamentary Debates," House of Commons, June 19, 1930, p. 471.
[100] Provisional census returns.
[101] In comparing these averages with those in Chart 10, it should be noted that the latter are per dwelling.

—— CHART 75 ——

INDEX NUMBERS OF MONEY WAGES, REAL WAGES, AND RENT,
IN GREAT BRITAIN: 1920-1932

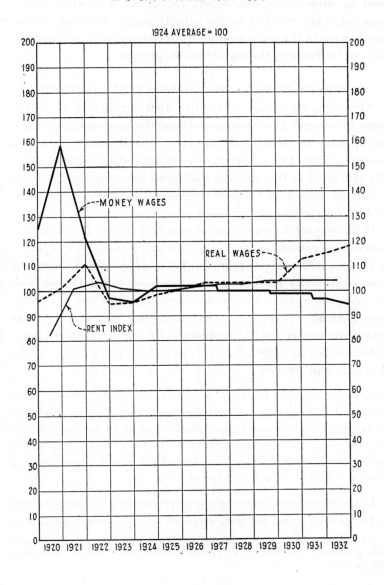

1924 AVERAGE = 100

MONEY WAGES

REAL WAGES

RENT INDEX

1920 1921 1922 1923 1924 1925 1926 1927 1928 1929 1930 1931 1932

partly responsible, there can be little doubt that the subsidy program contributed to this bettering of conditions. However, as clearly shown, this does not imply a corresponding improvement in slum conditions, which, nearly all authorities agree, were not really reached by the subsidy policy. Instead, the new houses were in the main secured by relatively well-paid workers and not by those in the lowest-income groups.

EUROPEAN OPINION ABOUT GOVERNMENT ASSISTANCE

Although, as shown, restrictive rent legislation is still in force in several European countries, the preponderant opinion appears to be strongly against its continuance as a permanent policy. The retention of such legislation there is generally defended on the ground that until the supply of housing is further increased there is danger of profiteering by landlords if restrictions are removed.

With respect to public assistance to housing through such methods as subsidies, loans, and tax exemption, there appears to be more difference of opinion. Although public aid had been granted in many European countries prior to the World War, the exceptional assistance undertaken after its close was at the time generally regarded as an emergency policy to meet an extraordinary crisis. A representative of the International Labour Office in 1928 held that apart from the Russian Soviet Republic and Austria

" the policy adopted has been merely one of granting financial aid to house building, with the aim of encouraging private enterprise by relief from taxation or by subsidies, so as to bridge over the interval until the gradual rise in rents (a parallel item in the policy) once more brings them to a level where house building offers a sufficient return on capital." [102]

In the Scandinavian countries government assistance, except in the case of rural settlers, appears to have been regarded as

[102] Pribram, Karl, " The Financing of House Building in Countries with Rent Restriction Legislation: I " (International Labour Review, September, 1928, p. 360).

an emergency policy. In the Netherlands likewise government assistance was rapidly curtailed as soon as the acute shortage was relieved, although there is some sentiment in favor of continuing to offer it to the lowest-income groups. In Switzerland,

TABLE 79

NUMBER OF NEW DWELLINGS AND NUMBER RECEIVING STATE AID IN SWEDEN, 1917–1929 [a]

Year	Number of dwellings provided	Number of dwellings receiving state aid	Per cent
1917	6,818	3,293	48.3
1918	5,203	1,478	28.4
1919	4,915	1,081	22.0
1920	4,524	3,385	74.8
1921	6,365	3,867	60.7
1922	6,360	3,069	48.3
1923	9,461	2,922	30.9
1924	11,901	2,405	20.2
1925	13,042	2,360	18.1
1926	14,221	1,288	9.1
1927	15,095	2,996	19.8
1928	16,399	1,162	7.1
1929	16,000 [b]	1,140	7.1
	130,304	30,446	23.4

(a) ILO, " Housing Policy in Europe," pp. 122 and 126.
(b) Approximate figures.

These figures include dwellings remodelled as well as strictly new construction. The net increase in dwellings is smaller than that shown in the table, since in every year certain dwellings were demolished. From 1917 to 1923 inclusive, the average number demolished was 426. In 1928 it was 1705; in 1929 it was 2200.

In addition to the dwellings shown as receiving state aid, some 206,-000,000 kroner have been loaned under a special fund created in 1904 by the Swedish government to facilitate the acquisition of dwelling-houses and agricultural holdings in rural districts, enabling 52,658 borrowers to acquire homes (p. 128).

The above figures relate to assistance furnished by the State. In addition, a considerable amount of assistance has been granted by some Swedish cities, but precise data are not available.

public assistance has been largely abandoned. In Italy and Czechoslovakia there appears to be no definite assurance of an early return to full reliance on private enterprise. Germany intends to terminate government aid in 1936. Belgium, in spite of a marked revival of commercial building, seems to have definitely adopted public aid as a permanent policy for certain classes of the population. What may be done in France after the completion of the Loucheur scheme can only be conjectured. Austria seems to be definitely committed to a policy of state-aided, or, rather, state-provided, housing.

In several countries where restrictive rent legislation and housing aid were withdrawn in whole or in part, there has been a marked increase in commercial building. This has been especially true in nearly all the Scandinavian countries, in several of which commercial building after 1927 exceeded the pre-War volume. Table 79 gives the number and proportion of state-aided dwellings in Sweden from 1917 to 1929, showing that whereas in 1920 and 1921 over 60 per cent of new dwellings received public aid, in 1928 and 1929, when there was a great increase in the volume of building, the proportion was only 7.1 per cent.

In Iceland there was a similar increase in private building after rent control ceased. A report by Edward M. Groth, consul at Copenhagen, Denmark, says:

" In 1917 rents were restricted by law and this control continued until 1926. With abolition of control, rents rose and with the incentive of higher returns a building boom began which continued until the end of the first half of 1931, after which construction practically ceased." [103]

In the Netherlands, where rent control has been terminated, and in Belgium there has likewise been a great increase in private, unaided, construction.

However, the assertion is frequently made that the cost of shelter of a reasonably satisfactory standard is beyond the

[103] Monthly Labour Review, April, 1932, p. 807.

means of the lower-income groups in nearly all European countries.[104]

In Great Britain there has been a sharp division of opinion over the nation's housing policy. Government assistance has been bitterly assailed as extravagant and socially unwise; yet one subsidy bill after another has been enacted. Conservative opinion in Great Britain has long been opposed to subsidies to housing in principle. On the other hand, the labor and other socialist elements in Parliament have shown a disposition to advocate public assistance as a permanent policy; some socialist writers have gone so far as to suggest that eventually housing may be provided rent-free in much the same way that education is furnished.[105]

The burden imposed on the Exchequer by the government's subsidy policy was greatly accentuated by the change in economic conditions in recent years, and in April, 1933, as already noted, Parliament voted to terminate subsidies except in a very restricted field. Already there had been some scaling down of the expenditure for government assistance. Moreover, private enterprise building, without any assistance, had been steadily gaining. Whereas during the period 1919 to March 31, 1928, of 1,105,000 houses built in England and Wales 724,000, or 65 per cent, were state-aided, of 750,000 houses built during the four fiscal years 1928–32 the percentage fell to 45; for the fiscal year 1932 alone it was 33. In the year ended March 31, 1933, it was 28.5.

The facts presented in this chapter show that whatever the justification of post-War intervention in housing in Europe may have been and whatever benefits it may have yielded, it has resulted in a dislocation of the entire building industry and has

---

[104] See article by Senator Dr. F. M. Wibaut, in the October, 1931, issue of Housing. Of conditions in France, Dr. Wibaut says: "In the Paris district — and one might say in the whole of France — private enterprise has not built a single dwelling for the worker on a profit-earning basis " (p. 223).

[105] Barnes, Harry, " Housing " (Ernest Benn, Ltd., London, 1923), and Simon, E. D., " How to Abolish the Slums " (Longmans, Green and Co., London, 1929).

been responsible for many evils, aside from an enormous burden upon the tax payers which in several countries will continue for many years. Moreover, the lower-income classes were not benefited to any such extent as was intended.

Some of the salient facts of the experience with restrictive rent legislation and with government aid to housing in Great Britain and some other countries are epitomized at the close of this chapter.

RESTRICTIVE RENT LEGISLATION IN THE UNITED STATES

Except for the Soldiers' and Sailors' Relief Act of 1918, a war measure intended to prevent evictions or unreasonable increases in rent in the case of certain families [106] of men in service, national legislation on rent control in the United States was limited to the District of Columbia and to two measures:

(1) The Saulsbury Resolution of 1918.

(2) The Ball Rent Act of 1919.

The Saulsbury Resolution, subject to certain conditions and exceptions, was designed to protect tenants in the District of Columbia, whose leases ran for one month or longer, from eviction or increases in rent until the declaration of peace with Germany or until the repeal of the resolution. The close of the War did not bring the expected relief, and in 1919 this resolution was repealed by the Ball Rent Act, which established a Rent Commission with wide powers to regulate residential rentals in the District.

The original legislation provided that the commission was to operate for two years, but subsequent amendments continued its existence until 1925. The original act was treated as emergency legislation; in 1925 the United States Supreme Court indicated that the emergency had ended and rent control automatically lapsed. An attempt to secure the passage of an act by Congress continuing control on a more or less permanent basis, " on the ground that rental property and apartments in the

[106] This act applied where the rent was not over $50 per month.

District of Columbia are affected with a public interest," was unsuccessful.

The operation of the act was the subject of much complaint by real estate interests, who charged that it was confiscatory in principle and unjust in its application. The Rent Commission on its own initiative could change any residential rent in the District regardless of any agreement made between landlord and tenant, and indeed could penalize a tenant who paid a rent that he had voluntarily agreed to pay if it was in excess of the amount that the commission decided he should pay. In one case the Court of Appeals remarked that the annual income allowed the landlord was so low " that it leaves the unpleasant impression that it was the purpose of the Commission to cut the income as close as possible to the line of confiscation without crossing it." The work of the Commission was often far behind its docket, and this resulted in further dissatisfaction.

Several states, notably Maine, Connecticut, Massachusetts, New Jersey, Nevada, and Virginia, enacted specific war measures for the control of rents. These were, however, generally concerned with families of men in service or with conditions coming within the description of emergencies. Procedure under them was limited, and in some cases their effects seem to have been chiefly in their moral influence on landlords.

Legislation of a more general character, intended to cover the post-War period, was enacted by New York, New Jersey, Massachusetts, Maine, Delaware, Illinois, Colorado, and Wisconsin, on the ground that a temporary emergency existed as a result of which tenants were liable to be victimized by landlords. It took two forms:

(1) Control of landlords through the courts.

(2) Control through specially created rent adjustment commissions, with varying degrees of power.

In most states such legislation was merely permissive, authorizing municipalities to set up rent-adjustment agencies.

The state of Wisconsin definitely provided for a rent commission with regulatory powers, largely similar to those of the commission established by the Ball Rent Act in the District of Columbia. The act was held unconstitutional, largely because by its terms it was limited in its operation to a single county.

Numerous attempts at rent control were made by cities. In many cases this was done without state legislation, reliance being placed chiefly on public opinion and the effect of publicity. Action was secured through local committees representing different interests. These committees held hearings in cases of dispute over rents and determined what constituted a fair rental. If a landlord failed to appear when a tenant's complaint was considered just, that fact was made public. A committee of New London, Connecticut, served as a general model. In all, more than eighty such committees were organized in various cities and a large number of disputes were settled without recourse to litigation.[107] In many such cities, however, these committees did not function actively.

By far the most important instance of state legislation intended to cover post-War conditions was that of the state of New York, and there its operation was chiefly limited to a few of the larger cities, especially New York City, Albany, and Buffalo; the New York acts provided for control through the courts. Twelve rent acts were passed by the New York legislature, all of which went into effect April 1, 1920.

Two of these acts were the subject of much controversy. In brief, they provided that an increase of more than 25 per cent in rent was to be deemed " presumptively unjust, unreasonable and oppressive." That is, the burden of proof was thrown on a landlord who attempted to secure a larger increase. The legislation was bitterly assailed by real-estate interests on the ground that it was confiscatory, but was upheld by the United States Supreme Court as a justifiable exercise of the police power of the state in an emergency.

In 1926 the New York rent laws were amended so as to exempt from their application apartments in New York City rent-

[107] Thesis of Miss Pauline Schubart of Columbia University (mss.). Furnished by courtesy of Widener Library, Harvard University.

ing for $20 per room per month or more and those in Albany and Buffalo renting for $15 or more per room per month. At the close of 1927 the State Board of Housing found that the temporary features of the existing maladjustment had disappeared. The Board therefore recommended that the rent laws then applying to New York City and to Buffalo should be allowed to lapse automatically on May 31, 1928.

Despite this finding, restrictive rent legislation was continued until July 1, 1929. Moreover, fresh agitation was started for its extension, with the result that a further act was passed by the New York legislature continuing control in New York City until May 1, 1930, for flats renting for not more than $15 per room per month. This act was declared unconstitutional by the Appellate Term of the Supreme Court of New York.[108]

RESULTS OF RENT CONTROL IN THE UNITED STATES

Where rent regulation was confined to local committees, whose activities were largely of an advisory character, it is the general opinion that considerable benefit was secured by preventing unreasonable exactions by landlords or unreasonable demands by tenants.

The experience with national regulation under the Saulsbury Resolution and the Ball Rent Act, indicated above, appears to have been distinctly unsatisfactory, particularly from the standpoint of property owners. As to the operation of the rent laws of the state of New York, there is wide difference of opinion. There is general agreement that these laws tended to discourage new building, but since at the same time considerable incentive to new construction was given by tax-exemption legislation, it is difficult to isolate the effects of the two conflicting types of legislation.

One obvious effect of rent control in New York was the creation of a substantial differential between the rents paid by old

---

108 Housing, in its issue of September, 1929, attributed this effort to secure continuation of these laws largely to political considerations. "While there was no longer a housing emergency, there was a political emergency. A municipal election and a political campaign impended" (p. 188).

and by new tenants. The State Board of Housing said, " The differential was created by and is now maintained by the Rent Laws." [109] A compilation of rentals paid in October, 1923, by a group of 1700 tenants of four-room apartments showed that whereas the mean rent paid by tenants of less than one year was $38.03, tenants who had been occupants from five to six years were paying $24.44 and those who had been occupants for fifteen years or more, $22.18. That on the whole the laws seemed to operate to the immediate benefit of the tenant is suggested by repeated efforts to secure their extension, even after the State Board of Housing had declared that the emergency which led to their enactment had ceased to exist.[110]

GOVERNMENT AID TO HOUSING IN THE UNITED STATES

With the possible exception of some very recent legislation, the only instance of federal aid to housing in the United States appears to be the provision of dwellings for war workers through the United States Housing Corporation and the United States Shipping Board in connection with the World War. As these projects were specifically intended to further the prosecution of the War, rather than to provide housing for any considerable part of the population, they are sharply differentiated from the experience with post-War housing assistance in Europe already discussed.

Both these wartime housing projects of the United States Government involved losses of many millions of dollars; this was perhaps inevitable on account of the necessity for haste and the general high level of cost as well as the abrupt abandonment of the work after the close of hostilities.

Several of the states have undertaken at various times to as-

[109] New York State Board of Housing, Legislative Document, 1928, No. 85, p. 10.

[110] For a more favorable opinion on the operation of rent control in the United States by a writer who holds that, on the whole, it accomplished its real purpose, securing justice for all within reasonable bounds, and that it did not seriously interfere with the erection of new dwellings, see Whitman, Marcus, " The Public Control of House Rents " (The Journal of Land and Public Utility Economics, July, 1925, pp. 343–361).

sist in providing housing. The results as measured by the number of dwellings provided are in most cases so meager that they need little further reference beyond the condensed summary at the close of this chapter. It may be worth while, however, to mention that tax and other official commissions in certain states were severe in their condemnation of government intervention. The South Dakota Tax Commission in its 1922 report said of certain exemptions on dwelling-houses, tools, furniture, and other items:

" After three years of operation we are thoroughly convinced that they are not only unworkable, but that they are vicious and should be repealed. It is clear to us that a flat reduction in dollars is not a fair way to grant an exemption, if in fact any exemption is fair. It means that property already taxed to the limit must be taxed more heavily to make up for the loss from exemption and that no good results can be discerned from the exemption allowed." [111]

A committee of the legislature of California, after reviewing experience with two land colonies, urged that the state " never enter into another land settlement scheme." [112] On the other hand, the policy of aiding veterans to acquire homes appears to have given general satisfaction.

Reviewing the disastrous results of a similar land-settlement scheme in Washington, the Land Settlement Board of that state said:

" The board believes that the whole land settlement scheme is uneconomic, un-American, socialistic, paternalistic, and contrary to the best interests of the settlers and State. . . .

" The board further believes that the whole scheme of financial State or Government aid to individuals, organizations or corporations, is fundamentally wrong and can only result in disaster; that the individual must be self-reliant, and not dependent upon the

[111] " Report of the Tax Commission of South Dakota, 1921–1922 " (State Publishing Company, Pierre, 1922), p. 6.

[112] Cleary, C. W., " Division of Land Settlement " (Reprint from the Monthly Bulletin, December, 1927, Department of Agriculture, State of California), p. 5.

Government for financial support; that the only reason that our country exists today is because of the independent self-reliance of our forefathers; that the present tendencies to ape the old customs of Europe would, if persisted in, finally result in the old order of things — landlord and tenant — which is, in effect, financial servitude for the farmer." [113]

Special mention may be made of the experience with tax exemption in New York City under a state law enacted in 1920 permitting counties or municipalities to grant exemption from local taxes until January 1, 1932, for all new dwellings, except hotels, erected prior to certain dates; this exemption did not apply to the land. New York City was the only community to take advantage of the legislation. Under it, over $900,000,000 of new dwelling-house construction, including apartment-houses, was completed. This large volume of construction has often been cited as proof of the efficacy of the law in stimulating new building. On the other hand, it has been pointed out that during the same period there was a building boom through the country, and that even without tax exemption there would have been a great increase in construction in New York City.

A serious charge against this legislation is that while land-owners, promoters, builders, and financing agencies reaped large profits, the tax-payers as a whole paid the bill, for during the period the exemption was in force it appears that the community lost nearly $200,000,000 in taxes, which means that the burden was shifted to others. Furthermore, the rents of these new buildings, which were not affected by the restrictive rent acts, were comparatively high. A still more serious complaint is that purchasers of these houses were victimized because of the large amount of inferior, shoddy, and even dishonest construction; a speaker at the National Housing Conference in Philadelphia in 1930 prophesied that some of the tax-exempt developments in New York would prove to be slum districts in the future. A similar charge has been made by the New York State

[113] Department of Conservation and Development, State of Washington, "Third Biennial Report" (Jay Thomas, Olympia, 1925), pp. 69–70.

Board of Housing, which said of such houses erected in Queens County:

" From a social point of view they threaten to become slum areas worse than our present congested tenement sections. The houses are cheaply built. Frequently they are shoddy. Many of the newer areas are without public improvements. In a few years' time the cesspools will have saturated the ground. Many miles of streets on which these houses stand are unpaved. In Spring thaws and long periods of wet weather they become almost impassable. Heavy fire apparatus is frequently delayed in reaching the center of such a block, if indeed it can reach the houses at all. Speed is the essence of fire fighting in these regions and a delay, even of minutes, may mean a holocaust. No fire retarding material is used in the construction. . . . A fire must be confined to one or two buildings or blocks are doomed. The lack of street paving is a great contributing factor in increasing the hazard." [114]

Similar criticism has been voiced with respect to apartment-house construction under this legislation. A mortgage broker of New York said:

" It was the shoe-string builders and mushroom operators who reaped in the main the benefits of the ten-year exemption. They unloaded the buildings just as soon as they were completed, at big profits. The tax inducement and the housing shortage attracted this class of builder. Painters and small contractors became builders overnight and the slapstick, cheaply-constructed apartment houses they built during that period stand as monuments to the folly of this legislation." [115]

It should be emphasized that not all tax-exempt construction falls in this category of shoddy housing. For example, the Metropolitan Life Insurance Company in 1921 undertook the erection of a group of five-story apartment-houses providing dwellings for more than 2000 families in Queens County, Long

[114] State of New York, Report of the State Board of Housing, Legislative Document, 1930, No. 84 (J. B. Lyon Co., Albany, 1930), p. 67.

[115] Alliger, Joseph K., President of the Sterling Investment Corporation. New York Times, November 15, 1931.

Island, that are often referred to as model homes. The buildings were carefully planned and constructed. The homes rented for $27 to $45 per month; the land was exempt from taxation until 1932. With this advantage the venture showed a fairly high rate of return. Whether the 6 per cent which the insurance company is allowed as its return will be earned in future can only be conjectured; the company has, however, been able to write down the cost by a substantial sum out of the excess of earnings over the 6 per cent rate during the period of exemption.

Another high-class housing project to take advantage of tax exemption in connection with limited dividends was that of the City Housing Corporation at Sunnyside, also in Queens County. About 1200 homes were erected, at a total cost for the buildings alone of over $8,000,000, or an average cost of over $6500. Sales prices ranged from $8000 upwards for single-family homes. As more than three-quarters of the owners and tenants had yearly incomes of $2500 or more (of families owning their homes nearly 30 per cent had incomes of $5000 or more), it will be seen that these houses served a section of the population in relatively comfortable circumstances.[116]

Such projects should not be confused with the cheap frame construction in Queens County referred to in the report of the State Board of Housing just quoted.

In 1926, tax exemption in New York was limited by law to limited-dividend companies whose operations were made subject to the supervision of the State Housing Board. Under this legislation several large apartment-house projects, such as that of the Amalgamated Cooperative Apartments, primarily for workers in the clothing trades, have been completed, involving the expenditure of several million dollars and providing housing for several thousands of families. Several other similar projects are contemplated.

Opinion as to the success of this legislation depends largely

[116] In the early part of 1933 a "strike" of several hundred purchasers of these homes was reported, on the ground that since incomes of workers had decreased, payments on account of mortgages should be reduced.

on the attitude of critics toward the basic principle involved. Should government aid special classes by exempting the property of limited-dividend companies from taxation? [117]

The Committee on Taxation of the President's Conference took a strong position against the principle of tax exemption. The Committee held that special exemptions to home-owners, even if restricted to the building as distinct from land, were inadvisable. It found that the practical results of such legislation had been " negative and inconclusive," but that general experience " creates a strong presumption against special favors or exemptions." [118] It pointed out that discrimination in such legislation for the purpose of vote-getting was likely. While recognizing that the principle of exemption had been applied in various fields, the Committee urged that the true interest of home-owners was to narrow the operation of this principle where it was already found rather than to extend it to homes.

With respect to the operation of the New York law, the Committee found that while this act may have stimulated building, it had " unfortunate by-products " such as a low quality of housing, while " little if any of the advantage of tax exemption was passed on to the purchaser or to the tenant. . . . In the absence of a critical shortage of housing, nothing can be said for such an exemption." [119]

[117] In this connection, Housing, in its issue of March, 1930, said, in describing one of these projects:

" When one learns that these new buildings, though only 6 stories high, are to be provided with automatic electric elevators, and with electric refrigeration for each apartment, as well as steam heat, hot and cold running water in several places in each apartment, hard wood floors, electric light and every modern convenience of living, one wonders whether tax exemption for that class of building is either warranted or desirable " (p. 4).

" People in crowded Manhattan who are able to afford living rooms that average 12 by 18 feet in size — as is contemplated in this new building — and who can afford such luxuries as automatic electric elevators and electric refrigeration, to say nothing of steam heat and hardwood floors, should certainly be able to pay the economic rent which such luxuries require, and not ask their fellow citizens to bear their burdens for them " (p. 5).

[118] The President's Conference on Home Building and Home Ownership, Vol. II, p. 112.

[119] *Ibid.*, p. 128–129.

The Committee further recorded its objection to exemptions in favor of limited-dividend companies.

It should be emphasized that in so far as any considerable section of the population is unable to secure adequate housing this is essentially a wage problem and not a housing problem. *A priori,* there is no more reason why the state should contribute to the rent bill of such families than to their grocery bill. Whether government aid is or is not justified, the fact is that if any section of the population really cannot afford proper shelter, this really means that their wages do not permit them to maintain a reasonable standard of living. Whether assistance shall be concentrated on housing or distributed over the entire budget is a matter of expediency.

But the proposal to grant public assistance to provide shelter for the great bulk of the population as a social policy involves a fundamentally different principle. This has been clearly stated by one prominent writer as follows:

" In every state of society at all times there is a group of persons who cannot pay for such accommodation any more than they can pay for ample supplies of good food and clothing. . . . It is equally wrong to describe the plight of this class, in regard to their inability to pay for decent homes, as a housing problem, as it is to call their lack of other necessities a food or clothing problem. . . . To the extent that better housing accommodation for those who suffer from poverty needs to be provided by public aid, it should be regarded as a charity, for the same reasons that giving food or clothing is a charity. One of the great mistakes in the past has been in regarding this charitable work in housing as distinct from other forms of charity. The confusion which occurs in discussing remedies for housing and the desirability or otherwise of applying public aid is largely due to this mistake. No one can object to giving charity in the form of shelter, as of other necessities. But it cannot be given for housing alone. If it is given as a relief of rent, as a subsidy toward cost of building, or as tax exemption, then whatever its direct object or result, it becomes in effect a contribution toward all necessities of life. . . .

" The real questions, however, are whether public aid to housing should be given on some ground of public responsibility for shelter that does not apply to other necessities, and whether this aid should be dispensed among those whose earnings are sufficient to enable them to live without state aid. . . . When . . . we are discussing the giving of state aid in the form of housing to citizens who can be self-supporting, we are discussing a form of *socialism* and not of charity." [120]

Tables 80–82 give epitomes of the experience in certain countries summed up in the form of debits and credits which deserve careful study by anyone attracted by the social promise of government housing projects. Without encroaching upon the ground covered by these tables, it may be remarked that our study of the history of government aid to housing in the country where it obtains most fully, Great Britain, indicates that rent restrictions first resulted in discouraging building so that a building shortage developed; and that as a result the government was lured into the building of houses. It is true that the shortage was diminished and practically eliminated; that the standard of housing was higher than previously known; that the effects on health were entirely beneficial; and that possibly the plan averted a revolution. On the other hand, the subsidies tended to increase the cost of building; there was little direct benefit to those classes who most needed it; many working-class families developed a habit of not paying an economic rent and will in future look with resentment on any effort to exact one; wages possibly were actually depressed by the plan; the building industry was seriously disrupted; housing became a political football; and, finally, generations to come have been saddled with an overwhelming financial burden from which they will have difficulty in recovering.

It is much easier to say what should have been done than it was then to look forward and clearly see the right way out. The aid essential to revamping the war-torn economic structure was

[120] Adams, Thomas, "Housing Conditions in the New York Region" (in "Buildings: Their Uses and the Spaces About Them") (Regional Survey of New York and Its Environs), Vol. 6, p. 281.

TABLE 80

Epitome of Results of Post-War Government Aid to Housing in Various Countries

Great Britain

Debits	Credits
Excessive cost. Average cost of the Addison houses (about 174,000) was about £1000. Various factors contributed to high cost. Local Authorities had little incentive to economy.	*Number of houses built.* Over 1,200,000 houses built with public assistance from Armistice to March 31, 1933, under the Addison, Chamberlain, and Wheatley Subsidy Acts.[b] Proportion of British population housed by such assisted building about $12\frac{1}{2}\%$.[c]
Subsidies themselves tended to increase cost. Disputed by many, but generally conceded.	*Standards generally high.* Assisted houses much better than those formerly erected; bathrooms the rule; hardwood floors and electrical and other conveniences common.
Heavy loss to state. Ultimate loss to National Treasury estimated at £400,000,000 (see p. 454). Further heavy loss in many cases to localities. Loss may be less if subsidies are reduced or rents increased.	*Effects on health.* Many claims that health and comfort of tenants have been improved, and death rate lowered. Reduction in death rate has been in progress over a long period of years; better housing only one factor.
Little direct benefit to poorer classes. Assisted houses often secured by persons not really in need of aid; the slum problem was hardly touched.[a] "The tragedy of Government Housing in the last ten years is that . . . the unskilled artisan with a large family is still miserably housed." Contended, on the other hand, that the building of 1,350,000 new subsidized houses must have relieved overcrowding.	*Political effects.* Often asserted that the government's housing-aid campaign averted a revolution.

(a) In 1930 a new Housing (Slum Clearance) Act was passed by the British Parliament. Ultimate cost originally estimated at £250,000,000.

(b) During this period over 100,000 assisted houses were erected under other Acts; also about 500,000 houses yearly were repaired or reconditioned. Over 950,000 houses were erected during this period by private enterprise *without* government aid.

(c) Does not include occupants of repaired or reconditioned buildings, nor persons in dwellings built with government assistance prior to the World War.

TABLE 80 (*continued*)

Debits

Many persons not paying a reasonable rent. Many working-class families with fairly good incomes paying less than one-tenth and often only about one-twentieth of their income for rent. Pre-War proportions for similar income classes much higher. In some cases tenants of subsidized houses had motor-cars.

Attitude of labor. Output of labor, especially brick-layers, far below pre-War levels, or a reasonable level. Charge that subsidy largely became a device to provide employment for building-trades labor.

Effect on wages. Contended by some observers, including labor officials, that housing subsidies and other "social services" operate to depress wages.

Employers. Building industry disturbed by frequent changes in subsidies. Many builders opposed to them.

Political. Housing aid a political issue. Demands that provision of housing be regarded as a state function on much the same basis as education. Demands for special subsidies for large families.

Intangible. Effect on morale of nation. Assertions that British working classes are being demoralized.

Credits

TABLE 80 (*concluded*)

CANADA

Debits	Credits
Little effect on housing situation. "It must certainly be admitted that the provision of homes for . . . 32,000 individuals . . . could have little effect in changing housing conditions of the industrial population." "It also served to show that there are some perils when municipal authorities engage directly in house building."	Total number of houses built (in 179 different municipalities), 6244.

NEW SOUTH WALES (DACEY GARDEN CITY SUBURB)

Debits	Credits
Financial difficulties speedily encountered. Rents frequently in arrears. When the Housing Board was abolished in 1924, some estates were bankrupt. *Labor.* "Failed to do its best." *Tenants.* Would not take proper care of houses. *Public dissatisfied.* "An enquiry revealed the unpleasant truth that socialism in building is very expensive. . . ."	From 1912 to 1923 Housing Board erected 818 houses.

INDIA

Debits	Credits
Annual loss to government originally estimated at $1,350,000.[d] At end of 1928 only 7277 rooms out of 16,524 completed were rented, despite reductions in rentals. Government called a halt on further construction until tenements already completed were fully occupied.	In or about 1923 the Bombay Government aided the construction of about 200 chawls, each containing 80 one-room tenements (16,500 rooms in all).

(d) This was on the basis of a total of 625 chawls containing 50,000 rooms, originally contemplated. Only about one-third of the program was ever carried out.

definitely viewed as a normal governmental function, and because of the War there was a feeling, too, that government morally owed something to the masses, and particularly to soldiers, in the form of shelter. Therefore government aid, started to meet an emergency, was quickly perverted into a long-time politico-economic obligation. The rental and housing emergencies resulting from the War have long since passed; yet most of the government aid pledged to housing still has to be paid for. Will the emergency housing built in 1925 in Great Britain justify taxing her people for it in 1975? What will be the new housing needs of that year? Will they in turn justify taxation payable in part in 2025?

This experience should be carefully studied and considered by all advocates of government housing assistance to the lowest-income groups. Our analysis indicates that a great economic burden has been placed on the British people for generations to come, and that this burden is still accumulating without justifiable benefits. Of course one cannot evaluate in pounds sterling the social benefits which have accrued to the nation from better homes. The economic burden may safely be evaluated, however, as at least £500,000,000. It seems clear that the British government might have aided housing after the War in ways which would have much better served and developed her social-economic structure. Relatively short-time self-liquidating loans to landlords with coincident deflation of rent restriction would have been much better. It would at least have encouraged and aided private industry and ownership, which are basic elements of the British economic organism, as of the political. Private enterprise is the life blood of British economy, the source of private and public income, and the means by which building construction, ownership, and tenantry function. Furthermore, self-liquidating loans on new housing might directly have increased the national productive and revenue resources, whereas the subsidies are a long-time drain upon them.

Contributions of public funds toward the capital cost of housing for private ownership or occupancy impose upon the bene-

TABLE 81

Epitome of Results of Rent Restriction in Great Britain

Debits	Credits
Landlord often deprived of a reasonable return. Generally admitted that rents of many houses are below an economic level. This true of practically all subsidy houses. "There can be no doubt that a considerable proportion of the working classes in Great Britain . . . could afford a higher rent."	Tenants enabled to retain their homes. Tenants protected from exploitation. Soldiers at front relieved of anxiety over housing for their families.
Many small owners unable to occupy their own houses. Such owners often compelled to allow tenants to remain for years in their homes at lower rentals than these owners themselves pay for other dwellings. "The owner was often poorer than the tenant himself."	*Political Effects.* Sometimes argued that it avoided revolution. Many who object to rent restriction in principle hold that it was inevitable under war conditions.
Gross abuses in subletting. Tenants often sublet part of building for more than they paid for the whole. "On the whole the Acts are more of a hardship than a boon to the very poor."	
Slum improvement prevented or delayed.	
New construction by private enterprise largely stopped, accentuating housing shortage.	
Subsidies held to be an inevitable sequel to rent restriction, even by many who oppose them in principle.	
Maintenance of buildings frequently neglected.	

TABLE 81 (*continued*)

Debits	*Credits*
Litigation between landlord and tenant vastly increased.	
Family budget dislocated.	
Wages held down in some countries because of low rents; in other cases low rents are an addition to " real " wages.	
Political. " Decontrol " of rents repeatedly postponed. Restriction still in effect in Great Britain (and over most of Europe). General disposition among tenants to retain permanently the abnormal advantages secured under the emergency of war. Conservatives in Great Britain are generally agreed that rent restriction is uneconomic and mischievous, but thus far have not been able to terminate it. Some Socialists, on the other hand, demand that housing be placed on more or less the same basis as education, i.e. a permanent function of the state. One writer, Barnes, even suggests " rent-free " houses.	

TABLE 82

Epitome of Government Assistance to Housing in the United States

Except for the Massachusetts Homestead Commission experience (covering only 12 houses) this record of experience is a post-War development.

State	Date	Nature of Legislation	Results
Massachusetts	1911	$50,000 state appropriation.	Only 12 houses built. Experiment abandoned and Commission abolished.
	1920	Act passed permitting state to provide shelter for residents in distress — an emergency measure.	No action taken.
New York	1920	Exemption of new houses, *not land*, from local taxation for ten years. New York City almost only municipality where exemption actually used.	Over $900,000,000 new construction; some critics hold construction would have gone on without the exemption. Taxable values of adjacent property increased in some cases; increased assessment on land tends to defeat real purpose of plan.[a] Little benefit to poorer classes; houses poorly built, involving serious fire and slum hazards.
	1926	State Housing Plan; exemption of dwelling in case of limited-dividend companies; low rentals fixed by state.	Several high-class projects, for wage earners, undertaken under this plan. Much favorable comment, but automatic elevators and electric refrigerators in some cases led to severe criticism.
New Jersey	1920	Similar to New York.	Law declared unconstitutional.
Louisiana	1921	Similar to New York, but limited to two cities, New Orleans and Shreveport.	Nothing done: neither city took advantage of legislation.

(a) In one case assessment of land on which tax-exempt buildings were erected was raised from $75,000 to $326,000.

TABLE 82 (*continued*)

State	Date	Nature of Legislation	Results
Oklahoma	1915	Permitted loaning of funds secured from sale of certain public lands to aid home ownership.	Law apparently chiefly intended to benefit farmers. Comparatively few loans made.
Wisconsin	1919	Permitted counties and municipalities to invest in stock of cooperative housing companies.	Garden Homes Company formed; built 105 houses. Disputes soon led to demand for private ownership; company dissolved.
North Dakota	1919	Provided for state loans at low interest rates.	About 50 houses built. Scheme abandoned after about two years' experience.
South Dakota	1917	Rural credit plan involving aid to housing as a subordinate feature.	Soon financially embarrassed. In process of reorganization.
		$500 exemption on all dwellings.	Abandoned after three years as unsound.
	1921	State loans at low rates.	Nothing done. Law declared unconstitutional.
California	1917	Land-settlement schemes at Durham and Delhi — state loans at low rates.	Both Durham and Delhi schemes were flat failures. Loss of state about $2,000,000; settlers' losses heavy. Legislative Committee advised that state "never enter into another colonization plan."
	1921	State loans at low rates for veterans only.	About 5000 homes financed up to 1929; state apparently satisfied with results.
Washington (State of)	1919	Land-settlement scheme at White Bluffs-Hanford. State loans.	Settlers dissatisfied. State deeded them the tracts at $1 each to avoid litigation. Loss of state about $500,000. State Board severe in condemnation of principle of public aid.

ficiaries of such appropriations an obligation to the remainder of the community, who must ultimately pay the bill. The British grants and subsidies might have been made upon the condition of lower construction costs and lower economic rents resulting directly therefrom. To meet the condition of lower costs, the contractor might have halved his normal margin of profit, and labor accepted a lower hourly wage, perhaps working more hours per week to make the weekly wage equal that for private work. By these means the long-time tax burden upon the community would have been more nearly if not fully justified. Government intervention which imposes an unrequited financial burden upon the community can hardly be called government aid.

Direct action to get by law that which the working of natural forces fails to provide usually ends in failure. For instance, money wages may be fixed by law, and the weekly hours of work. But costs of production, which determine what those nominal wages may buy, will be fixed by the interplay of psychic and physical forces which statute law may color but cannot control. The natural laws that govern the growth and use of property are grounded in social psychology. People's ideas, though constantly confused by the complexities of group life, appear as a composite result in the economic structure; each group builds its own economic order, but always subserviently to natural law. These truths are illustrated repeatedly in history: in the framework of Athenian society, the early English manorial system of land tenure, the community of the American Indian, and the chaotic international situation with which the London Economic Conference undertook to deal. In dealing with housing provision government should try to promote harmony between psychic and economic forces. The shelter which its social welfare demands can be supplied only through its economic structure. Except in a communistic society direct provision of housing through public funds without a return at least equal to that from private provision is injurious to the general economy and ultimately to social standards as well.

Lessons may be drawn from the experience outlined in this chapter for our own guidance in the matter of government aid. Recent legislation involves both government grants to the capital cost of housing (including tax exemption) and financial assistance in the form of self-liquidating loans. Such grants tend to increase housing cost and rent. At best, there is the added cost of government administration of the grants and resulting increased tax collection. Where the use of labor-saving devices is barred and other uneconomic conditions imposed upon the recipient of capital aid, a further increase in housing cost may be expected. Tax exemption increases tax burdens on other property, thus reducing public revenue resources. Whether the government grant be to Housing Authority, limited-dividend corporation, or wholly private owner, the real cost which the community must pay is the same. Whatever immediate advantage there may be in government participation of this kind, it does becloud the facts, it does tend to fool the public, it does undermine public revenue resources, it does increase the cost of housing and reduce the general buying power of the community. Reduced buying power is likely to affect even the occupants of the " assisted " housing. Government participation in capital cost for sectional private benefit is a balky mule that may kick to pieces the wagon to which it is harnessed.

As opposed to the unsatisfactory results from capital grants, financial assistance in the form of self-liquidating credit has usually worked to community and national benefit. The need for such assistance seems obvious in the case of large-scale slum clearances and rehousing projects, usually requiring state authority to enforce. Furthermore, the state has unique ability to finance at the lowest justifiable rates. Full prevention of slums and blighted areas can never occur, but most that is worst in kind and degree can be assuaged by government aid in wise planning and zoning, in large-scale financing through consolidated self-liquidating loans, and wise building regulations.

We normally spend two and a half billion dollars a year on new homes. The waste of labor and materials in such construction is variously estimated as from 25 to 50 per cent. If we figured it as 30 per cent, or the same proportion the federal government is now granting on certain housing projects, this waste would equal seven hundred and fifty million dollars. According to the evidence this chapter presents, the effect of these grants would increase the amount of this wastage and further increase the burden of taxation in doing so. A small fraction of whatever the government may annually grant to the capital cost of housing under existing law, or one-thousandth part of the amount now wasted in construction, if directly applied to the reduction of this wastage might eliminate it in the course of a decade. Engineering and legal talent coupled with the necessary federal and state authority through well-directed research in building structure and the revision of our antiquated and unscientific building codes would certainly accomplish this desirable end. Would it not?

In general the relationship between government and its people in the matter of housing provision should reflect a control-and-develop policy. Government housing aid should be of a sort to strengthen the economic position and not weaken it; it must increase, not decrease, the nation's income, its total unpledged wealth, and the average man's power to earn and to buy. Aid of this sort involves sound planning of all features of community growth including the safeguarding of economic resources through which that growth year by year may be attained; and through which the inevitable obsolescence in slum and blighted area may be concurrently liquidated. And aid of this sort includes building and sanitary regulation, technically responsive to the ever-changing needs for the protection of body and health on the one hand and improvement in methods of building on the other; zoning laws governing sectional growth, and laws regulating the use of public services; and promotion of the home asset through the control and development of housing credit in order that it may be sound and liquid.

CHAPTER XII

Rationalization

THE most obvious need of our time is an improved distribution. Given such distribution, we could all move on with assurance to that constant desideratum, improved productive efficiency per capita. But together with such practical aims, we need fresh ethical and spiritual stimulus and a higher motive than that of mere profit. In no department of economics are these truisms more bitterly true than in all that relates to housing. And housing is today perhaps the very crux of our whole economic, monetary, moral tangle.

Near Santiniketan, India, not far from the International College of Rabindranath Tagore, there lies a village of the Santals, an ancient race of simple folk numerous in that section. For centuries almost unnumbered the Santals, notwithstanding relative poverty, have joyfully, peacefully, and busily maintained their racial life in physical decency and well-being, continually actuated by richness of spirit. The Santals like comfort; their villages are clean and well built. Raised above the mud of the surrounding soil and its plant growth, their homes are cleaner far than many of our complicated homes and hotels, not to mention our clubs, roadside inns, and college dormitories.

Intermingled with Santal villages are those of other tribes, neither poorer nor richer, whose ways of life are not fine but squalid. In India as elsewhere, it is wealth of spirit that makes the home decent, not economic wealth. Wealth of spirit is what we need in the United States; economic wealth may then take care of itself. Therein is shown the road to sound economy in production and distribution and to decent living. Spirit alone can make living decent.

In these days, especially in the United States, false standards of respectability are in the ascendant. So many pens and tongues have asserted the inability of large portions of our population to possess a respectable home that the public is beginning to believe it. A third of our people — some say two-thirds — is said to live in squalor and indecency because of lack of income. Have our lives become so controlled by the almighty dollar that spiritual values have disappeared? Unselfishness, industry, and love will make a home decent and healthy, however humble and simple it may be. A national spirit founded on such a belief would make the nation sound and strong. Not all the bathtubs and radios in the world will make decent a home that is ruled by love of pleasure, selfishness, and animosity. How are we building our nation — with the qualities that lead to health and decency, or those that bring sickness and indecency?

In Great Britain the ethical protest against the " slum " has risen into a wave of passionate action that is patriotic in the noblest sense. The feeling that this crying evil must be abolished in England's green and pleasant land is finding expression in legislation and building schemes which, whether or not soundly conceived, will beneficially affect many human lives. Similar effort in Germany seems more wisely directed toward preventive means, though by no less fine a spirit of social justice than in England. Happy, healthful homes are a nation's very heart, source of its life, seat and symbol of its soul. Houses that are fit to be true homes are, therefore, its best material asset, for they develop and safeguard the good life for its people.

In these days of social and political reconstruction, when an over-stimulated public interest moves hastily over dangerous ground, any action dealing with this fundamental necessity, shelter, should be most carefully scrutinized. Housing plays so important a rôle in the economic life of every country that its position as a revenue producer, alike to individual and state, should be safeguarded and improved by every possible means.

If the reader to whom the subject appeals as vital to human welfare will glance at the sections and chapter headings that marshal our almost unwieldy numbers of facts, graphically presented in the highly significant charts, he will see that the first three chapters establish the major premise that this fundamentally necessary item of housing is unreasonably expensive; the next section of seven chapters analyzes the industry and factors of cost, and shows what changes are most needed. In Chapter XI we differentiate between the several types of government participation, and set forth certain drawbacks attending on it as it is commonly understood and crudely demanded in sweeping slum clearance and paternalistic provision. We do not merely criticize such demands; we also offer alternatives. A solution much better suited to our economic principles would be that the housing industry develop modern efficiency within itself. Better housing throughout the country is economically possible and socially urgent, but it is to be accomplished through industrial and engineering efforts rather than by government intervention. The technical skill of our time can most certainly cope with this problem; and engineering is the turbine that can transform the wildly wasteful rapids of social forces into useful power.

The pages of this book present a formidable array of evidence on the present status of shelter in our country. That it is an item of major, of primary, importance as an economic factor and government revenue resource; that it is heterogeneous, obsolescent, ill-defined, almost undefinable, unstandardized, wildly various, therefore difficult to appraise, finance, or liquidate; that it is costly, unmanageable, hard to purchase, socially inadequate; that it expresses but ill the spirit of the time or the life it shelters; all these points have been made and substantiated. They may all be gathered together in the one indictment directly or indirectly pressed home on every foregoing page, that *the housing industry is out of date.* In comparison with all other major industries, it is antiquated in methods and procedure.

If an important industry, providing for a basic need, is obviously out of balance with other economic factors, backward, lagging, and antiquated, the general welfare certainly demands that it be subjected to reason, comparison, and reform. Our food and our clothing represent great advances in scientific production and cooperative marketing; our shelter needs to be brought within the power of the same forces.

This process of comparing, balancing, and harmonizing is rationalization. In the last decade or two, the word " rationalization " has been used in special and limited senses, as for international industry, or trade. In a broad sense of " bringing up to date " we shall use it to cover the changes needed by the housing industry.

The need of rationalization appears more plainly in the housing industry, so definitely behind other comparable businesses, than in housing itself. Its inefficiency is glaring, but mass production methods thus far have not appealed to either user or producer. As individuals or families, we rather like our houses; but we heartily detest and really suffer from the difficulties of building or buying or renting them. The product as well as the process must be overhauled. Disregarding faddists who want to build houses of untried materials and in extraordinary forms, and likewise the conservative critics who sneer at experiments, we again emphasize the point that sound reasoning will necessarily involve a review of structure. The next volume will undertake such a review; and the esthetic and spiritual arguments against mass production are also postponed.

Except for new phases and meanings such as those stated by E. A. Filene,[1] mass production is almost as old as mankind. Viewed as production for the benefit of numbers instead of for the profit of the producer, it is merely a phase of increasing productive technique. Mass production is specialized and standardized production by group effort for the benefit of the masses.

[1] Filene, E. A., " Successful Living in This Machine Age " (Simon and Schuster, New York, 1932).

Such rationalization will inevitably utilize extensive research, every possible improvement in machinery, elimination of waste, better methods of distribution, all resulting in lower real prices to the immediate consumer.

Broad social betterment through housing depends upon a more cooperative view of its function, so well outlined by Henry Wright,[2] and upon much greater efficiency in its provision. The instantaneous prestige of any housing scheme shows how deep and real is the human need so universally felt. Yet " slum clearance and low-cost housing," grants of federal and state funds, redemption of " blighted areas," all are inadequate if they mean only more housing or new housing. Enormous building programs at public expense might mean only burdens to the taxpayers and injury to the welfare of future generations. We need to differentiate between what is essential or helpful and what is superficial or wasteful, and we need even more definitely to use modern, scientific, economical technique in the provision of shelter.

What, then, will rationalization accomplish? Of the long list of disabilities outlined in Chapter IV there is not one that would not be at least ameliorated, at most removed, by rationalization. Instead of the disorganized, heterogeneous, overnumerous units of the present industry, handicapped by seasonal demands, we should have a much smaller number of plants manufacturing material for houses, products finished to the point of final assembly. These establishments would work all the year round, and serve the entire country.

Structural reform also would integrate the house as product. Each house would be a whole, assembled on the chosen site with a speed now incredible. Such construction is not only desirable but it is long overdue and it is almost here. The buyer of the house will get more nearly what he wants, and, in a hundred situations in life that can be imagined, speedy erection will be of inestimable advantage.

The managerial drawbacks of the present condition of

[2] Wright, Henry, " A Manual of Housing," Architecture, July and August, 1933.

things, the old-fashioned, inharmonious ways of numerous small operators and their continued use of ancient hand tools, would quickly disappear. Small contractors would become assemblers, as keepers of general stores have become managers of chain stores. As to individual adjustments it is impossible to generalize, unless to suggest that building many houses quickly and well is sure to mean both pleasure and profit to any builder whose personal capacity is sturdy enough to survive desirable and long overdue changes in the industry.

Houses will be built of the same materials as they are now, and of others too; but into no single house will go the many varied materials that are now so wastefully combined. Certainly modern manufacturing technique will meet no insurmountable difficulty in fashioning and finishing the major parts of the house so efficiently that they may flow quickly from the factory into the completed home. And do so without the messiness, confusion, and intolerable waste of time, labor, and materials incident to the present methods of building. But it is well to recognize clearly the difference between mass production of houses and that of cloth, tools, automobiles, etc. In the latter case, parts are both made and assembled in the factory, and the finished product is transported to the consumer. In the case of houses, the parts may be finished in the factory, but they can be only partially assembled there; they must then be transported as parts and assembled finally on the consumer's property. Instead of twenty or thirty separate agencies, each supplying portions of a house, one complete and independent house-building agency, selected by the purchaser for its characteristic quality, will in each case be the means by which materials and accessories will be brought together and the completed product prepared for actual use.

In this new and entirely different set-up, we shall have a smaller number of processes than at present, fewer agencies, and fewer channels of distribution. The purchaser will be able to deal directly with the agency he selects, and the product will be certified. The producer will give complete service skilfully, assuming full responsibility for his product. He will not build speculatively, though where desired he will arrange financing for the purchaser.

In houses as they are now built, obsolescence is inevitable, and its rate will be more rapid as inventions multiply. Modern life accelerates every kind of change and favors shift, as it does improvement. This perfectly inevitable pressure, driving people to frequent migration and constant " betterment," calls for a form of housing that will be changeable, flexible to new demands, and cheap enough to offset the quicker rate of obsolescence.

When a standardized unit of structure becomes the unit of production cost and of commercial value (and also the unit of specification for engineer and architect) the difficulties of financing, regulation and legislation will be greatly lessened. Hampering unscientific ordinances will be displaced by unified, rational codes; usury laws will be healthily regulated, and tax legislation restored to a logical basis. In imagination one can see much antiquated rubbish going down the stream before the spring flood of rationalization. Will the flood, however, mean disaster to present interests? Unfortunately, this process of bringing so large and extended an industry up to date cannot be accomplished without temporary hardship to some. Yet the industry is so extensive and so protected by conservative influences, tradition, laws, trade rules, and vested interests, that its own inertia will absorb the shocks of the necessary adjustments.

Socially, mass production of housing is so desirable that the effect it will have on labor and employment cannot be harmful in the long run. The change may be revolutionary but all to the advantage of low-income groups and the average man generally. The building trades will be equally benefited by the steady employment which mass production would promote. Their members are certainly not pleased by the unemployment which existing conditions enforce. The huge, intricate, tangled mass of the building industry as it now exists, the excessive number of crafts, the separate jurisdictions, the quarrels, the strikes, the seasonal employment — all these with their concurrent waste we shall gladly forget.

All current comment agrees that the present situation is intolerable. The national recovery acts under which we are so hopefully working will succeed on one condition, that the cost of production in man-hours, including administration both private and public, shall be reduced. In housing this implies mass production (rationalization) and it is only by means of this sort that the buying power of the individual and the nation will increase. In the matter of wages, larger buying power might surely be expected from harmonizing wage scales between the different industries. At present the standard wage in the building trades is disproportionately high and in the textile industry disproportionately low, and recovery programs might inadvertently fail if such discrepancies should be perpetuated.

In our present economic system, real costs and real wages are defined in terms of individual time-effort, the number of man-hours required for production. These man-hours must include all who contribute to cost in office, factory, or field, whether directly or indirectly, whether in private or public service. Endless evidence on the cost of shelter in the modern world shows that, if the masses are to obtain essential housing from the income the present system provides, its cost must become relatively less. Its portion of the yearly economic effort, and of the family budget, is now spent wastefully. Whether viewed as a part of national income or of national expenditure, it is one of the largest items and yet of them all it seems the most unsoundly managed. Either the peoples of the civilized world are piling up too much of their accumulating wealth in housing structure, or they are not getting the housing they might properly demand. The reason is obvious, the present cost of housing is too great. Endless effort devoted to reducing the cost of the present structure has thus far been without avail. The only answer to this insistent need is a new conception of the structural elements with which our shelter is to be designed and of the manner by which they are to be made and combined into a home.

For the basis of home credit something tangible is demanded but also something rational, something comparable to other credit bases. The present-day home, whether single or multiple, is of infinite variety, of indefinable character, of irrational value. There are thirty million homes in this country, each one essentially different from every other, each one requiring separate consideration and appraisal as a credit basis. Without losing individuality in the appurtenances of the home, these thirty millions could, by a standardization of structure, become one million from the point of view of credit determination, and thus substantial savings in home financing might be effected. Such savings might amount to 29/30 of appraisal and other overhead costs; furthermore, the kind of credit resulting would mean better risk and a lower rate, advantageous both to buyer and lender. Clearly, the financing of the home demands a simplified building structure and a simpler, sounder method of providing it.

If our people are to continue to live under the present economic regime, reduction in the cost of shelter seems essential. Through a reduction in building costs those who are now unable to pay an economic rent for what they require could make the grade, and all classes would benefit by increased housing production. In our own frontier days, " house-raisings " or " bees " for doing this or that expressed a primitive kind of social cooperation now amplified into our complex building organization and financing means. Relying on wise regulation by government, private initiative would move to lower the cost of housing. Organizers and inventors, with their new processes and materials, will be the vital force that through individual effort will best express social cooperation.

The annual savings that might be expected from rationalization of the housing industry in the United States would count heavily in the national recovery program. By eliminating waste and improving the character and amount of housing provided, this essential industry would brace and fortify our entire economic structure.

Thus far we have apparently ignored the objections to mass production and standardization that rise most speedily to almost any reader's mind. " My home ordered from a factory, one of forty thousand exactly alike? No, thank you! " says the proud house-owner. " Miles of modern dwellings, monotonous as so many bricks? No, thank you! " says the ambitious city-planner. " Machine-made houses? *Quelle horreur!* " says the conservative architect who studied at the Beaux Arts.

If we were advocating what they think we are, their reactions might be justified. Of course, dull monotony in design and effect, since ever-present, could reappear in factory-made houses. But has sameness increased or decreased in mass-produced clothing? And are not houses, though more durable, like clothing in being partly molded and characterized by the life they contain? Mass production of houses does not necessarily mean the building of ten thousand or a hundred thousand dwellings all of the same design and form and texture and color. It means first of all determining the greatest common divisor of modern building structure and then making it freely available in multiform types. There is excellent reason, backed by eminent architectural authority, for the belief that the mass-produced house of the future will give a far wider and more varied expression to the spirit of the times than anything we have today.

Just as the Woolworth Building mistakenly covers an efficient modern structure with an ancient wrapper, so most of the modern domestic architecture of the " Century of Progress " Exposition is esthetically poor because it clothes an old structure in an unrelated modern-looking exterior. The surface appearance should harmonize with the structure beneath. Yet the Chicago architectural exhibits clearly indicate the general groping for means whereby to express in a building structure the technical developments and new social concepts of our present civilization. From this viewpoint the architecture of the Exposition as a whole calls for a modernized building structure in harmony with what it is trying to reflect.

As regards beauty, a rich variety of effect and a wide range of form, color, and texture will be made available for the benefit of the whole people by mass production. The architect will be able to plan more freely and there will be marvelous new developments in materials. When the benefit of mass production reaches the householder in lower costs, the demand for more and better housing will increase. In the United States at the present time, outside of multi-family dwellings as we have seen, not one house in five has architectural service. Has this no connection with the unemployment among architects? Mass production in the provision of shelter would put architectural talent, even of the highest grade, to work for the benefit of the masses, on a scale certainly larger than today. And the effort now wasted in unnecessary estimates, altered specifications, salesmanship, and, far above all, the attempt to arrange infinite irrelevant detail for each separate house, would be saved for creative work and efficient service. Instead of being forced, as he fears, into the iron mold of a " standardized house," the individual will have free choice in the matters in which variety gives real character.

The scope of the architect, then, his practical opportunity to meet individual demand, community demand, esthetic and utilitarian requirements, will be enlarged without harmful restrictions being imposed upon layout or plans or design. The best or most useful designs, beautiful because of their adaptation to use, will be the most successful, and therefore the most common. Thereby common, or community, beauty will increase and esthetic needs be better satisfied. The architectural effect of the modern German group housing is certainly preferable to the heterogeneous clutter of traditional types. It forecasts the use of mass production and finely illustrates the advantages that will thereby be brought to the masses.

In Chapters II and III we emphasize the suburban home. That type does very truly represent American housing, and dominates our ways of life and social thinking. There is no reason to suppose that the advantages of mass-produced housing, including all the characteristic American good qualities, cannot be just as well supplied to individual dwellings as to communal developments. In both cases, expert talent giving careful study to group life will provide air, light, sunlight, to the comfort of all occupants, and will also attend to the social recreational side of community life, playgrounds, parks, museums, landing fields, stadia.

The most practical consideration is, however, the most pressing. Decrease in the cost of housing is, above all, what the consumer demands, what government, what society demands. He would be a bold economist indeed who should assert that society would benefit by an increase in the cost of housing, whether he meant through inflation or through an increase in the labor cost of production. Yet for years, in fact generations, housing cost has been increasing through the continuing relative decrease in the cost of practically everything else.

When waste shall have been eliminated and the costs reduced, when a guaranteed product is available, those who are now buying inefficient housing, and paying a great deal too much for what they get, will probably spend the same 20 per cent of their annual income on shelter and employ the same amount of labor to produce it. But they will get far more for their money, and that will mean an increase in the buying power of the day's work, whether in building construction or other work. The resultant enormous demand for better and cheaper housing will mean more work for all those now employed so inefficiently. There is no part of the body public that will not respond to the stimulus and life imparted by new conditions in the housing industry.

In the realm described as " social invention " there will be finer developments than any achieved so far. Comprehensive, intelligent planning for cities and whole regions will make good use of efficient building methods. Programs of " decentralizing " industries away from crowded cities, and " homesteading " schemes will be well served by a rationalized housing industry that can deliver for swift assembly " adequate dwellings at the lowest possible cost."

Nor are these forecasts Utopian visions. Whether or not our present civilization is going to pieces, and whether or not great changes are to occur, particularly the long overdue improvement in our technique of distribution, two things stand out clearly from the maze of the social, political and economic problems that confront us. Authoritative opinion and likewise the data presented in this book make it clear that housing provision (and probably the entire building industry) are obsolete and on the verge of being rationalized. The technique of building construction is bound to be harmonized with other productive means, and there is but one way in which that harmony may be brought about. The disabilities of the housing industry require drastic and profound change, a major operation, a revolution. Genuine rationalization will effect all this, and it is surely coming. Nobody can prevent it.

Just as the right catalytic agent starts and accelerates the beautiful and orderly process of synthesis in some great conglomerate mass of hydrocarbons, there must be for the building industry an agent by means of which its huge, heterogeneous, unwieldy mass may change from chaos to order. It is useless to think that such a disorganized, diverse, antiquated conglomeration can contain its own reagent. But once provided with a persuader, its scattered warring particles would with reasonable celerity join into an effective new formation. Complex as the change may seem, it is in reality the variegated mass of social and economic elements in the industry that is complex. But their realignment should prove relatively simple. To suit mass production, a new conception of building structure is needed, a conception that will annul the present obvious disabilities of the industry. Such a conception would precipitate the rationalization of housing, would effect the benefits we have described.

If an engineer or architect were to step forward with an efficient means of doubling the output of shelter for the use of mankind, it would not be, as the " overproduction " terrorizers suggest, a national calamity. It might mean new labor processes, new financing, new laws, new standards; and the workers would have a new enthusiasm to put into their work. Though it would involve vast changes in a really huge section of American industry and apparently cut out many jobs, the change would actually so increase the purchasing power of the buying public that it would take the entire product of all the revamped agencies to provide the housing which the American public would buy. Spending the same percentage of income as now, our population, to a man, would buy " more of a house " in size and appurtenances and demand such an output as to employ all those directly displaced by mass-productive technique. It would give people more work because it would so greatly increase their efficiency in producing the housing which is wanted.

The new line-up of productive forces may be revolutionary. It will be, however, a revolution spread over a decade or more, for the struggle against tradition and inertia will be difficult. But in some length of time the disturbance will be absorbed. Meantime the entirely different concept of this basic industry will be to stimulate economic reconstruction and spiritual recovery.

The change in methods of building needed to adapt housing to mass needs is clearly an engineering problem of great size and moment. Its solution, even in part, will have vast social significance. The elements of the problem have not been clear, owing to its great scope and very involved nature. The means of its solution, though obscured by those same conditions, involve a new conception of building structure, one that will fulfil the requirements of modern industry — scientific efficiency, mass production, speedy assembly, facile marketing — and will also open new fields to invention, design, and to the creation of domestic and civic beauty. With such a conception the third volume of this book will deal.

Appendix

APPENDIX

(Supplementary Material to Indicated Chapters)

GENERAL LACK AND DEFECTS OF STATISTICAL DATA

PREPARATION of the material in this volume has been handicapped at almost every point by a lack of authoritative, comprehensive statistical data. In spite of the extraordinary amount of discussion of the housing problem in recent years, there is an almost incredible lack of simple basic facts.

For example, in the United States there is no reliable information on the total value of dwelling-houses. Apparently only a single state, Connecticut, keeps a record of the value of dwelling-houses separately from the land. A few states report the total value of all buildings or of "structures" but do not distinguish between houses and other buildings. The United States Census would be the logical source of this information, but has not kept such records. The Census reports the production of radishes, parsnips, and okra, separately; the value of these crops in 1929 was about $1,000,000. But for real property amounting in 1922 to more than $176,000,000,000, it made no separation as between land and buildings, to say nothing of a classification of buildings by type.

Again, in the case of a matter so apparently simple as determining the number of workers in the industry, there is a lack of definite figures, and estimates by individual students vary widely. One reason for this is that the Census does not always show separately the number of workers in a given occupation who are engaged in the building industry. For example, electrical workers are reported as a group with no indication of the number engaged in building alone. The classification basis used by the Census in its census of occupations has sometimes been challenged.

A matter of special importance so far as this book is concerned is that in almost no case is information given for the dwelling-house branch of the industry alone.

The responsibility for these defects in Census data does not in the main rest on the Bureau of the Census but rather on the legislation directing its inquiries. The inclusion of a single additional inquiry in the Census schedule ultimately involves a considerable expenditure and the Census cannot depart from its instructions. Apparently it is easier to get an inquiry concerning the production of pop-corn inserted in the Census schedule than one covering the value of dwelling-houses erected in a given year. The defects in Census statistics here pointed out are a reflection upon the log-rolling appropriation methods of the Congress and not upon the statistical methods of the Bureau of the Census.

In this absence of complete official data it has been necessary to rely upon partial statistics issued by various governmental bureaus and upon the records of various private agencies affiliated with the building industry. Even then, it has frequently been necessary to make approximate computations for the dwelling-house industry alone.

A further difficulty arises from the lack of standard nomenclature. Thus such terms as " family " and " dwelling " as used by the Census have a different significance than they have when used in ordinary conversation. Moreover, their significance is not the same in all censuses or in all countries. For example, prior to 1930 the term " family " as used by the Census applied to a group of persons, whether related by blood or not, who lived together in one household, usually sharing the same table. The definition counted as a single family all the occupants of a hotel, boarding-house or lodging-house and all the occupants of an institution, however numerous. In 1930, however, the Census revised its definition and applied the term to what may be called private families, i.e., a group of persons related either by blood, marriage, or adoption who live together as one household, usually sharing the same table. Single persons living alone were counted as families, as were two or more related persons occupying permanent quarters in a hotel.

Likewise, the term " dwelling " for Census purposes covers everything from a room in a factory, or even a freight-car used as an abode, to an entire apartment-house regardless of the number of families housed. Prior to 1930 it also included hotels, boarding-houses, institutions, and the like.

A "home" for Census purposes in the United States signifies the abiding place of a single family and therefore may not relate to an entire dwelling. A large apartment-house, for instance, would include a great many homes. The number of homes and the number of families as shown by census reports are identical.

The definitions used by the Canadian Census are broadly similar to those used by the United States Census prior to 1930. The Canadian Census, however, distinguishes between "dwelling-houses" and apartment-houses. In most of the other countries mentioned in this book a dwelling is defined as representing the total number of rooms intended for occupation by one household and definitely separated from other premises. In general, the term "dwelling" as used in foreign countries excludes hotels and institutional buildings.

A particularly troublesome feature of government statistics on housing is that it is frequently impossible to coordinate them. Thus the United States Bureau of Labor Statistics has published what is probably the most valuable information on the cost of living in the United States. It shows the income and expenditures of families by income groups. The Census in 1930 classified rented homes on the basis of rentals paid by rental groups, but there is no way of determining the family income or the family expenditures for any particular group of families falling in a given census rental group. Again, in its 1930 returns, the Census did not give average figures for rentals paid or for the value of homes owned, but instead reported medians. These medians may, when related to such a large body of statistics, differ very considerably from averages, and it would therefore be unsafe, for example, to multiply the number of owned homes by the median value in an attempt to arrive at an estimated total value.

It is especially to be regretted that owing to the lack of an appropriation the United States Bureau of Labor Statistics has been unable to make a nation-wide investigation of the cost of living since 1918. That study was taken when family budgets were more or less distorted by War conditions. The previous study by the Bureau was in 1901. It is reasonably certain that the percentage allotment of the budget has undergone important changes since then, but in the absence of a broad basis of statistical data it is very difficult to estimate such changes.

These comments, we repeat, are not in any sense intended as a criticism of the Bureau of the Census, the United States Bureau of Labor Statistics (which, with the Department of Commerce, have been extremely helpful in this study), or any other government bureau, the investigations of which are very largely regulated by the legislation directing their inquiries. They are merely cited here as an explanation of the difficulty of drawing definite conclusions on many points discussed in the text.

CHAPTER I

TABLE A

APPROXIMATE VALUES OF MAJOR ITEMS IN THE TOTAL WEALTH OF VARIOUS NATIONS IN 1895, AS ESTIMATED BY MULHALL a

(In millions of pounds)

	Farms	Rail-roads	Houses b	Merchan-dise	Sun-dries	Total	% houses to total
United Kingdom	2,077	985	2,490	805	5,449	11,806	21.0
France	3,093	663	2,159	601	3,174	9,690	22.3
Germany	2,508	555	1,755	677	2,557	8,052	21.8
Russia	2,710	349	1,019	515	1,832	6,425	15.8
Austria	1,797	371	719	367	1,258	4,512	15.9
Italy	1,399	184	503	223	851	3,160	15.9
Spain	1,212	108	280	148	632	2,380	11.8
Portugal	164	23	77	32	115	411	18.7
Sweden and Norway	278	40	152	80	240	790	19.2
Denmark	254	14	69	37	132	506	13.6
Holland	295	46	178	104	257	880	20.2
Belgium	354	75	175	118	266	988	17.7
Switzerland	172	44	91	49	136	492	18.5
Danubian states	508	36	136	83	263	1,026	13.3
Greece	109	6	31	15	61	222	13.9
Europe	16,930	3,499	9,834	3,854	17,223	51,340	19.1
United States ..	4,142	2,260	4,446	1,563	3,939	16,350	27.2
Canada	305	186	145	103	264	1,003	14.4
Australia	392	139	174	88	283	1,076	16.2
Argentina	198	88	107	53	170	616	17.4
Totals	21,967	6,172	14,706	5,661	21,879	70,385	20.9

(a) Mulhall, Michael George, " Industries and Wealth of Nations " (Longmans, Green and Co., London, 1896), Table No. XXXIV, p. 392.

(b) Mulhall's figures in many cases are rough estimates, and can be considered only as approximating actual conditions. His valuations for houses include the value of the site, and are arrived at by assuming that the value was 16½ times the annual rental. The more commonly used formula adopts a ratio of 10 times the annual rental. From this it appears that Mulhall's valuations of "houses " considerably exceed the true value of dwellings only.

TABLE B

MEDIAN VALUES OF OWNED NON-FARM HOMES, AND AVERAGE VALUES
OF FARM DWELLINGS IN THE UNITED STATES IN 1930, BY STATES

	Owned Non-farm Homes a (Median values, including site)			Farm Dwellings b (Average values, excluding site)
	Urban	Rural	All non-farm	
New England				
Maine	$4,632	$2,460	$3,233	$1,450
New Hampshire .	4,388	2,439	3,533	1,738
Vermont	5,849	2,882	4,031	1,727
Massachusetts ..	6,516	4,345	6,249	3,050
Rhode Island ...	6,348	3,900	6,153	2,965
Connecticut	7,507	6,098	7,013	3,708
Middle Atlantic				
New York	8,477	4,720	7,492	2,296
New Jersey	8,245	5,397	7,426	3,218
Pennsylvania ...	5,830	3,432	5,206	2,038
East North Central				
Ohio	5,961	2,816	5,201	1,619
Indiana	4,427	1,931	3,654	1,358
Illinois	6,799	2,565	5,867	1,803
Michigan	6,007	2,545	5,067	1,596
Wisconsin	5,523	3,112	4,781	1,888
West North Central				
Minnesota	4,906	2,811	4,297	1,704
Iowa	4,255	2,739	3,657	2,212
Missouri	5,104	2,178	4,050	1,099
North Dakota ..	4,694	2,127	2,762	1,408
South Dakota ...	4,318	2,648	3,180	1,432
Nebraska	4,323	2,862	3,717	1,719
Kansas	3,304	2,120	2,768	1,271
South Atlantic				
Delaware	5,724	3,632	4,878	1,789
Maryland	4,817	3,614	4,525	2,051
District of Columbia	9,246	———	9,246	4,197
Virginia	4,558	2,259	3,392	1,226

(a) USDC, Bureau of the Census, "Population Bulletin, Families 1930"
(GPO, Washington, 1933), p. 38.
(b) USDC, Bureau of the Census, "Agriculture, General Statistics 1930"
(GPO, Washington, 1932), p. 40.

TABLE B (*continued*)

	Owned Non-farm Homes (*Median values, including site*)			Farm Dwellings (*Average values, excluding site*)
	Urban	Rural	All non-farm	
West Virginia ..	$5,059	$2,363	$3,620	$941
North Carolina .	4,257	1,826	2,763	653
South Carolina ..	4,271	1,645	2,710	519
Georgia	4,029	1,810	2,869	483
Florida	3,908	1,557	2,892	807
East South Central				
Kentucky	4,390	1,662	3,268	664
Tennessee	3,850	1,657	2,903	602
Alabama	3,785	1,671	2,710	408
Mississippi	2,896	1,454	2,074	377
West South Central				
Arkansas	3,151	1,290	2,090	391
Louisiana	4,289	1,012	2,730	447
Oklahoma	3,673	1,214	2,512	620
Texas	3,744	1,809	2,998	708
Mountain				
Montana	3,356	1,429	2,364	910
Idaho	3,253	1,575	2,433	1,117
Wyoming	4,062	2,193	3,136	991
Colorado	3,875	1,770	3,209	1,074
New Mexico	2,954	——— c	——— c	526
Arizona	4,050	1,361	2,363	1,011
Utah	3,797	1,893	3,098	1,189
Nevada	4,815	——— c	2,541	1,624
Pacific				
Washington	3,762	2,301	3,316	1,318
Oregon	4,161	2,224	3,574	1,317
California	5,914	3,659	5,491	1,895

(*c*) Less than $1000.

ESTIMATED VALUE OF DWELLING-HOUSES IN THE
UNITED STATES

TABLE C

APPROXIMATE VALUATION OF BUILDINGS IN THE UNITED STATES BY
MAJOR CLASSES IN 1930

Residential		*Per cent*
Dwellings, including apartments	$70,000,000,000	60.9
Hotels, lodging-houses, etc.	4,000,000,000	3.5
Total residential	$74,000,000,000	64.4

Non-residential		
Amusement buildings	$ 1,250,000,000	1.1
Churches	2,000,000,000	1.7
Manufacturing buildings	4,750,000,000	4.1
Public and private garages	2,500,000,000	2.2
Institutions	3,500,000,000	3.1
Office-buildings	5,000,000,000	4.3
Public buildings	3,000,000,000	2.6
Public utilities buildings	2,500,000,000	2.2
Schools, colleges, and libraries	5,000,000,000	4.3
Stores and warehouses	5,000,000,000	4.3
Sheds, stables, and barns	5,500,000,000	4.8
Miscellaneous	1,000,000,000	0.9
Total non-residential	$41,000,000,000	35.6
Grand total	$115,000,000,000	100.0

NOTE. This estimate allows for normal depreciation, but not for the abnormal deflation prevailing in 1930 and since. Except for this the values here given would be broadly applicable as of January 1, 1933, but somewhat too high, as new construction in 1930–32 did not fully offset normal depreciation and fire losses.

The valuation of $70,000,000,000 is considerably less than that indicated by the Census of 1930. An exact comparison cannot be made, first because the Census did not separate the value of the building from that of the land, and second because, as already noted, it did not report average values but simply median figures; for rented homes, moreover, it gave only median rentals, with no estimate of capital values.

The Census reported the median value of 10,503,386 owned non-farm homes at $4778, and the median rental value of 12,351,-549 rented non-farm homes at $27.15 per month, roughly $325 per year. If the median for owned homes were to be regarded as approximately the average and the value of rented homes as eight times the annual rental,[1] a grand total of roughly $91,500,000,-000 (including several hundred thousand homes for which no returns were secured) would be suggested, as follows:[2]

Owned non-farm homes	$51,000,000,000
Rented non-farm homes	32,500,000,000
Farm homes including $1,000,000,000 for sites	8,000,000,000
	$91,500,000,000

It seems reasonably certain that Census *averages*, if available, would be higher than the median figures, and would result in an estimate of well over $100,000,000,000 as the value of all homes including land. Assuming the total to be approximately $110,000,-000,000, an allowance of $30,000,000,000 for the sites would leave a total for the houses alone of $80,000,000,000. This is $10,000,-000,000 more than the value assigned to houses in Table C. Some estimates based on Census medians suggest a much greater difference. Casual analysis, therefore, might indicate that an estimate of $70,000,000,000 is discredited by the median figures of the Census. But the use of any figure greatly in excess of this total at once implies a total national wealth far in excess of any current estimates.

As shown in Chapter V, the value of dwelling-houses may be taken as at least 60 per cent of the value of all buildings. If the former valuation be placed at $80,000,000,000, this would indicate a value for all buildings of nearly $135,000,000,000. The value of all buildings in turn is almost certainly less than 30 per cent of the total wealth of the country, and appears to range between 25 and 30 per cent. If the mean of 27.5 per cent be used, a

[1] See Chapter III.

[2] Some estimators use a ratio of ten times, or even higher, but as shown on p. 132 the use of such ratios may result in excessive valuations. Based on an " economic " rent of 14 per cent as computed in Chapter III, the ratio would be about seven times instead of eight times; but since the actual rent may be somewhat less than an economic rent, it seems better to use the last-named ratio here.

valuation of $135,000,000,000 for all buildings would suggest a total national wealth in 1930 of $500,000,000,000. Had values continued to increase from 1922 [3] to 1930 at the same average rate as that indicated by the Census valuations of 1912 and 1922, the indicated total in 1930 would have been more than $500,000,000,-000. However, according to the Census there was a shrinkage of $20,000,000,000 in the value of farm lands alone between 1920 and 1930. The shrinkage in urban real-estate values since the peak year 1925 may safely be estimated at a still higher figure. In certain industries, notably textile manufacturing and street railways, there was a heavy decline in capital values after 1922. While capital investment in some other fields increased, we may be reasonably sure that the annual rate of increase in *total* national wealth was materially smaller during the period 1922–30 than in the preceding ten-year period.

Ingalls [4] estimated the total national wealth in 1929 at $450,-000,000,000, but some of his figures are unduly liberal. The Chamber of Commerce of the United States cited an estimate of $400,-000,000,000, as of 1930; but an estimate by the National Industrial Conference Board, Inc., which has devoted considerable research to the problem, placed the total in 1930 at only $330,-000,000,000. [5] While this seems over-conservative, it affords ground for rejecting any estimate approaching $500,000,000,000.

The estimate of $70,000,000,000, which was based on a large amount of research, therefore seems more in harmony with the indicated value of other items comprising total national wealth than one of $80,000,000,000. It is also more in line with the indicated values of other classes of buildings given in Table C.

A further rough check on the $70,000,000,000 valuation may be made by comparing the value of homes estimated on that basis with the average amount of mortgage indebtedness upon them. The value of all *homes*, including the site, would be $90,000,000,-000, of which $82,000,000,000 represents the value of non-farm

[3] This is the date of the latest Census estimate of national wealth.

[4] Ingalls, W. R., New York Times Annalist, October 23, 1931.

[5] The Conference Board's estimate for 1929 was $362,000,000,000. In comparing the Board's estimate with that in Table 1, p. 11, allowance should be made for the fact that the National Industrial Conference Board did not include public streets and highways, which in Table 1 are given a value of $27,000,000,000.

TABLE D

ESTIMATES OF THE TOTAL INCOME OF THE PEOPLE OF THE UNITED
STATES ANNUALLY, 1909–1929

(In billions of dollars)

| | NBER [a] | | NICB [b] | |
	Current dollars [c]	1913 dollars	Current dollars [c]	1913 dollars
1909	29.6	31.3	28.8	30.2
1910	31.4	32.4	31.4	32.2
1911	31.9	32.9	31.2	32.2
1912	34.0	34.7	33.0	33.6
1913	35.7	35.8	34.4	34.4
1914	35.6	35.2	33.2	32.9
1915	37.2	36.6	36.0	35.8
1916	43.3	39.6	45.4	41.6
1917	51.3	40.2	53.9	41.9
1918	60.4	40.1	61.0	40.2
1919	65.9	38.0	68.3	38.8
1920	74.0	37.6	74.3	37.5
1921	63.4	36.7	54.3	32.1
1922	65.9	40.6	60.0	37.9
1923	74.3	45.2	70.5	44.1
1924	77.1	46.8	70.0	43.7
1925	81.9	48.4	77.5	46.9
1926	85.5	50.4	79.3	47.7
1927	88.2	52.9	78.1	48.2
1928	89.4	54.0	81.0	50.6
1929	—	—	84.0	52.5

(a) King, W. I., " The National Income and Its Purchasing Power " (National Bureau of Economic Research, Inc., New York, 1930), pp. 94 and 100.

(b) National Industrial Conference Board, Inc., " Bulletin," March 20, 1931, p. 406.

(c) In dollars current at the time, not the current devalued dollar of 1934.

The income here given as computed by the National Bureau of Economic Research is termed " entire realized income " and is defined in the report substantially as follows:

" Realized income consists, in the main, of the amounts received by individuals in the form of wages, salaries, pensions, compensation for injuries, interest, dividends, rents, royalties, services of durable consumers' goods, and profits withdrawn from business." (" The National Income and Its Purchasing Power," p. 42.)

The total includes an item of "imputed" income (amounting since 1922

homes,[6] or an average value per home of $3500. In view of the
fact, brought out in the Appendix of Chapter X, that the average
size of mortgages on many groups of owned homes in 1928–29
ranged from $3500 to $5000 or more, this average value may seem
discredited. It should be remembered, however, that the average
value of owned homes is undoubtedly much in excess of the average

TABLE E

ESTIMATED EXPENDITURES IN THE UNITED STATES IN 1926 FOR LUX-
URIES AND CERTAIN OTHER ITEMS [a]

Passenger automobiles	$11,955,907,443	
Tobacco	2,087,110,000	
Soft drinks, ice cream, candy, and chewing-gum	1,803,480,000	
Theaters, movies, and similar amusements	1,055,420,000	
Jewelry, perfumes, and cosmetics	806,820,000	
Sporting goods, toys, etc.	487,030,000	$18,195,767,443
Building construction		6,787,000,000
Education		2,255,251,327
Life insurance		2,624,000,000
Taxes collected		
By federal government	$ 3,207,000,000	
By state governments	1,264,285,840	
By local governments	4,083,793,000	8,555,078,840

(a) "Can the States Afford to Educate Their Children?" (National Education Association, Washington, 1929), pp. 16–20.

---

to about $5,250,000 annually) covering "the estimated value of the services
rendered to their owners by durable direct or consumers' goods," as for instance the rental value of a house occupied by the owner. It does not include
such items as "the income which might be imputed to housewives and householders for services rendered to their own families" or "income arising from
changes in the value of property." (*Ibid.*, pp. 73 and 75.)

The difference between the figures of the National Industrial Conference
Board and those of the National Bureau of Economic Research is largely due
to the inclusion by the latter of this allowance for "imputed" income, which is
not included by the former.

6 This valuation is reached by assuming that the value of the site in the
case of non-farm homes was about 25 per cent of the total value of the homes.
As shown in Chapter VII, the ratio of site value to total value in the case of new
homes would be nearer 20 per cent, probably somewhat less. But since in the

value of rented and owned homes taken together. Moreover, the average amounts of mortgage debt noted in the Appendix of Chapter X, applied in many cases to urban homes, often of high value. All in all, this estimate of $3500 as the average value of all non-farm homes, owned and rented, is not seriously out of line with the average amount of mortgage debt on owned homes reported on p. 587.

Independent estimates are closely in line with the total of $70,-000,000,000. Nystrom [7] placed the value of all dwellings in 1927 at $64,800,000,000, as a conservative estimate. New construction from 1927 to 1930 amounted to several billions, but allowing for normal depreciation and fire losses the indicated total in 1930 would be close to $70,000,000,000.

A very similar valuation is indicated by a report of the National Bureau of Economic Research, Inc.,[8] which placed the value of all non-farm homes in 1927 at $77,200,000,000. Making an arbitrary deduction of 25 per cent for the value of the site, this would suggest a value for houses alone of about $58,000,000,000. Adding the census figure of $7,000,000,000 for farm dwellings, the indicated total is $65,000,000,000, almost exactly the same as that arrived at by Nystrom for the same year.

In view of the various comparisons here presented, we may then accept the figure of $70,000,000,000 as a fair estimate of the 1930 value of dwelling-houses in the United States.

TABLE F

ESTIMATED "COST OF PLAY" IN THE UNITED STATES, ABOUT 1928

Pleasure motoring ($\frac{2}{3}$ of total cost of passenger automobiles) $5,000,000,000
Vacations and travel (transportation element primarily)   2,000,000,000

---

case of all houses standing at a given date many would have suffered very extensive depreciation over a period of years, it seems proper to assign the site a higher proportion of total value than that allowed in the case of *new* homes. The value of the sites in the case of farm homes has been arbitrarily placed at $1,000,000,000, or only one-eighth of the total value; even this valuation may be over-liberal.

[7] Nystrom, Paul H., "The Economic Principles of Consumption" (The Ronald Press Co., New York, 1929), p. 378.

[8] King, Willford I., "The National Income and Its Purchasing Power" (National Bureau of Economic Research, Inc., New York, 1930), p. 378.

TABLE F *a* (continued)

Moving pictures	1,500,000,000
Newspapers, tabloids, light fiction (in part)	1,000,000,000
Radio	750,000,000
Phonographs, pianolas, etc.	250,000,000
Telephone (pleasure factor only)	100,000,000
Flying, bicycling, etc. (pleasure factor only)	25,000,000
Entertaining, visiting, night clubs, road houses (food and service factor)	3,000,000,000
Candy, chewing-gum, hard and soft drinks (in part)	2,000,000,000
Tobacco (in part)	1,500,000,000
Collections, hobbies, pets	1,000,000,000
Shows, theatres, concerts, religious revivals, lectures, etc.	500,000,000
Gifts (in part)	500,000,000
Golf	500,000,000
Social clubs (upkeep factor only)	250,000,000
Children's toys	250,000,000
Indoor games: cards, billiards, pool, chess, etc.	100,000,000
Playgrounds, camping, hiking	100,000,000
Dancing, jazz palaces, etc.	100,000,000
Amusement parks	100,000,000
Processions, celebrations, pageants	50,000,000
Swimming and bathing beaches	50,000,000
Musical instruments (non-automatic)	50,000,000
Hunting and fishing	50,000,000
Gambling, including stock exchanges (commission element only)	50,000,000
Horse-racing	50,000,000
Football	50,000,000
Baseball	50,000,000
Sport clothes	50,000,000
Prize-fighting	15,000,000
Tennis and allied games	15,000,000
Yachting and boating	10,000,000
Field sports	10,000,000
Winter sports	10,000,000
Indoor sports: gymnasiums, basketball, bowling, etc.	10,000,000
Grand total	$21,045,000,000

(*a*) Chase, Stuart, "Play" in "Whither Mankind," edited by Charles A. Beard (Longmans, Green and Co., New York, 1930), pp. 336–337.

CHAPTER II

TABLE G

DISTRIBUTION OF DWELLINGS IN THE UNITED STATES IN 1930, BY TYPE
AND BY STATES [a]

State	Single-family	Two-family	Multi-family	Totals
New England				
Maine	155,406	13,929	3,653	172,988
New Hampshire	89,813	8,907	2,992	101,712
Vermont	72,356	5,778	1,321	79,455
Massachusetts	511,051	126,274	65,897	703,222
Rhode Island	81,152	23,065	11,076	115,293
Connecticut	214,588	46,302	19,662	280,552
Middle Atlantic				
New York	1,299,216	275,924	159,916	1,735,056
New Jersey	580,836	99,590	40,717	721,143
Pennsylvania	1,852,481	125,051	31,464	2,008,996
East North Central				
Ohio	1,335,303	107,024	32,566	1,474,893
Indiana	757,409	24,877	7,499	789,785
Illinois	1,153,819	163,079	88,229	1,405,127
Michigan	925,348	74,544	18,953	1,018,845
Wisconsin	559,919	55,032	9,250	624,201
West North Central				
Minnesota	503,600	31,007	7,444	542,051
Iowa	583,180	16,622	4,199	604,001
Missouri	727,440	64,372	17,613	809,425
North Dakota	133,030	3,712	961	137,703
South Dakota	149,928	3,584	822	154,334
Nebraska	316,419	7,292	2,268	325,979
Kansas	447,213	13,260	3,271	463,744
South Atlantic				
Delaware	52,234	2,016	690	54,940
Maryland	318,246	22,890	4,981	346,117
District of Columbia .	74,649	6,805	3,449	84,903

(a) USDC, Bureau of the Census, " Population Bulletin, Families 1930 "
(GPO, Washington, 1933), p. 55.

TABLE G (*continued*)

State	Single-family	Two-family	Multi-family	Totals
		Number of Dwellings		
Virginia	466,083	22,550	3,942	492,575
West Virginia	336,834	13,301	2,614	352,749
North Carolina	589,545	21,844	2,903	614,292
South Carolina	329,370	13,334	2,561	345,265
Georgia	564,540	32,411	5,517	602,468
Florida	332,547	13,657	4,039	350,243
East South Central				
Kentucky	533,615	27,286	5,428	566,329
Tennessee	528,242	24,815	5,096	558,153
Alabama	523,935	27,270	3,360	554,565
Mississippi	428,086	18,422	1,982	448,490
West South Central				
Arkansas	403,295	14,065	2,021	419,381
Louisiana	438,565	16,334	3,481	458,380
Oklahoma	501,347	19,990	5,322	526,659
Texas	1,211,505	56,996	13,375	1,281,876
Mountain				
Montana	122,144	3,357	1,353	126,854
Idaho	99,803	2,510	679	102,992
Wyoming	51,509	1,605	455	53,569
Colorado	230,607	8,304	3,637	242,548
New Mexico	87,921	3,824	785	92,530
Arizona	93,854	3,644	1,135	98,633
Utah	100,743	3,787	1,258	105,788
Nevada	23,064	569	261	23,894
Pacific				
Washington	368,917	8,843	4,779	382,539
Oregon	239,069	4,941	2,548	246,558
California	1,333,334	43,492	26,355	1,403,181
Totals	22,833,110	1,728,087	643,779	25,204,976
Percentages	90.5	6.9	2.6	100.1

TABLE H

PROPORTIONS OF APARTMENTS, WITH ONE, TWO, THREE, AND MORE THAN THREE
ROOMS EACH, ERECTED IN NEW YORK CITY, 1912–1932 a

New York City

Year	One room	Two rooms	Three rooms	More than three rooms
1912	0.37	3.76	19.98	75.89
1913	0.06	1.78	19.04	79.12
1914	0.15	1.38	20.12	78.35
1915	0.12	1.35	25.35	73.18
1916	0.27	1.21	27.68	70.84
1917	0.41	2.15	28.68	68.76
1918	0.00	2.77	30.86	66.37
1919	0.86	2.16	37.32	59.61
1920	0.16	2.01	33.10	64.73
1921	0.26	1.64	37.32	60.78
1922	0.09	2.47	41.12	56.32
1923	0.18	3.58	43.70	52.54
1924	0.50	4.87	43.23	51.40
1925	0.67	6.61	49.10	43.62
1926	0.61	7.16	52.34	39.89
1927	0.76	8.51	54.43	33.30
1928	1.22	9.98	54.79	34.01
1929	1.82	10.32	54.81	33.05
1930	5.10	14.61	49.08	31.21
1931	9.32	16.20	49.79	24.69
1932	6.40	17.02	50.94	25.64

Borough of Manhattan (only)

Year	One room	Two rooms	Three rooms	More than three rooms
1912	1.01	8.72	27.35	62.92
1913	0.02	4.58	19.98	75.42
1914	0.24	3.15	15.81	80.80
1915	0.36	3.85	27.31	68.48
1916	0.78	3.03	23.46	72.73
1917	1.08	4.64	24.92	69.36
1918	0.00	9.10	30.67	60.23
1919	9.56	12.50	33.09	44.85
1920	0.17	5.70	29.34	64.79
1921	1.29	2.87	28.23	67.61
1922	0.38	5.21	33.92	60.49
1923	0.67	8.61	37.90	52.82
1924	1.92	10.09	38.80	49.19
1925	1.27	8.52	35.55	54.66
1926	1.59	8.91	34.36	55.14
1927	2.22	8.07	44.88	44.83
1928	3.53	11.53	41.44	43.50
1929	5.54	10.41	41.56	42.49
1930	11.04	19.38	33.87	35.72
1931	28.03	24.05	21.48	26.44
1932	27.21	23.48	22.40	26.91

(a) Furnished by Tenement House Department, City of New York.

TABLE I

DISTRIBUTION OF FAMILIES IN THE UNITED STATES BY TYPE OF
DWELLING, 1930 [a]

	Single-family	Two-family	Three-family	Totals
New York	294,037	273,136	1,155,781	1,722,954
Chicago	209,685	232,680	400,213	842,578
Philadelphia	364,457	48,784	45,386	458,627
Detroit	209,981	81,452	78,860	370,293
Los Angeles	282,382	22,610	63,516	368,508
Total 5 cities	1,360,542	658,662	1,743,756	3,762,960
Other urban	9,641,319	2,202,478	1,765,767	13,609,564
All urban	11,001,861	2,861,140	3,509,523	17,372,524
Rural and farm ...	11,831,249	595,034	105,856	12,532,139
Total	22,833,110	3,456,174	3,615,379	29,904,663

	Per cent	Per cent	Per cent	Per cent
New York	17.1	15.9	67.0	100
Chicago	24.9	27.6	47.5	100
Philadelphia	79.5	10.6	9.9	100
Detroit	56.7	22.0	21.3	100
Los Angeles	76.7	6.1	17.2	100
Total 5 cities	36.2	17.5	46.3	100
Other urban	70.8	16.2	13.0	100
All urban	63.3	16.5	20.2	100
Rural and farm ...	94.4	4.8	0.8	100
Total	76.4	11.6	12.1	100

(a) USDC, Bureau of the Census, " Population Bulletin, Families 1930 "
(GPO, Washington, 1933), pp. 10 and 72.

TABLE J

PERCENTAGE OF FRAME DWELLINGS IN THE UNITED STATES IN COMMUNITIES OF
OVER 2500 INHABITANTS, BY STATES, ABOUT 1924 a

State	Population represented (per cent)	Dwellings of wood construction (per cent)
Washington	85.8	98
Oregon	77.2	97
Idaho	65.1	95
New Hampshire	41.8	95
Indiana	82.5	90
Louisiana	84.3	90
Maine	61.8	90
Montana	68.3	90
North Carolina	54.3	90
Oklahoma	61.5	90
Wyoming	45.3	90
South Carolina	77.9	89
Wisconsin	74.3	88
California	53.4	85
Connecticut	59.8	85
Florida	59.6	85
Georgia	62.3	85
Iowa	68.6	85
Kansas	46.5	85
Massachusetts	49.7	85
Michigan	76.9	85
New York	28.6	85
North Dakota	53.6	85
Texas	45.9	85
Ohio	82.1	83
Alabama	49.5	80
Nebraska	75.2	80
New Jersey	68.7	80
South Dakota	45.8	80
Tennessee	54.4	80
Illinois	95.5	78
West Virginia	72.6	77
Arkansas	37.4	75
Delaware	25.0	75
Mississippi	27.0	75
Minnesota	59.0	75
Missouri	85.8	74
Kentucky	66.1	70
New Mexico	57.6	70
Virginia	77.9	68
Colorado	89.8	59
Maryland	96.7	57
Pennsylvania	38.5	55
District of Columbia	100.0	20
Utah	61.2	15
Arizona	43.3	10

(a) USDC, Bureau of Foreign and Domestic Commerce, " Domestic Market Possibilities for Sales of Paints and Varnishes " (GPO, Washington, 1925), p. 20.

CHAPTER III

The position of shelter in family budgets in countries other than the United States is briefly as follows.

In Canada the percentage of the budget allocated to food is comparatively low and that for shelter fairly high. Up to a few years ago, the outlay for shelter was generally estimated at 22.5 per cent. This proportion was more or less representative of several other comparatively new countries, such as Australia, New Zealand, and the Argentine Republic, which, though distinctly modern, are still mainly agricultural communities. More recently, a revision of the Canadian budget placed the allowance for shelter at 18.5 per cent, or about the same as in the United States; the food ratio, however, was still estimated at 35 per cent. The old and new distributions of the Canadian budget are shown below: [1]

	Per Cent of Budget	
	Old budget	*New budget*
Food	35.0	35.0
Fuel and light	9.1	8.0
Housing	22.6	18.5
Clothing	14.3	18.5
Miscellaneous	19.0	20.0
	100.0	100.0

In Great Britain the relative cost of shelter appears to have risen slightly during the greater part of the Nineteenth Century. From 1900 to 1914 there was comparatively little change, and at the outbreak of the World War, it was generally agreed, it represented about one-sixth of the total expenditure of wage-earning families. There appears to be no authoritative distribution of the budget of British wage-earning families as a whole. Estimates of the proportion expended for food range all the way from 40 to 65 per cent or more, that for sundries from 4 to 15 per cent or even 20 per cent. From such conflicting data as are available we may conclude that an allowance of 54 per cent for food, 12 per cent for clothing, 16 per cent for shelter, 7 per cent for fuel and

[1] NICB, "The Cost of Living in Foreign Countries," 1927, p. 78.

light, and 11 per cent for sundries is fairly representative of the budgets of a large proportion of wage-earning families just prior to the World War.

TABLE K

MEDIAN MONTHLY RENTALS OF RENTED NON-FARM HOMES IN THE UNITED STATES, 1930 [a]

State	Median Monthly Rental Value Urban homes	Rural non-farm homes
New England		
Maine	$23.88	$14.08
New Hampshire	20.93	13.94
Vermont	24.19	13.34
Massachusetts	30.54	18.34
Rhode Island	24.99	14.12
Connecticut	29.70	21.96
Middle Atlantic		
New York	43.19	19.81
New Jersey	38.80	23.81
Pennsylvania	31.29	13.26
East North Central		
Ohio	32.12	14.58
Indiana	25.81	12.09
Illinois	43.32	13.45
Michigan	41.34	15.06
Wisconsin	33.45	14.79
West North Central		
Minnesota	30.34	15.67
Iowa	26.40	14.89
Missouri	28.97	11.45
North Dakota	34.81	15.74
South Dakota	29.26	16.15
Nebraska	27.89	15.65
Kansas	23.26	13.13
South Atlantic		
Delaware	29.86	14.69
Maryland	27.71	12.86
District of Columbia	44.28	———

(a) USDC, Bureau of the Census, "Population Bulletin, Families 1930" (GPO, Washington, 1933), p. 39.

TABLE K (*continued*)

State	Median Monthly Rental Value Urban homes	Rural non-farm homes
Virginia	$19.57	$— ⎤
West Virginia	26.15	— ⎟
North Carolina	15.75	— ⎟ *b*
South Carolina	11.32	— ⎟
Georgia	13.71	— ⎟
Florida	20.04	— ⎦
East South Central		⎤
Kentucky	20.77	— ⎟
Tennessee	16.94	— ⎟
Alabama	13.60	— ⎟ *b*
Mississippi	12.62	— ⎟
West South Central		⎟
Arkansas	16.45	— ⎟
Louisiana	19.66	— ⎦
Oklahoma	26.56	12.13
Texas	21.87	11.07
Mountain		
Montana	27.61	14.26
Idaho	24.20	13.55
Wyoming	26.73	15.23
Colorado	26.76	13.21
New Mexico	23.01	— *b*
Arizona	26.67	14.37
Utah	24.85	13.40
Nevada	33.15	14.73
Pacific		
Washington	27.37	13.74
Oregon	26.19	12.53
California	35.22	19.96

(*b*) Less than $10.

The abnormal conditions incident to the War, and especially the limitations imposed by restrictive rent legislation,[2] sharply reduced the ratio for shelter, which in many countries fell to 10 per cent or less. This does not mean that there was a corresponding reduction in the true cost of shelter, but simply that a part of

[2] For a discussion of such legislation, see Chapter XI.

TABLE L

ESTIMATES OF THE "PROBABLE USEFUL LIFE" AND OF RATES OF
DEPRECIATION FOR CERTAIN TYPES OF RESIDENTIAL BUILDINGS [a]

	Frame		Masonry, with frame interior		Masonry, slow-burning		Masonry, fireproof	
	Probable useful life	Depreciation rate	Probable useful life	Depreciation rate	Probable useful life	Depreciation rate	Probable useful life	Depreciation rate
	years	per cent	years	per cent	years	per cent	years	per cent
Single-family dwellings....	33	3	50	2	50	2	50	2
Two-, three-, or four-family dwellings....	30	$3\frac{1}{3}$	33	3	40	$2\frac{1}{2}$	45	$2\frac{1}{4}$
Row houses....	30	$3\frac{1}{3}$	35	$2\frac{6}{7}$	40	$2\frac{1}{2}$	45	$2\frac{1}{4}$
Apartments and flats without elevators....	25	4	30	$3\frac{1}{3}$	35	$2\frac{6}{7}$	40	$2\frac{1}{2}$
Hotels and elevator apartments.......	22	$4\frac{1}{2}$	25	4	30	$3\frac{1}{3}$	35	$2\frac{6}{7}$

(a) United States Treasury Department, Bureau of Internal Revenue, "Depreciation Studies, Preliminary Report" (GPO, Washington, 1931), p. 3.

the cost was borne by the public through subsidies or some other form of aid. No recent distribution of British budgets is available.[3]

Information on family budgets in France usually relates to individual cities or restricted areas. From such data it appears that the outlay for shelter, about 12 per cent, represents a considerably smaller proportion of the budget than in either Great Britain or Germany. That ratio is also indicated for Sweden by some cost-of-living studies, although others place it as high as 15 per cent. In Norway the ratio is considerably higher, approximating that for the United States. In Belgium the proportion is much lower, ranging below 10 per cent for wage-earning groups, according to most cost-of-living surveys.

In those oriental countries where the expenditure for food rep-

[3] Some years ago both employees and representatives of labor agreed that a new cost-of-living survey in Great Britain was not advisable under the conditions then prevailing.

resents a distinctly high percentage of the budget, the ratio for shelter often falls appreciably below the percentages for European countries; the high relative cost of food in the East is in the main at the expense of the sundries item.

TABLE M

ECONOMIC RENTAL OF SINGLE-FAMILY HOMES AND OF APARTMENT-HOUSES IN
THE UNITED STATES, 1913–1918, AS COMPUTED BY UNITED STATES
HOUSING CORPORATION [a]

Single-Family Homes

	Low	Median	High	Revised median
Maintenance	0.8	1.4	2.5	2.8
Service	0.3	0.5	0.6	1.0
Insurance	0.1	0.2	0.3	0.2
Taxes and assessments	1.1	1.4	1.9	1.4
Vacancies and bad accounts	0.5	0.7	1.0	0.7
Depreciation and obsolescence [b]	3.0	3.0	4.0	3.0
Administration	0.3	0.5	0.5	0.5
Total expense	6.1	7.7	10.8	9.6
Interest [b]	5.0	6.0	7.0	6.0
Gross rental, justified	11.1	13.7	17.8	15.6
Gross rental, obtained	7.5	9.2	11.0	13.8
Deficit from justified rental	3.6	4.5	6.8	1.8
Net earnings on investment	1.4	1.5	0.2	4.2

Apartments

	Low	Median	High	Revised median
Maintenance	1.2	1.9	4.9	3.8
Service	0.7	1.6	2.9	3.2
Insurance	0.1	0.2	0.3	0.2
Taxes and assessments	1.1	1.5	2.0	1.5
Vacancies and bad accounts	0.5	1.0	1.7	1.0
Depreciation and obsolescence [b]	3.0	3.5	4.5	3.5
Administration	0.4	0.5	0.6	1.0
Total expense	7.0	10.2	16.9	14.2
Interest [b]	5.0	6.0	8.0	6.0
Gross rental, justified	12.0	16.2	24.9	20.2
Gross rental, obtained	9.1	11.5	14.5	17.2
Deficit from justified rental	2.9	4.7	10.4	3.0
Net earnings on investment	2.1	1.3	2.4 [c]	3.0

(a) USDC, Bureau of Industrial Housing and Transportation, " United States Housing Corporation Report " (GPO, Washington, 1920), Vol. I, p. 47. The report stated that the results were based on past experience, and the revised median, not in the published report, was apparently intended to reflect conditions prevailing in 1920.

(b) Estimated and assumed.

(c) Apparently a deficit.

In Great Britain an economic rental is ordinarily reckoned at a somewhat lower percentage, frequently at about 10 per cent. While this may have been due at times in part to a lower rate of interest, apparently a more important factor is the smaller allowance for maintenance and depreciation charges in Great Britain, which in turn may be attributed to the predominance of brick construction already noted in Chapter II. One computation of an economic rental of a British cottage home is given in Table N; the item of local taxes given there is slightly larger than that used in the computation of the economic rental of American homes in Table M. The allowance for the other items, however, is appreciably smaller. The allowance of ½ of 1 per cent for sinking fund may be considered as representing depreciation. This may seem too low, but the life of a British house of brick is a good deal longer than that for an American frame house. If it be taken at seventy-five years, an allowance of ½ of 1 per cent yearly would completely amortize the original cost and leave a substantial amount for obsolescence. Much of the difference between the total economic rent in the United States and that of the British cottage is thus accounted for.

TABLE N

Economic Rental of a British Cottage Home, 1922 or 1923 [a]

	£	s.	d.	£	s.	d.	Per cent[b]
Interest on £75 at 6%	4	10	0				
Interest on £300 at 5½%	16	10	0	21	0	0	5.6
Sinking funds, £375 at ½% ...				1	17	6	0.5
Local taxes				10	0	0	2.67
Repairs				5	7	3	1.43
Insurance					5	3	0.07
Administration				2	2	6	0.57
Vacancies, etc.				1	12	6	0.43
				42	5	0	11.27

(a) Barnes, Harry: " Housing; The Facts and the Future " (Ernest Benn, Limited, London, 1923), p. 191.

(b) Reckoned on basis of total cost, including land.

CHAPTER IV

ORGANIZATIONAL DISABILITIES

Herbert Hoover [1]

Disability. "We have a larger proportion of adequate housing than any country in the world, but we still lag far behind our national ideals of homes for all our people. . . . There are problems of architecture, esthetic questions and questions of interior convenience, as well as problems of construction — all of which have large importance and enter into rural as well as urban homes."

Solution.[2] "The real solution probably lies in some radical departure in house construction and economics, as it does not appear to us that we are likely to have such relative readjustments as will correct this situation."

American Construction Council [3]

Disability. "Faulty engineering, unreliable architects, inexperienced and incompetent contractors, inferior grades of materials, poor mechanics, inadequate and poor inspection and other bad factors too frequently enter into building work. . . . Every element in the industry must bear its proportionate share of the blame for the vicious practices not infrequently found in building projects today, and for permitting practices within its ranks that do not measure up to proper standards."

Ernest J. P. Benn (author and economist) [4]

Disability. "In considering housing and building, it should always be remembered that the building trade is a protected trade.

[1] Address at opening session of the President's Conference on Home Building and Home Ownership, September 24, 1930 (New York Times, September 25, 1930.)

[2] Quoted (from a statement by Mr. Hoover in 1926) by Goodrich, Ernest P., "The Houses of the Future" (Building Age, September, 1930, p. 35).

[3] "Better Buildings." Quoted by Haber, William, "Industrial Relations in the Building Industry" (Harvard University Press, Cambridge, 1930), p. 578.

[4] "The Return to Laissez Faire" (D. Appleton and Company, New York, 1929), p. 145.

That is why building is something of a problem all over the world. There is an almost total absence of foreign competition in connection with building. Furthermore, the restraint of transport facilities gives a new share of protection to the building industry, and the builders of Essex are not in effective competition with the builders of Norfolk. This natural protection or shelter sets a premium on laziness and dilatory methods in the building trade the world over. It accounts for the almost total absence of machinery in the building trade, for the difficulties of mass production, and has the effect of keeping the whole of the human race not only short of houses but living all the time behind what is the standard of comfort known to be possible."

W. A. Starrett (*builder, president of the Thompson-Starrett Company* [5]

Disability. " When an industry ranks among the first two or three in a great industrial nation and no one engaged in it makes a living except indirectly, something is wrong. The answer is that building, while conducted with high technical efficiency, is, economically, the most disorganized major activity known to modern business, agriculture perhaps excepted. It is as fiercely competitive as the jungle and it is at the mercy of the customer to an extraordinary extent."

Ernst & Ernst (*certified public accountants*) [6]

Disability. " The construction industry . . . does not function as an industry. It is rather an agglomeration of industries, without proper unity, form, organization or coordination. To refer to it as a single industry . . . is a figure of speech. There are interests devoted to real estate development of various kinds; there are contractors for large projects; there are thousands of small contractors; there are material manufacturers and dealers, mortgage bankers and bond houses, building and loan associations, road builders, dam builders, architects, carpenters, electricians, paper hangers and ditch diggers. All are lumped under ' construction,' yet most have their separate organizations and interests, their diverse influences and directions. This is the curse of the industry.

[5] " Fierce Competition and Losses " (Quoted from the Saturday Evening Post by The Builder's Record, August, 1928, p. 2).

[6] " Ills of the Construction Industry " (Weekly Bulletin, April 28, 1931).

The fault lies mainly within the industry, and partly with the public, but it is remediable if given proper attention."

ARCHITECTURAL DISABILITIES

Howard T. Fisher (*architect*) [7]

Disability. "The house, among all the important tools of the twentieth century, is unique in the inefficiency and clumsiness of its design. The age that has produced the ocean liner, the skyscraper and the zeppelin has as yet done but little towards solving one of the most important and basic needs of mankind. . . .

"Of all the productions of our present day, the house alone is considered in terms of the past."

Solution. Modernization of plan, structure and mechanical equipment. Improved layout of rooms, changes in insulation and heating methods.

Ernest P. Goodrich (*engineer and author*) [8]

Disability. "Today new conveniences and equipment constitute 48 per cent of the total cost of the house: Heat and lighting, $8\frac{1}{2}$ per cent; floor finishes, 12 per cent; interior finish and decoration, 12 per cent; plumbing and utility construction, $15\frac{1}{2}$ per cent. But these new factors have not been efficiently incorporated into the design of the house."

Solution. "Improved construction methods are now commercially practical if the architect has initiative, a sympathetic understanding of construction problems and can design without adhering too closely to past construction methods."

CONSTRUCTION DISABILITIES

Engineering News-Record [9]

Disability. "It is no secret that the average house today is a shoddy affair, of high first cost, and soon reduced to a condition

[7] "New Elements in House Design" (The Architectural Record, November, 1929, p. 397).
[8] "Revolution in Housing Needed to Lower Costs" (New York Times, January 19, 1930).
[9] June 12, 1930 (editorial).

requiring constant maintenance; that it is built as it was built a great many years ago, by hand methods, with every piece cut in the field by men whose horizon is limited to the locality in which they live, whose training is of a sort that makes them impervious to the adaptation of new methods, whose financial capacity does not permit of modern research or study, in case they do recognize their value, and who themselves often are the victims of profiteering materials dealers. Today there are available better automobiles, better furniture and even better office buildings than were available only ten years ago, and they cost less. But the average house not only costs more today than it did in the days of our fathers and grandfathers, but it is an inferior product."

Solution. " The question is one of method primarily, and material only in second order. Wood, steel, gypsum, brick or concrete will each find its proper place in the scheme after the important matter of method has been disposed of.

" The basic need is to transform the house-building field from a poorly organized craft into an industry such as serves the office-building field, for instance. Transfer as many as possible of the cutting and fitting jobs to the shop, where they can be controlled and improved and lowered in cost; use those materials which modern research has developed, and use them in their proper place; reduce field labor costs to a minimum; and, finally, make a sincere effort to give the house purchaser a better structure at a reasonable cost.

" If engineers and industrialists would give to house building the thoughtful planning and technical foresight that they have lavished on other branches of industry, a remarkable renaissance would soon be under way. . . . Solving the house-building muddle is not a problem for citizens' committees, congressmen or philanthropists. It is up to the engineer, the organizer and the financier."

Ernest Flagg (architect) [10]

Disability. " For the last 300 or 400 years there has been no forward progress in house building. If one compares the frame

---

[10] " Reducing Costs by the Proper Designing of Houses," in " Housing Problems in America," 1923, Vol. IX, p. 96.

house of today with that of our ancestors who landed on these shores 300 years ago, there will appear little change. Except for heating, lighting and plumbing there has been no improvement. The design is generally not so good and the construction more flimsy. There is the same unhealthy cellar, the same waste of space, the same intolerable heat under the roof, the same difficulty to heat in winter and the same need for constant repairs."

Solution. Standardization of parts; use of a modular system; factory methods of production.

Robert P. Lamont (*when Secretary of Commerce*) [11]

Disability. " Without doubt the major obstacle to an extensive increase in home ownership in this country is financial. The traditional single-family house handed down from our ancestors costs too much for the wage-earner. Instead of taking thought to reduce that cost, as we have reduced the cost of the automobile, for instance, we have accepted the substitute multi-family dwelling, the tenement. That is not only social shortsightedness; it is economic shortsightedness. The market for good housing within the range of the poor man's pocketbook is the richest untapped market in the world."

Solution. " It would be a gratuitous reflection on modern science and engineering technique to suggest that the production of such housing is impossible. Until the last few years it has never been tried. Let the same initiative that produced the skyscraper be turned to the production of low-cost dwellings and the results will surprise a world bred in a tradition of housing that has not changed fundamentally in five thousand years. Awareness, housing-consciousness to replace the widespread apathy to housing — that is the first requisite."

Franklin D. Roosevelt (*when Governor of New York*) [12]

Disability. " There is no question that the recent rush to remedy a housing shortage in almost every state of the nation has resulted

[11] The President's Conference on Home Building and Home Ownership, Vol. IV, p. viii.

[12] Address before American Construction Council, May, 1925. (Quoted by William Haber: " Industrial Relations in the Building Industry," pp. 577–578.)

in the erection of buildings which either go up in smoke or fall apart during our lifetime. Up to 1915 the United States has had an unenviable reputation for its fire loss and for its annual repair bill caused by cheap and unenduring methods. Since 1915 our building methods have not improved — they have in thousands of instances deteriorated."

R. L. Davison (engineer and author) [13]

Disability. "One must face the fact that the great majority of houses are in reality not the well designed and well built houses of Colonial or English tradition suggested by the word home, but flimsily built boxes turned out by the mile by speculative builders without the benefit of an architect."

Solution. Formation of a central research organization to develop better methods of construction; substitution of new materials; thinner walls; better insulation methods.

Lawrence Veiller (secretary of the National Housing Association) [14]

Disability. "The great mass of houses in America, especially homes of working people, are built by speculative builders who seek to make a quick profit. Consequently, there is an incentive to slight the work, to build cheaply, to substitute inferior materials, and no incentive to good workmanship. They have little or no concern whether the house lasts a long time or soon needs repairs, for they will have sold the house long before that time and will have no concern with it. The more they can ' skin ' it, as the phrase goes, the more profit for them. As a result, the great mass of our houses in America are badly built. Many need repainting and repairs within a few months after the family has moved in. The plumbing wears out quickly, everything has to be renewed much sooner than it should; so that this kind of building is a very distinct discouragement to investment in a home on the part of the average man. This is undoubtedly one of the factors in the great increase in the number of rented homes in the United States in recent years."

[13] "New Construction Methods" (The Architectural Record, October, 1929, p. 384).
[14] "The Housing Problem in the United States" (National Housing Association Publications, New York, 1930), pp. 21–22.

Royal Barry Wills (architect) [15]

Disability. "Materials in themselves out of date are assembled at the site in a hit or miss fashion by skilled labor not properly directed or organized. Bricks are laid one upon another by hand, as they were when the Romans built their aqueducts. Wood is sawed and nailed by hand. Work that should be done under factory conditions is done on the job in the most expensive way possible."

MANAGEMENT DISABILITIES

Committee on Elimination of Waste, Federated American Engineering Societies [16]

Disability. "Yet it is a rare exception to find a construction job planned to co-ordinate the various divisions of work with the necessary materials. . . . The average contractor . . . largely regulates deliveries of materials by visits to the job, or through advices received from the job superintendent, stating that he will need this or that at such a time. Such a method of planning must result in delaying the job for want of material or at other times in burdening the job by an over-supply of material. Frequent lay-offs result in dissatisfaction of the workmen, loss of good mechanics, and higher labor turnover."

"Contractors, by failure to make thorough studies to determine the amount, type, and best location of plant and equipment, add another contribution to waste."

". . . General failure of the industry as a whole to develop and use a greater amount of mechanical equipment is an established fact. Greater strides have been made in almost every other industry in the application of mechanical means as labor-saving devices and production stimulants. . . ."

"In construction . . . a great deal of waste occurs in cutting lumber, breakage of brick, loss of mortar, and damages to materials. In scaffolding the waste of lumber is appalling. New lumber and thin boards are used until one-half of this is ruined before the finish of the job. . . ."

[15] "This Vicious Circle of Jobs by Hand" (The American Architect, June, 1930, p. 22).

[16] "Waste in Industry" (McGraw-Hill Book Co., Inc., New York, 1921), pp. 72–73, 78–79, 90.

F. H. McGraw and Johnson Heywood (authors) [17]

Disability. " There are something like 250,000 contractors in the United States. Most of them are small. A very large majority of them are ex-superintendents or ex-foremen who have succumbed to the common American urge to go into business for themselves. Many of them are excellent rule-of-thumb mechanics, some of them can handle men to advantage, but mighty few of them are executives of sufficient capacity to plan work accurately or of sufficient progressiveness to adopt modern labor-saving machines and methods. Then in some of the large cities there are real-estate operators with practically no knowledge of construction methods who undertake to do their own building. Instead of saving the contractor's profit, they generally succeed in wasting so much that it costs them far too much to build. It is chiefly this army of more or less incompetent contractors and real-estate men that gives the construction industry the reputation of being inefficient."

LABOR DISABILITIES

Brick and Clay Record [18]

Disability. " The productivity of labor in building material factories has been increased and the economies have been passed on to the consumer. But there the economy has stopped. The productivity of building labor has increased little and in many cases has decreased considerably. Brick layers, for instance, lay fewer brick per hour but they receive much more money for this labor.

" So we have the rather interesting spectacle of building labor standing practically alone of all trades in their lack of increased productivity, yet receiving for this inefficient labor a vastly higher return than other workmen."

" Building labor wages are too high. They are out of line with the wages in other industries and are putting the price of homes beyond the ability of the workingmen to pay."

Solution. " We believe that a substantial and general reduction in building labor would contribute tremendously to the prosperity of the country and of the building trades themselves."

[17] " Does Building Cost Too Much? " (World's Work, December, 1930, p. 43).

[18] " Building Labor Wages Are Too High " (Brick and Clay Record, October 21, 1930, p. 465).

Lawrence Veiller [19]

Disability. ". . . The cost of the average small home in the United States has risen 19 per cent during the past six years and is still climbing. The chief reason for this is in the high wages paid to labour in the building industry and in the manufacture of materials that enter into a building. One observer commenting on this said recently:

' The cost of housing through public indifference and timidities of politicians has been permitted to mount out of all proportion to other items in the cost of living. A thousand dollars worth of automobile or of many other articles today means more than twenty years ago, while a thousand dollars worth of building construction means considerably less.'

". . . In this increased cost of building labor many thoughtful observers find the reasons for the ever-mounting cost of building construction. This increase in the cost of building is out of keeping with increased costs of other commodities. Official figures show that since 1913, food prices in the country have increased by 59 per cent; clothing by 65 per cent; and fuel and light by 81 per cent; house furnishing by 105 per cent; while building costs increased by 110 per cent."

National City Bank of New York [20]

Disability. " Due principally to this high level of wages and to the many restrictions imposed by the unions which have prevented offsetting economies, building costs have been maintained at levels which not only act as a brake upon new construction but are responsible for the enormous increase in rents which bears so heavily upon the population of our cities, including the wage-earners themselves."

FINANCING DISABILITIES

Herbert Hoover [21]

Disability. " The finance of home building, especially for second mortgages, is the most backward segment of our whole credit sys-

[19] " The Town Planning Review," Vol. XIII, No. 4, December, 1929, p. 249.
[20] Monthly Circular, June, 1930.
[21] Address before Conference on Home Building and Home Ownership (New York Times, September 25, 1930).

tem. It is easier to borrow 85 per cent on an automobile and repay it on the installment plan than to buy a home on that basis — and generally the house requires a higher interest rate."

" The whole process of purchase and finance involves a ceremony like a treaty between governments, and yet the home is certainly as good collateral as an automobile; it depreciates more slowly, if at all. . . ."

Clyde A. Mann, (*Director of Certified Building Registry*) [22]

Disability. " Home building has been starved by the system of loans that disregarded differences in grade. The margin of safety necessary for the poorest has been exacted of quality construction — 50 to 60 per cent of a fair valuation. This has increased second mortgage needs at usurious interest and discounts and has increased the cost of the houses built, increased the costs both to the builder and to the buyer. A needless waste has put its chilling hand upon home building."

Solution. Certified construction.

LEGISLATIVE DISABILITIES

United States Senate, Committee on Reconstruction and Production [23]

Disability. " The building codes of the country have not been developed upon scientific data, but rather on compromises; they are not uniform in principle and in many instances involve an additional cost of construction without assuring more useful or more durable buildings."

United States Department of Commerce, Building Code Committee [24]

Disability. " Unless a building code is drafted with extreme care concerning the correctness of its numerous requirements and their relation to each other, obsolete provisions are apt to creep in, also unexpected applications develop which are objectionable and ex-

[22] " The Cost of Cheapness in Home Construction " (National Real Estate Journal, March 3, 1930).
[23] Quoted in Report of the Building Code Committee, July, 1922 (GPO, Washington, 1922), p. 1.
[24] Report of July, 1925 (GPO, Washington, 1925), pp. 17–18.

pensive. There is, furthermore, an essential difference between a building specification and a building code, based on the police power, which those who draft building codes frequently fail to appreciate. Codes written by competent architects and engineers often take the form of specifications for good practice instead of stating minimum safe limits."

Wilbur L. Cross (Governor of Connecticut) [25]

Disability. "The income of our towns and cities is now derived largely from a tax on real estate. This class of wealth, which represents less than 20 per cent of the total wealth of the State, is paying fully 60 per cent of the cost of our schools, and our town, county, and state governments. So large a tax on real estate not only affects the owner and the rent-payer; it also enters materially into the cost of the products of manufacturing concerns."

Building Investment [26]

Disability. "The increasing number of tax sales in the various counties of New York State is sufficient evidence of the toll being taken by high real estate taxes and their disastrous results. . . . The question is receiving serious consideration by the National Government and organizations interested in the economic and social welfare of the country. There can be little questioning of the fact that high taxes have discouraged home ownership and that a little relief on this score would prove quite stimulative to the home-owning movement."

National Association of Real Estate Boards [27]

Disability. "Archaic usury legislation keeps money from the second mortgage field, makes interest rates high because it is hard to get, and keeps many people from home-ownership."

Solution. "In 1929," according to Mr. Reep,[28] "American bankers, attorneys and experts on the land agree that the usury

[25] Message to Legislature of Connecticut (United States Daily, February 16, 1931, Supplement).
[26] "Real Estate Taxes: A Tariff in Restraint of Trade?" (Building Investment, February, 1931, pp. 29–30).
[27] Press Article 17, pp. 1 and 4.
[28] S. N. Reep, a prominent authority on home financing.

laws should be amended and that the maximum interest charges authorized by statute on second mortgage financing should be permitted to correspond, as nearly as can be ascertained, to the actual cost of that type of financing in various parts of the country, so that more capital will be attracted to this field and real estate made more liquid."

DISABILITIES DUE TO THE HOME-OWNER

William Haber (author) [29]

Disability. "The most important single agent in the building industry is the owner. His demand determines the kind and size of building and the time when it is to be begun and finished. His insistence that a structure be completed on a definite date is responsible for many wasteful competitive practices. The contractor can do little to correct bad policies, nor can he hold out against the exorbitant demands of labor or other groups, when he is confronted by the owner's insistence for a completed structure at a specified time, usually determined without much consideration for possible contingencies. . . .

"The attitude of the building owner and the contractor is one of total disregard for consequences. 'I want what I want when I want it,' has characterized their approach to the problem. All seek labor when labor is fully employed. Workers are rushed to finish a job and therefore must shirk on thoroughness or efficiency. When the peak is passed, the best mechanics are available; materials and equipment are idle. . . ."

James S. Taylor (Chief of the Division of Building and Housing, United States Department of Commerce) [30]

Disability. "Men are lured, by what seems attractive, to make important decisions, and live to regret their choice . . . many families would be better satisfied with their houses if they used more discrimination in picking out good ones, and did not 'fall' for showy features — or, in effect, demand them, even when they may have been provided at the expense of items they later find they

---

[29] "Industrial Relations in the Building Industry," pp. 51 and 96.

[30] "New Trends in Home Design" (Address before National Association of Real Estate Boards, June 26, 1929, pp. 3, 9, and 10).

really need — or of shoddy structures that quickly deteriorate and multiply the owner's repair bills."

". . . The bathroom is one of the most conspicuous features of many new small houses. I recall one in a row house selling for less than six thousand dollars. Although small, it looked fit at least for a millionaire screen star, with its floor of black and white tile, buff colored tile wainscoting, special wallpaper showing sea scenes, and the built-in bathtub, with shower attachment, in a kind of alcove. The bathtub on legs is going out of style even in the lower priced new houses. . . . Of the houses covered in our survey, three fourths had tile floors in the bathroom, and about one half, tile wainscoting."

" I need not go into the growing part which electricity is playing in the home. You all know of its use for lighting, electric irons, toasters, refrigeration, operation of vacuum cleaners and washing machines, and most recently for heating by means of large hot water storage tanks which consume current, provided at special rates, during the hours after midnight when other power requirements are at a minimum. All this involves a more expensive wiring, and additional electric outlets, and leaves less of the owners' dollar for the structure of the house itself."

John M. Gries (former Chief of the Division of Building and Housing, United States Department of Commerce) [31]

Disability. " A survey shows 1112 different sizes, varieties and styles of [plumbers'] traps. It seems probable that these will be reduced to 117."

" At present [32] there are approximately 600 different sizes and styles of window sash. . . . To my mind it would seem that 150 different sizes and varieties would satisfy the desires of all designers and reduce very materially the stock which the retailer must carry."

Solution. Reduction in number of styles, sizes, etc.; development of new materials; standardization of window openings and of various parts; possibly elimination of the cellar.

[31] " New Materials, Processes and Standardization " (In " Housing Problems in America," 1923, Vol. IX, pp. 57–58).
[32] In 1923.

*Walter W. Hoops (Vice-president of Carrol-Dean Murphy,
   Inc.)* [33]

Disability. " If 95 per cent of all automobiles were built to
order . . . according to the owner's fancy . . . the automobile
industry . . . wouldn't be an industry. . . . Yet . . . the so-
called building industry is just such a non-industry . . . and
many of the difficulties to which it is recurrently subject arise because it is what it is."

Solution. Organization of great corporations, handling all
phases of the industry: construction, marketing, financing, etc.

International Housing Association [34]

Disability. " If we look back on the manner in which, since the
beginning of the 19th century, building has been carried on all the
world over, we shall find that in all parts of the globe people used
to have certain types of structure for dwellings of a certain kind,
types repeated a thousandfold with slight changes, i.e., with the
variations as to construction and material, due to local usages and
custom. Is it not strange that no objection to this was taken in
former times and that opposition came forward in our age of
rationalisation only? The same people who in their workshop or
factory are striving after the elimination of the slightest chance of
idle running, with a view to obtaining a maximum of output with
a minimum of effort, think they cannot follow that economic principle in the field of housing, because individuality might be sup-
pressed thereby."

GENERAL DISABILITIES

Ernest P. Goodrich (engineer and author) [35]

Disability. " Subdividers preserve the vicious, inherited tendency toward long narrow lots, which is wasteful of land and an
obstacle to the building of better homes."

" The process of producing houses is distributed through so
many agencies — the plumber, the carpenter, the electrician, the

[33] " Wanted — A Building Industry " (Brick and Clay Record, July 29,
1930, p. 156).
[34] " Housing Policy of Frankfort on the Main," p. 19.
[35] *Vide supra.*

hardware dealer, the glazier, the tinsmith, the mason, the brick-layer, the plasterer, the hod carrier, the laborer — that the pros-pect of success in trying to secure further piecemeal economies in connection with existing competitive methods is hopeless." "Health, safety, happiness, education and social progress are being sacrificed. . . . Satisfaction and happiness are sought out-side the home. . . . The high cost of homes . . . postpones mar-riage. It affects morals."

Solution. "The solution must be sought along sound economic lines and in scientific research. . . . The world is not going to reach a solution of its housing problems by feeding spoonfuls of State aid or private philanthropy to those who cannot afford to build, buy or rent decent homes at present costs. Charity will pro-vide only temporary relief."

Lewis Mumford (critic) [36]

Disability. "What we actually achieve in the shoddy industrial suburbs of Long Island City, Brooklyn, Detroit, Chicago, St. Louis, is only a hollow counterfeit, so badly built that the houses will require complete renovation before the last installment has been paid off; and often, as in Long Island City, with very genuine fire hazards and health hazards."

". . . Municipalities have permitted the subdivision and sale of land without adequate utilities — thus temporarily concealing the eventual costs of the isolated house; likewise . . . these munici-palities have permitted dangerous or short lived forms of con-struction and unhygienic designs."

Solution. "The alternative to such low-grade building, below every standard of honesty and technical decency, is group housing and community planning; for only by this means can we escape the waste of small-scale operations . . . a higher type of house can be created in row units or in apartments than can be conceived of at the same price level in separate units. . . ."

[36] "The Chance for Civilized Housing" (The New Republic, September 17, 1930, pp. 115–117).

SUMMARY OF DISABILITIES

I. *General*
Local nature
Complexity
Subcontracting evils: frequent failures
Irresponsible contractors
Sub-group consciousness
Irregular demand
Curtailment of construction in winter
Extensive use of credit
Owner's insistence on time limit
Owner's refusal to support contractor against demands of
labor

II. *Architectural*
Houses poorly designed
Accessories not efficiently incorporated into the structure
Lack of sufficient supervision
Vagueness in plans and specifications
Tradition over-emphasized
Larger projects preferred

III. *Constructional*
Dwelling-house industry backward
Hand methods: much material cut on the job
No economies of mass production
Few labor-saving devices
Shifting nature of work
Lack of scientific, coordinated effort
Shoddy construction
Needless weight of materials
Needlessly thick walls
Excessive cost
Lack of light and ventilation
Inflammable construction

IV. *Managerial*
Excessive number of contractors
Small size of average contracting concern
Many incompetent contractors
The speculative builder
Lack of efficient routing
Lack of proper equipment

Waste of materials
Use of inferior material
Seasonal unemployment

V. *Labor*
Large number of crafts
Frequent disputes
Jurisdictional disputes
Use of skilled labor for unskilled work
Reduction in skill
High wages

VI. *Financial*
Inadequate organization
Obsolete laws
High cost of second-mortgage funds
Failure of lending agencies to consider quality
Usury laws
Heavy foreclosure costs

VII. *Legislative*
Building codes unscientific, excessive, chaotic
Complicated and expensive administration
Large proportion of taxes derived from real estate
High taxes discouraging to home ownership

VIII. *Attitude of Consumer*
Tendency of purchaser to exceed his means
Concentration of leasing dates
Expenditures for automobiles, recreation, etc., placed ahead
of outlay for shelter
Owner's insistence on individuality of design
Emphasis on non-essentials
Demand for expensive fads and novelties
Excessive number of styles, types, sizes, etc.

IX. *Miscellaneous*
Wasteful subdivision methods
Building material dealers not interested in reducing costs
Decline in quality
Lack of proper oversight by municipalities
Accidents

CHAPTER V

EQUIPMENT AND OPERATIONS OF THE GENERAL CONTRACTOR

Equipment

1. For layout of lines and grades
    Transit or level, rod.
    Sledge hammer, axe, hammer, nails.
    String, stakes, and batter boards.
2. Excavating equipment
    Shovels, picks, wheelbarrows, chains and drag, scraper; axe and
        saw for trees, shrubs, roots.
    Trucks.
    Pumping equipment, either hand or power type.
3. Concrete equipment
    Mixer, barrows, hose, water barrel, pails.
    Reinforcing rod-cutting tool.
4. Forms
    Wire cutters, form oil and brush for applying.
    Form lumber; if new material, it is reused for other structural
        parts of the building, or may be taken from contractor's yard
        stock, especially supports and braces, which are reused several
        times.
5. Staging
    Staging lumber, horses, brackets.
    Ladders, rope, nails, bolts.
    Runways for concrete foundation wall work.
    Platform at mixer.
6. Construction sheds
    Field office and material shed; doors, sash, roofing.
    Bench, shelves, racks.
    Temporary telephone and wiring; gong for telephone.
    Temporary electric light and power line.
    Stove to heat office (if in winter).
    Privy.
7. First-aid kit
8. Electric power tools
    Saw, floor-sander.
9. Small truck for getting miscellaneous material to job and for trans-
        portation of workmen.

10. Tarpaulins for covering materials.
11. Time cards, job records, etc.
12. Miscellaneous
      Hinges and padlocks for temporary doors.
      Wire brush for concrete surfaces.
      Paint and brush for steel and ironwork field coat.
      Asphaltum paint for wood sills, columns, etc., in contact with concrete; brush for same.
      White lead for exterior woodwork points.
      Broom, sponge, pail; shovels for snow.
      Sandpaper, putty, glue.
      Building paper for protection purposes.
      Cloth screens for temporary window closing during plastering.
      Straw and canvas for protecting new masonry and concrete work from cold and rain.

Operations

1. Layout and excavating
      a. Staking out; lines and levels.
      b. Hand labor:
            Stripping loam.
            Excavating trenches, etc.
      c. Backfill and rough grading.
      d. Dry wells and connections to roof leaders.
      e. Septic tank (or sewer), dry wells, and connections.
      f. Water supply, temporary and permanent.
      g. Driveway excavating, cinder fill.
      h. Gas supply to house.
2. Foundation work
      a. Wood forms.
      b. Concrete footings and walls.
      c. Waterproofing.
      d. Inserts and openings, such as bolts for sills, openings for sewer, water, gas service pipes.
      e. Concrete floors.
      f. Foundations for chimney, boiler, columns, steps, etc.
      g. Retaining walls.
      h. Cellar area window units, to be built in.
3. Framing
      a. Iron columns, steel girders, steel framing work.
      b. Wood frame and boarding, rough stairs, partitions, etc.

4. Exterior finish
   a. Exterior trim.
   b. Window and door frames, sash, louvres, blinds.
   c. Steel sash for garage.
   d. Porch and piazza columns, railings, etc.
       Porch and piazza ceilings.
   e. Wall covering; waterproof paper, clapboards, special board-
       ing.
   f. Garage doors and fittings.
   g. Metal flashing in connection with carpentry work.
   h. Glass and glazing:
       Of steel sash.
       Of broken panes.
5. Insulation
   a. Board type material put up by carpenters.
6. Grounds, strapping, and furring
   a. Blocking for fixtures.
   b. Cutting for plumbing and heating work.
7. Inside finish
   a. All wood trim, stair work, mantels, cabinets, paneling, doors.
   b. Application of all finish hardware.
8. Finish wood floors (sometimes sublet)
9. Underfloor for cork tile and linoleum floors
10. Miscellaneous
    a. Basement storeroom and shelves.
    b. Meter board.
    c. Underground garbage receiver.
    d. Whitewash cellar walls.

CONSTRUCTION MATERIAL PURCHASED BY THE GENERAL CONTRACTOR

1. Materials for forms
   Lumber, nails, tie wire, form oil.
2. Materials for concrete
   Cement, sand, stone, lime.
   Reinforcing rods.
3. Steel work
   Lally columns.
   Steel girders.
   Steel angle for garage door sill.
4. Wood frame
   All framing and boarding material.
   Spikes, nails, bolts, hangers.

5. Exterior wood trim and millwork
    General trim.
    Special detailed mouldings, columns, doorways, lattice, etc.
    Wood window frames and sash, blinds and shutters.
    Louvres.
    Steel windows, glass, putty.
    Door frames, garage door frame and doors, track, hardware.
    Nails, putty, white lead for joints.
6. Exterior wall covering
    Building papers.
    Siding and finish boards.
7. Insulating materials and nails
8. Grounds, blocking, furring, nails
9. Inside finish
    Trim, casings, etc.
    Stair work.
    Mantels.
    Cabinets, case work.
    Paneling.
    Doors, exterior and interior.
10. Finish floors
    Flooring material.
    Paper between floors.
11. Underfloor for cork tile and linoleum floors
    Gypsum board.
12. Miscellaneous
    Sheathing for platform over piazza flat roof.
    Cellar partition sheathing and framing.
    Cellar partition sheathed doors.
13. Material for dry wells and cesspools
    Concrete blocks, bricks and mortar, manhole cover.
    Drain tile, cement.
14. Material for septic tanks
    Septic tank (if purchased ready-made).
    If built at site: forms, cement, sand, gravel, reinforcing rods.
    Drain tile connections.
15. Filling of gravel or cinders
    For porch and piazza floor slabs.
    For garage floor.
    For driveway and walks.
16. Miscellaneous
    Form oil, form tie wire.

White lead for outside joints of woodwork.
Elastic cement for gutter joints and flashing.
Flashing (window and door head), copper strips bent to shape.
   Sheet lead over column caps on piazza and for joints in wood
     gutters.
   Lead goosenecks for wood gutters.
   Shelf over entrance doorway; copper in roll; copper nails.
Putty for steel sash glazing.
Putty for broken glass.
Whitewash for cellar walls.
17. All construction hardware
   Bolts for anchoring sills, basement, and garage door frames.
   Plates and anchors for steel girders.
   Joist hangers.
   Spikes, framing nails, board nails, form nails, floor nails, siding
     nails, lath nails, finish nails, $1\frac{1}{2}$-inch, 2-inch, $2\frac{1}{2}$-inch,
     $3\frac{1}{2}$-inch brads, tacks, screws.
18. Miscellaneous hardware not included in finish hardware
   Cellar window butts and fastenings.
   Bulkhead door hinges and bolt.
   Garage door track and hangers.
   Blind and shutter hardware.
   Iron pipe for closet poles.
19. Underground garbage receiver

SUBCONTRACTORS NECESSARY ON A TYPICAL HOUSE CONSTRUCTION

	Amount of
	subcontract
1. Excavating	
Steam shovel contractor	
Blasting rock	$ 180.00
2. Roofing and sheet metal work	
Slate roofs, tar and gravel flat roof decks, copper ⎫	
dormer roofs ⎬	1,087.00
Gutters and conductors, flashings ⎭	
3. Metal lath and plaster	1,092.00
4. Masonry	
Chimneys ⎫	
Incinerator ⎬	380.00
Firestopping ⎭	
Flagstone walks and steps	200.00
5. Ceramic tile work	200.00
6. Cork tile floors	75.00

7. Linoleum floors 90.00
8. Finish wood floors (sometimes done by general contractor) 200.00
9. Electric wiring, radio, telephone 280.00
10. Electric fixtures 250.00
11. Plumbing, heating, oil burner 3,100.00
12. Painting 625.00
13. Hardware 200.00
14. Shades and screens 240.00
15. Wallpapering 70.00
16. Weatherstripping 170.00
17. Finish grading 400.00
18. Landscape (planting of trees and shrubs) 250.00

EMPLOYERS' ORGANIZATIONS

A. Local Organizations

Builders' exchanges. These, which are among the earliest associations
of builders, are concerned with matters of daily routine, prices of
materials, credits, etc.; also with such matters as building codes,
mechanic's lien legislation, and accident prevention.

Master builders' associations. These are interested primarily in the
maintenance of high standards in the industry. They also deal
with building codes, credits, accident prevention, etc., usually in
cooperation with a local building congress, if there is one.

Building-trades employers' associations. Labor problems are the special
field of these organizations, particularly the making of agreements
with trade unions with respect to wages and hours of work. They
also are actively interested in plans for reducing the frequency of
strikes and jurisdictional disputes, and in local legislation.

Building congresses. These are distinguished from the preceding organizations in that they embrace all interests in the industry, including labor. They ordinarily do not deal with such matters as
wage agreements, but with broader issues, such as apprenticeship
problems, trade ethics, seasonal employment, accident prevention,
and other matters of *general* interest to the industry. A special
activity of some building congresses has been the promotion of
craftsmanship by awarding prizes or medals, or honorary membership in the congress, to workers showing exceptional skill in
their craft.

Associations of building-material manufacturers and dealers. These are
extremely common. They are especially interested in market conditions. Sometimes it has been charged that they have become
agencies for price maintenance.

B. National Organizations in Special Fields

National associations of employers in specific trades. These organizations are concerned mainly with trade practices, contract forms, and methods of estimating and bidding. An example is the National Association of Steam and Hot Water Fitters.

National associations of building-material manufacturers and dealers.[1] The purposes of these associations have been largely promotional. They frequently engage in joint research and in joint publication of its results. A local branch, having met a new problem, turns over its data to the central group, which allows all others to participate in the benefits of the solution. The associations also engage in joint publication of advertising matter promoting the use of the material in question, and such publication is of considerable value technically as well as serving to interest a wider public in a specific commodity.

National Association of Builders' Exchanges (Pittsburgh, Pa.). This organization, composed of local, state, and interstate builders' exchanges, is, like them, largely concerned with routine trade matters.

National Association of Building-Trades Employers (Cleveland, Ohio). This is composed of local associations of the same name, and like them is primarily concerned with wage agreements, hours of work, and methods for reducing the frequency of strikes and jurisdictional disputes. In a sense it is a counter-organization to the Building Trades Department of the American Federation of Labor.[2]

National Erectors' Association (New York, N. Y.). This organization is concerned almost exclusively with labor problems. In recent years it has been the aggressive champion of the open shop, and is thus distinctly different from other organizations already described which, ostensibly at least, maintain a neutral attitude on the question of union recognition.

Associated General Contractors of America (Washington, D. C.). As the name suggests, this is essentially an organization of *general*

---

[1] The names and addresses of a few of these organizations follow:

Associated Metal Lath Manufacturers, Inc.	Chicago, Ill.
Association of Plumbing and Heating Contractors	Kansas City, Mo.
Common Brick Manufacturers Association of America	Cleveland, Ohio
National Lumber Manufacturers Association	Washington, D. C.
National Builders' Supply Association	Detroit, Mich.
Portland Cement Association	Chicago, Ill.
Tile and Mantel Contractors Association of America	Rochester, N. Y.

[2] Haber, William, "Industrial Relations in the Building Industry" (Harvard University Press, Cambridge, 1930), p. 456.

contractors. Its primary object is the promotion of higher standards in the industry. It devotes much time to trade practices and codes of ethics; it is also actively interested in apprenticeship problems. It is not especially concerned with wage questions; on union matters it is presumably neutral, although many of its members operate on the closed-shop basis.

National Association of Building Owners and Managers (Chicago, Ill.). This organization occupies a specific and limited field, namely the financing, ownership, and operation of large office

TABLE O

PRINCIPAL INDUSTRIES OF THE UNITED STATES RANKED ACCORDING TO NUMBER
OF EMPLOYEES AND VALUE OF PRODUCTS OR SERVICE [a]

Industry	Employees	Annual value of products or service [b]	Value per employee [c]	Estimated investment [b]
1. Agriculture [d]	10,241,000	$16,963,000	$ 1,656	$57,000,000
2. Construction	3,051,000	7,000,000	2,294	——f
3. Railroads	2,184,000	7,396,000	3,386	27,800,000
4. Textiles	1,110,000	5,342,000	4,812	4,100,000
5. Machinery	858,000	5,020,000	5,851	——f
6. Lumber	474,000	2,254,000	4,755	8,000,000
7. Iron and steel	438,000	3,711,000	8,473	5,000,000
8. Automobiles	430,000	4,745,000	11,035	3,000,000
9. Oil	158,000	2,377,000	15,044	11,000,000
10. Coal [e]	748,000	1,727,000	2,309	2,500,000
11. Electricity	230,000	1,783,000	7,752	9,500,000
12. Clothing	466,000	3,239,000	6,951	1,000,000
13. Publishing	296,000	2,482,000	8,389	1,200,000
14. Telephone and telegraph	381,000	935,000	2,454	2,600,000
15. Meat	120,000	3,050,000	25,418	1,200,000
16. Rubber	141,000	1,255,000	8,901	1,000,000
17. Shoes	207,000	1,061,000	5,126	700,000
18. Baking	160,000	1,268,000	7,925	600,000
19. Paper	124,000	972,000	7,839	1,200,000
20. Tobacco	132,000	1,091,000	8,265	——f

(*a*) Compilation by Evans Clark in New York Times, March 25, 1928.

(*b*) In thousands of dollars.

(*c*) Computed from Mr. Clark's data.

(*d*) Although agriculture is broadly speaking an "industry," in recent statistical literature the term industry frequently is given a somewhat narrower definition.

(*e*) A better comparison would be with figures including all kinds of mining.

(*f*) No data.

buildings and large apartment buildings. It is not actively concerned with labor problems.

National Association of Real Estate Boards (Chicago, Ill.). This organization also operates in a special field, that of the realtor,
buying, selling, and renting real estate. It is largely concerned
with financial and legal problems. It maintains an extensive sta-

TABLE P

ESTIMATED PER-CAPITA EXPENDITURE FOR BUILDING IN THE UNITED STATES,
YEARLY, 1902–29

(In 1913 dollars)

Year	Estimate A[a]	Estimate B[b]	Year	Estimate A[a]	Estimate B[b]
1902	$26.5		1916	$28.0	$29.52
1903	25.2		1917	16.6	20.18
1904	29.4		1918	14.1	17.20
1905	37.7		1919	19.5	21.02
1906	35.6		1920	14.7	15.93
1907	30.5		1921	16.4	20.45
1908	27.4		1922	25.6	26.62
1909	35.8	$37.88	1923	26.2	25.28
1910	32.6	34.74	1924	27.8	27.84
1911	31.1	33.23	1925	29.4	32.54
1912	32.2	34.37	1926	30.3	32.22 [c]
1913	28.9	31.05	1927	30.5	33.30 [c]
1914	26.3	29.42	1928	31.4	34.88 [c]
1915	26.8	29.08	1929	26.2	

(a) Furnished by the Lehman Corporation, New York City.
(b) King, W. I., "The National Income and Its Purchasing Power" (National Bureau of Economic Research, Inc., New York, 1930), p. 336.
(c) Preliminary estimate.

tistical department and publishes the *National Real Estate Journal,* as well as various pamphlets and books on real estate matters.

C. National Organizations Representing the Industry as a Whole

National Congress of the Building and Construction Industry. Apparently the chief activity of this organization, formed in 1920, is to
foster the formation of *local* building congresses. It is an inclusive
organization, embracing labor, banking, and insurance interests,
and public officials, as well as contractors, manufacturers of building materials, and dealers. The general scope of its activities has
already been indicated under *Building congresses.*

American Construction Council (New York, N. Y.). Organized in
1922, this is an association of associations, and as such is intended
to embrace every interest in the building industry — architects,

TABLE Q

PERCENTAGE DISTRIBUTION OF ESTIMATED ANNUAL COST OF NEW BUILDING CONSTRUCTION FOR CITIES COVERED BY THE UNITED STATES BUREAU OF LABOR STATISTICS, BY TYPES OF DWELLINGS, 1922–1932

	1922	1923	1924	1925	1926	1927	1928	1929	1930	1931	1932
Residential buildings											
One-family dwellings	30.7	28.4	28.9	28.2	25.9	24.4	23.1	19.4	20.3	23.2	21.2
Two-family dwellings	9.6	11.7	11.4	8.5	6.9	6.4	4.9	3.7	3.6	3.5	2.4
One-family and two-family dwellings combined with stores	1.8	1.4	1.5	1.5	1.3	1.1	.9	.5	.5	.3	.4
Multi-family dwellings	17.2	17.8	17.4	18.6	21.9	22.7	25.1	18.4	12.8	11.8	8.1
Multi-family dwellings and stores combined	1.3	1.7	1.7	2.0	2.2	2.8	2.9	1.3	.8	.8	.1
Hotels	3.0	3.4	2.8	4.5	4.0	2.1	3.7	10.7	1.6	.2	(a)
Lodging houses	.1	(a)	(a)	(a)	(a)	(a)	(a)	(a)	.2	(a)	(a)
All other	1.0	.7	.8	1.3	1.1	.9	1.1	1.4	1.9	.9	.4
Total[b]	64.6	65.1	64.6	64.7	63.3	60.5	61.8	55.4	41.6	40.8	27.7
Non-residential buildings											
Amusement buildings	2.1	1.7	1.9	3.1	3.7	4.0	2.7	1.6	2.9	2.1	3.1
Churches	1.7	1.5	1.8	1.7	1.8	1.8	1.6	1.5	2.0	1.7	2.2
Factories and workshops	4.4	5.2	5.4	4.5	5.0	4.4	4.9	5.3	7.3	4.4	4.2
Public garages	1.3	1.7	2.5	2.2	2.1	2.3	2.3	1.8	1.8	1.0	.6
Private garages	3.0	3.6	3.1	2.3	2.2	2.0	1.8	1.8	2.2	2.1	2.6
Service stations	.3	.3	.3	.3	.4	.5	.5	.7	1.5	.9	1.7
Institutions	1.4	1.2	1.1	1.4	1.4	2.3	2.1	2.8	3.9	5.2	4.1
Office buildings	6.1	5.6	5.9	6.9	7.2	7.5	8.3	9.0	10.7	9.6	2.5
Public buildings	.8	.7	.9	.6	.9	1.5	.9	3.3	5.7	11.5	25.8
Public works	1.0	1.6	1.4	1.2	1.2	1.4	1.2	1.7	3.0	3.9	6.2
Schools and libraries	5.9	5.0	4.9	4.3	4.2	4.8	4.6	4.8	8.4	10.1	10.7
Sheds	.3	.3	.3	.2	.2	.2	.2	.2	.3	.3	.6
Stables and barns	.1	(a)	(a)	(a)	(a)	(a)	(a)	(a)	(a)	(a)	.1
Stores and warehouses	6.8	6.2	5.8	6.4	6.0	6.7	6.8	9.6	8.5	6.0	6.5
All other	.3	.2	.2	.2	.4	.2	.2	.3	.4	.4	1.3
Total[b]	35.4	34.9	35.4	35.3	36.7	39.5	38.2	44.6	58.4	59.2	72.3
Grand total	100.0	100.0	100.0	100.0	100.0	100.0	100.0	100.0	100.0	100.0	100.0

(1932 not included in the ten-year average given in Table 39)

(a) Less than 1/10 of 1%.

(b) These totals may be in error by 1/10 of 1%.

contractors, building-material manufacturers and dealers, banking, insurance and real estate interests, public officials, labor, and numerous others.

Its membership, and likewise its field, are closely similar to those of the building congress, but whereas the building congress movement functions mainly through local organizations, the American Construction Council aims to deal only with problems of national scope. A question concerning only a locality or a specific trade would be left to some other organization. The council aims to coordinate the activities of its member organizations rather than to attempt direct administration. Its work is largely educational.

It leaves such matters as wage agreements to other organizations and concentrates its effort on such issues as the elimination of unsound and unethical practices, and major sources of waste. It has accordingly devoted much attention to the promotion of sound and honest construction, and to the reduction of seasonal fluctuations in building activity. It has also been actively interested in problems arising out of apprenticeship.

TABLE R

DISTRIBUTION OF THE NUMBER OF REPORTS RECEIVED FROM ALL CLASSES OF CONTRACTORS IN CONNECTION WITH THE CENSUS OF CONSTRUCTION, 1929 [a]

State	Total number of reports received	Number Reporting Business Amounting to $25,000 and Over		Under $25,000 (Number)	Number Reporting per 100,000 Population	Contractors doing business of $25,000 and over
		Number	Per cent of total		All contractors	
United States	149,798	34,794	23.2	115,004	122.0	28.3
Alabama	628	192	30.6	436	23.7	7.3
Arizona	358	105	29.4	253	82.3	24.1
Arkansas	648	125	19.3	523	34.9	6.7
California	14,811	2,763	18.7	12,048	261.0	48.6
Colorado	1,490	197	13.2	1,293	144.0	19.0
Connecticut	4,862	860	17.7	4,002	302.7	53.4
Delaware	275	88	32.0	187	115.4	37.0
District of Columbia	836	310	37.1	526	171.7	63.7
Florida	1,473	253	17.2	1,220	100.5	17.2
Georgia	683	206	30.2	477	23.5	7.1
Idaho	325	36	11.1	289	73.1	8.1
Illinois	9,672	2,904	30.0	6,768	127.0	38.0
Indiana	3,757	776	20.6	2,981	116.0	24.0

(a) This includes all replies received up to and including January 15, 1931. Construction Section of Distribution Division, USBC.

TABLE R (continued)

State	Total number of reports received	Number Reporting Business Amounting to $25,000 and Over		Under $25,000 (Number)	Number Reporting per 100,000 Population	Contractors doing business of $25,000 and over
		Number	Per cent of total		All contractors	
Iowa	3,198	485	15.2	2,713	129.6	19.7
Kansas	1,616	325	20.1	1,291	86.0	17.3
Kentucky	1,659	356	21.4	1,303	63.5	13.6
Louisiana	830	218	26.3	612	39.5	10.4
Maine	893	147	16.5	746	112.0	18.4
Maryland	2,279	441	19.4	1,838	139.9	27.1
Massachusetts .	7,129	1,654	23.2	5,475	168.0	39.0
Michigan	7,274	1,599	22.0	5,675	150.0	33.0
Minnesota	2,922	685	23.4	2,237	114.0	26.8
Mississippi	461	104	22.6	357	22.9	5.2
Missouri	3,076	854	27.8	2,222	84.8	23.6
Montana	523	140	26.8	383	97.4	26.1
Nebraska	1,367	267	19.5	1,100	99.4	19.4
Nevada	155	23	14.9	132	170.3	25.3
New Hampshire	758	128	16.9	630	163.0	27.5
New Jersey ...	8,697	1,718	19.8	6,979	215.0	42.4
New Mexico ...	230	46	20.0	184	54.3	10.9
New York	21,277	6,160	29.0	15,067	169.0	48.9
North Carolina.	670	300	44.8	370	21.1	9.5
North Dakota .	537	111	20.7	426	79.0	16.3
Ohio	9,304	2,331	25.0	6,973	140.0	35.1
Oklahoma	1,189	324	27.2	865	49.5	13.5
Oregon	1,330	273	20.5	1,057	140.0	28.6
Pennsylvania ..	14,292	2,986	20.9	11,306	148.4	31.0
Rhode Island ..	1,226	239	19.4	987	178.5	34.7
South Carolina .	413	123	29.8	290	23.8	7.1
South Dakota ..	449	82	18.3	367	64.8	11.8
Tennessee	1,353	404	30.0	949	51.7	15.5
Texas	3,984	1,098	27.8	2,886	68.4	18.8
Utah	867	146	16.8	721	170.5	28.7
Vermont	340	64	18.8	276	94.8	17.8
Virginia	1,204	329	27.4	875	49.8	13.6
Washington ...	1,916	426	22.2	1,490	122.8	27.2
West Virginia .	982	198	20.2	784	56.9	11.5
Wisconsin	5,413	1,155	21.4	4,258	184.2	39.3
Wyoming	217	40	18.4	177	96.4	17.7

CHAPTER VII

TABLE S

Structure	1914	1920	1921	Average [b]
Excavation	2.0	1.6	1.9	1.8
Stone masonry	7.3	6.7	7.3	7.0
Brick masonry	11.3	11.5	13.6	12.3
Rough carpentry	12.8	15.7	11.5	13.6
Cement work	4.1	4.2	4.1	4.2
Cut stone	0.4	0.3	0.3	0.3
Structural steel	0.6	0.8	0.7	0.7
Roofing and spouting	2.5	2.0	2.3	2.2
Labor — general	1.2	0.8	1.0	1.0
Sheet metal work	1.7	1.7	1.8	1.7
Hardware — rough	0.5	0.5	0.5	0.5
Flue lining and crocks	0.1	0.1	0.2	0.2
Finish				
Finish carpentry	13.3	13.9	12.6	13.3
Plastering	5.3	6.3	5.6	5.9
Painting and glazing	5.0	3.7	4.5	4.2
Stairwork	1.9	2.7	2.6	2.5
Tile work	0.3	0.2	0.2	0.2
Cabinet work	1.1	0.9	0.8	0.9
Hardware — finish	0.5	0.6	0.7	0.6
Paperhanging and decorating	2.1	1.8	2.2	2.0
Art glass	0.4	0.2	0.3	0.3
Parquetry floor	2.4	2.4	2.7	2.5
Accessories				
Plumbing and gas fitting	8.4	9.0	9.2	8.9
Heating	8.3	7.2	7.6	7.5
Electric wiring	1.5	1.3	1.4	1.4
Lighting fixtures	2.2	1.5	1.8	1.7
Range and connection	1.1	1.1	1.4	1.2
Gas water heater and connection	0.6	0.6	0.5	0.6
Miscellaneous [c]				
Iron fence and clothes poles	0.8	0.5	0.5	0.6
Grading — general	0.2	0.1	0.1	0.1
Sodding and seeding	0.1	0.1	0.1	0.1
Numbering houses	[d]	[d]	[d]	[d]
	100	100	100	100

(a) " Proceedings of the Philadelphia and National Conferences on the Construction Industries " (issued in Philadelphia, April 15, 1921), p. 47. The allocation to structure, finish, accessories and miscellaneous was made by the authors.

(b) True average, based on actual amounts.

(c) Strictly speaking, part of cost of " home " rather than " house."

(d) — less than $\frac{1}{10}$ of 1%.

TABLE T

DISTRIBUTION OF CONSTRUCTION COSTS OF RESIDENTIAL BUILDING, BETWEEN MA-
TERIALS AND LABOR, IN 15 CITIES OF THE UNITED STATES IN 1931–1932,
BY PRINCIPAL OPERATIONS [a]

	Per cent of total cost	Percentage Division, by Principal Operations		
		Material	Labor	Total
Excavating and grading	1.3	1.5	98.5	100
Brickwork	14.8	58.4	41.6	100
Carpenter work	27.3	67.1	32.9	100
Tile work	3.5	56.0	44.0	100
Concrete work	11.7	63.5	36.5	100
Plastering and lathing	8.2	33.4	66.6	100
Painting	4.2	38.5	61.5	100
Papering	0.5	44.6	55.4	100
Roofing	1.8	67.7	32.3	100
Electric wiring and fixtures	4.5	64.0	36.0	100
Heating and ventilating	6.6	75.3	24.7	100
Plumbing	10.1	79.7	20.3	100
Miscellaneous	5.5	75.2	24.8	100
	100	62.7 [c]	37.3 [c]	100

SIMILAR DISTRIBUTION FOR A BRITISH COTTAGE, 1923 [b]

Bricklaying	44.3	66	34	100
Masonry	1.8	37	63	100
Carpentry	11.0	71	29	100
Joinery	18.1	37	63	100
Slating	4.1	78	22	100
Plumbing	3.5	72	28	100
Tinsmithing	2.7	75	25	100
Painting	4.5	36	64	100
Glazing	0.7	85	15	100
Plastering	8.2	51	49	100
Miscellaneous	1.1	50	50	100
	100	59	41	100

(a) USBLS, Monthly Labor Review, October, 1932, pp. 764, 766, and 769.
(b) Barnes, Harry, " Housing " (Ernest Benn, Ltd., London, 1923), p. 398.
(c) Weighted average.

CHANGES IN PRICES OF SPECIFIC BUILDING MATERIALS

In the case of lumber, there has been a more or less constant upward trend, due to the drain on the forests at a rate in excess of growth, and also to the accompanying increase in transportation costs due in part to the longer hauls to most markets.

Thus the Aldrich report on wholesale prices shows that between 1856 and 1891 the index number for plain white oak boards, first

TABLE U

PERCENTAGE DISTRIBUTION OF THE COST OF MATERIALS AND OF LABOR IN DWELLING-HOUSE CONSTRUCTION

A. United States

Material [a]	Per Cent of Total Cost of Materials	
	Frame house	Brick house
Lumber	45.0	25.9
Brick	4.2	23.9
Cement	3.5	3.5
Sand	2.4	2.8
Lime	2.2	2.9
Glass	2.3	2.4
Lath	2.6	1.4
Plumbing	10.3	11.4
Heating	8.4	8.1
Electric	3.6	3.7
Roofing	5.6	7.0
Finish hardware	2.5	2.5
Paint and varnish	4.0	2.9
Miscellaneous	3.4	1.6
Total	100.0	100.0

Labor [b]	Per Cent of Total Cost of Labor	
	Frame house	Brick house
Carpenters	49.6	32.2
Bricklayers	6.2	21.5
Hod carriers	2.2	6.7
Plasterers	7.9	8.8
Plumbers	8.7	7.6
Electricians	2.6	2.5
Painters	10.0	6.3
Common labor	6.3	9.9
All others	6.5	4.5
Total	100.0	100.0

(a) Lincoln, A. B., and Gayne, T. K., "Small House Construction Costs" (Home Owners' Institute, Inc., New York), p. 4.

(b) USDC, Division of Building and Housing (quoted in Housing Betterment, April, 1922, p. 236).

TABLE U (continued)

B. England — Cottage Type [c]

Operation	Materials Cost, Per Cent		Labor Cost, Per Cent	
	1901	1923	1901	1923
Bricklaying	50.3	49.4	37.2	37.0
Masonry	1.2	1.1	2.8	2.7
Carpentry	12.5	13.2	7.9	7.9
Joinery	11.0	11.5	28.1	27.8
Slating	5.3	5.5	2.0	2.1
Plumbing	5.0	4.1	2.4	2.4
Tinsmithing	4.4	3.4	1.6	1.6
Painting	2.9	2.7	6.4	7.0
Glazing	1.0	1.1	0.3	0.3
Plastering	5.5	7.1	9.9	9.9
Miscellaneous	0.9	0.9	1.4	1.4
Total	100.0	100.0	100.0	100.0

(c) Barnes, Harry, "Housing" (Ernest Benn, Ltd., London, 1923), pp. 397–398.

quality, 1 inch thick, rose from 100 to 318, and that for white pine boards, clear, extra, unplaned, from 100 to 183. In the same period the index for common building brick rose only from 91.4 (it was 103 in 1855) to 117. The index for lime during this period rose from 142 to 150. On the other hand, the index number for pine doors fell from 109 to 78, presumably reflecting the development of factory methods of production. The index for window glass, size 10 by 14, was somewhat lower in 1891 than it was in 1856, and the indices for several items such as carbonate of lead and putty were decidedly lower.[1]

From 1890 to the beginning of the World War, prices of nearly all items of lumber continued to rise. Prices of brick moved very irregularly but on the whole showed no advance for the period. Portland cement prices declined, the index dropping from 125 in 1895 to 100 in 1913. Plate glass showed a much sharper drop. The index for window glass rose from 82 in 1890 to 152 in 1901, declining to 100 in 1913.

[1] United States Senate Committee on Finance, "Wholesale Prices, Wages and Transportation 1893" (GPO, Washington, 1893), Part I, pp. 6–48.

TABLE V

Average Cost of New Houses Erected in the United States in or about 1840, by States [a]

State	Number of Houses Built			Number of men employed	Value of Construction	
	Brick and stone	Wooden	Total		Total [b]	Average per house [c]
Maine	34	1,674	1,708	2,482	$ 733,067	$ 429
New Hampshire	90	434	524	935	470,715	898
Massachusetts	324	1,249	1,573	2,947	2,767,134	1,759
Rhode Island	6	292	298	887	379,010	1,272
Connecticut	95	517	612	1,599	1,086,295	1,775
Vermont	72	468	540	912	344,896	639
New York	1,233	5,198	6,431	16,768	7,265,844	1,130
New Jersey	205	861	1,066	2,086	1,092,052	1,024
Pennsylvania	1,995	2,428	4,423	9,974	5,354,480	1,211
Delaware	47	104	151	299	145,850	965
Maryland	389	592	981	2,026	1,078,770	1,100
Virginia	402	2,604	3,006	4,694	1,367,393	455
North Carolina	38	1,822	1,860	1,707	410,264	220
South Carolina	111	1,594	1,705	2,398	1,527,576	896
Georgia	38	2,591	2,629	2,274	693,116	263
Alabama	67	472	539	882	739,871	1,373
Mississippi	144	2,247	2,391	2,487	1,175,513	492
Louisiana	248	619	867	1,484	2,736,944	3,157
Tennessee	193	1,098	1,291	1,467	427,402	332

TABLE V (continued)

State	Number of Houses Built			Number of men employed	Value of Construction	
	Brick and stone	Wooden	Total		Total[b]	Average per house[c]
Kentucky	485	1,757	2,242	2,883	1,039,172	465
Ohio	970	2,764	3,734	6,060	3,776,823	1,012
Indiana	346	4,270	4,616	5,519	1,241,312	269
Illinois	334	4,133	4,467	5,737	2,065,255	462
Missouri	413	2,002	2,615	1,966	1,441,573	551
Arkansas	21	1,083	1,104	1,251	1,141,174	1,034
Michigan	39	1,280	1,319	1,978	571,005	433
Florida Territory ...	9	306	315	689	327,913	1,041
Wisconsin Territory ...	7	509	516	644	212,085	411
Iowa Territory	14	483	497	324	135,987	274
District of Columbia ...	60	33	93	142	168,910	1,816
Total	8,429	45,684	54,113	85,501	$41,917,401	$ 774

(a) USDS, "Compendium of the Enumeration of the Inhabitants and Statistics of the United States as obtained at the Department of State, from the Returns of the Sixth Census (1840) " (Thomas Allen, Washington, 1841), p. 364.
(b) Presumably the cost.
(c) Computed by the authors.

TABLE W

INDEX NUMBERS OF GENERAL WHOLESALE PRICES, BUILDING-MATERIAL PRICES, AND WAGE RATES IN THE BUILDING TRADES, UNITED STATES, 1840–1932

(1913 = 100)

(For description of index numbers see note at end of table.)

Year	General wholesale prices	Building-material prices	Building-trade wages	Building costs, industrial frame type (eastern cities)
1840	103	73	29	
1841	102	74	29	
1842	95	72	29	
1843	89	70	29	
1844	89	69	29	
1845	90	71	29	
1846	93	71	30	
1847	93	72	31	
1848	89	70	31	
1849	87	65	30	
1850	90	68	29	
1851	93	65	30	
1852	90	67	30	58
1853	96	69	30	59
1854	99	76	31	62
1855	99	69	32	53
1856	99	69	32	54
1857	99	70	33	58
1858	89	69	32	53
1859	88	66	34	54
1860	88	67	34	57
1861	88	73	34	58
1862	103	100	36	61
1863	130	118	40	75
1864	167	148	50	86
1865	190	121	56	92
1866	168	125	57	95
1867	151	119	63	96
1868	142	116	63	96
1869	135	111	64	96
1870	125	109	63	89
1871	119	101	62	93
1872	122	111	62	92
1873	121	115	60	92
1874	117	103	60	87
1875	112	96	57	77
1876	104	92	53	76
1877	97	84	50	70
1878	89	78	48	67
1879	85	77	46	64

TABLE W (*continued*)

INDEX NUMBERS OF GENERAL WHOLESALE PRICES, BUILDING-MATERIAL PRICES,
AND WAGE RATES IN THE BUILDING TRADES, UNITED STATES, 1840–1932

(1913 = 100)

Year	General wholesale prices	Building-material prices	Building-trade wages	Building costs, industrial frame type (eastern cities)
1880	94	87	48	68
1881	93	88	54	71
1882	95	92	56	77
1883	93	90	56	75
1884	87	86	57	68
1885	82	84	57	68
1886	81	86	57	71
1887	81	84	57	71
1888	83	83	60	70
1889	83	83	57	69
1890	81	82½ a	58	68
1891	80	78	59	66
1892	75	74	60	66
1893	77	73	60	65
1894	69	70	59	65
1895	70	68	60	64
1896	67	69	60	63
1897	67	66	61	61
1898	70	70	62	62
1899	75	77	63	68
1900	81	81	66	74
1901	79	78	69	77
1902	84	80	73	80
1903	86	82	77	82
1904	86	79	79	84
1905	86	85	82	87
1906	89	95	86	95
1907	94	100	90	96
1908	90	92	91	91
1909	97	95	92	94
1910	101	98	94	96
1911	93	98	96	97
1912	99	99	98	99
1913	100	100	100	100
1914	98	93	102	97
1915	100	94	103	98
1916	122	119	106	107
1917	168	156	113	132
1918	188	174	125	163
1919	199	204	145	210

TABLE W (continued)

Index Numbers of General Wholesale Prices, Building-Material Prices, and Wage Rates in the Building Trades, United States, 1840-1932

(1913 = 100)

Year	General wholesale prices	Building-material prices	Building-trade wages	Building costs, industrial frame type (eastern cities)
1920	221	265	197	268
1921	140	172	200	198
1922	139	172	188	189
1923	144	192	207	210
1924	141	180	224	208
1925	149	179	233	208
1926	143	176	248	212
1927	137	165	257	212
1928	140	165	258	212
1929	138	171	262	213
1930	124	159	273	208
1931	102	137	276	177 b
1932	93	126	235	157 b

(a) This figure is given with fraction, as it was used in splicing the USBLS index from 1890 to the index taken from the Aldrich reports. See Table Y.

(b) Approximate.

Explanatory Memorandum:

General wholesale price index from 1840 to 1913. This is the index of the USBLS on a 1913 base. Beginning with 1913 it is the USBLS index transferred from a 1926 base to a 1913 base. In adopting its new base year, the USBLS also greatly enlarged its list of commodities.

Building-material price index. This is an approximate index constructed by splicing the index numbers as found in the Aldrich (Senate Finance Committee) report with those of the USBLS from 1890 on, putting them all on a 1913 base. Such splicing of index numbers is not altogether satisfactory, but it is believed that the index thus constructed is reasonably accurate, perhaps as accurate as the original data.

Building-trades wage index. The actual rates of wages with an explanation of the way they were obtained can be found in Table Y.

Building cost index. This is the index of the American Appraisal Company for eastern cities. An index for the entire country could have been employed, but in view of the fact that the western sections of the country had not been developed during the early years covered by this table, an index for eastern cities seemed somewhat better. For the years 1931 and 1932 a figure for eastern cities was not available, but was approximated from data for eastern states.

During and after the War, prices of nearly all building materials rose violently, reaching a peak in most cases in 1920 or 1921. The index for white pine boards (No. 2 barn) rose from 100 in 1913 to 277½ in 1920, that for common brick from 100 to 333, and that for Portland cement from 100 to 178. Similar advances in numerous other products could be cited.[2]

The decline in building-material prices in the past few years has been fairly general.

TABLE X

ESTIMATED AVERAGE HOURLY EARNINGS IN VARIOUS INDUSTRIES IN THE UNITED STATES, 1890–1926 [a]

Year	Build- ing trades	Metal trades	Coal mining (Bitum.)	Boots and shoes	Cotton goods	All mfg.	Un- skilled labor (Prob- able)	All in- dustries
1890	.341	.319	.180	.169	.097	.199	.148	.211
1891	.341	.313	.169	.167	.095	.202	.150	.213
1892	.348	.323	.179	.171	.095	.203	.149	.215
1893	.347	.322	.188	.173	.101	.205	.149	.216
1894	.339	.312	.171	.171	.095	.200	.147	.211
1895	.341	.313	.158	.173	.094	.200	.146	.210
1896	.343	.317	.147	.172	.099	.205	.147	.213
1897	.346	.317	.138	.173	.096	.203	.148	.212
1898	.348	.316	.170	.173	.093	.204	.149	.215
1899	.361	.322	.185	.175	.092	.209	.149	.220
1900	.374	.332	.204	.178	.103	.216	.151	.228
1901	.391	.340	.231	.178	.104	.219	.157	.235
1902	.413	.352	.244	.186	.107	.227	.161	.244
1903	.436	.363	.267	.195	.111	.236	.165	.255
1904	.443	.364	.271	.200	.109	.236	.167	.257
1905	.454	.366	.276	.204	.111	.239	.169	.261
1906	.481	.378	.293	.207	.120	.248	.175	.272
1907	.498	.389	.288	.216	.135	.257	.182	.281
1908	.505	.367	.293	.212	.134	.250	.181	.279
1909	.510	.369	.292	.220	.130	.252	.187	.282
1910	.520	.386	.299	.219	.133	.260	.188	.288
1911	.531	.396	.305	.222	.135	.263	.191	.293
1912	.544	.399	.320	.223	.148	.274	.195	.302
1913	.557	.406	.316	.241	.149	.285	.204	.313
1914	.567	.413	.323	.243	.153	.287	.207	.316
1915	.569	.413	.337	.237	.158	.287	.214	.319
1916	.587	.455	.379	.259	.179	.320	.237	.348
1917	.624	.504	.484	.287	.213	.364	.286	.394
1918	.684	.663	.599	.336	.267	.448	.395	.482
1919	.780	.747	.699	.449	.338	.529	.440	.558
1920	1.052	.875	.784	.559	.480	.663	.475	.688
1921	1.076	.855	.846	.529	.350	.607	.370	.640
1922	1.006	.797	.834	.501	.330	.574	.360	.608
1923	1.107	.840	.864	.523	.371	.620	.407	.662
1924	1.188	.887	.811	.516	.372	.636	.413	.683
1925	1.229	.921	.724	.513	.350	.645	.427	.696
1926	1.313	.961	.719	.528	.328	.647	.433	.712

(a) Douglas, Paul H., "Real Wages in the United States, 1890–1926" (The Pollak Foundation, Newton, Massachusetts, 1930), pp. 96, 101, 108, 135, 152, 182, 205. In this connection, see Chart 54.

2 USBLS, "Wholesale Prices 1890–1926" (GPO, Washington, 1927), pp. 158–170.

TABLE Y

ESTIMATED APPROXIMATE HOURLY WAGE RATES OF BUILDING-TRADES WORKERS
IN THE UNITED STATES, 1840–1932

Caution. These figures are intended to indicate the trend of wage rates over considerable periods, and may be inaccurate for any given year. For sources, see footnote.

1840–1889

Year	Hourly Rate A	Hourly Rate B	Year	Hourly Rate A	Hourly Rate B
1840	$ .148	$ .137	1865	$ .290	$ .262
1841	.148	.144	1866	.295	.314
1842	.150	.147	1867	.322	.366
1843	.147	.155	1868	.322	.348
1844	.148	.160	1869	.329	.389
1845	.150	.159			
1846	.154	.147	1870	.322	.319
1847	.161	.149	1871	.317	.317
1848	.160	.149	1872	.318	.313
1849	.156	.151	1873	.311	.315
			1874	.309	.294
1850	.148	.162	1875	.294	.286
1851	.153	.160	1876	.275	.266
1852	.154	.160	1877	.254	.235
1853	.157	.169	1878	.246	.244
1854	.162	.170	1879	.238	.264
1855	.166	.171			
1856	.168	.168	1880	.247	.261
1857	.169	.171	1881	.278	.276
1858	.166	.158	1882	.287	.296
1859	.175	.163	1883	.288	.302
			1884	.292	.326
1860	.174	.178	1885	.295	.307
1861	.174	.177	1886	.296	.332
1862	.185	.184	1887	.295	.316
1863	.208	.201	1888	.311	.298
1864	.250	.254	1889	.295	.365

A — From 1840 to 1889 the figures were obtained by translating the index numbers given in the Aldrich (Senate Finance Committee) Report into actual rates. This method is admittedly somewhat unsatisfactory but should indicate the general trend ("Wholesale Prices, Wages and Transportation," GPO, Washington, 1893, Part I, p. 173).

B — These are simple averages for five trades — bricklayers, carpenters and joiners, painters, and plasterers (from 1850 on), and laborers — as computed by us from *daily* rates quoted in the report of the USBLS, " History of Wages in the United States from Colonial Times " for the State of New York. Figures which cover only five occupations in a single state are not altogether satisfactory; the basic data themselves are more or less uncertain. The two sets of figures together, however, give an approximation of the trend.

TABLE Y (*continued*)

ESTIMATED APPROXIMATE HOURLY WAGE RATES OF BUILDING-TRADES WORKERS
IN THE UNITED STATES, 1840–1932

1890–1932

	C Authors' computation	D Douglas' computation		C Authors' computation	D Douglas' computation
Year			Year		
1890	$ .300	$ .341	1912	$ .502 a	$ .544
1891	.303	.341	1913	.515 a	.557
1892	.309	.348	1914	.530	.567
1893	.309	.347	1915	.530	.569
1894	.303	.339	1916	.550	.587
1895	.306	.341	1917	.580	.624
1896	.310	.343	1918	.650	.684
1897	.314	.346	1919	.750	.780
1898	.319	.348			
1899	.327	.361	1920	1.02	1.052
			1921	1.03	1.076
1900	.341	.374	1922	.96	1.006
1901	.355	.391	1923	1.07	1.107
1902	.375	.413	1924	1.15	1.188
1903	.394	.436	1925	1.20	1.229
1904	.405 a	.443	1926	1.28	1.313
1905	.422 a	.454	1927	1.32	1.352
1906	.440 a	.481	1928	1.33	1.359
1907	.461 a	.498	1929	1.35	
1908	.468 a	.505			
1909	.473 a	.510	1930	1.41	
			1931	1.43	
1910	.486 a	.520	1932	1.22	
1911	.494 a	.531			

(*a*) Interpolated.

From 1890 to 1903 the rates in column C are taken from USBL reports; from 1904 to 1912 they have been approximated by using the USBLS index for union rates in general as a basis; from 1913 to 1927, they are taken from the NBER report on " Recent Economic Changes," Vol. I, p. 435; since 1927 from the Monthly Labor Review.

Rates in column D are from Paul H. Douglas' book " Real Wages in the United States, 1890–1926 " published by the Pollak Foundation, Newton, Massachusetts, p. 135, down to 1926; from 1926 to 1928, from Paul H. Douglas, "Movement of Money and Real Earnings in the U. S., 1926–1928 " (University of Chicago Studies in Business Administration, 1930, p. 32).

TABLE Z

AVERAGE HOURLY RATES OF WAGES IN THE BUILDING TRADES OF THE
UNITED STATES AND GREAT BRITAIN, 1914–1932

	United States [a]	Great Britain [b] (pence)	
1914	$0.53	8.7	$0.17
1915	.53	9.0	.18
1916	.55	9.7	.19
1917	.58	11.7	.23
1918	.65	15.9	.32
1919	.75	20.1	.40
1920	1.02	26.4	.53
1921	1.03	22.6	.45
1922	.96	18.2	.36
1923	1.07	17.3	.35
1924	1.15	18.4	.37
1925	1.20	18.4	.37
1926	1.28	18.5	.37
1927	1.32	18.5	.37
1928	1.33	18.1	.36
1929	1.35	18.0	.36
1930	1.41	17.6	.35
1931	1.43	17.2	.34
1932	1.22	16.7	.33

(a) For the sources of these figures, see footnote to Table Y, p. 574.

(b) 1914 through 1927, Ministry of Labour, " Nineteenth Abstract of Labour Statistics of the United Kingdom " (His Majesty's Stationery Office, London, 1928), pp. 100–101.

1928 through 1930, Ministry of Labour, " Twentieth Abstract of Labour Statistics of the United Kingdom " (His Majesty's Stationery Office, London, 1931), p. 97.

1931, Board of Trade, " Statistical Abstract of the United Kingdom " (His Majesty's Stationery Office, London, 1933), p. 117.

1932, Ministry of Labour, " Ministry of Labour Gazette," February, 1933, p. 42.

Rates converted from pence into cents on basis of 1d. = 2 cents. In computing the British averages, the average hourly rate for six skilled occupations (bricklayers, masons, carpenters and joiners, plasterers, plumbers, and painters) was given a weight of 70 per cent and that for laborers a weight of 30 per cent. British rates are those prevailing on December 31 in each year.

TABLE AA

COURSE OF ACTUAL HOURLY WAGE RATES IN THE BUILDING TRADES,
GREAT BRITAIN, 1914–1932 [a]

(In pence)

Trade	August 4, 1914	December 31, 1920	December 31, 1932	Per cent increase, 1914–1932
Bricklayers	9.9	27.5	18.1	83
Masons	9.8	27.5	18.1	85
Carpenters and joiners	9.8	27.4	18.1	85
Plumbers	9.6	27.8	18.1	89
Plasterers	9.7	27.5	18.3	89
Painters	8.8	27.1	18.0	105
Laborers	6.6	23.8	13.5	105

NOTE. In the early part of 1933, hourly rates in thirty-six of the thirty-nine towns included in the above averages were reduced by about ½d. per hour for skilled workers and ¼d. for laborers.

(a) "The Ministry of Labour Gazette" (Great Britain), February, 1921, p. 62, and February, 1933, p. 42.

CHAPTER IX

A list of the states having statutory requirements for the registration of architects, with their administering boards, is here presented:[a]

State	Date of act	Administering board
Alabama	1931	State Board of Registration of Architects
Arizona	1921	State Board of Registration for Architects, Engineers, Land Surveyors and Assayers
California	1901	State Board of Architectural Examiners
Colorado		State Board of Examiners of Architects
District of Columbia	1924	Board of Examiners and Registrars of Architects
Florida	1915	State Board of Architecture
Georgia	1919	State Board for the Examination and Registration of Architects
Idaho	1929	Department of Law Enforcement
Illinois	1927	Department of Registration and Education — Division of Registration (Examining Committee)
Indiana	1929	State Board of Registration for Architects
Iowa	1927	State Board of Architectural Examiners
Kentucky	1930	State Board of Examiners and Registration of Architects
Louisiana	1910	State Board of Architectural Examiners
Michigan	1919	State Board of Examiners for the Registration of Architects, Engineers, and Surveyors
Minnesota	1921	State Board of Registration for Architects, Engineers, and Land Surveyors
Mississippi		State Board of Architecture
Montana	1917	State Board of Architectural Examiners
New Jersey		State Board of Architects
New Mexico	1931	State Board of Examiners for Architects

(a) Table based on data supplied by Pencil Points Press, Inc., New York City.

State	Date of act	Administering board
New York	1910	State Board of Examiners and Registration of Architects
North Carolina	1915	State Board of Architectural Examination and Registration
North Dakota	1919	State Board of Architecture
Ohio	1910	State Board of Examiners of Architects
Oklahoma	1925	State Board of Examiners of Architects
Oregon	1919	State Board of Architect Examiners
Pennsylvania	1919	State Board of Examiners of Architects
South Carolina	1917	State Board of Architectural Examiners
South Dakota	1925	State Board of Engineering and Architectural Examiners
Tennessee	1921	State Board of Architectural and Engineering Examiners
Utah	1927	Department of Registration and Education
Virginia	1925	State Board for Examination and Certification of Professional Engineers, Architects, and Land Surveyors
Washington	1921	Department of Licenses
West Virginia	1921	State Board of Examiners and Registration of Architects
Wisconsin	1925	Board of Examiners of Architects and Civil Engineers

In general, such legislation is for the expressed purpose of " safeguarding life, health and property." As a rule the laws forbid the use of the title " architect " or " registered architect " where this indicates a willingness to accept a fee for services, unless the legal requirements have been complied with. The commonest requirements are the passing of an examination or other evidence of competency, registration with the proper state board, and payment of fees.

As a prerequisite to taking examinations the laws of most states require that the applicant shall be at least 21 years of age, and shall be a citizen of the United States or have declared his intention of becoming one. In a few states the age limit is 25 years; in several there is no age requirement. Frequently it is stipulated that the applicant shall be of good moral character.

The educational requirements for taking examinations vary widely. They may be summarized thus:

In nine states (Alabama, Colorado, Florida, Mississippi, Montana, New Mexico, Utah, Virginia, Washington) and the District of Columbia there is no requirement.

In two states (Louisiana and Tennessee) only a grammar-school education is demanded.

In ten states (Illinois, Kentucky, New Jersey, North Carolina, North Dakota, Oklahoma, Oregon, Pennsylvania, South Dakota, and Wisconsin) the applicant must have had a high-school education or its equivalent.

In six states (Georgia, Idaho, Iowa, Ohio, South Carolina, West Virginia) in addition to a high-school education the applicant must have had training in certain additional subjects.

Three states (California, Indiana, and Michigan) require a diploma from an architectural college or some equivalent; in Arizona a diploma from a technological institution is required.

In New York, the law requires, in addition to passing the examination and satisfactory completion of a high-school course, two years' training in an institution (approved by the Board) conferring the degree of Bachelor of Science, and at least five years' practical experience after completion of the high-school course; in lieu of this a diploma or satisfactory certificate from an approved architectural school or college, plus three years' subsequent actual experience, may be accepted. The law further provides that after January 1, 1937, every candidate for examination for a certificate to practice as a registered architect shall present evidence that he satisfactorily completed the course of study in a college or school of architecture registered by the department as maintaining a satisfactory standard, and that prior to the beginning of his course of study in such college or school of architecture he satisfied the prerequisites for admission thereto.

The above requirements are in many cases not rigid; a certain amount of practical experience may count as the equivalent of training in an educational institution. The laws of many states provide that examinations may be waived by the administering boards if other satisfactory evidence of competency is offered; for instance, a stated period of practical experience in an architect's office, possession of a diploma from an approved architectural school or college, or registration in another state having similar requirements.

In the case of non-residents, evidence of ten years' practice of architecture in another state or a certificate of registration in such state is often accepted as evidence of competency, without examination.

A provision is found in the laws of many states requiring only a "practical examination" by persons who have for more than ten years been engaged in the lawful practice of architecture outside the given state.

Examinations cover tests in the science of planning and arrangement, the art of design, and a knowledge of the strength of material, stresses, etc., writing of specifications, and general architectural practice. Some states furthermore require an examination in the history of architecture and its place in social economy.[1]

---

[1] In California the examination covers:

Group 1. Architectural design.
    a. History.
    b. Theory.
    c. Design. 2 days.

Group 2. Architectural engineering.
    a. Structural design.
    b. Strength of materials. 1 day.

Group 3. Architectural practice.
    a. Office practice.
    b. Legal questions.
    c. Materials and specifications.
    d. Superintending.
    e. Mechanical engineering. 1 day.

CHAPTER X

Results of a Special Questionnaire Study

As noted on p. 347, Professor D. S. Tucker of the Massachusetts Institute of Technology was engaged to make a special questionnaire study of home-financing methods for the purposes of this book. In addition to securing data on financing, this inquiry developed considerable collateral information. The replies covered a definite class of housing in a price range considerably above that applicable to wage-earning groups. On many points the number of replies obtained was too small to permit of reliable conclusions.

Before sending out the general questionnaire, a special intensive survey was made of a limited section near Boston. It was intended to be confined to homes costing not over $10,000, and to new homes or to homes recently acquired. Perhaps the most interesting facts brought out by this preliminary survey, which was based on only sixteen replies, were that every purchaser resorted to some financing, and that the initial down payment made by the buyers averaged less than 9 per cent. The average cost of these homes was $5606 and the average debt $4456. The average annual earnings of the principal wage-earner were $2278; miscellaneous income of certain owners brought the average total income up to $2490. The average ratio of cost of the home to income was therefore 2.35.

In the larger survey, 8293 inquiries were sent to home-owners (names of whom had been obtained through extensive correspondence with real-estate dealers and others). In general, these were from relatively large communities, towns and cities of less than 30,000 population not being adequately represented. In all, 1155 answered questionnaires were secured, of which 1088 were regarded as usable. Of these 1088 homes, 932 were classed as single-family homes and 156 as "income-bearing" homes, these representing two-family homes, homes taking roomers, or homes deriving income from garages. Some of the results are briefly summarized below.

The average number of rooms in 918 single-family homes was 6.6. The lowest average for any state was 4.2 in Washington; the highest 8.4 in Maryland. In general, the survey indicated that the largest number of rooms was found in houses on the Atlantic seaboard. The average number for homes in the North was less than for homes in the South, and considerably smaller for homes in the West than for homes in the East.

The average price paid was $8098 per home. This compares with an average value for *owned* mortgaged homes reported in a special study by the United States Census in 1920 of $4938. One explanation of the difference is that many of the homes covered by this special survey were comparatively new, which means that they were built in a period of high construction costs; this, however, is not a complete explanation. Owing to the small number of replies received from certain states and regions in this survey, no comparisons can be made with the Census averages covering nearly 1,900,000 owned mortgaged homes.

The average initial or " down " payment (which in some cases included property as well as cash) for this special group of homes was $3185. In 210 cases part of the cash was obtained from personal notes of the purchaser, as distinct from mortgage borrowing to cover the balance of the purchase price. In addition, 84 of the group of 918 owners received gifts — averaging $3447 per recipient — to aid them in making their initial payment.

Only 4.3 per cent of these homes were paid for in full at the time of purchase. In 12.3 per cent of the cases the purchaser supplied no cash out of his own resources. Eighteen per cent of the purchasers contributed cash up to 10 per cent of the price, and 22.1 per cent contributed cash from 10 to 20 per cent. Combining the figures it appears that the number of purchasers furnishing less than 20 per cent of the purchase price was 481, or 52.4 per cent of the entire group of 918 owners of single-family homes.

Of the group of 918 reporting owners, 712, or 77.6 per cent, financed in part by first mortgage; 359 used second mortgages. Thus slightly over half the purchasers using a first mortgage also resorted to second-mortgage borrowing. Third mortgages were reported for only 15 homes. Land contracts were employed by 188 owners, or 20.5 per cent of the total number. Most of such financing was reported by owners in Michigan and a belt of states running west of Michigan (see p. 360). Very few land contracts were reported from states east of Michigan. Only four instances of the use of ground rents were reported, all in the city of Baltimore.

The average first mortgage on new homes amounted to a little over 53.5 per cent of the average value of the home, indicating an average face value for first mortgages of approximately $4400. Second mortgages represented approximately 27.4 per cent of the purchase price, indicating an average second-mortgage face value of about $2200. The average balance due on land-contract financing was $4933.

The average ratio of debt of all kinds to the value of new homes was 77.5 per cent. In 1920, the ratio of mortgage debt to value of all owned homes, as reported by the Census, was 42.6 per cent. No conclusion can safely be drawn from this comparison, since for the small group of homes so studied the indebtedness was of recent origin, while, as already shown, the sample covered by this survey was too small.

The average nominal interest rate on first mortgage borrowing was 6.2 per cent. The state average in New Hampshire was 4.9 per cent and in Texas 7.7 per cent. Including discounts where suffered, and incidental fees, the " true interest rate " on first mortgages was 6.4 per cent or only a trifle above the average nominal rate. In fact, the difference is so small as to raise a question whether this question was clearly understood. The " true interest rate " on first mortgages ranged from 5 per cent in New Hampshire to 8.3 per cent in Idaho.

The nominal interest rate on second mortgages was 6.3 per cent with a range in the state averages from 6 to 7.7 per cent. The true interest rates on such mortgages were much higher, depending on whether the mortgage was taken by the seller of the property or by a dealer. Where taken by the seller, the average " true interest rate " on second mortgages appears to have been about 11.2 per cent. Where taken by mortgage dealers it ranged from 9.3 to 17 per cent.

The average interest rate in the cases of financing by land contracts was 6.7 per cent.

The average duration of first mortgages was 5.7 years. As this average presumably included many mortgages taken out through building and loan associations and running for 10 to 12 years, a considerable number must have been for terms of only a few years.

For second mortgages the average term was 4.6 years. A relatively long term in Pennsylvania — 7.2 years — is presumably explained by the fact that in that state second mortgages are extensively made by building and loan associations. In every other state the average term of second mortgages was shorter than that for first mortgages.

First mortgages were paid off much more slowly than any other form of indebtedness, the average rate of reduction during the first few years after purchase of the home being only about 4 per cent annually. This may be explained by efforts to reduce borrowings on personal notes and on second mortgage. Thus second mortgages were reduced on the average at the rate of over 20 per cent per year. Balances due on land contracts were reduced at the average rate of 13.6 per cent per year.

Income-bearing Houses

For income-bearing homes only 156 returns were received as against 918 for single-family homes. Some of the general facts brought out by the replies for income-bearing homes were:

A higher purchase price ($10,346 vs. $8098 for single-family homes)
A larger initial payment ($3600 vs. $3085 for single-family homes)
A larger personal borrowing
A smaller average of gifts
A more frequent use of first and second mortgages
About the same ratios of mortgage debt to purchase price
About the same nominal rates of interest on mortgages
A somewhat more frequent use of third mortgages (but still rare)

Ratio of Purchase Price to Income

As to the average relationship between the purchase price of a single home and the owner's income, Professor Tucker summarized his findings as follows:

Average state ratios of purchase price to income	Characteristics of home financing in that state
0 — 1.1	Ownership of a single-family home more economical than rent. Not true of any state as a whole.
1.2 — 1.5	Money expenses, exclusive of accrued costs, less than rent. Ownership common. Initial payments small. Annual reduction of debt large.

1.6 — 2.1   Money expenses, exclusive of accrued costs, rather more than normal rent. Ownership still common. Annual reduction of the debt rather smaller. Initial payments somewhat larger.

2.2 — 2.7   Ownership at least twice as expensive as rent. Annual reduction of the debt very moderate. Initial payments still larger.

2.8 — 3.0   Annual debt reduction substantially zero. Disappearance of the building and loan association. Initial payments very large. Debt finally liquidated, if ever, by sale of the house.

3.1 and over   Home-ownership an undesirable credit risk. Not true of any state as a whole.

RESULTS OF A QUESTIONNAIRE BY THE RAILROAD COOPERATIVE BUILDING AND LOAN ASSOCIATION OF NEW YORK CITY

In 1931, this association canvassed its membership by questionnaire on various matters bearing on home financing. Some of the results especially pertinent to the discussion of this subject in Chapter X are briefly summarized below. The percentages given by the association are in many cases approximate. The membership of the association is located within fifty miles of New York City, an area characterized by a high percentage of home-ownership.

Question	Number of replies	Number Replying Yes	Number Replying No	Per Cent Yes	Per Cent No
Do you own the house you now live in?	755	614	141	81	19
Is there a mortgage on your home?	613	522	91	85	15
Have you found your first mortgage a burden?	538	126	412	23	77
Did you purchase a house already built?	611	427	184	69	31
Is there a second mortgage on your home? ..	594	123	471	21	79
If you built your home, was an architect employed to draw the plans?	187	110	77	58	42

Of 683 replies to a question as to how the portion of the purchase price paid by the owner was provided:

557 or 81 per cent reported that the funds were saved
38 or 6 per cent reported that the funds were inherited
78 or 12 per cent reported that the funds were borrowed
10 or 1 per cent reported that the funds were a gift

For 571 replies to a question as to the proportion of total cost possessed by the owner in cash or in land and cash, approximate results were as follows:

Proportion of total cost possessed %	Number of replies	Per cent of all replies %
0	6	1
5	6	1
10	58	10
20	172	30
30	91	16
40	83	15
50	69	13
60	37	6
70	12	$2\frac{1}{3}$
80	2	$0\frac{1}{3}$
90	2	$0\frac{1}{3}$
100	33	5

From this it appears that the largest group was that possessing 20 per cent of the total cost in cash or in land and cash while this group, with that so possessing 30 per cent of the cost represented 46 per cent, or nearly one-half, the total number of owners replying on this point.

The commissions paid for second-mortgage funds ranged from 2.5 to 30 per cent, the highest frequency falling in the 10, 15, 20, and 25 per cent brackets. The average percentage paid by these groups was 13.6.

Of 751 persons replying on the question of the desirability of home ownership, 521, or 70 per cent, expressed a desire to own their homes; 230, or 30 per cent, replied in the negative.

The reasons given by the 230 replying in the negative were distributed as follows:

	Number of replies	Per cent of total
Taxes and carrying charges	103	45
Home a " frozen asset "	79	34
No family	35	14
Miscellaneous	13	7
	230	100

TABLE BB

NUMBER OF BUILDING SOCIETIES IN GREAT BRITAIN AND AMOUNTS
ADVANCED ANNUALLY ON MORTGAGE, 1913–1931 [a]

	Number of societies	Amount advanced on mortgages during year	Balance due on mortgages	Other assets
1913	1,551	£ 9,131,017	£ 60,733,464	£ 4,582,434
1920	1,271	25,094,961	68,811,690	18,248,668
1925	1,092	49,822,473	145,857,119	23,339,539
1926	1,064	52,150,941	171,220,815	22,635,219
1927	1,054	55,886,903	197,748,150	25,597,932
1928	1,035	58,664,684	227,532,832	40,931,949
1929	1,026	74,718,748	268,141,456	44,604,427
1930	1,026	88,767,426	316,313,559	54,851,402
1931	1,013	90,253,133	360,176,859	59,008,511

(a) Board of Trade, " Statistical Abstract for the United Kingdom " (His Majesty's Stationery Office, London, 1933), p. 220.

AVERAGE SIZE OF MORTGAGES ON HOMES IN THE UNITED STATES

The average size of first mortgages on homes when taken out through building and loan associations is between $3400 and $3500. (Data furnished by John M. Wyman, associate editor of the American Building Association News.)

In the case of life-insurance companies the average is higher. A representative of the Metropolitan Life Insurance Company stated in 1928 that the average amount of its loans on homes ranged from around $3700 to $4100. The averages for this company from 1928–1931, excluding loans on apartments, ranged from $4200 to $4500. (Norton, W. S. See footnote 22, p. 355.)

The average mortgage of the Prudential Life Insurance Company on dwellings other than apartments in the first half of 1930 was nearly $5500. For the first half of 1932 it was a little more than $5000. (New York Times, July 10, 1932.)

The average savings-bank loan on a home is larger. A representative of the National Association of Mutual Savings Banks estimates the average for the entire country at $5700 to $5900. (Data furnished by John W. Sandstedt, Executive Secretary, National Association of Mutual Savings Banks.) An exact statement cannot be made, since many banks do not segregate mortgages on homes from those on other properties. The average here given may be influenced considerably by loans on apartment-houses.

The average size of first mortgages as shown by the special questionnaire study made for the purposes of this book, covering a limited number of homes of rather high cost, in 1928, was approximately $4400. (Tucker, D. S., Special Report.)

These averages are substantially larger than that shown for owned mortgaged homes not on farms in the census report on " Mortgages on Homes in 1920," that average being $2102, which included any outstanding junior indebtedness. The difference is largely explained by the fact that many of the mortgages covered by the Census were taken out at a time when building costs were much less than now, while the original indebtedness on many of these homes has been substantially reduced. Moreover, the ratio of debt to value has for some time been rising. (See p. 392.)

A survey by the National Association of Real Estate Boards in 1927 indicated that second mortgages on homes usually were from $1000 to $2000 each, sometimes for less than $500, and seldom for as much as $3000. (Brigham, H. R., " Junior Financing of Homes." In Annals of Real Estate Practice, Vol. V, p. 321.)

CHAPTER XI

TABLE CC

Average Tender Prices of British Subsidy Houses, June 1919 to March 1933 [a]

Monthly prices	Non-parlour	Parlour	Monthly prices	Non-parlour	Parlour
1919 June	£643	£785	1928 January	£389	£437
July	713	833	April	378	431
October	750	834	July	366	434
			October	369	427
1920 January	782	856			
April	817	914	1929 January	341	422
July	870	955	April	348	401
October	888	958	July	337	377
			October	344	419
1921 January	834	932			
April	697	798			
July	665	752	Quarterly averages		Non-parlour
October	573	667			
			1930 March quarter		£335
1922 January	494	560	June "		335
April	395	446	September "		337
July	378	413	December "		351
October	346	407			
			1931 March "		345
1923 January	346	373	June "		331
April	355	390	September "		333
August	351	408	December "		327
October	358	416			
			1932 March "		317
1924 January	386	445	June "		311
April	415	442	September "		295
July	428	495	December "		299
October	451	500			
			1933 March "		295
1925 January	438	501			
April	438	496			
July	444	513			
October	447	503			
1926 January	456	493			
April	434	495			
July	455	502			
October	453	522			
1927 January	427	492			
April	421	479			
July	418	483			
October	395	438			

(a) As shown by contracts let by, or by direct building schemes of, Local Authorities.

Bibliography

It is obvious that a work of this kind must be dependent upon current statistical material of all kinds for its sources rather than upon books which will always be somewhat out of date. In presenting the following bibliography, no attempt has been made to list all of these current sources; the serious student may find a complete list in the footnotes to the text. There are a number of books, however, likewise referred to in the footnote references, which seem worthy of being listed in the following consolidated bibliography because of their permanent value.

Aldridge, Henry R., " National Housing Manual, The " (National Housing and Town Planning Council, London, 1923).

Aragonés, Pedro Ortiz Y, " Casas Baratas " (Imprenta Torrent, Madrid, 1929).

Barnes, Harry, " Housing " (Ernest Benn, Ltd., London, 1923).

Benn, Ernest J. P., " Return to Laissez-Faire, The " (D. Appleton and Company, New York, 1929).

Bernan, Walter (Meikleham, R.), " History and Art of Warming and Ventilating Rooms and Buildings, On the " (George Bell, London, 1845).

Bishop, J. L., " History of American Manufactures from 1608 to 1860 " (Edward Young and Company, Philadelphia, 1864).

Bowley, A. L., and Hogg, M. H., " Has Poverty Diminished? " (P. S. King and Son, Ltd., London, 1925).

Carr-Saunders, A. M., and Jones, D. C., " Social Structure of England and Wales, The " (Oxford University Press, London, 1927).

Chase, Stuart, " New Deal, A " (The Macmillan Company, New York, 1932).

Chase, Stuart, " Play " in " Whither Mankind," edited by Charles A. Beard (Longmans, Green and Company, New York, 1930).

Clark, V. S., " History of Manufactures in the United States, 1607 to 1860 " (The Carnegie Institute of Washington, 1916).

Clarke, John J., " Housing Problem, The " (Sir Isaac Pitman & Sons, Ltd., London, 1920).

Colquhoun, Patrick, " Treatise on the Population, Wealth, Power and Resources of the British Empire " (Joseph Mawman, London, 1815).

Cooper, Thomas, " Some Information Respecting America " (J. Johnson, London, 1794).

Coxe, Tench, " View of the United States of America, A " (William Hall and Wrigley & Berriman, Philadelphia, 1794).

Douglas, Maj. C. H., " Economic Democracy " (Harcourt, Brace and Howe, New York, 1920).

Douglas, Paul H., " Real Wages in the United States, 1890–1926 " (Published by Houghton Mifflin Company, Boston, 1930 for The Pollak Foundation, Newton, Mass.).

Douglas, Paul H., and Jennison, Florence Tye, " Movement of Money and Real Earnings in the United States, 1926–1928, The " (University of Chicago Press, Chicago, 1930).

Federated American Engineering Societies, Committee on Elimination of Waste in Industry, " Waste in Industry " (Washington, D. C., 1921).

Fremantle, Lt.-Col. F. E., " Housing of the Nation, The " (Philip Allan and Company, Ltd., London, 1927).

Gregg, Richard B., " Economics of Khaddar " (S. Ganesan, Triplicane, Madras, India, 1928).

Haber, William, " Industrial Relations in the Building Industry " (Harvard University Press, Cambridge, 1930).

Hollander and Barnett, " Studies in American Trade Unionism " (Henry Holt and Company, New York, 1906).

Houghteling, Leila, " Income and Standard of Living of Unskilled Laborers in Chicago, The " (The University of Chicago Press, Chicago, 1927).

Hubbard, T. K., and Hubbard, H. V., " Our Cities To-day and
To-morrow. A Survey of Planning and Zoning Progress in
the United States " (Harvard University Press, Cambridge,
1929).

King, W. I., " National Income and Its Purchasing Power, The "
(National Bureau of Economic Research, Inc., New York,
1930).

Lorwin, Lewis L., " The American Federation of Labor " (The
Institute of Economics of The Brookings Institution, Washington, D. C., 1933).

Mulhall, Michael George, " Dictionary of Statistics " (George
Routledge and Sons, Ltd., London, 1899).

Mulhall, Michael George, " Industries and Wealth of Nations "
(Longmans, Green and Company, London, 1896).

National Bureau of Economic Research, Inc., " Recent Economic
Changes in the United States," Report of the Committee on
Recent Economic Changes of the President's Conference on
Unemployment, Herbert Hoover, Chairman; including the
reports of a special staff of the National Bureau of Economic
Research, Inc. (McGraw-Hill Book Company, Inc., New
York, 1929).

Nystrom, Paul H., " Economic Principles of Consumption, The "
(The Ronald Press Co., New York, 1929).

Pitkin, Timothy, " Statistical View of the Commerce of the United
States of America, A " (Durrie & Peck, New Haven, 1835).

Report and Recommendations of a Committee of the President's
Conference on Unemployment, " Seasonal Operation in the
Construction Industries " (McGraw-Hill Book Company,
Inc., New York, 1924).

President's Conference on Home Building and Home Ownership,
The John M. Gries and James Ford, General Editors; Dan H.
Wheelwe and Blanche Halbert, Associate Editors.

Volume I, " Planning for Residential Districts "

Volume II, " Home Finance and Taxation "

Volume III, " Slums, Large-Scale Housing and Decentralization "

Volume IV, " Home Ownership, Income and Types of Dwellings "

Volume V, " House Design, Construction and Equipment "

Volume VI, " Negro Housing "

Volume VII, " Farm and Village Housing "

Volume VIII, " Housing and the Community — Home Repair and Remodeling "

Volume IX, " Household Management and Kitchens "

Volume X, " Homemaking, Home Furnishing, and Information Service "

(National Capital Press, Inc., Washington, 1932).

Schoenhof, Jacob, " History of Money and Prices, A, being an inquiry into their relations from the 13th century to the present time " (G. P. Putnam's Sons, New York, 1896).

Simon, E. D., " How to Abolish the Slums " (Longmans, Green and Company, London, 1929).

Streightoff, Frank Hatch, " The Standard of Living Among the Industrial People of America " (Houghton Mifflin Company, Boston and New York). (Hart, Schaffner & Marx prize economic essay).

Tugwell, R. G., Munro, Thomas, and Stryker, R. E., " American Economic Life " (Harcourt, Brace and Company, New York, 1925).

Veiller, Lawrence, " How England is Meeting the Housing Shortage " (Spottiswoode, Ballantyne and Company, Ltd., London, 1920).

Webb, A. D., " New Dictionary of Statistics, The " (George Routledge and Sons, Ltd., London, 1911).

Weeden, W. B., " Economic and Social History of New England, 1620–1789 " Two Volumes (Houghton Mifflin Company, Boston, 1890).

Whipple, Sherman L., and Waters, Thomas Franklin, " Puritan Homes " (Ipswich Historical Society, Publication No. XXVII, Salem, 1929).

Whitaker, Charles Harris, " Joke about Housing, The " (Marshall Jones Company, Boston, 1920).

Whitten, Robert, and Adams, Thomas, " Neighborhoods of Small Homes — Economic Density of Low Cost Housing in America and England " (Harvard University School of City Planning, Harvard University Press, Cambridge, 1931).

Wolman, Leo, " Growth of American Trade Unions, 1880–1923 " (National Bureau of Economic Research, Inc., New York, 1924).

Wolman, Leo, " Outline of the American Labor Movement, An " (Workers Education Bureau of America, New York, 1923).

Wood, Edith Elmer, " Housing of the Unskilled Wage Earner, The; America's Next Problem " (The Macmillan Company, New York, 1919).

Wood, Edith Elmer, " Housing Progress in Western Europe " (E. P. Dutton and Company, New York, 1923).

Wood, Edith Elmer, " Recent Trends in American Housing " (The Macmillan Company, New York, 1931).

Woodbury, Coleman, " Apartment House Increases and Attitudes toward Home Ownership " (The Institute for Economic Research, Chicago, 1931).

Acknowledgments

In addition to the many published sources to which he turned, the author wishes to acknowledge the special assistance rendered him by the following organizations and individuals. They were kind in answering difficult questions, and in supplying no end of data otherwise unobtainable.

American Appraisal Company
American Brass Company
American Hotel Association
American Telephone and Telegraph Company
Brookings Institution
Cadwell, W. H., Agent, Jackson Mills of the Nashua Manufacturing Company
Canadian Bank of Commerce
Cellarius, H. F., Secretary-Treasurer of the United States League of Building and Loan Associations
Celotex and Metal Lath Interests
Chicago Homes Economic Council
City Housing Corporation
Copper and Brass Research Association
Department of Pensions and National Health, Canada
Department of Trade and Commerce, Canada
Dodge, F. W., Corporation
Dominion Bureau of Statistics, Canada
Fidelity-Phenix Fire Insurance Company
Foreman, H. E., Engineer; The Associated General Contractors of America, Inc.
Hunt, Leigh W., Assistant Commercial Attaché to the United States Department of Commerce, Brussels

Interstate Commerce Commission
Lehman Corporation, The
Lockwood Greene Engineers, Inc., New York
Massachusetts Department of Labor and Industries
Metropolitan Life Insurance Company
National Association of Building Owners and Managers
National Electric Light Association
National Lumber Manufacturers Association
Norton, W. S., Comptroller, Metropolitan Life Insurance Company
Philadelphia Housing Association
Plumbing and Heating Industries Bureau
Sandstedt, John W., Executive Secretary of the National Association of Mutual Savings Banks
Taylor, Stanley, Merchandising Consultant, *The American Architect*
Tenement House Department, Borough of Manhattan, New York City
United States Bond and Mortgage Company of New York
United States Department of Commerce
Ward, H. H., Deputy Minister of Labour, Canada
Wyman, John W., Associate Editor of the *American Building Association News*

Index